基础培训

新东方AP考试指定辅导教程

AP
物理C
力学和电磁学
Mechanics & Electromagnetism

祁恩云·编著

浙江教育出版社·杭州

图书在版编目(CIP)数据

AP物理C.力学和电磁学 / 祁恩云编著. —杭州：
浙江教育出版社，2015.6
ISBN 978-7-5536-3158-5

Ⅰ.①A… Ⅱ.①祁… Ⅲ.①力学—高等学校—入学
考试—美国—教材 ②电磁学—高等学校—入学考试—美国
—教材 Ⅳ.①O4

中国版本图书馆CIP数据核字（2015）第139049号

AP物理C：力学和电磁学

出版发行	浙江教育出版社
	（杭州市天目山路40号　邮编：310013）
编　　著	祁恩云
责任编辑	孔令宇　古　羽　路淑双
责任校对	刘文芳
责任印务	温劲风
封面设计	大愚设计+李　韬
印　　刷	三河市龙大印装有限公司
开　　本	880mm×1230mm　1/16
印　　张	31.5
字　　数	536 000
版　　次	2015年11月第1版
印　　次	2015年11月第1次印刷
标准书号	ISBN 978-7-5536-3158-5
定　　价	79.00元
联系电话	0571 - 85170300 - 80928
电子邮箱	bj62605588@163.com
网　　址	www.zjeph.com

前　言

　　美国大学理事会（College Board）推出的美国大学先修课程AP（Advanced Placement）是面向优秀高中生的大学基础课程。AP物理课程是AP考试项目的一个重要组成部分，分为物理1、物理2和物理C。AP物理C由"力学"和"电磁学"两门课程组成，是为报考理工科的学生设置的。物理C这两门课程都需要微积分的知识，因此算是有一定难度的课程，尤其对于想要自学的学生而言难度更大。作者在加拿大为高中生讲授多年高中物理和AP物理课程，有丰富的SAT物理、AP物理教学和考试经验；在国内有多年的大学物理教学经验和教授高中学生SAT、AP物理的经验。作者参考国外高中、大学物理教材、主流考试辅导教材，结合中国学生的数理基础、英语语言水平，并整理多年的教学案例，编著了这本适合中国学生的AP物理C备考教材。教材内容以英文为主，以便考生适应英文考试；同时，配以简要的中文和生僻词汇注释，方便考生快速理解和掌握所学的内容。

教材特点

1. 考试内容全部用英文进行讲解。
2. 侧边页用中文概述对应位置的英文知识点。
3. 每章的练习题和书后的模拟题均与真题的形式相同。
4. 全面覆盖AP物理核心知识点。
5. 用中文总结知识点，中文解答习题。

教材使用说明

　　本书既可作为国际学校、国际班、考试辅导机构的辅导教材，也很适合考生自学。本教材适合有微积分基础的高中在读学生。英文能力较强的学生要以英文内容学习为主，知识框架学习需看每章后的总结和每页侧边页的中文概述；英文能力中等的学生需要中、英文兼顾掌握知识点和物理英文术语；而对于英文能力不太强、高中物理又很好的学生来说，要重点学习每页侧边页的中文概述和每章后的中文总结，并在英文内容中学习英文术语。书中每章都有适量的英文练习题供考生巩固所学，学完全部知识点后还有三套全真模拟题来检验学习成果，最终找到知识弱点后加以强化。之后就可到官网下载历年真题进行最后的考前训练。

AP物理C考试介绍

　　AP物理C力学和电磁学是两个独立的考试科目，依据准备报考的专业，学生可以只参加力学部分或电磁学部分的考试，也可以两个科目的考试都参加。两科考试独立评分，分别给出成绩。AP物理考试采用5分制，一般情况下，美国大学要求4分以上可以抵学分，而名牌大学则多数要求5分。AP成绩是影响大学录取的重要因素。

　　AP物理C力学：考试时间为90分钟。由两部分组成，多项选择题（multiple-choice question）部分与问答题（free-response question）部分，各占总成绩的50%，考试时间各占45分钟。第一部分共有35道选择题；第二部分有三道问答计算题，每道题通常又包含几个小问。两部分都可以使用计算器，还会给考生提供一个常用物理公式和常数表。

力学作为物理学的一部分，是研究自然界最基本的运动形式的一门科学。力学的考试内容基于AP物理1的力学内容，融入向量和微积分的知识，给出力学概念的最基本定义，基本物理定律的积分、微分形式。难点在简谐振动、力矩、转动惯量、角动量和刚体转动。

AP物理C电磁学：电磁学也是物理学中一门重要的基础学科，是经典物理学的基本组成部分之一，与近代自然科学、技术的许多领域有着密切的联系，是大学工程学院和理学院不可缺少的基础课程之一。考试时间与形式同物理C力学。电磁学是一门较难的课程，不但要用到向量、微积分运算，还有一些新的知识。难点在高斯定理、环路定理的理解和应用，以及场强、电势、电磁感应和暂态电路的计算。

力学考试内容和所占比例		电磁学考试内容和所占比例	
内容	比例	内容	比例
运动学	18%	静电场	30%
牛顿定律	20%	静电场中的导体、电解质及电容	14%
功和能	14%	电路	20%
动量	12%	磁场	20%
圆周运动和转动	18%	电磁感应和麦克斯韦方程组	16%
振动和万有引力	18%		

考试指南

AP物理C考试中选择题有A、B、C、D和E五个选项，其中只有一个是正确答案，选错不扣分。选择题主要考查对概念的理解和评估知识的广度，通常计算比较简单，有些题目甚至不用计算，依据分析判断即可得出答案。

问答题考查考生深入理解基本物理概念和原理及其在复杂问题中的应用，利用数学工具，如微积分，给出物理概念和原理的公式表达，并用之来解决复杂的物理问题。按评分标准，问答题每一正确步骤都可以得到相应的分数，解答问答题的应试策略如下：

1. 做问答题前，通读所有的题目，先做有把握的题。

2. 做好时间分配，不要在一道题上耗费太多时间，因而导致没有时间完成其他题目。

3. 解题过程中，尽量写下所有的步骤，以免遗漏采分点。标清楚题号，以免漏题。

4. 通常问答题会有几个部分，要尽量回答每一个问题，因为每部分的分数都是独立的，即使前面的题目没有答对，也不影响后面题目的得分。

5. 在计算过程中，要注意单位，以免因单位错误或遗漏而丢分。

6. 要清楚恰当地标出所有图形图表标记，如图形图表的名称、x和y坐标轴和单位等。

从2015年开始，AP物理C整个考试过程中都可以使用公式表和计算器（之前只在问答题中可以使用），这意味着对定量计算的要求在提高，选择题中也会出现较难的题目；同时实验部分的题目也在加强。考试总体趋势是：难度在增加。

希望考生通过本教材的学习，全面、快速掌握AP物理 C考试内容，尽早熟悉和融入美国教育体系，在考试中取得理想成绩，成功迈进美国名校的大门。

祁恩云

致 谢

　　教材的编写和出版得到了俞敏洪老师的大力支持，在此深表谢意。感谢王国明先生在图表制作和编审工作中所做的大量工作。同时感谢我的女儿，王雨桐，根据自己对AP课程学习和考试的切身体验，对本书编写形式和内容提出的有益建议，并参与本书的编审工作。本书在编写过程中难免有疏漏与不妥之处，还望各位同行和读者指正，不胜感谢！

祁恩云

作者简介

　　祁恩云：于哈尔滨理工大学任教，从事大学物理教学多年，具有丰富的物理教学经验；曾作为公派访问学者在加拿大阿尔伯塔大学进行合作研究；曾任温哥华功力数理学院（Vancouver Power Math and Science Academy, Canada）教师。有多年加拿大数学、物理教学经验，精通北美标准化考试SAT II和AP数理课程教学。

目 录

PART ONE

力学
Mechanics

1

Vectors
向量

Introduction: Vectors will show up almost all places in our study of physics and obey certain rules for vector operations. The principal objective of this chapter is to learn the rules for the arithmetic, algebra and calculus of vectors. It is important to deal with them.

1.1 Scalar and Vector
1.1 标量和向量

There are two kinds of physical quantities—**scalar and vector**. A scalar is a quantity which has magnitude but no associated direction, such as mass, time and energy. They are specified completely by giving a number and units. A vector is a quantity which has direction as well as magnitude, such as displacement, velocity, force… etc.

Scalars can be equated with scalars, and vectors can be equated with vectors, but scalars can never be equated with vectors.

Drawing a diagram of a particular physical situation is always helpful in physics, and this is especially true when dealing with vectors. On a diagram, a vector is generally represented by an arrow whose direction is in the direction of the vector and whose length is proportional to the vector's magnitude.

When we write the symbol for a vector, we always use boldface type. Thus for velocity we write **v**. In handwritten work, the symbol for a vector can be indicated by putting an arrow over it, a $\vec{F}$ for force.

Vector notation: Vector **A**

Its magnitude and direction may be represented by a line OP directed from the initial point O to the terminal point P and denoted by $\overrightarrow{op}$.

物理量有两种：标量和向量。

标量是只有大小的物理量。

向量是既有大小又有方向的物理量。

标量和向量是两类不同的物理量，永远不会相等。

向量用有方向的线段图示。在印刷体中用黑体字符表示向量，**F**。手写时则在相应的物理量符号上方加上小箭头，$\vec{F}$。

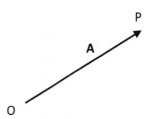

Figure 1-1 Vector notation

The two vectors A and B are added in following way: Triangle method and Parallelogram method.

向量加法遵循三角形法则和平行四边形法则。

To add **A** and **B**, the tip of **A** is placed at the tail of **B**. The arrow drawn from the tail of the first vector to the tip of the second represents the sum, or **resultant**, of the two vectors. This method is known as the tail-to-tip method of adding vectors.

向量平移后不变。

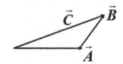

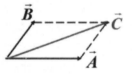

Note that vectors can be translated parallel to themselves to accomplish these manipulations.

A second way to add two vectors is the parallelogram method. It is fully equivalent to the tail-to-tip method.

Subtraction of vectors, and *Multiplicatio*n of a Vector by *a Scalar*:

Figure 1-2 Addition of two vectors

Given a vector **V**, we define the negative of this vector (-**V**) to be a vector with the same magnitude as **V** but opposite in direction.

V + (-V) = 0

The difference between two vectors, **A − B** is defined as

A − B = A+ (-B)

两向量差等于第一个向量加上第二个向量的相反向量，由此向量减法转化成向量加法。

Thus our rules for addition of vectors can be applied as shown in Figure 1-3.

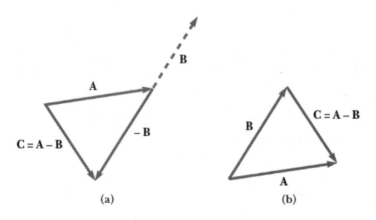

Figure 1-3 Subtracting two vectors: **A − B**

The subtraction between two vectors is the vector that extends from the head of the 2nd vector to the head of the 1st vector.

两向量相减：两向量顶端相连指向被减向量。

A vector **A** can be multiplied by a scalar c. We define c**A** to be a vector whose magnitude is $|c|$ A and whose direction is same as **A** if c > 0, but is opposite to **A** if c < 0.

向量数值乘法：方向不变或反向。

1.3 Components and Resultants of Vectors   1.3 向量分解与合成

An advantage of using vector components is that complicated vector problems can be replaced by algebraic manipulation.

解决复杂向量合成问题。

There are generally two ways to write vectors: using polar coordinates and using Cartesian coordinates.

向量的两种表达方式：

极坐标和直角坐标。

Unit vector $\overrightarrow{A_0}$ is a vector with magnitude 1 and in same direction with $\overrightarrow{A}$, denoted $\overrightarrow{A_0} = \dfrac{\overrightarrow{A}}{A}$ or $\overrightarrow{A} = A \overrightarrow{A_0}$.

单位向量：在某一方向上大小为1的向量，等于向量与向量大小相除。

For a fixed Cartesian system, unit vectors $\vec{i}$, $\vec{j}$ and $\vec{k}$ which have unit magnitude and only indicate directions, are unit vectors along OX, OY, OZ and are mutually perpendicular to one another.

直角坐标系中三个坐标轴方向单位向量是：**i，j，k**。

A component of a vector is the projection of the vector on an axis. Components may be in two or three dimensional coordinate system.

The components of a vector **A** in three dimension are a_x, a_y, a_z.

$$\vec{A} = a_x \vec{i} + a_y \vec{j} + a_z \vec{k}$$

magnitude: $\left|\vec{A}\right| = A = \sqrt{a^2_x + a^2_y + a^2_z}$

direction: $\cos\alpha = \dfrac{a_x}{A}$ $\cos\beta = \dfrac{a_y}{A}$ $\cos\gamma = \dfrac{a_z}{A}$

α, β, γ are angles formed by the vector and three axes.

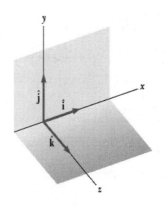

Figure 1-4 直角坐标系单位

向量

三维向量分量、大小、方向表示。

A vector in two dimensions can be represented as

A $= A_x \vec{i} + A_y \vec{j}$ or   **A**=<A$_x$, A$_y$>

二维向量分量、大小及方向表示。

Components are $A_x = A\cos\theta$ and $A_y = A\sin\theta$

Magnitude of A is: $A = \sqrt{A_x^2 + A_y^2}$

Direction of A is: $\tan\theta = \dfrac{A_y}{A_x}$

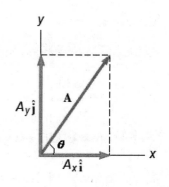

θ: the angle formed by the vector **A** and positive x axis.

Resultants of vectors：If two vectors **A** + **B** = **C** ，and

$$\mathbf{A} = A_x\,\vec{i} + A_y\,\vec{j} \qquad \mathbf{B} = B_x\,\vec{i} + B_y\,\vec{j}$$

Figure 1-5 向量在二维直角坐标中的分量

We have $\mathbf{C} = C_x\vec{i} + C_y\vec{j}$ = **B** + **A** = $(A_x + B_x)\vec{i} + (A_y + B_y)\vec{j}$

And obviously $C_x = A_x + B_x$ and $C_y = A_y + B_y$

Example 1.1: Suppose vectors **A**=<-3,-1>, **B**=<-1,4>, find the magnitude of **A+B**

向量直角坐标表达：<a,b>

Solution:

A+B = <-3+(-1),-1+4> = <-4,3>

Example 1.2: Given the two dimensional position vector

R=(2.5**i**–3**j**) (m)，

向量直角坐标表达：ai+bj

a. find the magnitude of R.

b. find the angle that R makes with the positive x-direction.

c. if R is parallel transported to another location in the plane, what happens to the answers to parts (a) and (b)?

Solution:

a. $R = \sqrt{2.5^2 + (-3)^2}$ = 3.91m

b. $\theta = \tan^{-1}(\dfrac{-3}{2.5}) = -50.2°$

c. If the vector is parallel transported to another location in the plan, its magnitude and direction are unchanged. The answers to parts (a) and (b) thus remain the same.

1.4 Dot Product (Scalar Product) of Vectors   1.4 向量点积

The dot product is often used in physic problems associated with work and power. It describes the projection of one vector onto another and results in a **scalar** product.

两向量点积的结果是标量。是一个向量对另一个投影。

1.4.1 Definition of Dot Product   1.4.1 点积定义

The scalar product of vectors **A** and **B** (denoted by **A·B)** is defined as
$$\mathbf{A \cdot B} = A\,B\cos\theta$$

$\mathbf{A \cdot B} = A\,B\cos\theta$
点积符合交换律。

Where θ is the angle between **A** and **B**. By definition, **A·B** is a scalar.

$\mathbf{A \cdot B} = \mathbf{B \cdot A}$

According to the definition, **A·B** = **B·A**, we have: **A·A** = A^2.

相同单位向量的点积。

In particular, $\vec{i} \cdot \vec{i} = \vec{j} \cdot \vec{j} = \vec{k} \cdot \vec{k} = 1$

$\vec{i} \cdot \vec{i} = \vec{j} \cdot \vec{j} = \vec{k} \cdot \vec{k} = 1$

If **A** and **B** are parallel vectors in the same direction, then **A·B** = AB. If **A** and **B** are parallel vectors in the opposite direction, then
   A·B = -AB.

两平行向量点积。
方向相同：**A·B** = AB
方向相反：**A·B** = -AB

According to the definition, **A·B** = AB cos θ = 0, means A = 0, or B = 0, or cos θ =0.

两向量相互垂直点积为零。

A and **B** are perpendicular if **A·B** = 0, given that **A** and **B** are none zero vectors.

A 垂直 **B**：**A·B** = 0

两不同单位向量点积为零。

In particular, $\vec{i} \cdot \vec{j} = \vec{j} \cdot \vec{k} = \vec{i} \cdot \vec{k} = 0$

$\vec{i} \cdot \vec{j} = \vec{j} \cdot \vec{k} = \vec{i} \cdot \vec{k} = 0$

1.4.2 Dot Product in Coordinate Form   1.4.2 向量点积坐标表示

In rectangular coordinate system, we have

$$\mathbf{A \cdot B} = A_x B_x + A_y B_y + A_z B_z$$

两个不为零的向量点积的结果可能为正、负、或零。

From the definition of scalar product **A·B** = $AB\cos\theta$, we see that: The angle θ between **A** and **B** can be found using

两向量的夹角公式

$$\cos\theta = \frac{\mathbf{A \cdot B}}{AB}$$

$\cos\theta = \dfrac{\mathbf{A \cdot B}}{AB}$

If **A·B** > 0, θ is acute; if **A·B** < 0, θ is obtuse.

Several physical concepts (work, electric and magnetic flux) require dot product we multiply the magnitude of one vector by the magnitude of the component of the other vector that is parallel to the first. That is why the dot product was invented.

力学中的功, 电磁学中的电通量和磁通量都由点积来定义。

Example 1.3

a. Find the angle between the two vectors **A** = **i** -2**j**+2**k** = (1, -2, 2),

B = 2**i**+3**j**-6**k** = (2, 3, -6).

b. Points A, B and C have coordinates (2, 3, 4), (-2, 1, 0) and (4, 0, 2)

respectively. Calculate $\angle$ BAC.

Solution:

a. $\cos\theta = \dfrac{\mathbf{A}\cdot\mathbf{B}}{AB} = \dfrac{(1,-2,2)\cdot(2,3,-6)}{\sqrt{1^2+(-2)^2+2^2}\cdot\sqrt{2^2+3^2+(-6)^2}} = \dfrac{-16}{21}$

$\theta = 139.6^0$

b. $\overline{AB} = (-2-2, 1-3, 0-4) = (-4,-2,-4)$
$\overline{AC} = (4-2, 0-3, 2-4) = (2,-3,-2)$

Use $\angle BAC = \dfrac{\overline{AB}\cdot\overline{AC}}{AB.AC} = \dfrac{(-4,-2,-4)\cdot(2,-3,-2)}{\sqrt{36}.\sqrt{17}} = \dfrac{1}{\sqrt{17}}$

$\angle$ BAC= $76°$

1.5 Cross Product (Vector Product) of Vectors   1.5 叉积（向量积）

1.5.1 Definition of Cross Product

1.5.1 叉积定义

The vector product of vectors **A** and **B** (denoted by **C** = **A**×**B**) is defined as a vector whose direction is perpendicular to both **A** and **B** and followed the right-hand rule, and whose magnitude is A B sin α where α is the angle between **A** and **B**.

两个向量叉积的结果是向量。方向垂直于这两个向量组成的平面，可用下图右旋法则确定。

Specifically, **A** × **B** = $\left(AB\sin\alpha \right) \vec{C}_0$

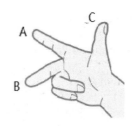

where $\vec{C}_0$ is a unit vector perpendicular to both **A** and **B**.

There are two equivalent ways to envision **the vector product right hand rule**.

1）Orient the index finger of your right hand along the direction of the first vector of the product and the middle finger along the direction of the second vector, as in Figure 1-6 a. The extended thumb then indicates the direction of the vector product **A**×**B**.

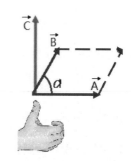

2）To find the direction, alternatively, points the four bunched fingers of your right hand in the direction of **A** and then curl them in the direction of **B**. Your thumb will be pointing in the direction of **A**×**B,** as shown in Figure 1-6 b. Always choose the smaller of the two possible angles for swinging your fingers from the first vector to the second vector of the product.

Figure 1-6 b: Right-hand rule 2

Obviously   **A**×**B** = - **B**×**A** ≠ **B**×**A**

叉积不符合交换律。

        A×**A** = 0

A×**B** = - **B**×**A** ≠ **B**×**A**

So, if **A**×**B** = 0 then **A** and **B** are parallel.

两向量平行叉积为零。

In the three dimensional coordinate system, **i**, **j** and **k** follow that

A 平行 **B**：**A**×**B** = 0

    i×**j** = **k**, **j**×**k** = **i**, **k**×**i** = **j** and **i**×**i** = **j**×**j** = **k**×**k** = 0

单位向量的叉积。

1.5.2 Cross Product in Matrix Form

1.5.2 向量叉积矩阵表示

If two vectors are defined in unit vector notation, the ***cross product as a*** vector is equal to the evaluation of the three by three matrix shown. Note that the second row is made up of the components of the *first* vector denoted in the cross product. Note also that you DON'T have to use the *right hand rule* to determine the direction as the direction is determined directly through the matrix evaluation.

两向量叉积结果可用一个 3×3 矩阵表示。

第二行是第一个向量的

分量。

矩阵的行列式直接给出两向量的叉积方向，不必再用右旋法则判断方向。

$$\vec{A} = a_x\vec{i} + a_y\vec{j} + a_z\vec{k}, \quad \vec{B} = b_x\vec{i} + b_y\vec{j} + b_z\vec{k}$$

$$\vec{A} \times \vec{B} = \begin{vmatrix} \vec{i} & \vec{j} & \vec{k} \\ a_x & a_y & a_z \\ b_x & b_y & b_z \end{vmatrix}$$

Example 1.4: If **A** = 2 I +3 **j** − 4 **k** and **B** = -3 I +2 **j** -3**k**,

a. find **A** × **B**.

b. verify that **A** × **B** is perpendicular to both **A** and **B**.

Solution:

a. **A** × **B** = $\begin{pmatrix} i & j & k \\ 2 & 3 & -4 \\ -3 & 2 & -3 \end{pmatrix}$ = - i +18 j +13 k

b. (**A** × **B**) · **A** = <-1, 18, 13 > · < 2, 3, -4 > = 0

And (**A** × **B**) • **B** = <-1, 18, 13 > • <-3, 2, -3 > = 0.

Hence **A** × **B** is perpendicular to both **A** and **B**.

1.6 Derivative of Vectors　　　　　　　　1.6 向量导数

In our study of motion in the next chapter, we will have frequent need to differentiate vectors which are functions of time.

Differentiation of a vector expressed in Cartesian form proceeds as follows for **i, j, k** are constant vectors.

直角坐标系中 **i, j, k** 可看做常数向量。

$$\frac{d\vec{A}}{dt} = \frac{d}{dt}(A_x i + A_y j + A_z k) = \frac{dA_x}{dt}i + \frac{dA_y}{dt}j + \frac{dA_z}{dt}k$$

The derivative of a vector also is a vector, whose components are the derivatives of the respective scalar component of the original vector. They also follow

向量的导数仍然是向量，遵循加法、乘法运算法则。

$$\frac{d(\vec{A} + \vec{B})}{dt} = \frac{d\vec{A}}{dt} + \frac{d\vec{B}}{dt}$$

$$\frac{d(\vec{A} \cdot \vec{B})}{dt} = \frac{d\vec{A}}{dt} \cdot \vec{B} + \vec{A} \cdot \frac{d\vec{B}}{dt}$$

$$\frac{d(\vec{A} \times \vec{B})}{dt} = \frac{d\vec{A}}{dt} \times \vec{B} + \vec{A} \times \frac{d\vec{B}}{dt}$$

$$\frac{d(\lambda \vec{A})}{dt} = \frac{d\lambda}{dt}\vec{A} + \lambda\frac{d\vec{A}}{dt}$$

Let **A** = A $\vec{A_0}$, $\vec{A_0}$ is the unit vector of **A**.

Then we have $$\frac{d\vec{A}}{dt} = \frac{d(A\vec{A_0})}{dt} = \frac{dA}{dt}\vec{A_0} + A\frac{d\vec{A_0}}{dt}$$

We know a vector changes with time including two parts: magnitude change with time and direction change with time also.

Example1.5: Differentiate the following vector with respect to t

A = $5t^2$**I** + 6t**j** + 8**k**

Solution:

Differentiate each Cartesian component with respect to t using the standard differentiation rules, so we obtain

$$\frac{d\vec{A}}{dt} = 10t\,\text{I} + 6\,\text{j}$$

第一章总结 向量

1. 标量和向量

标量：数值量。只有大小，可以为正、负、或零。

向量：既有大小又有方向的空间量，表示为 **A**。向量的大小是正的标量，|**A**| = A。

单位向量：大小为 1 的向量。直角坐标系三个坐标轴 x，y，z 方向的单位向量为 **i**，**j**，**k**。

$$\left|\overrightarrow{A_0}\right| = 1; \quad \overrightarrow{A_0} = \frac{\overrightarrow{A}}{A} \quad \text{or} \quad \overrightarrow{A} = A\,\overrightarrow{A_0}$$

向量的分解：向量 **A** 可以分解成 $\mathbf{A} = A_x\vec{i} + A_y\vec{j}$. A_x, A_y 是向量 **A** 在 x，y 方向的分量。

$$A_x = A\cos\theta$$

$$A_y = A\sin\theta$$

向量的合成：已知向量 **A** 在 x，y 方向的分量 A_x, A_y，则 $\mathbf{A} = A_x\vec{i} + A_y\vec{j}$

$$A = \sqrt{A_x^2 + A_y^2}$$

$$\text{tg}\,\theta = \frac{A_y}{A_x}$$

2. 向量的加减

1）在坐标系中

$$\mathbf{A} \pm \mathbf{B} = \left(A_x \pm B_x\right)\vec{i} + \left(A_y \pm B_y\right)\vec{j} + \left(A_z \pm B_z\right)\vec{k}$$

2）在平面或空间图形中用三角形或平行四边形法则求和。

3. 向量的乘积

1）数量乘法：c**A**

2）点积（标量乘积）：$\mathbf{A} \cdot \mathbf{B} = AB\cos\theta$

$$\mathbf{A} \cdot \mathbf{B} = A_x B_x + A_y B_y + A_z B_z$$

3）叉积（向量乘积）

$$\vec{A} = a_x\vec{i} + a_y\vec{j} + a_z\vec{k}$$

$$\vec{B} = b_x\vec{i} + b_y\vec{j} + b_z\vec{k}$$

$$\vec{A} \times \vec{B} = \begin{vmatrix} \vec{i} & \vec{j} & \vec{k} \\ a_x & a_y & a_z \\ b_x & b_y & b_z \end{vmatrix}$$

大小：$\left|\vec{A} \times \vec{B}\right| = AB\sin\theta$

方向：Right hand rule

4. 向量的导数

向量看作是向量大小和单位向量的乘积，用乘法法则求导。

Chapter 1 Vectors Practice

Multiple Choice Questions

1. Which one of the following contains only vector quantities?

    A. mass, time

    B. temperature, displacement

    C. force, velocity

    D. weight, distance

    E. acceleration, speed

2. Vectors **A** and **B** are shown as below, which figure is represented by 2**A-B**?

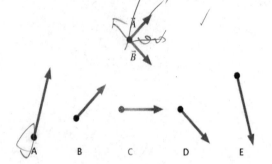

    A   B   C   D   E

3. If **A**=$2\vec{i}$ +$3\vec{j}$ and **B**=$\vec{i}$ -$5\vec{j}$, the resultant vector of 3**A**+2**B** equals

    A. $3\vec{i}$ -$2\vec{j}$

    B. $5\vec{i}$ + $\vec{j}$

    C. $7\vec{i}$ -$9\vec{j}$

    D. $8\vec{i}$ - $\vec{j}$

    E. $2\vec{i}$ +$3\vec{j}$

4. An airplane heads due north with an airspeed of 75m/s. The wind is blowing due west at 18m/s. What is the airplane's speed relative to the ground?

A. 57m/s

B. 73m/s

C. 77m/s

D. 93m/s

E. 98m/s

5. An airplane flies with velocity 400.0 km/h, 140.0^0 (40.0^0 north of west). Which of the following are the components of this velocity? (Assume positive x = east and positive y = north.)

    A. v_x = – 306 km/h, v_y = 257 km/h

    B. v_x = – 257 km/h, v_y = 306 km/h

    C. v_x = 306 km/h, v_y = – 257 km/h

    D. v_x = – 257 km/h, v_y = 306 km/h

    E. None of the above

6. Vector **A** has a magnitude of 8 and vector **B** has a magnitude of 4. The magnitude of **A+B** is can't be

    A. 12

    B. 2

    C. 4

    D. 5

    E. 10

7. **A** and **B** are vectors, and θ is the angle between them. What can you do to maximize **A·B**?

    I. Maximize the magnitude of A.

    II. Maximize the magnitude of B.

    III. Set θ to 90^0.

A. I only

B. III only

C. I and II only

D. I, II and III

E. None of the above

8. Two vectors **A** and **B** are in the plane of the page and have magnitudes 3 and 4 respectively. Which of the following statements is NOT true about **A** × **B**?

A. It is a vector that is perpendicular with the page.

B. It has a magnitude that is less than or equal to 12.

C. It has no component in the plane of the page.

D. The angle it makes with **B** is the same with the angle it makes with **A**.

E. It is the same as **B** × **A**.

Answers and Explanations

Multiple Choice Answers

1. C   2. A   3. D   4. C   5. A   6. B   7. C   8. E

Multiple Choice Explanations

1. C。选项 B 中温度是标量，位移是向量。C 中加速度为向量，速率为标量。

2. A。2A-B 的方向由 B 的矢端指向 2A 的矢端。

3. D。3A+2B=3($2\vec{i}$ +3 $\vec{j}$)+2($2\vec{i}$ -5 $\vec{j}$)=($6\vec{i}$ +9 $\vec{j}$)+($2\vec{i}$ -10 $\vec{j}$)=$8\vec{i}$ - $\vec{j}$

4. C。$v_{地}$ = $v_{飞机}$ + $v_{风}$ =75 $\vec{j}$ -18 $\vec{i}$ ， $v=\sqrt{75^2+18^2}$ =77m/s

5. A。 v_x =vcos140°, v_y =vsin140°

6. B。A+B 的最大值是 8+4=12，最小值是 8-4=4。

7. C。A·B=ABcosθ, θ =90° 时 A·B=0

8. E。A×B = - B×A ≠ B×A

Kinematics
运动学

Introduction: *Kinematics* is the description of how objects move and is defined to be the study of motion without regard to mass and force. The description of the motion of any object must always be given relative to some particular reference frame. If we know *where* and *when* an object is in space, we can completely describe its motion in terms of quantities like distance, displacement, speed, velocity, and acceleration.

2.1 Motion in One Dimension   2.1 一维运动

2.1.1 Some Concepts   2.1.1 基本概念

Frame of Reference: The selected body in order to determine the position of other body.

参照系

If we choose different objects as the reference frames to describe the motion of a given body, the indications will be different.

Coordinate system: It is fixed on the frame, relative to which position, velocity, acceleration and orbit of the object can be specified quantitatively.

坐标系

Particle: It is an ideal model. In some circumstances, we can treat a body as a particle, and concentrate on its translational motion and ignore all the other motions.

质点

Time instant and time interval: Time t is a given instant, and time interval Δt is the difference of two given instants. We use the former to describe the state of the object, the latter to describe the process.

时刻和时间间隔

Units: when dealing with the laws and equations of physics it is very important to use a consistent set of units. Today the most important system of units is the System International, which is abbreviated **SI**. In SI units, the standard of length is the meter, for time is the second, and for mass is the kilogram—kg, m, and s.

国际标准单位：kg, m, s

2.1.2 Position, Displacement and Distance

2.1.2 位置、位移和路程

Position: An object's position is its location at a given point in time. The vector from the origin of the coordinate system to the object's position is known as the position vector, **x**(t).

位置：坐标原点指向所在点的向量 x(t)

Displacement: As an object moves, its position changes with time, this change in position is called displacement, **Δx=x₂−x₁**, during the time interval Δt =t₂−t₁. Its direction points from the object's initial position x₁ to its final position x₂, regardless of the path actually taken.

位移：位置的变化 Δx =x₂−x₁

Position and displacement are both vectors, they have magnitude and direction.

位置和位移都是向量。

In one dimensional motion, a vector pointing to the right has a positive value, whereas, one pointing to the left has negative value. So negative signs just tell you the direction is opposite to the right.

一维运动用正负表示方向。

A graph of the position as a function of time is called an x versus t graph; it might appear as in Figure 2-1.

Distance S is a scalar that represents the total amount traveled by an object. The total distance traveled is not necessarily equal to the magnitude of the change in the position vector during the time interval **Δt** if the particle changes direction or moves back and forth along the axis while moving from x_1 to x_2.

路程：Δs，是标量

$$\Delta s \geq |x_2 - x_1|$$

$$\Delta s \geq |x_2 - x_1|$$

Units for position, distance and displacement are meters (m).

Example 2.1: The position vector of a particle is given by the following function of time, x(t)=4.00–(2.00)t –(3.00)t^2 (m), Where the time t is expressed in seconds on a stopwatch?

a.   What is the position vector of the particle at the instant t=0?

b. What is the position vector of the particle when the stopwatch indicates t=3.00s?

c. What is the change in the position vector during the three second interval between these time instants?

Solution:

a. x(0)=4m

b. x(3)= -29m

c. **Δx**=x(3) − x(0)=-33m

2.1.3 Velocity and Speed

The most obviously aspect of the motion of a moving object is **how fast it is moving**—its speed or velocity.

1. Average speed and average velocity

The **average speed** of a particle during a time interval Δt is defined as the total distance traveled along its path divided by time interval.

$$v_{ave} = \frac{\Delta s}{\Delta t}$$

The average speed is a positive scalar quantity, not a vector.

Average velocity is defined in terms of displacement, the displacement during a time interval divided by the time interval.

$$V_{ave} = \frac{x_2 - x_1}{t_2 - t_1} = \frac{\Delta x}{\Delta t}$$

Shown in Figure 2-1. Average speed and average velocity have the same magnitude when the motion is all in one direction. In other cases they may differ.

2. Instantaneous Speed and Instantaneous Velocity

The **instantaneous velocity** (speed) at any moment is defined as the average velocity (speed) over on infinitesimally short time interval. That is, to be evaluated in the limit of Δt becoming extremely small, approaching zero. We can write it as V for one-dimensional motion.

$$V = \lim_{\Delta t \to 0} \frac{\Delta x}{\Delta t} = \frac{dx}{dt} \quad , \quad v = \lim_{\Delta t \to 0} \frac{s}{\Delta t} = \frac{ds}{dt}$$

2.1.3 速度和速率

速度是描述物体运动快慢的物理量。

1. 平均速率和平均速度

平均速率：$v_{ave} = \dfrac{\Delta s}{\Delta t}$

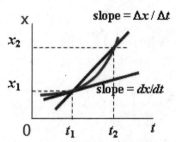

Figure 2-1 x − t graph and velocity

平均速度：$V_{ave} = \dfrac{\Delta x}{\Delta t}$

是向量，用正负表示方向。

一维同方向运动，位移的大小是路程。

2. 瞬时速率和速度

瞬时速度是平均速度的极限，是 x–t 图中曲线切线的斜率。

是运动方程的一阶导数。瞬时速率是平均速率的极限。

The velocity V is a vector quantity whose magnitude v is equal to the instantaneous speed. Shown in Figure 2-1.

$$|V| = v$$

$$V = \lim_{\Delta t \to 0} \frac{\Delta x}{\Delta t} = \frac{dx}{dt}$$

瞬时速度的大小是瞬时速率。$|V| = v$

From above, we have $dx = v(t)dt$

Integral two sides from t_1 to t_2, we have

$$\Delta x = \int_{t_1}^{t_2} v(t)dt$$

Area under the velocity-time graph gives you displacement.

V-t 图中曲线下面积是位移。

In summary from above, we know

$$\overline{V}_{ave} = \frac{x_2 - x_1}{t_2 - t_1} = \frac{\Delta x}{\Delta t}$$: the slope of the secant line.

$$v = \lim_{\Delta t \to 0} \frac{\Delta x}{\Delta t} = \frac{dx}{dt}$$: the slope of the tangent line.

$$\Delta x = \int_{t_1}^{t_2} v(t)dt$$: the displacement is the area under the V-t graph.

平均速度计算：平均值定理

$$\overline{V}_{ave} = \frac{\int_{t_1}^{t_2} v(t)\,dt}{dt}$$

$$\overline{V}_{ave} = \frac{x_2 - x_1}{t_2 - t_1} = \frac{\Delta x}{\Delta t} = \frac{\int_{t_1}^{t_2} v(t)\,dt}{dt}$$: instantaneous speed $v = |V|$

平均速率计算：

$$\overline{v}_{ave} = \frac{\int_{t_1}^{t_2} |V(t)|\,dt}{dt}$$

Average speed $\overline{v}_{ave} = \dfrac{\int_{t_1}^{t_2} |V(t)|\,dt}{dt}$, usually it is not equal to $\overline{V}_{ave}$.

Example 2.2 Given x as a function of t: A jet engine moves along an experimental track. We will treat the engine as a particle. Its position as a function of time is given by the equation

x=2.10t^2+2.80 (m).

a. Determine the displacement of the engine during the time

interval from t_1=3.00s to t_2=5.00s.

b. Determine the average velocity during this time interval.

c. Determine the magnitude of the instantaneous velocity at t=5.00s.

Solution:

a. At t_1=3.00s, the position x_1=2.10*3.00^2+2.80=21.7m

At t_2=5.00s, the position x_2=2.10*5.00^2+2.80=55.3m

The displacement is thus $\Delta_x = x_2 - x_1$ =33.6m

b. The average velocity can then be calculated as

$$V_{ave} = \frac{x_2 - x_1}{t_2 - t_1} = \frac{\Delta x}{\Delta t} = \frac{33.6m}{2.00s} = 16.8\text{m/s}$$

c. The instantaneous velocity at t=5.00s equals the slope of the tangent to the curve. We can calculate v for any time t using the given formula

$$x = 2.10\,t^2 + 2.80 \text{ (m)}$$

$$v(t) = \frac{d}{dt}\,x = \frac{d}{dt}(2.10\,t^2 + 2.80) = 4.20t$$

when t=5.00s, v = 4.20*5.00=21.0m/s

2.1.4 Acceleration

Acceleration specifies **how rapidly the velocity of an object is changing.** An object whose velocity is changing is said to be accelerating.

Average acceleration is defined as the change in velocity divided by the time taken to make this change:

$$a_{avg} = \frac{\Delta v}{\Delta t}$$

It is the slope of the secant line shown in Figure 2-2.

2.1.4 加速度

加速度是描述物体速度变化快慢的物理量。

平均加速度：速度-时间曲线图割线的斜率

$$a_{avg} = \frac{\Delta v}{\Delta t}$$

The area under the *v-t* curve between t_1 and t_2 corresponds to the *displacement* of the particle during that time interval:

Acceleration is also a vector, but for one-dimensional motion, we need only use a plus or minus sign to indicate direction relative to a chosen coordinate system.

The **instantaneous acceleration**, a, is defined as the limiting value of the average acceleration as we let change of t approach zero:

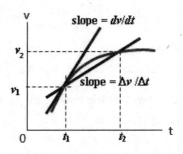

Figure 2-2 Acceleration in v-t graph

$$a= \lim_{\Delta t \to 0} \frac{\Delta v}{\Delta t} = \frac{dv}{dt} = \frac{d^2 x}{dt^2}$$

$$a= \lim_{\Delta t \to 0} \frac{\Delta v}{\Delta t} = \frac{dv}{dt} = \frac{d^2 x}{dt^2}$$

Instantaneous acceleration at t_1 is the slope of the tangent line at the point.

瞬时加速度是平均加速度的极限。

$\frac{d^2 x}{dt^2}$ is the second derivative of x with respect to time.

V-t 图曲线切线的斜率是加速度。

$a = \frac{dv}{dt}$, $dv = adt$. So integral both sides, we have

加速度是速度的一阶导数，是运动方程的二阶导数。

$$\Delta v = \int_{t_1}^{t_2} a(t)dt$$

In summary from Figure 2-2, we have:

$a_{ave} = \frac{\Delta v}{\Delta t}$: slope of the secant line of AB.

平均加速度—割线斜率
瞬时加速度—切线斜率

$a = \frac{dv}{dt}$: slope of the tangent line at A.

$\Delta x = \int_{x_1}^{x_2} dx = \int_{t_1}^{t_2} vdt$: area under the *v-t* curve between t_1 and t_2

位移： $\Delta x = \int_{t_1}^{t_2} vdt$

$\Delta v = \int_{t_1}^{t_2} a(t)dt$: area under the a-t curve between t_1 and t_2

V-t 曲线下的面积

速度变化： $\Delta v = \int_{t_1}^{t_2} a(t)dt$

$a_{ave} = \frac{\Delta v}{\Delta t} = \frac{\int_{t_1}^{t_2} a(t)dt}{dt}$

$a-t$ 曲线图中曲线下面积

平均值定理求平均加速度

Example 2.3: A particle is moving in a straight line so that its

position is given by the relation, x=2.10t^2+2.80 (m), calculate

a. its average velocity during the time interval from t_1=3.00s to

t_2=5.00s.

b. its instantaneous acceleration as a function of time.

Solution:

a. V=$\dfrac{dx}{dt}$=4.20t m/s

$$a_{avg} = \frac{\Delta v}{\Delta t} = \frac{V(5)-V(3)}{5-3} = 4.20 m/s^2$$

b. $a = \dfrac{dV}{dt}$ =4.20m/s^2

The particle is moving in a constant acceleration.

2.1.5 Motion at a Constant Acceleration (UAM)

2.1.5 匀加速运动

Uniform acceleration motion (UAM) is a special case of motion at a=constant. For an object with uniform acceleration a, initial velocity

v_0 and position x_0, we have

加速度为常数。

a=$\dfrac{dv}{dt}$=Constant,

solving the differential equation, we can get

速度方程:

V(t)=v_0+ at

V(t)=v_0+at

and V=$\dfrac{dx}{dt}$=v_0+ at, solving this differential equation, we have

X(t)=x_0+ $\displaystyle\int_0^t (v_0 + at)dt$

运动方程:

X(t)=x_0+v_0t+$\dfrac{1}{2}at^2$

X(t)=x_0+v_0t+$\dfrac{1}{2}at^2$

Eliminate t from above to get an equation that relates velocity directly to position. It is a useful equation for solving questions.

$$v^2 - v_0{}^2 = 2a(x - x_0)$$

And $\overline{V} = \dfrac{V + V_0}{2}$

匀加速运动的重要方程：

$$v^2 - v_0{}^2 = 2a(x - x_0)$$

匀加速运动的平均速度：

$$\overline{V} = \dfrac{V + V_0}{2}$$

Graphs for uniformly accelerated motion in the special case of constant acceleration tell us:

匀加速运动图像给出：

1. The a(t)=constant graph is a horizontal line. The area under the line in some interval Δt is the change of velocity Δv.

1. 在匀加速运动在 a-t 图中是一条水平线。直线下的面积是速度变化，Δv。

2. V(t)= v_0 +at. The V(t) graph is a line that may have a nonzero slope. A positive slope corresponds to positive acceleration, and a negative slope to negative acceleration. The area under the line is the change of position Δ x-displacement in corresponding time interval.

2. V-t 图中匀加速运动是一条斜率为正或负的直线。直线下的面积代表位移。

3. X(t)= x_0 + v_0 t+ $\dfrac{1}{2}at^2$. The X(t) graph is a parabola if there is nonzero acceleration.

3. X-t 图是一个抛物线，曲线每点的斜率是该点的速度。

Falling Objects:

自由落体—匀加速运动

At a given location on the Earth and in the absence of air resistance, all objects fall with the same constant acceleration, a = g =9.80m/s^2 downward pointing to the center of the Earth. We call g the acceleration due to gravity. Since the motion is vertical we will substitute y in place of all x. It is arbitrary whether we choose y to be positive in the upward direction or in the downward direction; but we must be consistent about it throughout a problem's solution.

重力加速度 g

y 轴方向正负选取依问题方便而定，同一问题正方向要保持一致。

Example 2.4: Suppose that a ball is dropped from a tower 70.0m high. How far will it have fallen after 1.00s, 2.00s and 3.00s? Assume y is positive downward. Neglect air resistance.

Solution:

y_0 =0 and v_0 =0. a=9.8m/s^2

Then after 1.00s, the position of the ball is $y(1)=\dfrac{1}{2}at^2$ =4.90m.

The ball has fallen a distance of 4.90m after 1.00s.

Similarly, after 2.00s, $y(2)=\dfrac{1}{2}at^2$ =19.6m

and after 3.00s, $y(3)=\dfrac{1}{2}at^2$ =44.1m.

2.2 Motion in Two Dimensions and Projectile Motion

2.2 二维运动和抛体运动

We can extend our definitions of velocity and acceleration in a formal way to two dimensional motions. Suppose a particle follows a path in the xy plane as shown in Figure 2-3.

2.2.1 Position function

$$\vec{r} = \vec{r}(t) = x(t)\vec{i} + y(t)\vec{j}$$

Its two components are

$$\begin{cases} x = x(t) \\ y = y(t) \end{cases}$$

These represent a parametric defined function with parameter t.

Eliminating parameter t, we will have   y=f(x)

It is the path equation of the particle or we call trajectory of the particle.

At time t_i, the particle is at point A, and at time t_f, it is at B. The vector $\mathbf{r_i}$ is the position vector of the particle at time t_i, and $\mathbf{r_f}$ is the position vector at time t_f.

Example 2.5: Known the position function of a particle moving in a plane is $\vec{r} = 2t\vec{i} + (2-t^2)\vec{j}$, it is in seconds and r is in meters.

Find

a. position vector at t=0s and t=2s.

b. the trajectory of the particle.

Solution:

2.2.1 位置方程

位置向量：$\vec{r} = \vec{r}(t)$ =xi+yj

位置向量的参数方程形式：

$$\begin{cases} x = x(t) \\ y = y(t) \end{cases}$$

消去参数 t 得到物体运动的轨道方程：y=f(x)

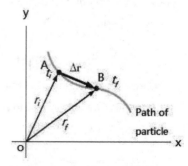

Figure 2-3 Position displacement and path of a particle

a. t=0s, r(0)=2j

Magnitude is r=2

$$\tan \theta = \frac{y}{x} = \frac{2}{0} = \infty \qquad \theta = 90°$$

t=2s, **r(2)=4i-2j**

Magnitude is r= $\sqrt{20}$ =4.47

$$\tan \theta = \frac{y}{x} = \frac{-2}{4} = -0.5 \qquad \theta = -26°32'$$

b. The parametric function for this particle is

$$\begin{cases} x = 2t \\ y = 2 - t^2 \end{cases}$$

Eliminating t we have the trajectory function

$$y = 2 - \frac{x^2}{4}$$

The particle's path is a parabola bending downward.

2.2.2 Displacement

The displacement vector is defined as the vector representing changing in position Δ**r**

$$\Delta \text{r=r}_f\text{-r}_i$$

This represents the displacement during the time interval Δt=t$_f$-t$_i$.
In unit vector notation, we can write

Hence Δ**r** = Δx**i**+ Δy**j**

Its magnitude of the displacement is the length of line segment AB,
$\left| \Delta \vec{r} \right|$

$$\left| \Delta \vec{r} \right| = \sqrt{(\Delta x)^2 + (\Delta y)^2}$$

S is the distance of the particle from A to B during time interval Δt=t$_f$-t$_i$, it is a scalar.

2.2.2 位移

位置的改变表示：Δ**r=r**$_f$**-r**$_i$

位移的直角坐标表示：
Δ**r** = Δx**i**+ Δy**j**

位移的大小：一般情况下位移的大小和路程不相等。

$$\left| \Delta \vec{r} \right| = \sqrt{(\Delta x)^2 + (\Delta y)^2}$$

Usually distance ΔS is not equal to the magnitude of displacement。

$$\Delta S \neq \left| \Delta \vec{r} \right|$$

Example 2.6: A particle is located at r_1=5i-7j at t1, r_2=-3i-5j at t2, find the displacement at this time interval.

Solution: r_2-r_1=-8i+2j

2.2.3 Velocity

Average velocity

Average velocity vector, over the time interval Δt=t_2-t_1, is defined as

$$\vec{V} = \frac{\Delta \vec{r}}{\Delta t} = \frac{\vec{r}_2 - \vec{r}_1}{t_2 - t_1}$$

which has a direction as same as that of $\Delta \vec{r}$.

Average speed: $\bar{v} = \dfrac{\Delta s}{\Delta t}$

Instantaneous Velocity

We consider shorter and shorter time intervals, that is, we let Δt approach zero so that the distance between points B and A also approaches zero. We define the instantaneous velocity vector as the limit of the average velocity as Δt approaches zero:

$$\vec{V} = \lim_{\Delta t \to 0} \frac{\Delta \vec{r}}{\Delta t} = \frac{d\vec{r}}{dt}$$

The direction of V at any moment is along the line tangent to the path at that moment (Figure 2-4).

Speed and velocity

$$\text{Speed } v = \lim_{\Delta t \to 0} \frac{\Delta s}{\Delta t}$$

In the limit Δt approaching zero, Δt can be written as dt, displacement $\Delta \vec{r}$ during the time interval dt can be written as $d\vec{r}$, we also have ds representing Δs. Approximately

$$\text{ds} = \left| d\vec{r} \right|$$

2.2.3 速度

平均速度：

$$\vec{V} = \frac{\Delta \vec{r}}{\Delta t} = \frac{\vec{r}_2 - \vec{r}_1}{t_2 - t_1}$$

平均速度方向：起点连向终点的方向，即位移方向

平均速率：$\bar{v} = \dfrac{\Delta s}{\Delta t}$

瞬时速度：$\vec{V} = \lim\limits_{\Delta t \to 0} \dfrac{\Delta \vec{r}}{\Delta t} = \dfrac{d\vec{r}}{dt}$

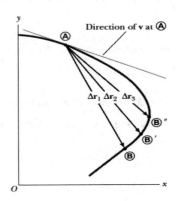

Figure 2-4 Direction of velocity

速度：时间间隔趋于零时，平均速度的极限。

瞬时速率：$v = \lim\limits_{\Delta t \to 0} \dfrac{\Delta s}{\Delta t}$

在微小时间间隔，位移的大小是路程：ds=$\left| d\vec{r} \right|$

Instantaneous speed: $v = \dfrac{ds}{dt} = \left| \dfrac{d\vec{r}}{dt} \right| = \left| \vec{V} \right|$

速度的大小是速率：$v = \left| \vec{V} \right|$

So the instantaneous speed always equals the magnitude of the instantaneous velocity at any time. In rectangular coordinates:

速度的分量表示：

$$\vec{V} = \dfrac{d\vec{r}}{dt} = \dfrac{dx}{dt}\vec{i} + \dfrac{dy}{dt}\vec{j} = V_x\vec{i} + V_y\vec{j}$$

$$\vec{V} = \dfrac{d\vec{r}}{dt} = V_x\vec{i} + V_y\vec{j}$$

$$V_x = \dfrac{dx}{dt}, V_y = \dfrac{dy}{dt}$$

Magnitude of velocity is: $V = \sqrt{V_x^2 + V_y^2}$

任意时刻速度大小：

$$V = \sqrt{V_x^2 + V_y^2}$$

The angle θ formed between $\vec{V}$ and +x direction can be determined

by: $\theta = \tan^{-1}\dfrac{V_y}{V_x}$

速度方向：$\theta = \tan^{-1}\dfrac{V_y}{V_x}$

2.2.4 Acceleration

2.2.4 加速度

Acceleration in two dimensions is treated in a similar way.

加速度定义类似速度定义。

Average acceleration is defined as: $\vec{a} = \dfrac{\Delta\vec{V}}{\Delta t} = \dfrac{\vec{V}_2 - \vec{V}_1}{t_2 - t_1}$

平均加速度：$\vec{a} = \dfrac{\Delta\vec{V}}{\Delta t}$

Instantaneous acceleration is defined as the limit of the average acceleration vector as the time interval Δt is allowed to approach zero.

瞬时加速度是平均速度的极限，是速度方程的一阶导数，运动方程的二阶导数。

$$\vec{a} = \lim_{\Delta t \to 0} \dfrac{\Delta\vec{V}}{\Delta t} = \dfrac{d\vec{V}}{dt} = \dfrac{d^2\vec{r}}{dt^2}$$

速度变化的方向是平均加速度的方向。

速度变化的极限方向是加速度的方向。

加速度指向曲线弯曲（凹）的一面。

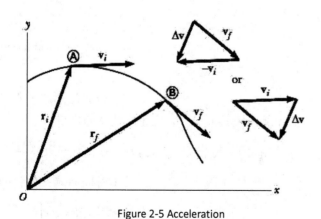

Figure 2-5 Acceleration

$$\vec{a} = \lim_{\Delta t \to 0} \frac{\Delta \vec{V}}{\Delta t} = \frac{d\vec{V}}{dt} = \frac{d^2 \vec{r}}{dt^2}$$

Using components of acceleration in x-y plane, we have:

$$\vec{a} = \frac{dV_x}{dt}\vec{i} + \frac{dV_y}{dt}\vec{j} = \frac{d^2x}{dt^2}\vec{i} + \frac{d^2y}{dt^2}\vec{j} = a_x\vec{i} + a_y\vec{j}$$

加速度直角坐标分量表示:

$$\vec{a} = a_x\vec{i} + a_y\vec{j}$$

Its magnitude and direction: $\quad a = \sqrt{a_x^2 + a_y^2} \qquad \phi = \tan^{-1}\frac{a_y}{a_x}$

加速度大小和方向:

$$a = \sqrt{a_x^2 + a_y^2}$$

$$\phi = \tan^{-1}\frac{a_y}{a_x}$$

The acceleration will be nonzero not only when the magnitude of the velocity changes, but also if its direction changes. For example, a person riding in a car traveling at constant speed around a curve, or a child riding on a merry-go-round, will both experience an acceleration because of a change in the direction of the velocity, even though its magnitude may be constant.

加速度的产生不仅是因为速率值的改变，速度的方向改变同样产生加速度。

Example 2.7: The position function of a particle is

$\vec{r} = 2\alpha t^2 \vec{i} + \beta t^3 \vec{j}$, where α and β are constants. Find the velocity

and acceleration of this particle.

Solution:

$$\vec{V} = \frac{d\vec{r}}{dt} = 4\alpha t\vec{i} + 3\beta t^2\vec{j} \qquad v = \sqrt{16\alpha^2 t^2 + 9\beta^2 t^4}$$

$$\vec{a} = \frac{d\vec{V}}{dt} = 4\alpha\vec{i} + 6\beta t\vec{j} \qquad a = \sqrt{16\alpha^2 + 36\beta^2 t^2}$$

Constant acceleration

匀加速运动

Now we consider motion in two dimensions for which the acceleration is constant both in magnitude and direction. That is a_x is constant, a_y is constant. The average acceleration in this case is equal to the instantaneous acceleration at any moment. The equations we derived for one dimensional motion apply separately to each perpendicular component of two dimensional motions. We

let $V_0 = V_{0x}$ i+ V_{0y} j be the initial velocity. According to the equations

we got above we can then write equations in the table below for two dimensions.

Table 2-1 Formula for Constant Acceleration in two Dimensions   二维匀加速运动分量公式

x Component(horizontal)	y Component(vertical)
$v_x = v_{x0} + a_x t$	$v_y = v_{y0} + a_y t$
$x = x_0 + v_{x0}t + \dfrac{1}{2}a_x t^2$	$y = y_0 + v_{y0}t + \dfrac{1}{2}a_y t^2$
$v_x^2 = v_{x0}^2 + 2a_x(x - x_0)$	$v_y^2 = v_{y0}^2 + 2a_y(y - y_0)$

The first two equations in Table 2-1 can be written in vector notation

V=v₀+at

r=r₀+v₀t+1/2 at²

Here, **r** is the position vector at any time. In practical situations, we usually use the component form given before with which we are very familiar.

二维运动的向量公式：

速度方程：**V=v₀+at**

运动方程：**r=r₀+v₀t+1/2 at²**

Projectile motion

Now we examine the motion of objects moving through the air in two dimensions near the Earth's surface, such as a golf ball, kicked football, and athletes doing the long jump or high jump. These are all examples of projectile motion, which we can describe as taking place in two dimensions. We just consider only its motion after it has been projected and is moving freely through the air under the action of gravity alone. Thus the acceleration of the object due to gravity is downward with magnitude a_y=g=9.8m/s^2. We choose upright as positive direction, then a_y = -g.

抛体运动

物体只在重力作用下运动——匀加速运动 a=-9.8m/s²

The x-component of the velocity is constant throughout the motion and equal to the initial x-component of the velocity

$v_x = v_{x0}$ (constant) because a_x =0m/s^2

So for horizontal motion: x(t)= $x_0 + v_{x0}t$

In vertical motion, a_y =constant= -g

水平方向加速度为零，物体做匀速直线运动。

竖直方向加速度为**-gj**，物体做匀加速运动。

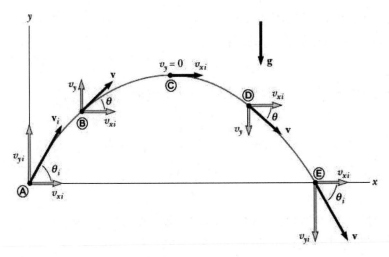

Figure 2-6 Project motion

$v_{x0} = v_0 \cos\theta_i$ $v_{y0} = v_0 \sin\theta_i$

For any time t, $\mathbf{V}(t) = v_0\cos\theta_i\mathbf{i} + (v_0\sin\theta_i - gt)\mathbf{j}$

Its magnitude is $V = \sqrt{v_x^2 + v_y^2}$

Direction can be calculated from $\tan\theta = \dfrac{v_y}{v_x}$;

θ is the angle between velocity V(t) and x axis in positive direction

Table 2-2 Kinematic Equations for Projectile Motion

(y positive upward)

Horizontal motion	vertical Motion
(a_x =0, v_x =constant)	(a_y = -g =constant)
$v_x = v_{x0}$	$v_y = v_{y0} - gt$
x(t)= $x_0 + v_{x0}t$	y(t) = $y_0 + v_{y0}t - \dfrac{1}{2}gt^2$
	$v_y^2 = v_{y0}^2 - 2gy$

加速度 $\vec{a} = -g\vec{j}$

初始条件：t=0 时，V_0，x_0

任意时刻 t 速度方程：

$\mathbf{V}(t) = v_0\cos\theta_i\mathbf{i} + (v_0\sin\theta_i - gt)\mathbf{j}$

速度大小和方向：

$V = \sqrt{v_x^2 + v_y^2}$

$\tan\theta = \dfrac{v_y}{v_x}$

θ：速度的方向与 x 轴夹角
抛体运动，y 向上为正。

运动方程： r(t)=xi+yj

运动方程的参数形式：

x(t)= $x_0 + v_{x0}t$

y(t)= $y_0 + v_{y0}t - \dfrac{1}{2}gt^2$

The equation for the trajectory y(x) of the particle is found by eliminating t from the equation above x(t) and y(t). We obtain

轨道方程：

$$y(x) = y_0 + v_{y0}\frac{x - x_0}{v_{x0}} - \frac{1}{2}g\left(\frac{x - x_0}{v_{x0}}\right)^2 \qquad \text{or}$$

$$y = (\tan\theta_i)x - \left(\frac{g}{2v_i^2\cos^2\theta_i}\right)x^2$$

$$y(x) = (\tan\theta_i)x - \left(\frac{g}{2v_i^2\cos^2\theta_i}\right)x^2$$

The equation for the trajectory y(x) is quadratic in x, indicating that the path in space is parabolic in shape. Two dimensional motions with a constant acceleration produce parabolic trajectories.

物体运动轨迹是抛物线

2.2.5 Solving problems involving projectile motion

2.2.5 抛体运动问题求解

You must avoid just plugging numbers into equations that seem to "work". As always, read carefully and draw a careful diagram. Follow the steps as below to crake all questions:

解决抛体运动问题的步骤：

1. Choose an origin and an XY coordinate system.

    1. 选择合适的原点和坐标。

2. Analyze the horizontal and vertical motion separately, given the initial velocity.

    2. 分别分析水平和竖直方向的运动。

3. List the known and unknown quantities, choosing a_y =-g or +g.

    3. 列出已知和待求物理量。

    Remember that v_x =constant, v_y =0 at the highest point of any trajectory that returns downward.

4. You may need to combine components of a vector to get magnitude and direction.

    4. 各向量分量求和解得向量的大小和方向。

2.3 Two types of Questions in Kinematics

2.3 运动学两类问题

A typical physics C kinematics question asks you to use calculus to find position, velocity or acceleration functions. In general, there are two kinds of problems to be solved.

考试中问题要求用微积分求位置、速度、和加速度方程。

1. Given position vector, find the velocity and acceleration by using derivation method.

    1. 已知位置方程，求导数可得速度和加速度方程。

2. Given acceleration (or velocity) and initial condition, find the velocity and position vector by means of vector integration

    2. 已知加速度（或速度）和初始条件，用积分计算可求

method.

速度（或位置）方程。

The following fundamental schematic is a guide to conversion between position, velocity and acceleration.

$$r(t) \underset{int\,egrate}{\overset{differentiate}{\rightleftharpoons}} V(t) \underset{int\,egrate}{\overset{differentiate}{\rightleftharpoons}} a(t)$$

First of all, if we know position function x=x(t), we can derive velocity and acceleration function by differentiation:

$$v(t) = \frac{dx}{dt} , \quad a(t) = \frac{dv}{dt} = \frac{d^2 x}{dt^2}$$

Secondly, if we know V(t) or a(t) plus initial condition, t=0: V=v_0

x=x_0, we can obtain velocity or position functions by integration:

$$x(t) = x_0 + \int_0^t V dt , \quad v(t) = v_0 + \int_0^t a dt$$

In graphical kinematics, the slope of a graph is related to the derivative of a function; the area under a graph is related to the integral of a function.

运动学图示问题：注意斜率和面积的意义。

Example 2.8: A particle moving in one dimension has a position function defined as: x (t)=t^4-4t.

已知运动方程求速度和加速度方程。

a. At what point in time does the particle change its direction along the x axis?

b. In what direction is the body traveling when its acceleration is 3m/s^2 ?

Solution:

a. The time the particle changing direction happens when velocity equals zero.

$$V(t) = \frac{dx}{dt} = 4t^3 - 4$$

Let V=0, solve the equation: t=1s

It happens at position x(1)=-3m

When t=0; x(0)=0, V(0)=-4m/s^2 ; it means the particle moves

starting from origin to left side at initial velocity 4m/s^2 .

When t=1s; X(1)=-3m, V(1)=0: it means after one second the particle arrived at 3m away from origin and velocity dropped to zero. It will move to right at next moment.

b. Acceleration function with time: $a = \dfrac{dv}{dt} = 12t^2$

a=3 m/s^2 =12t^2,   it happens at t=0.5s

at t=0.5s, x(0.5)=-1.94m, V(0.5)=-3.5m/s

It means at that time the particle is at 1.94m left and moves to left.

Example 2.9: An object moving along x-axis, its acceleration

function with time t (unit is second) is a = 4t m/s^2 . When t=0, the

object rests at 10m away from origin in positive direction of x-axis.

Try to find out velocity and position function respect to time.

已知加速度及初始条件求速度和运动方程。

Solution:

Known: t=0, V(0)=0 and x(0)=10m and $a = \dfrac{dv}{dt} = 4t$

Therefore: $dv = 4tdt$

$$\int dv = \int 4tdt$$

$$v = 2t^2 + c$$

When t=0, V=0, V= 2t^2 m/s

And, $v = \dfrac{dx}{dt} = 2t^2$

$$dx = 2t^2 dt$$

$$\int dx = \int 2t^2 dt$$

$$x = \frac{2}{3}t^3 + c$$

When t=0, x=10m, so we have $x = (\frac{2}{3}t^3 + 10)$ (m)

Example 2.10: An object is moving in a straight line at $a = \frac{dV}{dt} = -kV^2 t$, k is a constant number. When t=0, v= v_0, find velocity function v(t).

已知加速度求速度方程。加速度是速度和时间的函数。

Solution:

By separating variables to two sides of the equation a(t), we have

$$-\frac{dV}{V^2} = -ktdt$$

And then integral both sides

$$\int_{V_0}^{V} -\frac{dV}{V^2} = \int_{0}^{t} -ktdt$$

Thus $\frac{1}{v} - \frac{1}{v_0} = -\frac{1}{2}kt^2$

Solve for v: v(t)= $\dfrac{2v_0}{2 - kv_0 t^2}$

Example 2.11: The acceleration of a particle is given by $\vec{a} = 3.0t^2\vec{i} - 2.0\vec{j}$, the initial conditions are when t=0, $\vec{r_0} = 0, \vec{V_0} = 1.0\vec{i}$ .Find its velocity and position function **v**(t) and **x**(t)

Solution:

The velocity function is

$$\vec{a} = \frac{d\vec{V}}{dt} \Rightarrow \vec{V} = \int \vec{a}dt + \vec{V_0} = t^3\vec{i} - 2.0t\vec{j} + 1.0\vec{i}$$

$$= (t^3 + 1.0)\vec{i} - 2.0t\vec{j}$$

The position function of the particle is

$$\vec{V} = \frac{d\vec{r}}{dt} \Rightarrow \vec{r} = \int \vec{V} dt + \vec{r}_0 = (\frac{t^4}{4} + t)\vec{i} - t^2 \vec{j}$$

2.4 Circular Motion / 2.4 圆周运动

2.4.1 Nature Coordinate System

When a particle is moving along a circle, its velocity is always at the tangent direction. For circular motion or general curved motion, it is convenient using nature coordinate system which is shown as Figure 2-7 to describe the velocity and acceleration of a particle.

$\vec{\tau}$ (or **T**): the tangent unit vector whose magnitude is 1 and direction is always at tangent.

$\vec{n}$: the normal unit vector whose magnitude is also 1 and direction points to the center.

2.4.2 Kinematics of Circular Motion

Instantaneous velocity in circular motion is always tangent to circle and usually speed v is not a constant, v=v(t). Velocity can be written as

$$\vec{v} = v(t)\vec{\tau}$$

We derive both sides of the equation above, the acceleration will be

$$\vec{a} = \frac{d\vec{v}}{dt} = \frac{dv}{dt}\vec{\tau} + v\frac{d\vec{\tau}}{dt}$$

The first part of **a**, $a_t = \frac{dv}{dt}$, is the tangent component of **a**.

2.4.1 自然坐标系

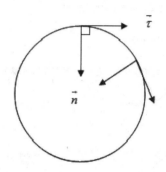

Figure 2-7 Nature coordinate system

圆周运动中，在每一点由切向和法向建立坐标系。

切向和法向单位向量：$\vec{\tau}, \vec{n}$

2.4.2 圆周运动学

圆周运动速度：沿切向

$$\vec{v} = v(t)\vec{\tau}$$

速度微分出现两个分量：

$$\vec{a} = \frac{d\vec{v}}{dt} = \frac{dv}{dt}\vec{\tau} + v\frac{d\vec{\tau}}{dt}$$

第一部分：$a_t = \frac{dv}{dt}$，沿切向

For a unit vector $\vec{\tau}$ we have

$$\vec{\tau} \cdot \vec{\tau} = 1$$

Derive the equation above, we obtain

$$\frac{d\vec{\tau}}{dt} \cdot \vec{\tau} + \vec{\tau} \cdot \frac{d\vec{\tau}}{dt} = 0$$

$$\vec{\tau} \cdot \frac{d\vec{\tau}}{dt} = 0 \quad \text{and} \quad |\vec{\tau}| \neq 0 \quad \left|\frac{d\vec{\tau}}{dt}\right| \neq 0$$

So we know: $\dfrac{d\vec{\tau}}{dt} \perp \vec{\tau}$

$\dfrac{d\vec{\tau}}{dt}$ is a vector whose limit direction is perpendicular to tangent

and points to the center of circle, normal direction **n**.

From the Figure 2-8, $d\tau /1 = \Delta l /r$, the magnitude of $\dfrac{d\vec{\tau}}{dt}$ is v/r

and;

$$a_n = \frac{v^2}{r} \vec{n}$$

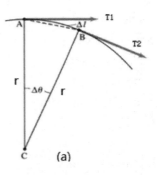

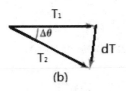

Figure 2-8 Direction of d τ /dt

加速度第二部分垂直切向，指向圆心—法向。

法向分量大小：

$$a_n = \frac{v^2}{r}$$

This acceleration is called the centripetal or radial acceleration, and it points towards the center of the circle.

So the total acceleration of circular motion is

$$\mathbf{a} = \mathbf{a}_t + \mathbf{a}_n = \frac{dv}{dt} \vec{\tau} + \frac{v^2}{r} \vec{n}$$

Uniform circular motion:

When an object is experiencing uniform circular motion, it is traveling in a circular path at a constant speed.

$$\frac{dv}{dt} = 0; \quad \mathbf{a} = \mathbf{a}_n = \frac{v^2}{r} \vec{n}$$

法向加速度方向指向圆心。

总加速度=切向加速度+法向加速度。指向曲线凹侧。

$$\vec{a} = \frac{dv}{dt} \vec{\tau} + \frac{v^2}{r} \vec{n}$$

匀速率圆周运动

$$\vec{a} = \frac{v^2}{r} \vec{n}$$

匀速圆周运动的加速度，也称之为向心加速度。加速度与速度垂直。

Thus the velocity and acceleration vectors are perpendicular to each other at every point for uniform circular motion. It is often described in terms of the frequency f as so many revolutions per second. The period T of an object revolving in a circle is the time required for one complete revolution. Period and frequency are related by

$$T = \frac{1}{f}$$

For an object revolving in a circle at constant speed v, we can write

$$v = \frac{2\pi r}{T}$$

Example 2.12 Acceleration of a revolving ball

A 100g ball at the end of a string is revolving uniformly in a horizontal circle of radius 0.500m. The ball makes 2.00 revolutions in a second. What is its centripetal acceleration?

Solution:

The revolution f=2，the ball's period is $T = \frac{1}{f} = 0.500s$, so

$$v = \frac{2\pi r}{T} = \frac{2*3.14*0.500}{0.500} = 6.28m/s$$

The centripetal acceleration is

$$a = \frac{v^2}{r} = 78.9m/s^2$$

2.4.3 Angular Quantities in Circular Motion

In the liner motion discussions, quantities as position, displacement, velocity, acceleration have been introduced. It is easy and simply to use angular quantities to describe circular motion. Suppose a particle P moves in a circular path with the center O in x-y plane as shown in Figure 2-9, the position vector **r** changes only in direction not in magnitude. Choose a reference line, ox, note that position vector **r** is at an angle θ to ox, and θ is varies with time

匀速率圆周运动周期和频率。

频率 f：每秒钟的转数

周期 T：每转一周用的时间

周期和频率的关系：

$$T = \frac{1}{f}$$

2.4.3 圆周运动角量描述

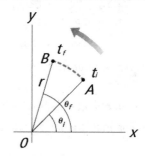

Figure 2-9 Angular quantities in circular motion

corresponding to the position vector's changing, specify the angular poison as a function of time, that is

$$\theta = \theta(t)$$

角位置 θ：位矢与 ox 夹角

If the particle moves from A to B in the time interval $\Delta t = t_f - t_i$ the position change is

$$\Delta\theta = \theta_f - \theta_i$$

角位移 $\Delta\theta$：逆时针为正

We define $\Delta\theta$ as the angular displacement. An angular displacement in the counterclockwise direction is positive, in the clockwise direction is negative.

The distance traveled along a circular path is $\Delta s = r\Delta\theta$.

路程与角位移关系：$\Delta s = r\Delta\theta$

We define the average angular velocity of the particle to be

$$\overline{\omega} = \frac{\Delta\theta}{\Delta t}$$

平均角速度：$\overline{\omega} = \frac{\Delta\theta}{\Delta t}$

The instantaneous angular velocity ω is the limit of this ratio as Δt is made to approach zero.

$$\omega = \lim_{\Delta t \to 0} \frac{\Delta\theta}{\Delta t} = \frac{d\theta}{dt}$$

瞬时角速度：平均角速度的极限，角位置方程一阶导数

$$\omega = \lim_{\Delta t \to 0} \frac{\Delta\theta}{\Delta t} = \frac{d\theta}{dt}$$

Angular speed has units of radians per second (rad/s), which can be written as s^{-1}. The angular velocity ω is either positive or negative, depending on whether the body is rotating counterclockwise (positive) or clockwise (negative).

角速度的单位：rad/s (弧度/秒) or rev/min (转/分)

If the instantaneous angular speed of an object changes from ω_i to ω_f in the time interval Δt, the object has an angular acceleration. The average angular acceleration α is defined as the ratio of the change in the angular velocity and the time interval.

$$\overline{\alpha} = \frac{\omega_f - \omega_i}{t_f - t_i} = \frac{\Delta\omega}{\Delta t}$$

平均角加速度：$\overline{\alpha} = \frac{\Delta\omega}{\Delta t}$

The (instantaneous) angular acceleration α is the limit in this equation as Δt approaches zero.

瞬时角加速度：

$$\alpha = \lim_{\Delta t \to 0} = \frac{\Delta\omega}{\Delta t} = \frac{d\omega}{dt}$$

$$\alpha = \lim_{\Delta t \to 0} = \frac{\Delta \omega}{\Delta t} = \frac{d\omega}{dt}$$

The unit of angular acceleration is commonly the radian per second-squared (rad/s^2 or the revolution per second-squared (rev/s^2).

角加速度的单位：rad/s^2 or rev/s^2

2.4.4 The Relationship of Linear and Angular Quantities

2.4.4 角量和线量的关系

From arc length formula ds=rdθ, we have

$$v = r\omega$$

Taking time differentiation of the equation above leads to

$$\frac{dv}{dt} = \frac{d\omega}{dt}r = r\alpha$$

This is the tangential component of linear acceleration

$$a_t = r\alpha$$

and $a_n = \omega^2 r$

The total acceleration **a** of the circular motion can be written as

a=a$_t$ + a$_n$

ds=rdθ

$$v = r\omega$$

$$a_t = r\alpha$$

$$a_n = \omega^2 r$$

2.4.5 Circular Motion with Uniform Angular Velocity and Acceleration

2.4.5 匀角速度和匀角加速度圆周运动

Uniform circular motion in polar coordinate system: r=constant and ω=constant, we have

$$\theta = \theta_0 + \omega t$$

θ_0 : initial angular position, when t=0, θ=θ$_0$

极坐标系中匀速圆周运动：

$$\theta = \theta_0 + \omega t$$

Uniform circular motion in Cartesian coordinate system:

$$x = r\cos(\omega t + \theta_0)$$

$$y = r\sin(\omega t + \theta_0)$$

直角坐标系中匀速圆周运动位置方程：

$$x = r\cos(\omega t + \theta_0)$$

$$y = r\sin(\omega t + \theta_0)$$

$$v_x = -r\omega\sin(\omega t + \theta_0)$$

$$v_y = r\omega\cos(\omega t + \theta_0)$$

速度方程：

$$v_x = -r\omega\sin(\omega t + \theta_0)$$

$$v_y = r\omega\cos(\omega t + \theta_0)$$

Circular motion with uniform angular acceleration: α=constant and initial condition: t=0, θ=θ_0, ω=ω_0; we can get

匀角加速度(α)圆周运动

$$\omega = \omega_0 + \alpha t$$

角速度： $\omega = \omega_0 + \alpha t$

$$\theta - \theta_0 = \omega_0 t + \frac{1}{2}\alpha t^2$$

角位置方程：

$$\theta = \theta_0 + \omega_0 t + \frac{1}{2}\alpha t^2$$

$$\omega^2 = \omega_0^2 + 2\alpha(\theta - \theta_0)$$

These three equations are similar to the equations of the motion on a straight line with constant acceleration motion. Table 2-3 compares the kinematic equations for rotational and linear motion.

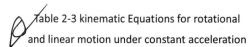
Table 2-3 kinematic Equations for rotational and linear motion under constant acceleration

Angular	Linear
$\omega = \omega_0 + \alpha t$	$v = v_0 + at$
$\theta - \theta_0 = \omega_0 t + \frac{1}{2}\alpha t^2$	$x - x_0 = v_0 t + \frac{1}{2}at^2$
$\omega^2 - \omega_0^2 = 2\alpha(\theta - \theta_0)$	$v^2 - v_0^2 = 2a(x - x_0)$
$\omega_{avg} = \dfrac{\omega + \omega_0}{2}$	$v_{avg} = \dfrac{v + v_0}{2}$

Example 2.13 Record player: An old-fashioned record player rotated at a constant angular speed of 4.8 rad/s. Find

匀角速度运动

a. the linear speed of the record at points 1.0 cm and 5.0 cm from the center.

b. the centripetal acceleration at these two points.

Solution:

a. at r=1.0 cm, v=rω=0.048 m/s

   at r=5.0 cm, v=rω=0.24 m/s

b. we obtain the centripetal acceleration $a_n = \dfrac{v^2}{r}$

   at r=1.0 cm, a_n=0.23 m/s^2

   at r=5.0 cm, a_n=1.15 m/s^2

Example 2.14: A wheel with a fixed axle is rotating and the angular   变速圆周运动

velocity is given as a function of the time by $\omega = 2t + 4t^2$, there

the unit of t is second. What is the angular acceleration at t= 0.3s?

solution:

According to $\alpha = \dfrac{d\omega}{dt}$, we have

$$\alpha = \dfrac{d\omega}{dt} = 2+8t$$

At t=0.3s, α=4.4m/s^2

Example 2.15 Rotating Wheel: A wheel rotates with a constant   匀角加速度运动
angular acceleration of 3.50 rad/s^2.

a. The angular speed of the wheel is 2.00 rad/s at t_0=0, through
what angular displacement does the wheel rotate in 2.00 s?

b. How many revolutions has the wheel turned during this time
interval?

c. What is the angular speed of the wheel at t=2.00 s?

Solution:

a. Δθ= $\theta - \theta_0 = \omega_0 t + \dfrac{1}{2}\alpha t^2$ =2*2+0.5 *3.5*4=11.0 rad

b. the number of revolutions: $n = \dfrac{11.0}{2\pi} = 1.75$ rev

c. $\omega = \omega_0 + \alpha t = 2 + 3.5*2 = 9.00 rad/s$

2.5 Relative Velocity   2.5 相对速度

We now consider how observations made in different frames of reference are related to each other. When the velocities are along the same line, simple addition or subtraction is sufficient to obtain the relative velocity. But if they are not along the same line, we must make use of vector addition.

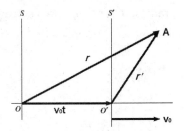

Figure 2-10 不同参照系下物体 A 的运动

We emphasize that when specifying a velocity, it is important to specify what the reference frame is. When determining relative velocity, it is useful to use a careful labeling process that makes things clear. Each velocity is labeled by two subscripts: the first refers to the object, the second to the reference frame in which it has this velocity.

确定速度时参照系的选择很重要。对不同参照系的速度要标示清楚。

A particle located at A is described by two observers, one in the fixed frame of reference S, and another in the frame S', which moves to the right with a constant velocity v_0. The vector r is the particle's position vector relative to S, and r' is its position vector relative to S', shown in Figure 2-10.

S'相对于 S 做匀速直线运动。两参照系 S、S'对物体在 A 点运动方程及速度描述不同：

We define the time $t=0$ as that instant at which the origins of the two reference frames coincide in space. At time t we have

相对 S 系，位置方程：r
相对 S' 系，位置方程：r'
$r'=r-v_0t$

$$r'=r-v_0t$$

If we differentiate the equation above with respect to time and note that v_0 is constant, we have obtain

相对速度：$V'=V-V_0$
V：绝对速度
V_0：牵连速度

$$V'=V-V_0$$

For example, suppose a boat is to cross a river to the opposite side, as shown in Figure 2-8.

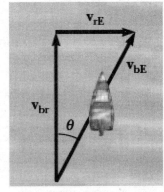

We let V_{br} be the velocity of the Boat with respect to the river.

Similarly, V_{bE} is the velocity of the Boat with respect to the Earth,

and V_{rE} is the velocity of the Water with respect to the Earth (river current). Note that V_{br} is what the boat's motor produces (against the water). Therefore, the velocity of the boat relative to the shore is

Figure 2-11 A boat across a river with constant velocity
船对水 V_{br}：相对速度
船对地面 V_{bE}：绝对速度

$$V_{bE} = V_{br} + V_{rE}$$

It is useful to remember that for any two objects or reference frames, A and B, the velocity of A relative to B has the same magnitude, but opposite direction, as the velocity of B relative to A.

$$V_{AB} = -V_{BA}$$

$$V_{AB} = V_A - V_B$$

水对地面 **V**$_{rb}$：牵连速度

$$V_{bE} = V_{br} + V_{rE}$$

两个相对运动的物体 A 和 B，A 相对于运动物体 B 的速度为 **V**$_{AB}$。

$$V_{AB} = V_A - V_B$$

V$_A$、**V**$_B$ 是物体 A 和 B 相对于地面的速度。

Example 2.16: An airplane whose airspeed is 200km/h heads due north. But a 100km/h wind coming from the northeast suddenly begins to blow. What is the resulting velocity of the plane with respect to the ground?

Solution:

Known: V_{pW} =200j km/h is the velocity of plane respect to air (wind). V_{WG} =100km/h(-cos45°i-sin45°j) is the velocity of wind respect to ground.

We need to ind: V_{PG} which is the velocity of the plane respect to ground. We have $V_{PG} = V_{pW} + V_{WG}$

V_{PG} =-100cos45° i +(200-100sin45°) j =-70.7km/h i +129km/h j

Magnitude of V_{PG} =137km/h

Direction of V_{PG} $\quad \theta$ =arctan$\dfrac{129}{-70.7}$ =115.6°, or 64.4^0 N of W

第二章总结 运动学

1. 描述运动的物理量

1）位置矢量：在直角坐标系中 **r(t)=x(t)i+y(t)j+z(t)k**。表示质点或物体在空间的位置，是时间的函数，给出物体在空间的轨迹。

2）位移向量：**Δr=r₂-r₁=Δx i+Δy j+Δz k**。是向量。表示物体空间位置改变。

路程：物体实际走过的距离，起点到终点的曲线长度。是标量。

3）速度：

平均速度：**V**$_{avg}$=Δ**r**/Δt

瞬时速度：**V**=d**r**/dt

速率：v=ds/dt

4）加速度：

平均加速度：**a**$_{avg}$=Δ**V**/Δt

瞬时加速度：**a**=d**V**/dt

2. 匀加速直线运动

1）一维运动—匀加速直线运动

2）二维运动—抛体运动（自由落体）

3. 运动学中的两类问题

1）由运动方程求速度、加速度。这类问题用求导数方法。

2）已知速度或加速度及初始条件求运动方程。这类问题由积分方法求得。

4. 圆周运动

角量描述：角位置—θ，角位移—$\Delta\theta$，角速度—$\omega = d\theta / dt$，角加速度—$\alpha = d\omega / dt$

角量线量关系：ds=rdθ，$v = r\omega$，$a_t = \dfrac{dv}{dt} = r\alpha ; a_n = \dfrac{v^2}{r} = r\omega^2$

匀速圆周运动：$T = \dfrac{2\pi}{\omega}, a = a_n = \dfrac{v^2}{r}$

一般圆周运动： $a_t = \dfrac{dv}{dt} = r\alpha; a_n = \dfrac{v^2}{r} = r\omega^2$

总加速度： $\vec{a} = \vec{a_t} + \vec{a_n}$

加速度大小： $a = \sqrt{a_t^2 + a_n^2}$ ，方向 $\tan\theta = \dfrac{a_n}{a_t}$

5. 相对运动

同一参照系内两物体 A、B 之间的相对运动。

$r_{BA} = r_B - r_A$ 或 $v_{BA} = v_B - v_A$

6. 一维运动函数图形

x-t 图的斜率是速度，V。

v-t 图中曲线下的面积是位移，Δx。

v-t 图中曲线的斜率是加速度，a。

a-t 图中曲线下的面积是速度变化，ΔV。

Chapter 2 Kinematics Practice

Multiple Choice Questions

1. Which of the following is/are true?

   I. If an object's acceleration is zero, then its speed must remain constant.

   II. If an object's speed remains constant, then its acceleration must be zero.

   III. If an object's acceleration is constant, then it must move in a straight line.

   A. I only

   B. II only

   C. I and II only

   D. I and III only

   E. II and III only

2. The acceleration of a particle that begins at rest at the origin is given by $a(t) = 3ti + 4tj$, where a is in m/s^2 and t is in seconds. The particle's distance from the origin at time $t = 2$ s is most nearly

   A. 6 m

   B. 7 m

   C. 8 m

   D. 9 m

   E. 10 m

3. At the top of a cliff 100 m high, a student throws a rock upward with the velocity 15.0 m/s. How long before he drops a second rock so both rocks arrive simultaneously at the bottom of the cliff?

   A. 5.05 s

   B. 3.76 s

   C. 2.67 s

   D. 1.75 s

   E. 1.56 s

4. An object moves in the *xy*-plane with a velocity given by $v(t) = 3t^2i + 4\sin 2t\, j$, where x and y are in meters and v is in meters per second. What is its displacement between $t=0$ and $t = 2$ s?

   A. $8i - 2(\cos 2)j$

   B. $8i - 2(\cos 4{-}2)j$

   C. $8i + 2(\cos 2)j$

   D. $8i + 2(\cos 4{+}2)j$

   E. $12i + 4(\sin 4)j$

5. An object moving horizontally with a speed v falls off the edge of a vertical cliff and lands a distance d from the base of the cliff. If it had landed a distance $2d$ from the base of the cliff, how fast would the object have been moving?

   A. v

   B. $\sqrt{2}\,$v

   C. 2v

   D. 4v

   E. It cannot be determined unless the height of the cliff is known.

Questions 6 and 7

The graph below shows the velocity *versus* time for an object moving in a straight line.

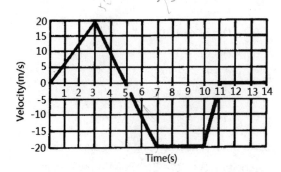

47

6. At what time after $t = 0$ does the object again pass through its initial position?

   A. 11 s
   B. 5 s
   C. 7 s
   D. 8.5 s
   E. 9.5 s

7. During which interval does the particle have the same average acceleration as $11s < t < 13$ s?

   A. $9\,s < t < 11\,s$
   B. $2\,s < t < 5\,s$
   C. $0\,s < t < 3\,s$
   D. $3\,s < t < 7\,s$
   E. $5\,s < t < 11\,s$

8. The velocity of a car traveling on a straight track along the x-axis is given by the equation $v(t) = -12t^2 + 6t + 2$, where v is in meters per second and t is in seconds. The vehicle's initial position is $x_0 = -1$ m. At which one of the following time is the car at the origin?

   A. Zero
   B. 1 s
   C. 2 s
   D. 3 s
   E. 4 s

9. The equation for the position x of a particle whose acceleration is given by the equation $a(t) = 6t - 3$ and starts at rest from the origin is

   A. $x(t) = 3t^2 - 3t$
   B. $x(t) = 6t^2 - 3t$
   C. $x(t) = t^3 - 3t^2/2$
   D. $x(t) = 6t^3 - 3t$
   E. $x(t) = 3t^3 - t$

10. An object moves along the x-axis with a velocity $v(t) = 3t^2 - 2t - 3$, where v is in m/s

and t is in seconds. What is the total distance traveled during the time interval $2 < t < 5$ s?

   A. 80 m
   B. 83 m
   C. 85 m
   D. 87 m
   E. 90 m

11. The position of a particle moving along the x-axis is given by the equation $x(t) = 1 + t^2 + t^3$, where x is in meters and t is in seconds. What is the average acceleration during the interval $t = 1$ to $t = 2s$?

   A. 6 m/s^2
   B. 9 m/s^2
   C. 11 m/s^2
   D. 13 m/s^2
   E. 20 m/s^2

12. Plane A is flying at 400 mph in the northeast direction relative to the earth. Plane B is flying at 500 mph in the north direction relative to the Earth. The velocity of Plane B as observed from Plane A is

   A. 900 mph, 52.5^{0}N of E
   B. 640 mph, 52.5^0 N of W
   C. 357 mph, 37.5^0 N of W
   D. 100 mph, 37.5^0 N of E
   E. 98.2 mph, 36.9^0 N of W

13. A train slows down as it rounds a sharp horizontal turn, slowing from 90.0 km/h to 50.0 km/h in the 15.0 s that it takes to round the bend. The radius of the curve is 150 m. Assume it continues to slow down at this time at the same rate. The magnitude of the acceleration at the moment the train speed reaches 50.0 km/h is

   A. 1.48 m/s^2
   B. 0.74 m/s^2
   C. 1.29 m/s^2

D. 0.55 m/s²

E. 1.65 m/s²

14. A ship can travel at a maximum speed of 8 km/h in any direction in still water. What is the maximum velocity of the ship relative to the shore if it is moving perpendicular to a 6 km/h current?

A. 2 km/h

B. 6 km/h

C. 8 km/h

D. 14 km/h

E. 10 km/h

15. A truck traveled 1200 meters south in 80 seconds and then 500 meters west in 20 seconds. The magnitude of the average velocity of the truck is most nearly

A. 10 m/s

B. 13 m/s

C. 17 m/s

D. 25 m/s

E. 30 m/s

16. A particle is moving along the curve $y = x^3 + 2x$ with a constant x-component of velocity of 4 m/s. What is the y-component of its velocity at $x = 2$ m?

A. 4 m/s

B. 14 m/s

C. 32 m/s

D. 56 m/s

E. 64 m/s

$y' = 3x^2 + 2$

17. An object moves in the xy-plane according to the equations $x(t) = t^3$ and $y = \cos t$, where x and y are in meters and t is in seconds. What is the magnitude of its velocity at $t = \pi$ s?

A. Zero

B. 1

C. π^3

D. $3\pi^2$

E. $9\pi^4$

18. Which one of the following statements is true concerning the motion of an ideal projectile launched at an angle of 45⁰ to the horizontal?

A. The speed at t=0 of the trajectory is zero.

B. The object's speed remains constant during the entire flight.

C. The horizontal speed decreases on the way up and increases on the way down.

D. The acceleration vector points opposite to the velocity vector on the way up and in the same direction as the velocity vector on the way down.

E. The vertical speed decreases on the way up and increases in the way down.

19. Two cars initially at the origin begin moving with velocities $v_1(t) = (2i + 3j)$ and $v_2(t) = (-i + j)$, where both velocities are in m/s. What is the rate at which the distance between the cars is increasing?

A. $\sqrt{2}$ m/s

B. 3 m/s

C. $\sqrt{15}$ m/s

D. $\sqrt{13}$ m/s

E. 5 m/s

20. An electric motor rotating a wheel at 120 rev/min is switched off. With constant negative angular acceleration of magnitude 2.00 rad/s², how long does it take the wheel to stop? Through how many radians does it turn while it is slowing down?

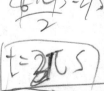

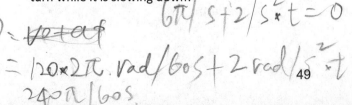

A. 3.14s; 39.5rad

B. 3.14s; 12.6rad

C. 6.28s; 39.5rad

D. 6.28s; 9.87rad

E. 12.6s; 12.6rad

21. A car is moving with decreasing speed on a circular-arc track of radius r=300m. Suppose that the speed of the car is v=9m/s,

tangential acceleration a_t is 0.2m/s^2 at one

instant. The car's total acceleration is

A. 0.2m/s^2, along tangential

B. 0.27m/s^2, pointing center of the circle

C. 0.34m/s^2, 53.4^0 with tangential

D. 0.47m/s^2, 36.6^0 with tangential

E. 0.34m/s^2, 36.6^0 with tangential

22. A particle is moving on a circle of radius r=1m. Its angular position is given by the

formula $\theta = 1 + 3t - 4t^2$. The speed and tangential acceleration at the end of 2 s is

A. -15m/s; -18m/s^2

B. 15m/s; 18m/s^2

C. 45m/s; 48m/s^2

D. -45m/s; -48m/s^2

E. 45m/s; -48m/s^2

Free Response Questions

1. A particle moves along a straight line, x. At time t=0, its position is at x=0. The velocity, V, of the object changes as a function of time, t, as indicated in Figure below.

   A. What is the position x of the particle at t=1s?

   B. What is the acceleration of the particle at t=2s?

   C. What is the position of the particle x at t=3s?

   D. What is the average velocity of the particle between t=0 and t=3s?

   E. What is the average speed of the particle between t=0 and t=3s?

   F. Make a plot of position x versus time

   between t=0 and t=3s. Indicate clearly in your plot at t=0, 1, 2, 3s what exactly the x positions are.

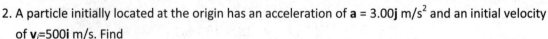

2. A particle initially located at the origin has an acceleration of **a** = 3.00**j** m/s^2 and an initial velocity of **v**$_i$=500**i** m/s. Find

   A. the vector position and velocity at any time *t* and

   B. the coordinates and speed of the particle at *t* = 2.00 s.

3. A car travels due east with a speed of 50.0 km/h. Raindrops are falling at a constant speed vertically with respect to the Earth. The traces of the rain on the side windows of the car make an angle of 60.0° with the vertical. Find the velocity of the rain with respect to

   A. the car and

   B. the Earth.

4. An object moves along the *x* axis according to the equation $x(t) = (3.00t^2 - 2.00t + 3.00)$ m. Determine

   A. the average speed between $t = 2.00$ s and $t = 3.00$ s,

   B. the instantaneous speed at $t = 2.00$ s and at $t = 3.00$ s,

   C. the average acceleration between $t = 2.00$ s and $t = 3.00$ s, and

   D. the instantaneous acceleration at $t = 2.00$ s and $t = 3.00$ s.

5. A projectile is fired up an incline (incline angle ϕ) with an initial speed v_i at an angle θ_i with respect to the horizontal ($\theta_i > \phi$), as shown in Figure below:

   A. Show that the projectile travels a distance *d* up the incline, where

$$d = \frac{2v_i^2 \cos\theta_i \sin(\theta_i - \phi)}{g \cos^2 \phi}$$

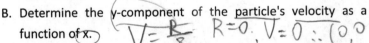

   B. For what value of θ_i is *d* a maximum, and what is that maximum value?

6. A particle starting from origin O moves along a parabola with equation $y = \frac{1}{4}x^2$ shown below. Suppose the particle moves so that the x-component of its velocity has the constant value $v_x = C$.

   A. On the diagram above, indicate the directions of the particle's velocity vector **v** and acceleration vector **a** at point R, and label each vector.

   B. Determine the y-component of the particle's velocity as a function of x.

   C. Determine the y-component of the particle's acceleration.
Suppose, instead, that the particle moves along the same parabola with a velocity whose x-component is given by $v_x = C/2(1+x^2)^{½}$

   D. Show that the particle's speed is constant in this case.

   E. On the diagram above, indicate the directions of the particle's velocity vector **v** and acceleration at point R again.

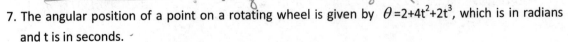

7. The angular position of a point on a rotating wheel is given by $\theta = 2+4t^2+2t^3$, which is in radians and t is in seconds.

   A. Find the point's angular position and its angular velocity

   B. What is its angular velocity at t=4s?

   C. Calculate its angular acceleration at t=2.0s

Answers and Explanations

Multiple Choice Answers

1. A　2. B　3. D　4. B　5. C　6. D　7. E　8. B　9. C　10. D　11. C　12. C　13. A　14. E　15. B
16. D　17. D　18. E　19. D　20. C　21. C　22. D

Multiple Choice Explanations

1. A。加速度为零，物体的运动速度保持常数或零不变；匀速率圆周运动加速度不为零；斜抛运动加速度为常数，物体的运动轨迹为抛物线。

2. B。当 t=0 时，x=0，v=0；$V=\int_0^2 adt = \frac{3}{2}t^2 i + 2t^2 j$，位置方程 $r=\int_0^2 Vdt = \frac{t^3}{2}i + \frac{2}{3}t^3 j$；当 t=2s 时，$r=4i+\frac{16}{3}j$，大小为 $r \approx 7m$。

3. D。　第一块石头落地所用时间：$y=y_0+v_0t_1-\frac{1}{2}gt_1^2=0$，$t_1=6.22s$；第二块石头落地所用时间：$y=\frac{1}{2}gt_2^2=100$，$t_2=4.47s$。当第二块石头在第一块石头抛出后 t_1-t_2=1.75s 扔出，两块石头同时落地。

4. B。$\Delta r= \int_0^2 Vdt = (t^3 i - 2\cos 2tj)_0^2 =$8i-(2cos4-2)j

5. C。水平距离 d=vt，2d=（2v）t 。

6. D。物体回到原点，$\Delta x = 0$；求得 t=8.5s。

7. E。在时间间隔（12,14）s 内，平均加速度 a=0；$\bar{a}=\frac{v_f-v_i}{\Delta t}$，任意速度相同的两点间的平均加速度都为零。

8. B。位移 $\Delta x = x - x_i = \int_0 vdt$，x=0 and x$_i$=-1m，求得 t=1s。

9. C。 a=6t-3, and $v_i = 0, x_i = 0$；$v = \int_0^t adt = 3t^2 - 3t$；$x = \int_0^t vdt = t^3 - \frac{3}{2}t^2$

10. D。 t=2s, v(2)=5m/s, t>2s, a=6t-2>0；所以 $\Delta x = \int_2^5 (3t^2 - 2t - 3)dt = 87m$

11. C。 $v = \frac{dx}{dt} = 2t + 3t^2$，v(1)=5m/s, v(2)=16m/s；$\bar{a} = \frac{v(2) - v(1)}{2-1} = 11m/s^2$

12. C。 飞机 B 相对于 A 的速度 $\mathbf{v}_{BA} = \mathbf{v}_B - \mathbf{v}_A$。大小为：$v_{BA} = \sqrt{v_B^2 + v_A^2 - 2v_B v_A \cos 45^0} = 357mph$

方向：$v_x = -400\cos 45^0, v_y = 500 - 400\sin 45^0$，$\tan\theta = \frac{v_y}{v_x}$，$\theta = 142.5^0$.

13. A。 切向加速度 $a_t = \frac{90 - 50}{3.6*15} = 0.74m/s^2$，法向加速度 $a_n = \frac{(50/3.6)^2}{150} = 1.29m/s^2$；

$a = \sqrt{(v^2/R)^2 + a_t^2} = 1.48m/s^2$

14. E。 $v = \sqrt{8^2 + 6^2} = 10km/h$

15. B。 位移大小 $\Delta r = \sqrt{1200^2 + 500^2} = 1300m$，平均速率 $\bar{v} = \frac{\Delta r}{\Delta t} = \frac{1300}{80 + 20} = 13m/s$

16. D。 $v_y = \frac{dy}{dt} = 3x^2\frac{dx}{dt} + 2\frac{dx}{dt}$，当 x=2m 时，$v_y = 56m/s$

17. D。 $v_x = \frac{dx}{dt} = 3t^2, v_y = \frac{dy}{dt} = -\sin t$；当 t=$\pi$ 时，速率为 $v = \sqrt{v_x^2 + v_y^2} = 3\pi^2$

18. E。 只有 E 的描述是正确的。

19. D。 两车的相对速度 $\mathbf{V} = \mathbf{V}_1 - \mathbf{V}_2 = 3i + 2j$，大小为 $v = \sqrt{3^2 + 2^2} = \sqrt{13}m/s$

20. C。 $\omega = \omega_0 - \alpha t = 0 \rightarrow \alpha = 2\pi$，$\theta = \omega_0 t - \frac{1}{2}\alpha t^2 = 4\pi^2$

21. C。 $a = \sqrt{(v^2/R)^2 + a_t^2} = 0.34m/s^2$，$\theta = \tan^{-1}(a_n/a_t) = 53.6^0$

22. D。 $\omega = 3 - 12t^2$　$\alpha = -24t$；V=-45m/s, a_n=-48m/s^2

Free Response Explanations

1. A. $x = x_0 + v_0 t = 3t$ and $t = 1, x(1) = +3m$

   B. $a = \dfrac{dv}{dt}$ 加速度是常数 t=1s 和 t=3s 之间， $a = -3m/s^2$

   C. X(3)=3m，曲线下的面积。

   D. 平均速度

   $$\overline{v}_{t=0, t=3} = \frac{x_3 - x_0}{3} = \frac{+3 - 0}{3} = +1 \ m/s$$

   E. 平均速率=路程/时间间隔=6/3=2m/s

   F. 位置-时间图（x-t 图）

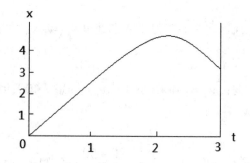

2. 当时间 t=0 时，**r**(0)=0，**v**(0)=5i，**a**=3j

   A. **v**= $\displaystyle\int_0^t 3j\,dt$ +v(0)=5 **i**+3t **j**

   r= $\displaystyle\int_0^t (5i + 3tj)\,dt = 5ti + \frac{3}{2}t^2 j$

   B. **v**(2)=**5 i +6 j** (m/s)

   当 t=2s 时，速率 V= $\sqrt{5^2 + 6^2}$

   位置为 **r**(2)=**5i+6j** (m)

3. 用**V**表示雨相对于车的速度；**V₁**表示雨对地的速度，方向竖直向下；**V₂**表示车对地的速度水平向右。有向量关系式：**V=V₁ - V₂**，分量式为：

   A. V_x=Vsin60=-V_2，有V=57.7km/h，at 60.0° west of vertical

   B. V_y=Vcos60=V_1，有V_1=28.9 km/h downward

4. $x(t)$=(3.00t^2-2.00t+3.00) m

   A. 平均速度： $\overline{V} = \dfrac{x(3) - x(2)}{3 - 2}$ =24m/s

   B. 任意时刻的瞬时速度方程： $V = \dfrac{dx}{dt} = 6t - 2$

   V(2)=10m/s

V(3)=16m/s

C. 平均加速度：$\bar{a} = \dfrac{V(3)-V(2)}{3-2}$ =6m/s^2

D. 加速度方程：$a = \dfrac{dV}{dt} = 6m/s^2$，加速度不随时间而变化，所以

$a(2) = a(3) = 6m/s^2$

5. A. 分别选 x、y 为抛体的水平和竖直运动方向。运动方程分别为

$x = v_i \cos\theta_i t$ （1）

$y = v_i \sin\theta_i t - \dfrac{1}{2}gt^2$ （2）

t 时刻抛射体落在斜面上，此时落点坐标关系为：$y = x\tan\theta_i$ （3）

解上述方程得：$x = \dfrac{2v_i^2 \cos^2\theta_i(\tan\theta_i - \tan\phi)}{g}$

$d = \dfrac{x}{\cos\phi} = \dfrac{2v_i^2 \cos\theta_i \sin(\theta_i - \phi)}{\cos^2\phi}$

B. 求 d 的最大值，令 $\dfrac{d}{d\theta_i}(d) = 0$，有

$\cos(2\theta_i - \phi) = 0$

$2\theta_i - \phi = \dfrac{\pi}{2}$，　$\rightarrow \theta_i = \dfrac{\phi}{2} + \dfrac{\pi}{4}$

6.

A. R 点的速度方向沿切向。水平方向加速度为零，所以加速度方向沿 y 轴向上。

B. $v_y = \dfrac{dy}{dt} = \dfrac{1}{2}x\dfrac{dx}{dt} = \dfrac{1}{2}cx$

C. $a_y = \dfrac{dv_y}{dt} = \dfrac{1}{2}c\dfrac{dx}{dt} = \dfrac{1}{2}c^2$

D. 因为 $v_x = \dfrac{c}{2(1+x^2)^{\frac{1}{2}}}$, $v_y = \dfrac{1}{2}cx$,

速率 $v = \sqrt{v_x^2 + v_y^2} = \dfrac{c}{2}$ 是一常数。

E. 速度的方向仍然是沿着切向，但此时速度的大小为常数，所以加速度的方向与速度方向垂直，指向曲线弯曲的一侧。

7. A. $\theta(0) = 2rad$; $\omega = 8t + 6t^2$, $\omega(0) = 0$

B. $\omega(4) = 128rad/s$

C. $\alpha = 8 + 12t$, $\alpha(2) = 32rad/s^2$

Chapter 3

Newton's Laws of Motion
牛顿运动定律

3.1 Newton's Three Laws

3.2 Type of Forces

3.3 Free Body Diagram——Solve Problems with Newton's Law

3.4 Centripetal Force

Introduction: We have discussed how motion is described in terms of velocity and acceleration. In this chapter, we deal with the questions of why objects move as they do; what makes an object begin to move? What cases a body to accelerate or decelerate? What is involved when an object moves in a circle? For each case the answer is that a force is required. **The cause of any change in an object's velocity is a force; we define force as an action capable of accelerating an object.** We will investigate the connection between force and motion, which is the subject called dynamics.

3.1 牛顿三定律

3.2 常见力

3.3 隔离物体受力分析—运用牛顿定律求解力学问题

3.4 向心力

力是物体运动速度发生改变的原因。

3.1 Newton's Three Laws

3.1 牛顿三定律

A force has direction as well as magnitude, and is indeed a vector that follows the rules of vector addition. Isaac Newton built his great theory of motion. Newton's analysis of motion is summarized in his famous three laws of motion.

力是向量，是既有大小又有方向的物理量。

3.1.1 Newton's First Law of Motion

3.1.1 牛顿第一定律

In an **inertial frame of reference, every body continues in its state of rest or of uniform speed in a straight line as long as no net force acts on it.**

The tendency of a body to maintain its state of rest or of uniform motion in a straight line is called **inertia.** So Newton's first law is also called **the law of inertia.**

The first law can be stated: $\mathbf{F}_{net} = 0 \implies \mathbf{a} = 0$

物体将保持静止或匀速直线运动状态不变，直到有外力改变这种状态为止。又称之为惯性定律。

惯性：由质量来衡量惯性大小。

第一定律数学表示

$\mathbf{F}_{net} = 0 \implies \mathbf{a} = 0$

57

$$F_{net} = \sum_{i=1}^{i=n} \vec{F_i} \qquad \text{the vector sum of n individual forces}$$

$$F_{net} = F_{net,x} + F_{net,y} + F_{net,z}$$

Reference frames in which Newton's first law does hold are called **inertial reference frames**—the law of inertia is valid in them.

Until a net external force is applied, the constant-velocity, straight-line motion of a body will continue unchanged.

Inertia: An object's resistance to being accelerated. The measure of an object's inertia is mass (kg).

Example 3.1: A 10-kg traffic light is suspended from a beam as shown in Figure 3-1. Find the tension in each of the three cables supporting the traffic light.

Solution:

F_{net} =0，so we have two component equations:

$$F_{net,x} = -T_1 \cos 60^0 + T_2 \cos 30^0 = 0$$

$$F_{net,y} = T_1 \sin 60^0 + T_2 \sin 30^0 - mg = 0$$

Then we obtain
T_1=85N and T_2=49N

3.1.2 Newton's Second Law

The **acceleration** of a body (as a vector) is directly proportional to the **net force F** (also a vector) acting on the body and is inversely proportional to its mass. The direction of the acceleration is in the direction of the net force acting on the body.

Mathematically, this can be stated as **F**$_{net}$ = m**a**,

$$\sum F_x = ma_x \qquad \sum F_y = ma_y \qquad \sum F_z = ma_z$$

Where the proportionality constant m is the *mass of the object being accelerated*.

From Newton's second law we can make the definition of force as

合外力：$\vec{F}_{net} = \sum_{i=1}^{i=n} \vec{F_i}$

合外力的分量形式：

$$F_{net} = F_{net,x} + F_{net,y} + F_{net,z}$$

牛顿第一定律适用于惯性参照系。

惯性：由质量量度。

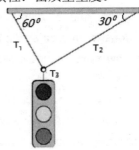

Figure 3-1 Traffic light

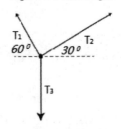

Figure 3-2 Free body diagram

3.1.2 牛顿第二定律

在合外力作用下，物体获得加速度。其大小正比于合外力，反比于物体质量；方向与作用于物体上的合外力方向一致。

F$_{net}$ = m**a**

力的定义：力是物体间相互

an action capable of accelerating an object.

As a force in the *x direction* will not make a body accelerate in the *y* direction, we can break both the *net force* and *acceleration* into their component parts and write three direction-related force equations:

$$F_{net,x} = ma_x$$

$$F_{net,y} = ma_y$$

$$F_{net,z} = ma_z$$

作用，使物体获得加速度。

X 方向的合外力不能改变物体在 y 方向的加速度。

加速度在直角坐标系中的分量形式

$$F_{net,x} = ma_x, \quad F_{net,y} = ma_y$$

$$F_{net,z} = ma_z$$

We need to be careful of *direction* as denoted by *positive* and *negative* signs.

注意：分力方向用正负表示

The two sides of Newton's second law represent different things. The left-hand side of the law involves the vector sum of the forces in the system. The right-hand side is the product of the mass and acceleration (a kinematic aspect of the system), which is the response of the system to the forces acting on it.

第二定律公式的左方是物体受到的合外力，右方是系统受合力作用的结果—物体产生了加速度。

In SI units with the mass in kilogram, the unit of force is called the **Newton** (N). One Newton, then, is the force required to impart acceleration of $1m/s^2$ to a mass of 1kg. Thus $1N=1kgm/s^2$.

力的国际单位是牛顿 N，$1N=1kgm/s^2$。

Newton's second law, like the first law, is valid only in inertial reference frames. In the none-inertial reference frame of an accelerating car, for example, **F**$_{net}$ = m**a** doesn't work in such an accelerating reference frame.

第二定律，同第一定律一样，只适用于惯性系。
在非惯性系（有加速度的参照系）中，牛顿定律不适用。

Sometimes the frictional force (such as air resistance) is a function of an object's velocity. These forces are called drag, or retarding force. Assume we drop a man from an airplane. Typically, the drag forces on a free falling object take the form $F_{drag} = -bv$, or

$F_{drag} = -kv^2$, where b and c are constant.

阻力一般是物体运动速度的函数：

$$F_{drag} = -bv \text{ or } F_{drag} = -kv^2$$

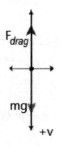

Example 3.2: For our problem, let's assume that the drag force of a man falling from a plane freely is F$_{drag}$=-bv. Find the man's a (t), v (t), and y (t) during his falling.

Solution:

Figure 3-3 Falling man with drag force

Downward as positive in y direction.

$$F_{net} = mg + F_{drag} = ma$$

$$mg - bv = m\frac{dv}{dt}$$

Initially at time t=0, v=0, a=g. After a long time, however, the man reaches terminal velocity v_t and a=0. At this point, F_{drag} = mg.

$$mg - bv_t = 0 \implies v_t = \frac{mg}{b}$$

To find velocity itself as a function of time we solve the differential equation above,

$$\frac{dv}{v - v_t} = -\frac{b}{m}dt$$

Integral both sides, we have

$$v = \frac{mg}{b}(1 - e^{-\frac{b}{m}t})$$

Now that we know v(t), we can solve for the acceleration by taking the derivative of v(t) with respect to t.

$$a = \frac{dv}{dt} = g\,e^{-\frac{b}{m}t}$$

Acceleration begins at g and over time declines to zero at terminal velocity.

$$v = \frac{dy}{dt} \rightarrow dy = vdt = \frac{mg}{b}(1 - e^{-\frac{b}{m}t})\,dt$$

Velocity begins at zero and increases until reaching terminal velocity. Integral both sides of the equation, we have

$$y = \frac{mg}{b}t + \frac{m^2g}{b^2}(e^{-\frac{b}{m}t} - 1)$$

Displacement begins at zero and increase as speed increases, until

$$F_{drag} = -bv$$

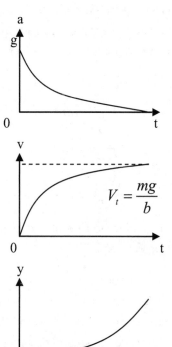

Figure 3-4 a-t, v-t, y-t graph of a falling body with drag force

$$a = \frac{dv}{dt} = g\,e^{-\frac{b}{m}t}$$

加速度从开始时的 g 以 e 指数的规律减小直至为零。

$$v = \frac{mg}{b}(1 - e^{-\frac{b}{m}t})$$

速度从零开始增加最终达到终极速度。

$$y = \frac{mg}{b}t + \frac{m^2g}{b^2}(e^{-\frac{b}{m}t} - 1)$$

位移从零开始指数增加，达

reaching a constant rate v_t. And then he is falling at constant speed.

到终极速度后线性增加.

3.1.3 Newton's Third Law of Motion

3.1.3 牛顿运动第三定律

Newton's second law of motion describes quantitatively how forces affect motion. Where do the forces come from? Newton realized that a force is exerted on a body and is exerted by another body. Action and reaction act on different objects. This is the essence of Newton's third law of motion.

Third law: **For very force exerted by one object on another, there is another force equal in magnitude and opposite in direction that is exerted back by the second object on the first.**

力是物体间的相互作用，作用力、反作用力大小相等，方向相反，作用在不同的物体上。

To avoid confusion, it is very important to remember that the action force and the reaction force are acting on different objects. These two forces would never appear together in a sum of forces in Newton's second law, because **a** is the acceleration of one

particular body and F_{net} must include only the forces on that body.

$$\mathbf{F}_{action} = -\mathbf{F}_{reaction}$$

$$\mathbf{F}_{action} = -\mathbf{F}_{reaction}$$

3.2 Types of Forces　　　　　　　3.2 常见力

Newton's Second Law is intimately related to force acting on a body. Solving Newton's law problems requires familiarity with the five kinds of forces you are likely encounter.

3.2.1 Gravitational Force—Weight

3.2.1 重力（引力）

Galileo claimed that objects dropped near the surface of the Earth will all fall with the same acceleration, **a=g**. The force that gives rise to this acceleration is called the force of gravity. So according to Newton's second law, the force of gravity can be written as

从地球表面下落的物体有相等的加速度，$g=9.8m/s^2$，垂直向下指向地心。

$$\mathbf{F}_g = mg$$

The gravitational force of the Earth acts on very object on or near the Earth, whether falling or not, and is of magnitude mg. Therefore very object near the surface of the Earth has at least one force acting on it, it is also called weight **W**.

$$w = mg$$

The direction of this force is down toward the center of the Earth (not necessarily perpendicular to the surface that the object sits on). If the y axis is upwards, we can write $\mathbf{F}_g = -mg\,\mathbf{j}$.

3.2.2 Normal Force F_N

A normal force is a force of support provided to a body by a surface in which the body is in contact. It is labeled $\mathbf{F}_N$ in the Figure 3-5.

The magnitude of F_N can be determined by Newton's second law and its direction always perpendicular to the surface the object is on and pointing away from the surface toward the object.

3.2.2 支撑力（法向力）N

支撑力垂直于两物体接触表面。

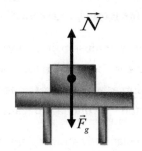

Figure 3-5 Normal force

3.2.3 Frictional Force F_f

Friction is produced by the atomic interaction between two bodies as they either slide over one another (this is called *kinetic friction)* or sit motionless in contact with one another—this is called *static friction*.

When two bodies come very close (i.e. rest against one another), there is a weak atomic bonding that occurs between the electrons of the one structure and the protons of the other (and vice versa). It is almost as though the atoms of the two bodies have melded to some degree. When the bodies try to move over one another, this bonding has to be sheared. That shearing is what produces the retarding effects we call friction.

Kinetic friction F_{fk} : Sometimes called *sliding friction*, kinetic friction occurs when one body slides over or against a second body. The direction of *kinetic friction* is always *opposite to* the direction of motion.

3.2.3 摩擦力F_f

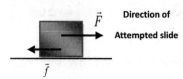

Figure 3-6 Friction force

动摩擦（滑动摩擦）力：两个接触物体有相对运动。方向与运动方向相反。

$$F_{fk} = \mu_k F_N$$

From experimentation, it has been observed that the amount of *kinetic friction* **F** $_{fk}$ that a body experiences is proportional to the size of the *normal force* F $_N$ exerted on the body by the structure it slides against.

$$F_{fk} = \mu_k F_N$$

μ_k is the *coefficient of kinetic friction, a dimensionless number that is a property of the two materials in contact.*

μ_k 是滑动摩擦系数，是一个没有单位的量。

Static friction F $_{fs}$ **:** If a book, for instance, sits on a table and a tiny external force is applied to the book *parallel to the table top*, the force may or may not move the book. There will be a force-of-opposition in this case provided by *static friction*.

静摩擦力

For values of the applied force below threshold, the frictional force is large enough to balance the applied force and the object does not move; the magnitude of the frictional force is exactly equal to the applied force and is "whatever it takes to prevent motion". The frictional force, present when the objects are not sliding relative to each other, is called static friction and has a variable magnitude with a maximum magnitude of

物体之间没有相对运动，只有相对运动趋势时受到静摩擦力。静摩擦力随受到的外力而变。但最大静摩擦力为 F $_{fs,max} = \mu_s F_N$

$$F_{fs,max} = \mu_s F_N$$

When μ_s is the coefficient of static friction, a dimensionless number is a property of the two materials in contact. The magnitude of static friction force F $_{fs}$ = F $_{apply}$, when F $_{apply}$ < F $_{fs,max}$.

μ_s 是静摩擦系数。

The friction force points parallel to the plane of contact between the two objects and in a direction that opposes the motion or incipient motion of the object.

Example 3.3: An object mass m is moving with constant velocity on a plane. The coefficient on the plane is μ . What is the angle θ when the apply force is minima?

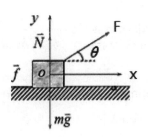

Figure 3-7 Example 3.3

Solution:

For this situation net force=0, we have

x direction: $F\cos\theta - \mu N=0$

y direction: $N+F\sin\theta -mg=0$

$$\rightarrow F = \frac{\mu mg}{\cos\theta + \mu\sin\theta}$$

When the denominator is maximum, F has minimum value.

So, $\dfrac{d}{d\theta}(\cos\theta + \mu\sin\theta)=0 \rightarrow \theta = \arctan\mu$

3.2.4 Tension Force F_t

3.2.4 张力F_t

Tension force is applied to a body by a rope, string, or cable.

Normally characterized by F_t or **T**, tension forces are always

applied *along the line of the cable* and *away from* the body in question.

An ideal pulley (massless, frictionless) changes the DIRECTION of the tension force but does not change the force's magnitude.

滑轮只改变力的方向。

3.2.5 Spring Force Fs—Hooker's Law

3.2.5 弹性力—胡克定律

$$F_s = -kx$$

$$F_s = -kx$$

k—spring constant

x—extension of spring

Springs in series: $\dfrac{1}{k_e} = \dfrac{1}{k_1} + \dfrac{1}{k_2}$

弹簧串联时等效弹性系数：

$$\sqrt{\dfrac{1}{k_e} = \dfrac{1}{k_1} + \dfrac{1}{k_2}}$$

Springs in parallel: $k_e = k_1 + k_2$

弹簧并联时等效弹性系数：

k_e : equivalent spring constant

$$k_e = k_1 + k_2$$

3.2.6 Fundamental Forces

In nature, there are only four certain forces which we called the fundamental forces. They are **the force of gravitation, the electromagnetic, strong, and weak force.** The forces we mentioned above (we might call the secondary forces), weight, the normal force, friction, drag, tension, spring forces, are some kinds of the fundamental forces. For example, weight is a kind of the force of gravitation and friction force is a kind of the electromagnetic force.

Depend on the strength from strong to weak; the order of the four fundamental forces is strong force, electromagnetic force, weak force and gravitational force. From the table 3-1, some characteristics of the fundamental forces are listed.

3.2.6 四种基本力

自然界中的所有力都可归纳为四种基本力。

四种基本力按照强度由强到弱可分为：强力、电磁力、弱力和引力。

Table 3-1 Four fundamental forces

Force	Couples with	Strength	Range
Strong	Quarks and particles composed of them	10^4	$\approx 10^{-15}$ m
Electromagnetic	Electrically charged particles	10^2	Unlimited
Weak	Most particles	10^{-2}	$\approx 10^{-17}$ m
Gravitational	All particles	10^{-34}	Unlimited

3.3 Free Body Diagram—Solve Problems with Newton's Law

3.3 隔离物体受力分析—运用牛顿定律求解力学题

Newton's second law tells us that the acceleration of an object is proportional to the net force acting on the object. The net force is the vector sum of all forces acting on the object.

When solving problems involving Newton's laws and force, it is very important to draw a diagram showing all the forces acting on each object involved. Such a diagram is called a free-body-diagram (F.B.D). Be sure to draw every force acting on that body; don't show forces that the body exerts on other objects.

General approach to solving Newton's law problems:

1. **Draw a sketch** of the situation.

2. **Draw a F.B.D for each body** in the problem, showing all the forces acting on that body, including any unknown forces that you have to solve for. Do not show any forces that the body exerts on other bodies.

3. **Choose a coordinate system** for each body. Newton's second law involves vectors, and it is usually important to resolve vectors into components. Choose an x and y axis in a way that simplifies the calculation.

4. **Apply** Newton's second law $\mathbf{F}_{net}$ = m$\mathbf{a}$ to the X and Y components separately for each body.

$$F_{net,x} = ma_x$$

$$F_{net,y} = ma_y$$

5. **Solve** the equation or equations for the unknown.

1. 画出物体状态草图。

2. 对每个物体进行受力分析。

3. 选择合适的坐标系。

4. 使用第二定律公式。

5. 解牛顿方程。

3.4 Centripetal Force   3.4 向心力

What causes the acceleration for a circular motion? Newton's second law tells us that a net force must act on the body along the direction of a. So tangential acceleration is along the direction of tangent, there must be a force—tangent force to make the speed changing.

$$F_t = ma_t = m\frac{dv}{dt}$$

Centripetal acceleration is perpendicular to the velocity and does not change an object's speed. Meantime, in order to produce an acceleration, there must be a force—centripetal force; otherwise, the object would move off in a straight line (obey Newton's First Law).

切向力（切向合外力）—切向加速度

$$F_t = ma_t = m\frac{dv}{dt}$$

向心力（法向合外力）—向心加速度

$$F_n = ma_n = m\frac{v^2}{r}$$

A particle moving with uniform speed v in a circular path of radius r experiences only a centripetal force.

When a car goes around a curve, there must be a net force towards the center of the circle of which the curve is an arc. If the road is flat, that force is supplied by friction, shown in Figure 3-8.

$$f_s = \mu mg = m\frac{v_{max}^2}{r}$$

If the frictional force is insufficient (or $v > v_{max}$) the car will tend to move more nearly in a straight line.

As long as the tires do not slip, the friction is static. If the tires do start to slip, the friction is kinetic, which is bad in two ways:

1. The kinetic frictional force is smaller than the static.

2. The static frictional force can point towards the center of the circle, but the kinetic frictional force opposes the direction of motion, making it very difficult to regain control of the car and continue around the curve.

Banking the curve can help keep cars from skidding. In fact, for every banked curve, there is one speed where the entire centripetal force is supplied by the horizontal component of the normal force, and no friction is required, see the Figure 3-9.

$$N\sin\theta = m\frac{v^2}{r}$$
$$N\cos\theta = mg$$

so $v_{max} = \sqrt{rg\tan\theta}$

Example 3.4: What Is the Maximum Speed of the Car?

A 1200kg car moving on a flat, horizontal road negotiates a curve, as shown in Figure 3-8. If the radius of the curve is 40.0 m and the coefficient of static friction between the tires and dry pavement is 0.400, find the maximum speed of the car and still make the turn successfully.

Solution:

In this case, the force that enables the car to remain in its circular

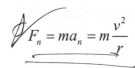

$$F_n = ma_n = m\frac{v^2}{r}$$

匀速率圆周运动物体只受向心力作用。

静摩擦力作为汽车转弯向

心力：$\mu mg = m\frac{v_{max}^2}{r}$

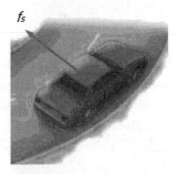

Figure 3-8 A car moves around a flat curve. Static friction force acts as centripetal force

当路面向弯路中心倾斜时，支持力分量可作为汽车转

弯向心力：$N\sin\theta = m\frac{v^2}{r}$

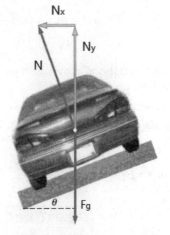

Figure 3-9 Banked curve, the component of normal force acts as centripetal force when the car's speed is limited.

path is the force of static friction. Hence, we have

$$f_s = m \frac{v^2}{r}$$

The maximum speed the car can have around the curve is the speed at which it is on the verge of skidding outward. At this point, the friction force has its maximum value f_s, max = $\mu_s N$.

$$v_{max} = \sqrt{\frac{\mu_s mgr}{m}} = \sqrt{\mu_s gr} = 13.0 \text{ m/s}$$

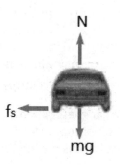

Figure 3-10 Example 3.4 The free-body diagram of the car

Example 3.5 The Conical Pendulum: A small object of mass m is suspended from a string of length L. The object revolves with constant speed v in a horizontal circle of radius r, as shown in Figure 3-11. (Because the string sweeps out the surface of a cone, the system is known as a *conical pendulum*.) Find an expression for v.

圆锥摆

Solution:

Because the object does not accelerate in the vertical direction, $\Sigma F_y = ma_y = 0$ and the upward vertical component of T must balance the downward gravitational force. Therefore,

$$T \cos \theta = mg \qquad (1)$$

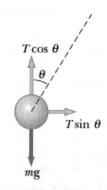

Figure 3-11 The conical Pendulum

$$T \sin \theta = ma_c = m \frac{v^2}{r} \qquad (2)$$

From equations above we have:

$$\tan \theta = \frac{v^2}{rg}, v = \sqrt{rg \tan \theta}$$

For $r = L \sin \theta$; therefore,

$$v = \sqrt{Lg \sin \theta \tan \theta}$$

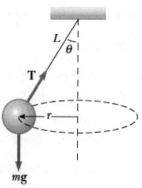

Figure 3-12 Free body diagram of the pendulum

Note: The speed is independent of the mass of the object.

第三章总结　牛顿运动定律

1. 牛顿三定律

1）第一定律：任何物体都有惯性，运动无需力来维持，力是物体之间的相互作用，是改变物体运动状态的原因。

$$如果\ F_{net}=0，那么\ a=0$$

2）第二定律：确定了力与加速度的瞬时向量关系，质量是物体惯性大小的量度。

$$F_{net}=ma$$

3）第三定律：作用力与反作用力成对出现，并属于同一性质。

$$F_{act}=-F_{react}$$

2. 常见力

重力：$w=mg$，方向竖直向下。

支持力：N，垂直于接触表面。

张力：T，方向沿着弦线。

最大静摩擦力：$F_s=\mu_s N$，方向平行于表面，与运动趋势相反。

滑动摩擦力：$F_k=\mu_k N$，方向平行于表面，与运动方向相反。

弹性力：$F=-kx$，并联使用时等效弹性系数 $k_e=k_1+k_2$

$$串联使用等效弹性系数\ k_e\ 满足\ \frac{1}{k_e}=\frac{1}{k_1}+\frac{1}{k_2}$$

万有引力：$F=-G\dfrac{mM}{r^2}$

3. 空气阻力：$F=kv$ 或 $F=kv^2$，阻力大小正比于速度或速度的平方

由 $mg-kv=ma$ 可求得

终极速度 $v_t=\dfrac{mg}{b}$

速度方程 $v=\dfrac{mg}{b}(1-e^{-\frac{b}{m}t})$

加速度方程 $a(t)=ge^{-\frac{b}{m}t}$

运动方程 $y(t) = \dfrac{mg}{b}t + \dfrac{m^2 g}{b^2}(e^{-\frac{b}{m}t} - 1)$

4. 匀速圆周运动

速度：速率不变，方向沿圆的切向。

加速度：$a_c = \dfrac{v^2}{r}$，指向圆心。

向心力：$F_c = m\dfrac{v^2}{r}$，是物体所受所有力的合力。

5. 任意圆周运动

$\mathbf{a} = \mathbf{a}_t + \mathbf{a}_n = \dfrac{dv}{dt}\vec{\tau} + \dfrac{v^2}{r}\vec{n}$

总加速度=切向加速度+法向加速度

合外力=切向力+向心力 $F_{net} = F_t + F_n$

切向力 F_t：改变速度的大小即速率

向心力 F_n：改变速度的方向

Chapter 3 Newton's Laws of Motion Practice

Multiple Choice Questions

1. Block A of mass $2M$ rests upon Block B of mass M. What is the ratio of the normal forces exerted by Block B on Block A to the normal force exerted by the ground on the block B?

   A. 5:2

   B. 3:2

   C. 1:1

   D. 2:3

   E. 2:5

2. A force of magnitude F pushes two blocks on a surface moving with a constant velocity v. What is the magnitude of the friction force acting on the 4 kg block?

   A. 4F

   B. 2F

   C. $\dfrac{4}{3}$ F

   D. $\dfrac{2}{3}$ F

   E. $\dfrac{1}{3}$ F

3. How much force is required to vertically lift an object of mass m with acceleration g?

   A. mg

   B. 2mg

   C. Mg^2

   D. $2mg^2$

   E. m/g

Base your answers to questions **4** and **5** on the following. A block of mass m is pulled along a rough horizontal surface by a constant applied force of magnitude F_1 that acts at an angle θ to the horizontal, as shown below. The acceleration of the block is a .

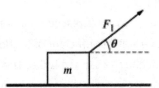

4. The normal force N exerted by the surface on the block and the coefficient of kinetic friction μ between the block and surface is

   A. $\mu = \dfrac{F_1 - ma}{mg - F_1 \sin\theta}$

   B. $\mu = \dfrac{F_1 \cos\theta - ma}{mg - F_1}$

   C. $\mu = \dfrac{F_1 - ma}{mg - F_1}$

   D. $\mu = \dfrac{F_1 \cos\theta - ma}{mg - F_1 \sin\theta}$

   E. $\mu = \dfrac{F_1 \cos\theta - ma}{F_1 \sin\theta}$

5. If the applied force is large enough, the block will lose contact with the surface, the magnitude of the greatest acceleration a_{max} is

A. $a_{max} = g \sin \theta$

B. $a_{max} = g \cos \theta$

C. $a_{max} = g \tan \theta$

D. $a_{max} = \frac{1}{2} g \cos \theta$

E. $a_{max} = g \cot \theta$

6. Block A with mass m is placed on a horizontal surface. The static coefficient of friction between A and the surface is 0.6. The magnitude of the force necessary to push it across the surface at a constant velocity is F_1. Block B, also of mass m is placed on top of the first block. The static coefficient of friction between A and B is 0.5. The force necessary to push this stack across the floor at constant velocity, F_2, is greater than F_1 because

A. the force of friction on Block B is greater
B. the coefficient of friction between Block A and the floor is greater
C. the weight of Block A is greater
D. the force of the floor on Block A is greater
E. of the additional frictional force between Block A and Block B

7. In the frictionless system shown below, all blocks have the same mass, and the entire system is accelerated by an applied force of magnitude F. What is the tension in the cord between blocks B and C?

A. $\frac{1}{2}$ F

B. $\frac{1}{3}$ F

C. F

D. 3F

E. 2F

Base your answers to questions **8** and **9** on the following situation. A ball of mass m is dropped down through the air in a gravitational field. The magnitude of the force of air resistance is $f=bv^2$ where b is a positive constant.

8. The magnitude of the acceleration of the ball at any time is

A. $g - b$
B. $g - bv^2/m$
C. $g + bv^2/m$
D. g/b
E. $bv^2 + g$

9. What is the terminal speed of the ball?

A. $mg/\sqrt{b}$

B. $\sqrt{mgb}$

C. $\sqrt{\dfrac{mg}{b}}$

D. $\sqrt{\dfrac{g}{b}}$

E. $\dfrac{\sqrt{mg}}{b}$

10. The maximum speed a car can travel around an unbanked curve depends on all of the following **EXCEPT**

A. The diameter of the curve.

B. The acceleration due to gravity.

C. The mass of the car.

D. The coefficient of kinetic friction between the road and the tires.

E. The surface of the curve.

11. When a block with a mass of 4 kg is hung from a spring, the spring stretches 12 cm. If a mass of 3 kg is then added to the spring, the spring will stretch an additional

A. 9 cm

B. 12 cm

C. 15 cm

D. 18 cm

E. 21 cm

12. Two skaters, one of mass 100 kg, the other of mass 50 kg are on a frozen pond (negligible friction). If the heavier person pushed the lighter one with a force F, the ratio of the magnitude of the acceleration of the lighter skater to that of the heavier is

A. 1:4

B. 1:2

C. 1:1

D. 2:1

E. 4:1

13. A ball attached to a string is whirled around a horizontal circle of radius r with a tangential velocity v. If the radius is changed to $2r$ and the magnitude of the centripetal force is doubled the new speed is

A. $v/2$

B. $v/\sqrt{2}$

C. $\sqrt{2}\,v$

D. $2v$

E. $4v$

14. A vehicle of mass 3000 kg travels along an unbanked circular turn without leaving the road. If the turn has a radius of 10 m, and the coefficient of kinetic friction between the road and the tires is 0.25, what is the maximum speed the vehicle can travel without slipping?

A. 5 m/s

B. 7.5 m/s

C. 10 m/s

D. 25 m/s

E. 16 m/s

15. A 60 kg adult and a 30kg child are passengers on a rotor ride at an amusement park. The floor moves downward when the rotating hollow cylinder reaches a certain constant speed v. Both passengers stay "pinned" against the wall of the rotor, as shown in the diagram below.

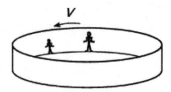

The magnitude of the frictional force between the adult and the wall of the spinning rotor is F. What is the magnitude of the frictional force between the child and the wall of the spinning rotor?

A. $\dfrac{1}{4}F$

B. $\dfrac{1}{2}F$

C. F

D. 2F

E. 4F

Questions **16** and **17**

An object with a mass of 5 kg is attached to a

1 meter long rope and whirled in a vertical circle.

16. At the bottom of its path, the rope has a tension of 95 N. The object is moving most nearly

   A. 2 m/s
   B. 3 m/s
   C. 6 m/s
   D. 9 m/s
   E. 15 m/s

17. Of the following, which is the greatest speed of the object for which the rope would become slack at the top of its circular path?

   A. 1 m/s
   B. 3 m/s

   C. 4 m/s
   D. 5 m/s
   E. 10 m/s

18. At what angle (relative to the horizontal) should a curve 52 m in radius be banked if no friction is required to prevent the car from slipping when traveling at 12 m/s? ($g = 9.8$ m/s^2)

   A. 28^0
   B. 32^0
   C. $16°$
   D. $10°$
   E. $8.2°$

Free Response Questions

1. A time-dependent force, **F**=(8.00 **i** -4.00t **j**) N, where t is in seconds, is exerted on a 2.00 kg object initially at rest.
   A. At what time will the object be moving with a speed of 10.0 m/s?
   B. What total displacement has the object traveled through at this time?
   C. How far is the object from its initial position when its speed is 10.0 m/s?

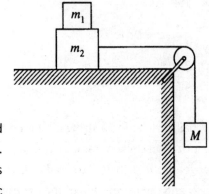

2. As shown in the diagram, a block 1 with mass m_1 is placed on block 2 with mass m_2 which is then placed on a table. A string connecting block 2 to a hanging mass M passes over a pulley attached to one end of the table. The static and kinetic coefficients of friction between blocks 1 and 2 are μ_{s1} and μ_{k1}. And μ_{s2} and μ_{k2} are coefficients of friction between block 2 and the tabletop. The mass and friction of the pulley are negligible.

   A. Determine the largest value of M for which the blocks can remain at rest.
   B. Suppose that M is large enough that the hanging block descends when the blocks are released. Assume that blocks 1 and 2 are moving as a unit (no slippage). Determine the magnitude a of their acceleration.

C. Now suppose that M is large enough that as the hanging block descends, block 1 is slipping on block 2. Determine the magnitudes of the acceleration of block 1 and block 2.

3. A block of mass m, which has an initial velocity v_o at time t = 0, slides on a horizontal surface. If the sliding friction force f exerted on the block by the surface is directly proportional to its velocity (that is, f = -kv) determine the following:

A. The acceleration a of the block in terms of m, k, and **v**.

B. The speed v of the block as a function of time t.

C. Determine the velocity of the ball when t=m/k sec.

D. Derive an equation for the distance the object travels as a function of time t.

E. The total distance the block slides.

4. A small block of mass m slides on a horizontal frictionless surface as it travels around the inside of a hoop of radius R. The coefficient of friction between the block and the wall is μ. The speed v of the block decreases. Find expressions for each of the following.

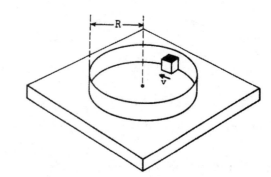

A. The frictional force on the block

B. The block's tangential acceleration a_t

C. The time required to reduce the speed of the block from an initial value v_0 to $v_0/2$

5. A ball of mass m is swung around on a string in a circle in s horizontal plane with a constant speed. The string makes an angle α with the vertical, shown in the figure below. The radius of the circle is R, it takes T sec for the ball to make one complete rotation, the direction of rotation is indicated in the figure; the ball, at S, is coming toward you. Q is the center of the circle. QP is vertical. SQ is in the +x-direction, QP in the +y-direction, and the +z-direction is tangent to the circle at S and points toward you. The gravitational acceleration is g; assume that the string is massless. Express your answers in terms of m, R, T, and g.

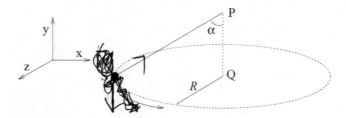

A. Make a free body diagram for the ball at S.

B. What is the velocity of the ball at S, and what is its angular velocity?

C. What is the ball's centripetal acceleration at S?

D. At S, what is the direction and magnitude of the sum of all forces acting on the ball? Indicated the net force in the figure or in a separate sketch, and make this force unambiguously.

E. What is α ?

6. A puck of mass m_1 is tied to a string and allowed to revolve in a circle of radius R on a frictionless horizontal table. The other end of the string passes through a hole in the center of the table, and a counterweight of mass m_2 is tied to it, shown in the figure. The suspended object remains in equilibrium while the puck on the tabletop revolves.

A. What is the tension in the string?

B. What is the radial force acting on the puck?

C. Determine the speed of the puck.

Answers and Explanations

Multiple Choice Answers

1. D   2. D   3. B   4. D   5. E   6. D   7. B   8. B   9. C   10. C   11. A   12. D   13. D   14. A   15. B
16. B   17. B   18. C

Multiple Choice Explanations

1. D。B 对 A 的支撑力 N=2Mg，地面对 B 的支撑力 N=3Mg

2. D。在 F 作用下，系统获得加速度 a：F=6a；4kg 物体作用于 2kg 物体上的作用力为 T，有 F-T=2a。

求得 T=2a/3

3. B。F-mg=mg, F=2mg

4. D。

竖直方向和外力为零：N+ $F_1 \sin\theta - mg = 0 \rightarrow N = mg - F_1 \sin\theta$

水平方向和外力为 ma： $F_1 \cos\theta - \mu N = ma \rightarrow \mu = \dfrac{F_1 \cos\theta - ma}{mg - F_1 \sin\theta}$

5. E。F_1 增加时，支持力减小直至为零，摩擦力也降为零。此时物体仍和平面接触，获得最大

速度 $a_{\max}$： $F \sin\theta = mg$, $F \cos\theta = ma_{\max}$

$\rightarrow a_{\max} = g\cot\theta$ 支持力 $N = mg\cos\theta$

6. D。摩擦力 $f = \mu N$ ，N 增加，所以 f 增加。

7. B。 $F = 3ma$ ，连接 B、C 的绳中张力为 T=ma；T=F/3

8. B。竖直方向受力：$mg - bv^2 = ma$，$\rightarrow a = g - \dfrac{bv^2}{m}$

9. C。物体达到终极速度时，和外力为零：$mg - bv^2 = 0 \rightarrow v = \sqrt{\dfrac{mg}{b}}$

10. C。$v_{\max} = \sqrt{\mu gR}$，与质量无关。

11. A。由 $m_1 g = kx_1$ 求出弹簧的弹性系数，$m_2 g = kx_2$ 求出 7kg 物体使弹簧的伸长 $x_2 = 21$cm，

所以 $\Delta x = x_2 - x_1 = 9$cm

12. D。两个人之间的作用力和反作用力大小相等：$m_1 a_1 = m_2 a_2 \rightarrow a_2 / a_1 = 2$

13. D。向心力 $F = m\dfrac{v^2}{r}$；$F \rightarrow 2F$，$r \rightarrow 2r$，所以 $v \rightarrow 2v$

14. A。汽车转弯所需向心力由摩擦力提供：$m\dfrac{v_{\max}^2}{R} = \mu mg$，$v_{\max} = \sqrt{\mu gR} = 5$m/s

15. B。大人所受摩擦力为 F，向心力为 $F_c = \dfrac{F}{\mu} = M\dfrac{v^2}{R}$

小孩所受向心力为 $F_c' = \dfrac{F'}{\mu} = m\dfrac{v^2}{R}$，$F' = F/2$

16. B。物体运动到竖直平面底部：$T - mg = m\dfrac{v^2}{r}$，求得 v=3m/s

17. B。物体运动到圆环轨道顶部时最小运动速度为：$mg = m\dfrac{v_{\min}^2}{r}$，

$\rightarrow v_{\min} = \sqrt{gr} = \sqrt{10} \approx 3m/s$

18. C。支持力在水平方向的分力提供向心力，

$N\cos\theta = mg$　竖直方向；　$N\sin\theta = m\dfrac{v_{\max}^2}{R}$　水平方向

求得，$\theta = 16^0$

Free Response Explanations

1. A. $F = ma, a = 2i - 2tj = \dfrac{dV}{dt}$, $V = 2ti - t^2 j \cdot v = \sqrt{4t^2 + t^4} = 10 \to t = 2.86s$

B. $\vec{\Delta r} = \int_0^{2.86} (2ti - t^2 j)dt = (t^2 i - \dfrac{t^3}{3} j)_0^{2.86} = 8.20i - 7.82j$

C. $|\Delta r| = 11.3m$

2. A. M 达到最大值且整个系统静止时，物块和桌面之间受到最大静摩擦力作用

$$F_s = \mu_{s2}(m_1 + m_2)g$$

对物体 M：Mg=T，（绳中张力的大小）

对（m_1+m_2）系统：T=$F_s = \mu_{s2}(m_1 + m_2)g$

$$\to M = \mu_{s2}(m_1 + m_2)$$

B. 增大 M 使（m_1、m_2）以相同的加速度运动时，整个系统有相同的加速度大小 a。

M: Mg-T=Ma

m_1+m_2: (m_1+m_2) a=T- $\mu_{k2}(m_1 + m_2)g$

$$\to a = \dfrac{Mg - \mu_{k2}(m_1 + m_2)}{M + m_1 + m_2}$$

C. 继续增加 M 使得 m_1、m_2 有相对运动时，m_2、M 有相同的加速度大小 a_2；m_1 物体的加速度大小为 a_1。

M: Mg-T=M a_2

m_1: $m_1 a_1 = \mu_{k1} m_1 g$

m_2: $T - \mu_{k2}(m_1 + m_2)g - \mu_{k1}m_1g = m_2a_2$

$$\rightarrow a_1 = \mu_{k1}g \; ; \quad a_2 = \frac{Mg - \mu_{k2}(m_1 + m_2) - \mu_{k1}m_1g}{M + m_2}$$

3. A. 物体所受和外力为 $-kv$，有牛顿第二定律有：

$$-kv = m \rightarrow a = -\frac{k}{m}v$$

B. 解微分方程：$\dfrac{dv}{dt} = -\dfrac{k}{m}v$ 得：$v = v_0 e^{-\frac{k}{m}t}$

C. 当 $t = m/k$ 时，其速度为 $v = \dfrac{v_0}{e}$，即速度减至 v_0/e 为初始速度的1/e

D. $x = x_0 + \displaystyle\int_0^t v dt = \frac{mv_0}{k}\left(1 - e^{-\frac{k}{m}t}\right)$

E. $x = \Delta x = \displaystyle\int_0^\infty v dt = \frac{mv_0}{k}$

4. A. $F_c = m\dfrac{v^2}{R}$

B. $F_t = -\mu m \dfrac{v^2}{R} = m\dfrac{dv}{dt}$; $\rightarrow a_t = \dfrac{dv}{dt} = -\mu\dfrac{v^2}{R}$

C. 求解 b 中的微分方程，$\rightarrow \displaystyle\int_{v_0}^{v_0/2}\frac{dv}{v^2} = \int_0^t -\frac{\mu}{R}dt$; $\rightarrow t = \dfrac{R}{\mu v_0}$

5. A.

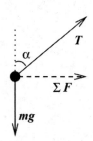

B. $\omega = \dfrac{2\pi}{T}, v = \omega R \rightarrow \bar{v} = \dfrac{2\pi R}{T}\hat{Z}$

C. $a = \dfrac{v^2}{R} \rightarrow \vec{a} = \dfrac{4\pi^2 R}{T^2}\hat{X}$

D. $\vec{F} = m\vec{a} = \dfrac{m4\pi^2 R}{T^2}\hat{X}$

E.
$T\sin\alpha = \dfrac{m4\pi^2 R}{T^2}, T\cos\alpha = mg$

$\tan\alpha = \dfrac{4\pi^2 R}{T^2 g}$

6. A. m_2 处于平衡状态，所以绳中张力 $T=m_2 g$

B. 绳中张力处处相同，m_1 受到指向转动中心的向心力 $F_c=m_2 g$

C. $m_2 g = m_1\dfrac{v^2}{R}$，$\rightarrow v = \sqrt{\dfrac{m_2}{m_1}gR}$

Work and Energy
功和能

Introduction: This chapter is devoted to the very important concept of energy and the closely related concept of work. Energy gives us one more tool to use to analyze physical situations. Energy is defined as the ability to do work, and work is one way of transferring energy from one system to another.

Energy has great importance for two reasons. Firstly, it is conserved. Secondly, it is a concept that is useful not only in the study of motion, but in all areas of physics and in other sciences as well.

We first examine the notion of work.

4.1 Work
4.1 功

4.1.1 Work Done by a Constant Force
4.1.1 恒力的功

For a single constant force acting parallel to the (straight-line) motion of an object, the work done on the object is defined to be **the product of the magnitude of the displacement and the component of force that is parallel to the displacement.** In equation form, we can write

恒力功定义：$W = \vec{F} \cdot \overrightarrow{\Delta r}$

力和位移的点积，单位是 J

$$W = F\Delta r \cos\theta = \vec{F} \cdot \overrightarrow{\Delta r}$$

Where F is the magnitude of the constant force, θ is the angle between the force and displacement vectors, and Δr is the magnitude of the displacement of the object. Work can be positive, negative or zero depending on θ.

In Figure 4-1, the work done by the normal force on the object and the work done by the gravitational force on the object are both zero because both forces are perpendicular to the displacement and have zero components along an axis in the direction of **Δr**.

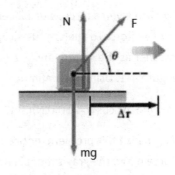

Figure 4-1 Work done by a force
F $W= F\Delta r \cos\theta$

The sign of the work depends on the direction of **F** relative to **Δr**. The work done by the applied force is positive when the projection of **F** onto **Δr** is in the same direction as the displacement. For example, when an object is lifted, the work done by the applied force is positive because the direction of that force is upward, in the same direction as the displacement of its point of application. When the projection of **F** onto **Δr** is in the direction opposite the displacement, W is negative. For example, as an object is lifted, the work done by the gravitational force on the object is negative. The factor cosθ in the definition of W takes care of the sign.

W 的正负与 θ 的关系:

$$\theta < 90^0, \qquad W > 0;$$

If an applied force **F** is in the same direction as the displacement **Δr**, then θ=0 and cosθ= 1. In this case, W=F**Δr**.

$$\theta > 90^0, \qquad W < 0;$$

$$\theta = 90^0, \qquad W = 0.$$

Work is a scalar quantity. Although it is defined in terms of two vectors, **work is a scalar—there is no direction associated with it**. **All types of energy and energy transfer are scalars**. This is a major advantage of the energy approach—we don't need vector calculations! In SI units, work is measured in Newton-meters. A special name is given to this unit, the Joule (J): 1J=1Nm.

功是标量。
各种能量都是标量。

When dealing with work, as with force, it is necessary to specify whether you are talking about work done by a specific object or done on a specific object. It is also important to specify whether the work done is due to one particular force, or the total work done by the net force on the object.

Example 4.1 Work done by constant force moving along a line

恒力作用下物体直线运动,
恒力对物体所做的功

A man cleaning a floor pulls a vacuum cleaner with a force of magnitude F=50.0 N at an angle of 30.0° with the horizontal. Calculate the work done by the force on the vacuum cleaner as the vacuum cleaner is displaced 3.00 m to the right.

Solution:

We are given a force, a displacement, and the angle between the two vectors. To analyze the situation, we identify the vacuum cleaner as the system and draw a free body diagram as shown in Figure 4-1. Using the definition of work,

$$W = \mathbf{F} \Delta \mathbf{r} \cos \theta = (50.0 \text{ N})(3.00 \text{ m})(\cos 30.0) = 130 \text{ N.m} = 130 \text{ J}$$

To finalize this problem, notice in this situation that the normal force n and the gravitational $Fg=mg$ do no work on the vacuum cleaner because these forces are perpendicular to its displacement.

Example 4.2 Work done by a constant force moving in a plane

恒力作用下物体在平面运动恒力对物体所做的功

A particle moving in the xy plane undergoes a displacement $\Delta \mathbf{r} = (2.0\mathbf{i}+3.0\mathbf{j})$m as a constant force $\mathbf{F}=(5.0\mathbf{i}+2.0\mathbf{j})$N acts on the particle.

a.   Calculate the magnitudes of the displacement and the force.

b.   Calculate the work done by **F**.

solution:

a.   We use the Pythagorean theorem

$$\Delta \mathbf{r} = \sqrt{(\Delta x)^2 + (\Delta y)^2} = \sqrt{2.0^2 + 3.0^2} = 3.6 \text{ m}$$

$$F = \sqrt{5.0^2 + 2.0^2} = 5.4\text{N}$$

b.   W=FΔr=(5.0i+2.0j) (2.0i+3.0j)=5*2+2*3=16j

4.1.2 Work Done by a Varying Force

4.1.2 变力的功

Consider a particle being displaced along the *x* axis under the action of a force that varies with position, F=F(x). The particle is displaced in the direction of increasing *x* from $x = x_i$ to $x = x_f$. According to Calculus of integration, the work done on the particle:

$$W = \int_{x_i}^{x_f} F_x dx$$

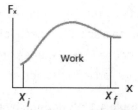

Figure 4-2 The work done by the component F_x of the varying force as the particle moves from x_i to x_f is *exactly* equal to the area under this curve

Example 4.3 Calculating Total Work Done from a Graph

A force acting on a particle varies with x, as shown in Figure 4-3. Calculate the work done by the force as the particle moves from x=0 to x=6.0m.

Solution:

The work done by the force is equal to the area under the curve from x=0 to x=6.0m.

$$W = 4*5 + \frac{1}{2}2*5 = 25J$$

物体一维运动：功是 F-x 图曲线下的面积

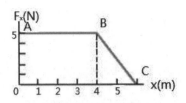

Figure 4-3 Example 4.3

4.2 Kinetic Energy and the Work—Kinetic Energy Theorem

4.2 动能和功—动能定理

An object in motion has the ability to do work and thus can be said to have energy. The energy of motion is called kinetic energy, K. The work done on the particle in moving through the small displacement d**r** due to the force **F** is

$$dW = \vec{F} \cdot \vec{dr}$$

To obtain a quantitative definition for kinetic energy, let us consider a rigid object of mass m that moves in a plane with an initial speed $v_i = v_A$. Moving along the curve shown in Figure 4-4 under the force of **F**$_{net}$ from A to B, work done on the object is:

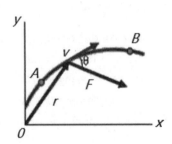

Figure 4-4 Work done on a particle moving from A to B under the force **F**

$$W_{net} = \int_{\vec{r}_A}^{\vec{r}_B} \vec{F}_{net} \cdot \vec{dr} = \int_{\vec{r}_A}^{\vec{r}_B} \text{ma.dr} = \int_{\vec{r}_A}^{\vec{r}_B} m\frac{d\vec{v}}{dt} \cdot \vec{dr} = \int_{\vec{r}_A}^{\vec{r}_B} m\vec{v} \cdot d\vec{v} = \int_A^B m$$

$$\frac{1}{2}\text{d}(\vec{v} \cdot \vec{v}) = \frac{1}{2}\int_{v_A^2}^{v_B^2} m\text{d}(v^2) = \frac{1}{2}mv_B^2 - \frac{1}{2}mv_A^2 = \frac{1}{2}mv_f^2 - \frac{1}{2}mv_i^2$$

We define the quantity $\frac{1}{2}mv^2$ to be the translational kinetic energy, K, of the object:

$$K = \frac{1}{2}mv^2$$

$$W_{net} = \int_{\vec{r}_A}^{\vec{r}_B} \vec{F}_{net} \cdot \vec{dr}$$

$$= \frac{1}{2}mv_B^2 - \frac{1}{2}mv_A^2$$

Kinetic energy is a scalar quantity and has the same units as work.

We can rewrite the W_{net} as:

平动动能定义：$K = \frac{1}{2}mv^2$

$$W_{net} = K_2 - K_1$$

Or $W_{net} = \Delta K$

动能是标量，单位是焦耳 J。

动能定理：$W_{net} = \Delta K$

Equation above is an important result. It can be stated in words:

In the case in which work is done on a system and the only change in the system is in its speed, the work done by the net force equals the change in kinetic energy of the system.

外力作用在机械运动物体的功等于系统动能的改变。

This is known as the **work-kinetic energy principle**. The work=kinetic energy theorem indicates that the speed of a particle will *increase* if the net work done on it is *positive,* because the final kinetic energy will be greater than the initial kinetic energy. The speed will *decrease* if the net work is *negative,* because the final kinetic energy will be less than the initial kinetic energy.

The work=kinetic energy theorem is important, but limited in its application— it is not a general principle. There are many situations in which other changes in the system occur besides its speed, and there are other interactions with the environment besides work. A more general principle involving energy is conservation of energy.

Example 4.4 Work to accelerate a car

How much work is required to accelerate a 1000kg car from 20m/s to 30m/s?

Solution:
We treat the car as a particle, then we can write that the net work needed is equal to the increase in its kinetic energy:

$$W_{net} = K_2 - K_1 = 2.5 \times 10^5 \text{J}$$

4.3 Conservative and Nonconservative Force

4.3 保守力和非保守力

We will find it important to categorize forces into two types: conservative and nonconservative. By definition, we call any force a conservative force if the work done by the force on an object moving from one point to another depends only on the initial and final positions and is independent of the particular path taken.

按照做功特点，力可分成两类：保守力和非保守力。

保守力做功与路径无关，只与起点和终点位置有关。

Which forces are conservative? Let us see what will happen to work done by the force of gravity, the force of spring and the force of friction.

4.3.1 F_g is a Conservative Force

Suppose that an object of mass *m* is raised along an arbitrary path in the *xy* plane, $A \rightarrow B$, as shown in Figure 4-5, the work done by gravity,

$$W_g = \int_A^B F_g \cdot dr = -\int_A^B mg\cos\theta dr$$

$$W_g = -\int_{y_i}^{y_f} mgdy = -mg(y_f - y_i)$$

Work done by $\overrightarrow{F_g}$ does not depend on the particular path taken!

So F_g is a conservative force.

4.3.2 Spring Force (Elastic force) is a Conservative Force

Consider a system consisting of a block plus a spring, as shown in Figure 4-6. The force that the spring exerts on the block is given by *Fs = – kx*.

$$W = \int_{x_a}^{x_b} Fdx = -\int_{x_a}^{x_b} kxdx = \frac{1}{2}kx_a^2 - \frac{1}{2}kx_b^2$$

*Work done by **Fs** does not depend on the particular path taken, too.*

So F_s is a conservative force.

4.3.3 Definition of Conservative Force

Consider an object that moves from point 1 to point 2 via either of two paths A and B, Figure 4-7. *Assume that a conservative force acts on the object, then*

$$_A\int_1^2 \overrightarrow{F} \cdot d\overrightarrow{r} = {_B}\int_1^2 \overrightarrow{F} \cdot d\overrightarrow{r}$$

Now consider the round trip. The total work done by the force in

4.3.1 重力是保守力

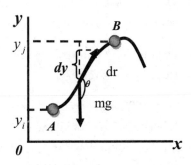

Figure 4-5 An object of mass m is raised along an arbitrary two dimensional path.

$$W_g = -mg(y_f - y_i)$$

4.3.2 弹簧弹性力是保守力

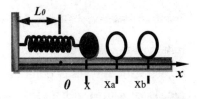

Figure 4-6 Spring-block system

$$W = \frac{1}{2}kx_a^2 - \frac{1}{2}kx_b^2$$

4.3.3 保守力的定义

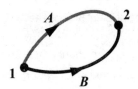

Figure 4-7 Moving from 1 to 2 via two different paths, A and B

making the round trip:

$$_A\int_1^2 \vec{F}d\vec{r} +_B \int_2^1 \vec{F}d\vec{r} =_A \int_1^2 \vec{F}d\vec{r} -_B \int_1^2 \vec{F}d\vec{r} = 0$$

Or $$\oint \vec{F} \cdot d\vec{r} = 0$$

We can give the definition of a conservative force in another equivalent way: a force is conservative if

The net work done by the force on an object moving around any closed path is zero.

From this definition of conservative forces, it shows an important aspect of such a force: the work done by a conservative force is recoverable in the sense that if positive work is done by an object on one part of the closed path , an equivalent amount of negative work will be done by the object on its return.

Obviously, not all forces are conservative. The force of friction is an example of nonconservative force apparently according to the definition of conservative force. Work done by kinetic friction force is always negative and not recoverable.

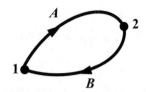

$$W= _A\int_1^2 \vec{F} \cdot d\vec{r} = _B \int_1^2 \vec{F} \cdot d\vec{r}$$

Figure 4-8 Round trip work

$$\oint \vec{F} \cdot d\vec{r} = 0$$

保守力定义：力对物体做功与路径无关，或绕任意闭合路径的功为零。

摩擦力做功与路径有关，是非保守力。

4.4 Potential Energy | 4.4 势能

Potential energy is the energy associated with the position of an object. Various types of potential energy can be defined and each type is associated with a particular conservative force.

Because the work done by a conservative force between two particles depends only on the two particles' initial and final positions or on the system's initial and final configurations, there must be a function determined by their configurations.

This function determined by the system's configuration is called **potential energy _U_** of the system.

We define the change in potential energy associated with a particular conservative force F as the negative of the work done by that force.

$$\Delta U = -W$$

势能是一种与物体位置相关的能量 U（r）。对应于不同的保守力势能具有不同的形式。

势能属于系统。

势能的增量等于保守力做功的负值。

$$\Delta U = -W$$

Therefore, for a conserved force F

$$\Delta U = -\int_{\vec{r}_i}^{\vec{r}_f} \vec{F} \cdot d\vec{r}$$

However, we cannot use this definition to define a potential energy for all possible forces. It doesn't apply to nonconservative forces like friction, because the integral in the equation above would not have a unique value depending on the end points. That is, ΔU would depend on path and we couldn't say that the U has a particular value at each point in space. Thus the concept of potential energy is meaningless for a nonconservative force.

如果势能增量与路径有关，就不能说势能在空间任意点有确定的数值。

对于非保守力，势能概念无意义。

For conservative force $F_g = mg$:

$$\Delta U = U_2 - U_1 = -W_g = mg(Y_2 - Y_1)$$

The gravitational potential energy, U, at any point a vertical height y about some reference point can be defined as

重力 mg 是保守力，对应的势能函数是： $U = mgy$

$$U = mgy$$

Position y of the particle relative to the reference position y = 0.

We can choose the potential energy to be zero at any point that is convenient, but we must be consistent throughout any given problem. The change in potential energy between any two points doesn't depend on this choice.

势能零点选择不同的位置，势能函数将有不同的表达式。但任意两点之间势能差却是相同的，不随零势能点的选择而变。

For conservative force $F_s = -kx$

弹性力 $F_s = -kx$ 是保守力。

As the block moves from point x_i to point x_f, the spring force $F = -kx$ does work on the block. By the potential definition, we have

$$\Delta U = -\int_{x_i}^{x_f} \vec{F} d\vec{r} = -\int_{x_i}^{x_f} \left(-kx\vec{i}\right) dx\vec{i}$$

$$\Delta U = \frac{1}{2}kx_f^2 - \frac{1}{2}kx_i^2$$

When the spring is at its relaxed length and the block is at x_i= 0, then $U(0) = 0$.

$$U - 0 = \frac{1}{2}kx^2 - 0$$

$$U(x) = \frac{1}{2}kx^2$$

势能函数：$U = \frac{1}{2}kx^2$

零势能点：$x = 0$，$U(0) = 0$

U(x) means the potential energy at x(compressed or stretched), and U(0) means U at x=0. It is usually convenient to choose the potential energy at x=0 to be zero: U(0)=0.

Potential energy summarized:

Potential energy – an object has the capacity or potential to do work even though it is not yet actually doing it. Energy can be stored, for later use, in the form of potential energy. Note that the mathematical form of each type of potential energy depends on the force involved.

势能总结：
能量可用势能的形式储存。

Important aspects of potential energy:

1.   A potential energy is always associated with a conservative force, and the difference of the potential energy between two points is defined as the potential energy at one point is negative to at another point of the work done by that force.

2.   The choice of where U = 0 is arbitrary and can be chosen wherever it is most convenient.

3.   Potential Energy Belongs to a System. Since a force is always exerted on one body by another body (the Earth exerts a gravity on a falling stone; a compressed spring exerts a force on a block; and so on), potential energy is not something a body "has" by itself, but rather is associated with the interaction of two (or more) bodies.

势能的特征：

1.   势能与保守力对应。势能差是保守力做功的负值。

2.   零点的选择可以任意。

3.   势能属于系统。

Example 4.5 Potential energy changes for a roller coaster

A 1000kg roller caster car moves from point A, Figure 4-9, to point B and then to point C.

a.   What is the gravitational potential energy at B and C relative to point A? Take y=0 at point A.

b.   What is the change in potential energy when it goes from B to C?

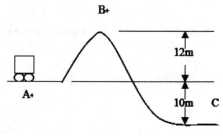

Figure 4-9 Roller coaster

c. Repeat 1 and 2, but take the reference point (y=0) to be at point C.

Solution:

a. We take upward as the positive direction, and measure the heights from point A, which means initially that the potential energy is zero.

At point B, $Y_B = 12m$,

$$U_B = mgy_B = 1000 * 9.8 * 12 = 1.2 * 10^5 J$$

At point C, $Y_C = -10m$

$$U_C = 1000 * 9.8 * (-10) = -9.8 * 10^4 J$$

b. From B to C, the potential energy change is

$$U_C - U_B = -2.2 * 10^5 J$$

The gravitational potential energy is decreased.

c. At point A, $Y_A = 10m$, $U_A = 1000 * 9.8 * 10 = 9.8 * 10^4 J$

At point B, $Y_B = 22m$, $U_A = 1000 * 9.8 * 22 = 2.2 * 10^5 J$

At point C, $Y_C = 0m$, $U_A = 1000 * 9.8 * 0 = 0$

The change in potential energy going from B to C is

$$U_C - U_B = -2.2 * 10^5 J$$

This is the same as in part b.

4.5 Calculating the Conservative Force from the Potential Energy Function

4.5 用势能函数计算保守力

In the one-dimensional case, the potential energy can be written as

$$U(x) = -\int F(x)dx$$

一维势能函数：

$$U(x) = -\int F(x)dx$$

And during an infinite small displacement dx, work done by conservative force is

$$dU = -F(x)dx$$

$$dW = F_{net} \cdot dr = (F_x + F_y + F_z)dx_i = F_x dx = F(x)dx$$

$$dW = F(x)dx = -dU$$

保守力为其对应的势能函数一阶导数的负值：

Thus we have $F(x) = -\dfrac{dU(x)}{dx}$

$$F(x) = -\frac{dU(x)}{dx}$$

In three dimensions, we can write the relation between F(x, y, z) and $U(x, y, z)$ as:

$$F_x = \frac{\partial U}{\partial x}, F_y = \frac{\partial U}{\partial y}, F_z = \frac{\partial U}{\partial z}$$

三维势能函数 U(x, y, z)：

$$\vec{F} = -(\frac{\partial U}{\partial x}\vec{i} + \frac{\partial U}{\partial y}\vec{j} + \frac{\partial U}{\partial z}\vec{k})$$

由势能函数求其对应保守力

Or $\vec{F}(x, y, z) = -(\dfrac{\partial U}{\partial x}\vec{i} + \dfrac{\partial U}{\partial y}\vec{j} + \dfrac{\partial U}{\partial z}\vec{k})$

Example 4.6 Determine F from U: Suppose $U(x) = ax^2$, where a is constant. What is F as a function of x?

由势能曲线求保守力

Solution:

Since U(x) depends only on x, this is a one-dimensional problem and we don't need to use partial derivatives, so

$$F(x) = -\frac{dU(x)}{dx} = -2ax$$

We can figure out that F(x)= - kx.

The introduction of potential energy allows us to generate a powerful and universally applicable principle for solving problems that are difficult to solve using Newton's laws.

Let us consider a conservative system (meaning only conservative forces do work) in which energy is transformed from kinetic to potential or vice versa. According to the work energy principle, the net work done on an object is equal to its change in kinetic energy:

只有保守力存在的机械系统，物体的动能和势能才可以相互转化。

$$W_{net} = \Delta K , \text{ and } W = -\Delta U$$

We combine the two equations, and obtain

$$\Delta K + \Delta U = 0$$

It also can be written as

$$K_2 - K_1 + U_2 - U_1 = 0$$

We now define a quantity E_m, called the total mechanical energy of our system, as the sum of the kinetic energy plus the potential energy of the system of any moment.

机械能：系统动能和势能和

$$E_m = K + U$$

$$E_m = K + U$$

The mechanical energy E_m of a system is the sum of its potential energy U and the kinetic energy K.

Now we can rewrite the above equation as

机械能守恒定律：

$$\Delta E_m = 0$$

$$\Delta E_m = 0$$

Or $E_{m2} = E_{m1}$

Equation above is a statement of conservation of mechanical energy for an isolated system. An isolated system is one for which there are no energy transfers across the boundary. The energy in such a system is conserved—the sum of the kinetic and potential energies remains constant (This statement assumes that no *nonconservative forces* act within the system).

孤立保守系统任意状态的机械能相等。

This is called the **principle of conservation of mechanical energy** for conservative forces.

If only conservative forces are doing work, the total mechanical energy of a system neither increases nor decreases in any process. It stays constant—it is conserved.

只有保守力存在的孤立系统的机械能守恒。

Example 4.7: A ball of mass m = 2.60 kg, starting from rest, falls a vertical distance h = 55.0 cm before striking a vertical coiled spring, which then compresses an amount y = 15.0 cm, shown at Figure 4-10. Determine the spring constant of the spring. Assume the spring has negligible mass.

Solution:

Choose the original position of the spring as zero potential energy. Using the Conservation of Mechanical Energy, we have

$$mgh = -mgy + \frac{1}{2}ky^2$$

Solving for k

$$k = \frac{2mg(h+y)}{y^2} = 1580\text{N}/\text{m}$$

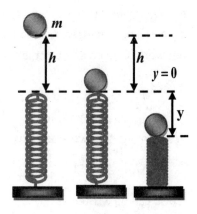

Figure 4-10 Example 4-7

Energy Diagrams and Equilibrium of a System

能量曲线和系统的平衡

Potential energy function, U(x) or E_P(x), can be converted to be a conservative force, F(x), graph. A block is moving between A and B, U(x) function is shown in Figure 4-11. The block experiences a force whose magnitude is proportional to the slope of the U(x) curve and its direction points toward decreasing potential energy.

从势能函数曲线可知物体受力函数。

Dashed horizontal line represents the total energy of the conservative systems. From the equation

$$F(x) = -\frac{dU(x)}{dx}$$

$$F(x) = -\frac{dU(x)}{dx}$$

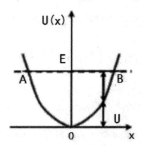

Figure 4-11 Elastic potential energy

We can calculate forces (magnitude and direction) at any point of the potential energy curve.

Point O at which the force is zero is called equilibrium point. In general, there are three types of equilibrium points: stable, unstable, and neutral equilibrium showing in Figure 4-12.

系统总能量为 E。

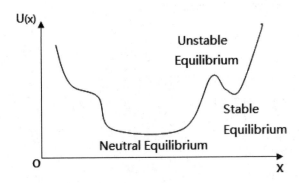

Figure 4-12 Three types of equilibrium points

O 点：平衡点，受力 F=0

任意位置物体受力 **F** 指向平衡点 O，物体在 AOB 间往复运动。

平衡点：$\dfrac{dU(x)}{dx}$ =0，势能曲线上的极值点。

三类平衡点：稳定、不稳定、随遇平衡。

对任何势能函数曲线确定平衡点：

For any curve of potential energy, we can discuss three types' equilibrium points.

1. The stable equilibrium position which happened at dU/dx =0 and U is minimum. It means if you put a particle at this point with zero kinetic energy, it could remain there forever at rest.

1. 稳定平衡位置：U 是极小值。物体将稳定在这个位置不动。

2. The unstable equilibrium position which happened at dU/dx =0 and U is maximums. It means if the particle gives a small displacement, it will end up far away from the equilibrium point.

2. 非稳定平衡位置：U 达到极大值。有扰动时物体将离开这个位置。

3. Neutral equilibrium interval which happened at dU/dx =0 and U = constant. Neutral equilibrium points are locations where the U curve is completely flat.

3. 随遇平衡位置：U 在此区间是常数。可在其间任一位置不动。

Example 4.8

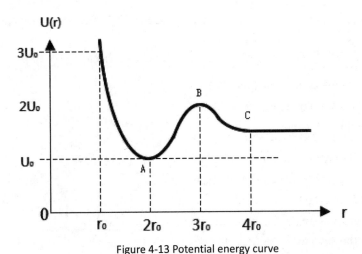

Figure 4-13 Potential energy curve

The graph above represents the potential energy U as a function of position r for a particle of mass m. if the particle is released from rest at position r_0 ,

a.   What will its speed be at position $3r_0$?

b.   What will happen if the particle is released from rest at $3r_0$?

Solution:

a.   According to the law of conservation of mechanical energy

$$E_m\big|_{r=r_0} = E_m\big|_{r=3r_0}$$

$$3U_0 = 2U_0 + \frac{1}{2}mv^2$$

Solving the equation, we have

$$v = \sqrt{\frac{2U_0}{m}}$$

b.   Because dU/dr=0 at point A, B and C (shown in the figure). F(r)=0 at position A, B and C.

Potential energy at point A, U (A), is minimum and at point B is maximum. So point A is a stable equilibrium position, point B is an unstable equilibrium position and point C is a neutral equilibrium position.

A 点是稳定平衡点，B 点非稳，C 点是随遇平衡点。

If a particle which is released from rest at point B were displaced a bit to either side of $3r_0$, a force would act to pull the particle away from the point.

如果物体在 B 点，任何一个微小扰动都会使物体最终远离这个位置。

Problem solving using conservation of mechanical energy:

机械能守恒问题解题步骤：

We can solve many problems in physics using the principle of conservation of mechanical energy. You should incorporate the following procedure when you apply this principle:

1. Define your isolated system, which may include two or more interacting particles, as well as springs or other structures in which elastic potential energy can be stored. Be sure to include all components of the system that exert forces on each other. Identify the initial and final configurations of the system.

1. 确定研究的系统。

2. Identify configurations for zero potential energy (both gravitational and spring). If there is more than one force acting within the system, write an expression for the potential energy associated with each force.

2. 选取合适的零势能点。

3. If friction or air resistance is present, mechanical energy of the system is not conserved.

4. If mechanical energy of the system is conserved, you can write the total energy $E_i = K_i + U_i$ for the initial configuration. Then, write an expression for the total energy $E_f = K_f + U_f$ for the final configuration that is of interest.

Because mechanical energy is conserved, you can equate the two total energies and solve for the quantity that is unknown.

3. 非保守力系统机械能不守恒。

4. 保守力系统中,确定起始和终点状态的机械能。应用机械能守恒定律。

4.7 Work-Energy Theorem

4.7 功–能原理

We now take into account nonconservative forces such as friction, since they are important in real situation.

实际的系统经常存在非保守力。

Let us express the work in the work-kinetic energy theorem in two parts, the work W_c due to conservative forces and the work W_{nc} due to the nonconservative forces:

动–能定理中外力的功,可分为保守力功和非保守力功。

$$W_{net} = W_c + W_{nc}$$

$$W_c + W_{nc} = \Delta K$$

Because a conservative force does work $Wc = -\Delta U$,

保守力的功 Wc 等于势能增量的负值: $Wc = -\Delta U$

Then $-\Delta U + W_{nc} = \Delta K$

Or $W_{nc} = \Delta K + \Delta U$

非保守力功 W_{nc} 的表达式给出功–能原理。

This equation represents the general form of the work-energy principles. It also represents the conservation of energy.

$$W_{nc} = \Delta K + \Delta U = \Delta E_m$$

$$W_{nc} = \Delta E_m = E_{m2} - E_{m1}$$

Work done by **nonconservative force** is equal to the change of mechanical energy.

非保守力（如摩擦力）存在时，其所做的功等于系统机械能的增量。

Example 4.9 Crate Sliding Down a Ramp

A 3.00kg crate slides down a ramp. The ramp is 1.00m in length and inclines at an angle of 30.0°, as shown in Figure 4-14. The crate starts from rest at the top, experiences a constant friction force of magnitude 5.00 N, and continues to move a short distance on the horizontal floor after it leaves the ramp. Use energy methods to determine the speed of the crate at the bottom of the ramp.

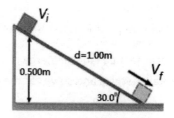

Figure 4-14 A crate slides down a ramp

Solution:

We choose the bottom of the ramp as reference position U(0)=0 at $y_f=0$. Work done by nonconservative force, friction force, W_{nc} is

$$W_{nc} = -F_r d = -5*1 = -5J$$

And it will be equal to

$$\Delta E_m = E_{mf} - E_{mi} = (\frac{1}{2}mv_f^2 + mgy_f) - (\frac{1}{2}mv_i^2 + mgy_i)$$
$$= \frac{1}{2}mv_f^2 - mgy_i = -5J$$

Solve the equation above: v_f = 2.54m/s

4.8 The Law of Conservation of Energy

4.8 能量守恒定律

Usually the mechanical energy does not remain constant but decreases. Because frictional forces reduce the total mechanical energy, they are called *dissipative forces*.

通常系统机械能都在减少，使机械能减少的作用力（如摩擦力）称为耗散力。

For each type of forces, conservative or nonconservative, it has always been found possible to define a type of energy that corresponds to the work done by such a force. And it has been found experimentally that the total energy E always remains constant.

$$E = K + U + \text{all other forms of energy}$$

That is, the change in the total energy, kinetic plus potential plus all other forms of energy, equals zero:

$$\Delta E = 0$$

This is one of the most important principles in physics. It is called the **law of conservation of energy**, stated as follows:

The total energy is neither increased nor decreased in any process. Energy can be transformed from one form to another, and transferred from one body to another, but the total amount remains constant.

能量守恒定律：

$$\Delta E = 0$$

能量守恒定律是物理学中最重要的基本定理之一。

经过任何一个过程，孤立系统的总能量既不能增加，也不能减少，只能从一种形式转化成另一种形式。

4.9 Power

4.9 功率

Power is the rate at which work gets done on a system. The average power, $\overline{p}$, when an amount of work W is done in a time t is

$$\overline{p} = \frac{W}{t}$$

The instantaneous power, P, is **the instantaneous time rate of doing work**

$$P = \frac{dW}{dt}$$

It is the measure of how fast work is done.

$$P = \frac{dW}{dt} = \frac{\vec{F} \cdot d\vec{r}}{dt} = \vec{F} \cdot \vec{v}$$

The SI unit of power is joules per second (J/s), also called the watt (W) (after James Watt):

1 watt = 1 W = 1 J/s

功率 P 描述做功快慢，是标量。

平均功率 $\overline{p} = \dfrac{W}{t}$

瞬时功率 $P = \dfrac{dW}{dt} = \vec{F} \cdot \vec{v}$

功率的单位：瓦特（W）。

One kilowatt-hour (kWh) is the energy transferred in 1 h at the constant rate of 1 kW= 1 000 J/s. The amount of energy represented by 1 kWh is

千瓦时：能量单位

$$1 \text{ kWh} = (10^3 \text{ W}) (3\ 600 \text{ s}) = 3.60 * 10^6 \text{ J}$$

Example 4.10 A car climbing a hill: A car with a mass of 900 kg climbs a 20° incline at a steady speed of 60 km/hr. If the total resistance forces acting on the car add to 500 N,

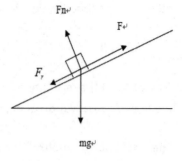

Figure 4-15 Example 4-10

a.   What is the power output of the car in watts?

b.   The car accelerates along a level road from 90 to 110km/hr in 6.0s. Assume the retarding force on the car is F_r = 700N throughout. Calculate the power needs of the car.

Solution:

a.   Note that the gravitational force is the only force which needs to be split into components. mg sin20° acts down the slope; mg cos20° acts into the slope. Fr represents the resistance forces.

The velocity is constant, so the forces must balance. Applying Newton's second law up the slope of the hill gives:

$$F - F_r - mg \sin 20^0 = 0$$

The force up the slope is then

$$F = F_r + mg \sin 20^0 = 500 + 3017 = 3517 \text{N}$$

The power output can then be found from, (60km/hr = 16.67 m/s)

$$P = Fv = 3517 * 16.67 = 58620 \text{W}$$

b.   The car accelerates from 25.0m/s to 30.6m/s. Thus the car must exert a force that overcomes the 700N retarding force plus that required give it the acceleration

$a = (30.6 - 25.0) / 6.0 = 0.93 \text{m/s}^2$, so

$$F = ma + F_r + mg\sin\theta = 900 * 0.93 + 700 + 3017 = 4517\text{N}$$

Since P = F.V, the required power increases with speed and the motor must be able to provide a maximum power output of

$$P = 4517 * 30.6 \approx 1.38 * 10^5 \text{W}$$

第四章总结 功和能

1. **功- W（J）**

   力是常数对物体做功：W=$\mathbf{F} \cdot \mathbf{\Delta r}$，功可以为正、负、或零。

   力随时间变化：W=$\int_A^B F \cdot dr$

   动能定理：W=ΔK，K 或者 KE 表示动能

2. **保守力 Fc：** $\oint F_c \cdot dr$ =0

   保守力做功与路径无关，只决定于起点和终点的位置。

   力学中常见的保守力有万有引力、弹簧弹性力。

3. **能量**

   动能：K=$\frac{1}{2}mv^2$

   势能：用 PE 或 U 表示，由保守力场中物体所在位置决定的能量。不同保守力场对应不同的

   势能表达形式。

   重力：F=mg，U=mgh

   弹性力：F=kx，U=$\frac{1}{2}kx^2$

   机械能：E_m=K+U

   总能量：E=K+U+其他

4. **功-能原理**：非保守力的功等于系统机械能的增量。

$$W_{nc} = \Delta K + \Delta U = \Delta E_m$$

5. **机械能守恒**：当只有保守力做功时，系统的总机械能守恒。

$$E_{mi}=E_{m2}，或 K_1 + U_1 = K_2 + U_2$$

   能量守恒：孤立系统的能量保持不变

6. **势能曲线图**

   保守力的功等于其对应的势能增量的负值：W= -ΔU

   势能曲线表达式为 U（x）：保守力 F=$-\dfrac{dU}{dx}$

如果 $\dfrac{dU}{dx}=0$，那么 **F**=0，满足此条件的点就是平衡点。

平衡点有三种：稳定平衡、不稳定平衡和随遇平衡。

7. 功率：用 P 表示。表示物体做功的快慢。

瞬时功率 $P=\dfrac{dW}{dt}$

平均功率 $\overline{P}=\dfrac{W}{\Delta t}$

F 为常数时 $P=\mathbf{F}\cdot\mathbf{v}$

Chapter 4 Work and Energy Practice

Multiple Choice Questions

1. The force vs distance graph is shown below. For an object being pushed along a straight line, starting at rest, if the object has a mass of 2 kg, its velocity at 4.0 m is

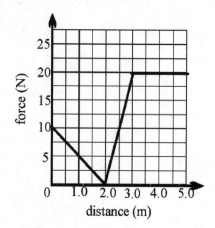

   A. 0.2 m/s
   B. 2.0 m/s
   C. 5.0 m/s
   D. 6.3 m/s
   E. 8.5 m/s

2. A ball of mass 16 kg on the end of a string is spun at a constant speed of 2.0 m/s in a horizontal circle with a radius of 1 m. What is the work done by the centripetal force during one complete revolution?

   A. 0 J
   B. 16 J
   C. 32 J
   D. 8 J
   E. 4 J

3. A force $\mathbf{F} = (2x\,\mathbf{i} + 5y^2\,\mathbf{j})$ N acts on an object as the object moves in the x direction from the origin to $x = 4.00$ m. The work done on the object by the force is

A. 4J

B. 8J

C. 16J

D. 18J

E. 32J

4. A particle is fired at an angle θ with ground out of a cannon. Which of the following graphs best represents its kinetic energy K as a function of time t?

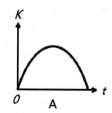

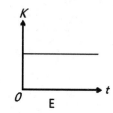

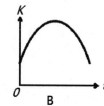

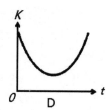

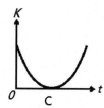

5. A block of mass m moving with initial velocity v_0 moves over a rough surface with coefficient of kinetic friction μ. How long does it take for the block to come to a complete stop?

A. $\dfrac{v_0^2}{2\mu g}$

B. $\dfrac{v_0}{2\mu g}$

C. $\dfrac{v_0^2}{2m\mu g}$

D. $\dfrac{v_0}{\mu g}$

E. $\dfrac{v_0^2}{\mu g}$

6. Two balls of equal size are dropped from the same height from the roof of a building. One ball has mass M and the other has a mass 2M. When the balls reach the ground, how do the kinetic energies of the two balls compare? (Neglect friction)

A. M has one-fourth the kinetic energy of 2M.
B. M has one-half the kinetic energy of 2M.
C. M has the same amount of kinetic energy as 2M.
D. M has twice the amount of kinetic energy as 2M.
E. M has four times the amount of kinetic energy as 2M.

7. What happens to the energy of a bouncing ball as it hits the ground with a certain downward velocity?

A. Gravitational Potential energy is converted into kinetic energy.
B. Elastic Potential Energy is converted into gravitational potential energy.
C. Kinetic energy is converted into heat energy.
D. Kinetic energy is converted into elastic potential energy and heat.
E. Kinetic energy is converted into gravitational energy.

8. What is the expression of the kinetic energy of an object of mass 5 kg whose acceleration is given by $a(t) = 4t - 5$ and that is initially at rest?

A. $5(4t-5)$
B. $5(2t^2-5t)$
C. $5(2t^2-5t)^2$
D. $2.5(2t^2-5t)^2$
E. $2.5(4t-5)^2$

9. A horizontal force F is used to push a 3.0 kg block, initially at rest, across a floor, with a constant acceleration of 2.0 m/s². If the frictional force between the block and the floor is 4 N, how much work is done by force F on the block to move it 15 meters?

A. 60 J
B. 90 J
C. 120 J
D. 150 J
E. 210 J

10. An object is dropped off a cliff of height h and is subjected to an average force of air resistance of F. If the object has a mass of m, the kinetic energy it gains during the fall will be equal to

A. mgh
B. $mgh + F$
C. $mgh - F$
D. $mgh + Fh$
E. $mgh - Fh$

Questions **11** to **15**

The diagram below shows a frictionless track. And the starting point is at origin.

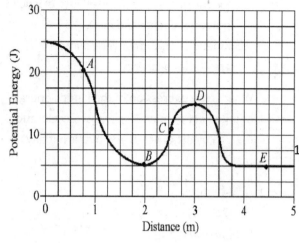

Potential Energy (J) vs Distance (m)

11. At which point would an object at rest be in unstable equilibrium?

12. At which point is an object at rest in stable equilibrium?

13. If an object is released at the beginning of the track, which of the following is true at point E?

   A. It is in static equilibrium.
   B. It is losing kinetic energy.
   C. It is in dynamic equilibrium.
   D. There is a net force acting on the object.
   E. Its kinetic energy is 25 J.

14. Which of the following best describes the motion of an object as it approaches point B, if it was released from rest at the beginning of the track?

   A. It is losing potential energy only.
   B. It is gaining kinetic energy only.
   C. It is gaining potential energy and gaining kinetic energy.
   D. It is losing potential energy and gaining kinetic energy.
   E. It is gaining heat energy, gaining kinetic energy, and losing potential energy.

15. If an object of mass 5 kg is released from rest at the beginning of the track, what is its velocity at point D?

   A. 1 m/s
   B. 1.4 m/s
   C. 2 m/s
   D. 2.2 m/s
   E. 3 m/s

16. An object with an initial potential energy U_0 experiences a conservative force given by $F(x) = 3x^2 + 2$ over the interval $0 < x < 2$. What is the equation for the potential energy U of this object?

   A. $U(x) = x^3 + 2x + U_0$
   B. $U(x) = -x^3 - 2x - U_0$
   C. $U(x) = -x^3 - 2x + U_0$
   D. $U(x) = -x^3 - 2x$
   E. $U(x) = x^3 + 2x$

17. The work done by an object is given by the equation $W(t) = 3t^2 - 5t + 1$, where W is in Joules and t is in seconds. What is the power delivered by the object at $t = 2$?

   A. 3 W
   B. 6 W
   C. 7 W
   D. 8 W
   E. 10 W

18. A 500 N student expends an average power of 250 W to climb a 6 m vertical rope at constant velocity. How long does it take for the student to climb the rope?

   A. 1 s
   B. 2 s
   C. 3 s
   D. 6 s
   E. 12 s

19. A 2.0kg block is initially at rest on a horizontal frictionless surface when a horizontal force in the positive direction of x

axis is applied to the block. The force is given by $F(x)=(6-3x^2)i$ N, where x is in meters and the initial position of the block is x=0. The speed of the block as it passes through x=2.0m is

A. 2m/s

B. 3m/s

C. 4m/s

D. 6m/s

E. 8m/s

20. A mass m is attached to the end of a spring with constant k. the mass is given an initial displacement x_0 from equilibrium, and an initial speed v_0. Its maximum stretch from equilibrium is

A. $x_{max} = x_0 + \dfrac{m}{k} v_0$

B. $x_{max} = \sqrt{x_0^2 - \dfrac{m}{k} v_0^2}$

C. $x_{max} = \sqrt{x_0^2 + \dfrac{k}{m} v_0^2}$

D. $x_{max} = \sqrt{x_0^2 + v_0^2}$

E. $x_{max} = \sqrt{x_0^2 + \dfrac{m}{k} v_0^2}$

Free Response Questions

1. Two objects are connected by a light string passing over a light frictionless pulley as shown in Figure on the right. The object of mass m_1=5.00 kg which is 4m height from the ground is released from rest.

   mq h

   zog

   A. Determine the speed of the m_2= 3.00kg object just as the m_1 object hits the ground.

   B. Find the maximum height to which the m_2 object rises.

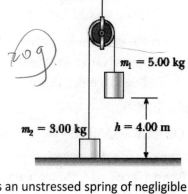

$m_1 = 5.00$ kg

$m_2 = 3.00$ kg $h = 4.00$ m

2. An object of mass m starts from rest and slides a distance d down an incline of angle θ. The coefficient of kinetic friction between the mass and the plane is μ. While sliding, it contacts an unstressed spring of negligible mass and spring constant k as shown in Figure below.

   A. Determine the object's speed when it reaches the spring.

   B. At what value x of the compression of the spring does the object reach its maximum speed.

   C. The object slides a distance x_{max} as it is brought momentarily to rest by compression of the spring. Find the value x_{max} of the compression.

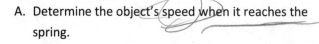

3. A uniform chain of mass M and length L hangs from a hook in the ceiling. The bottom link is now raised vertically and hung on the hook as shown below.

A. Determine the increase in gravitational potential energy of the chain by considering the change in position of the center of mass of the chain.

B. Write an equation for the upward external force F(y) required to lift the chain slowly as a function of the vertical distance y.

C. Find the minimum work done on the chain to lift the bottom of the rope to any position y.

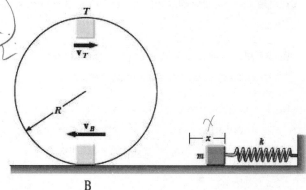

4. The graph below shows the potential energy U(x) of a particle with mass m=1kg as a function of its position x.

A. Identify all points of equilibrium for this particle.

B. Describe the motion of the particle if its total energy is 2J.

C. What are the particle speeds at x=2.0m and 4.0m if its total energy is 4J?

D. Can the particle reach the positions x = 0.5 m and 5.0m if the total energy is 4J? Explain.

E. On the grid below, carefully draw a graph of the conservative force acting on the particle as a function of x, for 0 < x < 7 meters.

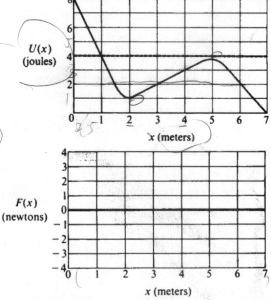

5. A block of mass 0.500 kg is pushed against a horizontal spring of negligible mass until the spring is compressed a distance x (shown in the Figure below). The force constant of the spring is 450 N/m. When it is released, the block travels along a frictionless, horizontal surface to point B, the bottom of a vertical circular track of radius R =1.00 m, and continues to move up the track. The speed of the block at the bottom of the track is v_B = 12.0 m/s, and the block experiences an average friction force of 7.00 N while sliding up the track.

A. What is x?

B. What speed do you predict for the block at the top of the track?

C. Does the block actually reach the top of the track, or does it fall off before reaching the top?

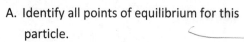

B

108

Answers and Explanations

Multiple Choice Answers

1. D   2. A   3. C   4. D   5. D   6. B   7. D   8. D   9. D   10. E   11. D   12. B   13. C   14. D   15. C
16. C   17. C   18. E   19. A   20. E

Multiple Choice Explanations

1. D。力-位移曲线下的面积是力对物体所做的功。W=40J=$\frac{1}{2}mv^2$，$\rightarrow v = 6.3m/s$。

2. A。向心力与物体运动速度方向垂直，所以做功为零。

3. C。$W = \int F \cdot dr = \int_0^4 2x \, dx = 16J$

4. D 物体在运动到最高点时速率最小。

5. D。由冲量定理：$-\mu mgt = 0 - mv$，$\rightarrow t = \frac{v_0}{\mu g}$

6. B。球落地时的动能 K=$\frac{1}{2}mv^2$，两球落地时速度相同。

7. D。小球撞击地面过程中动能 K 转化成势能+热。

8. D。$v = \int_0^t (4t-5)dt = 2t^2 - 5t$，K=$\frac{1}{2}mv^2 = 2.5(2t^2 - 5t)^2$

9. D。F-f=ma，得 F=10N。W=Fd=150J

10. E。K=W=（mg-F）h

11. D。D 点是非稳平衡点。

12. B。B 点是稳定平衡点。

13. C。E 点是中性平衡点，物体所受和外力为零。

14. D。到达 B 点时，部分势能转化为动能，此时是物体所能达到的最大动能。

15. C。顶点处的势能将有 10J 转化为 D 点的动能 K=$\frac{1}{2}mv^2 = 10J \rightarrow v = 2m/s$

16. C。 $W=-\Delta U$。 $U-U_0 =-\int_0^x (x^2 +2)dx =-x^3 /3-2x$

17. C。 瞬时功率 $P=\dfrac{dW}{dt}$ =6t-5；t=2s 时，P=7w

18. E。 学生爬上 6m 高时要克服重力做功 W=mgh=3000J，t=$\dfrac{W}{P}$ =12s

19. A。 W= $\int_0^2 (6-3x^2)dx =4J=\dfrac{1}{2}mv^2 \rightarrow v=2m/s$

20. E。 $\dfrac{1}{2}kx_0^2 +\dfrac{1}{2}mv_0^2 =\dfrac{1}{2}kx_{max}^2$, $x_{max} =\sqrt{x_0^2 +\dfrac{m}{k}v_0^2}$

Free Response Explanations

1. A. 5kg 物体 m_1 释放之前系统的机械能：$m_1gh=20g$ J

   m_1 落地时，两个物体以相同的速度运动，系统的机械能：$m_2gh+\dfrac{1}{2}(m_1 +m_2)v^2$

   整个系统不受外力作用，机械能守恒。

   $\rightarrow v=4.43m/s$

   B. 3kg 的物体 m 在 h=4m 处，以初速度 v=4.43m/s 做上抛运动，在最高点 h_{mac} 处，v=0

   由机械能守恒：$mgh_{max} =mgh+\dfrac{1}{2}mv^2 \rightarrow h_{max} =5m$

2. A. 令系统零势能点在弹簧原长位置处 O。物体从斜面距离为 d 处运动到零势能点位置，非保守力的功等于系统机械能的增量。非保守摩擦力 f= $\mu mg\cos\theta$ 做负功：

   -fd= $\dfrac{1}{2}mv_o^2 -mgd\sin\theta$

   $\rightarrow v_o =\sqrt{2dg(\sin\theta -\mu\cos\theta)}$

   B. 沿斜面方向和外力为零时，物体的加速度为零，速度达到最大值，有

   $mg\sin\theta -\mu mg\cos\theta -kx=0$

   $\rightarrow x=\dfrac{mg(\sin\theta -\mu\cos\theta)}{k}$

C. 物体压缩弹簧从 O 点达到最大距离 x_{max} 时，摩擦力的功等于系统机械能的增量。

$$-\mu mg \cos\theta x_{max} = (\frac{1}{2}kx_{max}^2 - mg\sin\theta x_{max}) - \frac{1}{2}mv_0^2$$

$$\rightarrow x = \frac{mg(\sin\theta - \mu\cos\theta) + \sqrt{m^2g^2(\sin\theta - \mu\cos\theta)^2 + 2mgkd(\sin\theta - \mu\cos\theta)}}{k}$$

3. A. 以链条底部为零势能点，设此位置为竖直方向坐标零点 O：

完全折叠时，势能改变为-（MgL/4-（MgL/2））=MgL/4

B. 外力 F 向上提起链条运动的任意时刻，从 O 点到链条最低点的距离是 y；此时折叠部分的质量为 m=yM/L，

所需最小外力为 $F(y) = \frac{M}{L}yg$

C. 链条长度每折叠 y，F 移动的距离为 2y：W= $\int_0^y Fd(2y) = \int_0^y \frac{M}{L}yg2dy = \frac{M}{L}y^2g$

或者：考虑位于距离底部 O 高为 x 的小质元 dm=$\frac{M}{L}dx$，将其由 x 位置移动到 2y-x 位置时外力所做的功，dW=dm g 2(y-x)

$$\rightarrow W = \int_0^y dW = \int_0^y \frac{M}{L}g2(y-x)dx = \frac{M}{L}y^2g$$

4. A. 保守力 F=$-\frac{dU}{dx}$=0 是粒子的平衡点，图中给出 X=2m 和 x=5m。

其中 x=2 是稳定平衡点，x=5m 是非稳定平衡点。

B. 粒子不可能出现在 x<1.5m 的位置处。在点 x=1.5m 和 3m 处粒子的动能为零势能为 U=2J，粒子将在这两点间运动，这两点作为转向点。粒子亦不可能处于 3<x<6m 区间。如果粒子出现在 x=6m 处，之后它将加速沿 x 轴正向运动。

C. 总能量 E=U+K

x=2m：4=1+$\frac{1}{2}mv^2$，$\rightarrow v = 2.4m/s$

x=4m：4=3+$\frac{1}{2}mv^2$，$\rightarrow v = 1.4m/s$

D. 在 x=0.5m 处，U（0.5）=6J。而系统的总能量为 E=U+K=4J，所以粒子不可能出现在此位置。

在 x=5m 处：U（5）=3.8J，小于物体的总能量，粒子可以在此出现。

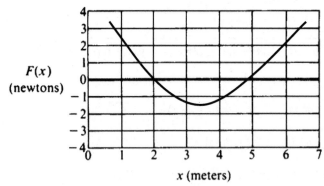

E.

5. A. 物体获得的动能等于弹簧压缩x时储存的势能：$\dfrac{1}{2}kx^2 = \dfrac{1}{2}mv_B^2 \rightarrow x = 0.4m$

B. 物体从底部运动到顶部摩擦力的功 W=-fs=$-7 \times \pi R = -7\pi$ J

由功能原理：W=ΔE，摩擦力的功等于系统机械能的增量。

$$\Delta E = mg2R + \dfrac{1}{2}mv_T^2 - \dfrac{1}{2}m_B^2 ,$$

$$\rightarrow v_T = 4.1m/s$$

C. 物体运动到顶部时，能保持其在轨道上不掉下来的最小速度是 v_{min}，此时重力充当物体圆周运动的向心力。

$$mg = m\dfrac{v_{min}^2}{R} ,$$

$$\rightarrow v_{min} = \sqrt{gR} = 3.3m/s < v_T$$

所以物体可以达到顶部。

Linear Momentum and Collisions
动量和碰撞

Introduction: Quantities found to be conserved are **energy, linear momentum, angular momentum, and electric charge**. We will eventually discuss all of these because the conservation laws are among the most important in all of science. In this chapter, we discuss linear momentum and its conservation. And then we make use of the laws of conservation of linear momentum and of energy to analyze collisions. When dealing with two or more bodies that interact with each other, as in collisions, the law of conservation of momentum is particularly useful.

能量、动量、角动量和电荷都遵循守恒定律。

5.1 Linear Momentum and its Relation to Force   5.1 动量和力

The linear momentum (or momentum for short) of an object is defined as the product of its mass and its velocity, represented by the symbol **P**.

$$\vec{P} = m\vec{v}$$

Momentum is a vector parallel to velocity and obeys superposition, such that the net momentum of a collection of objects is the vector sum of the momentum of each object.

Differentiate **P**=m**v** with respect to time,

$$\frac{d\vec{p}}{dt} = \frac{d(m\vec{v})}{dt} = m\frac{d\vec{v}}{dt} = m\vec{a}$$

$$\vec{F}_{net} = \frac{d\vec{p}}{dt}$$

We obtain Newton's second law in terms of momentum: *The time*

动量（线动量）定义：

$$\vec{P} = m\vec{v}$$

单位：kg m/s

动量是向量，与速度方向一致，遵循向量叠加。

牛顿第二定律动量形式：

$$\vec{F}_{net} = \frac{d\vec{p}}{dt}$$

物体动量时间变化率等

rate of change of the momentum of a particle is equal to the net force acting on the particle and in the direction of that force.

于作用于物体上合外力。

5.2 Impulse and Theorem of Momentum　　5.2 冲量和动量定理

From Newton's second law, we have

$$d\vec{p} = \vec{F}dt$$

During the infinitesimal time interval dt, the momentum changes by $d\vec{p}$ because of the action of the net force **F**. If we integrate this over the duration of some time interval (t_i, t_f), we obtain

$$\int_{t_i}^{t_f} \vec{F}dt = \int_{P_0}^{P} d\vec{P} = \vec{P} - \vec{P}_0 = \Delta \vec{P}$$

Impulse is defined

$$\vec{J} = \int_{t_i}^{t_f} \vec{F}dt$$

So　　$$\vec{J} = \vec{P} - \vec{P}_0 = \Delta \vec{P}$$

The impulse of the force F acting on a particle equals the change in the momentum of the particle. This is the impulse-momentum theorem-relationship between impulse and force. This statement is equivalent to Newton's second law.

From this definition, we see that impulse is a vector quantity having a magnitude equal to the area under the force-time curve, as described in Figure 5-1.

Because the force imparting an impulse can generally vary in time, it is convenient to define a time-averaged force.

$$\overline{F} = \frac{1}{\Delta t} \int_{t_i}^{t_f} Fdt$$

The figure tells us that the impulse is the area under the F(t) graph. The average force is this area divided by Δt, which equals the height of a rectangle of width Δt, that contains the same area as the integral impulse.

冲量定义：力的时间累积

$$\vec{J} = \int_{t_i}^{t_f} \vec{F}dt$$

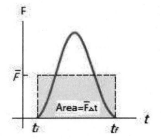

Figure 5-1 Average force

冲量：F-t 图曲线下面积

冲量单位：1N*s=1kgm/s
动量定理：力在一段时间内作用于物体上的冲量等于物体的动量改变。

$$\vec{J} = \vec{P} - \vec{P}_0 = \Delta \vec{P}$$

动量定理与牛顿第二定律等价。

平均冲力 $\overline{F} = \frac{1}{\Delta t} \int_{t_i}^{t_f} Fdt$

Example 5.1 Teeing off: A golf ball of mass 50 g is struck with a club. The force exerted by the club on the ball varies from zero, at the instant before contact, up to some maximum value and then back to zero when the ball leaves the club. Thus, the force–time curve is qualitatively described by Figure 5-1. Assuming that the ball travels 200 m and the launch angle θ is 45°, estimate the magnitude of the impulse caused by the collision. What is the average force on the ball during the collision with the club? We *assume* that the time interval is 0.01 s.

击球时平均冲力

Solution:

The range of a projectile is

$$R = \frac{v_0^2}{g} \sin 2\theta$$

So $v_0 = \sqrt{Rg}$ = 44m/s ; Direction of velocity V_0 is θ = 45°

v_0 : 出射速度

$$I = \Delta P = P_f - P_i = mv_0 - 0 = 2.2 \text{kgm/s} ;$$

direction is the same with V_0

$$\overline{F} = \frac{I}{\Delta t} = \frac{2.2}{0.01} = 220\text{N}$$

5.3 Conservation of Momentum

5.3 动量守恒定律

Let **P** represent the total momentum of a system of n interacting objects

$$\vec{P} = m_1\vec{v}_1 + m_2\vec{v}_2 + \cdots + m_n\vec{v}_n = \sum \vec{P}_i$$

物体系统（由 n 个物体组成）总动量： $\vec{P} = \sum \vec{P}_i$

We differentiate with respect to time:

$$\frac{d\vec{P}}{dt} = \sum \frac{d\vec{P}_i}{dt} = \sum \vec{F}_i$$

$$\frac{d\vec{P}}{dt} = \sum \frac{d\vec{P}_i}{dt} = \sum \vec{F}_i$$

F_i represents the net force on the object. The force **F** $_i$=**F** $_{ext}$+**F** $_{int}$

F $_{ext}$: external forces on objects of the system, exerted by objects outside the system

F_i:第 i 个物体所受合外力

F $_{ext}$:各个物体所受外力和

F_{int}:物体之间相互作用的

F $_{int}$: internal forces that objects within the system exert on other objects in the system.

内力和

All the internal forces cancel each other in pairs. Thus we have

内力全部成对抵消为零

$$\frac{dp}{dt} = \sum F_{ext}$$

$$\frac{dp}{dt} = \sum F_{ext}$$

If the net external force is zero, then d**P**/dt =0, so

如果 $\sum F_{ext}$ =0,

P = constant.   Or

$\triangle$ **P**=0

有 $\triangle$ **P**=0,或**P**=常数

We have：**When the net external force on a system is zero, the total momentum remains constant.**

动量守恒定律：系统所受合外力为零时，系统的总动量保持守恒。

This is the **law of conservation of momentum**. It is also be stated as

The total momentum of an isolated system of bodies remains constant.

或孤立系统总动量守恒。

In three dimensions: if $F_{net,x}$=0, then $\triangle P_x$=0

系统在哪一方向合外力为零，在哪一方向的动量守恒：

If $F_{net,y}$=0, then $\triangle P_y$=0

If $F_{net,z}$=0, then $\triangle P_z$=0

若 $F_{net,x}$=0, 那么 $\triangle P_x$=0

Example 5.2 Railroad cars collide

A 10,000 kg railroad car traveling at a speed of 24.0m/s strikes an identical car at rest. If the cars lock together as a result of the collision, what is their common speed afterward?

Solution：

The initial total momentum is simply $m_1 v_1$(since v_2=0), to the right in the +x direction. After the collision, the total momentum will be the same, and it will be shared by both cars which have the same speed v′. Then

$$(m_1 + m_2) v' = m_1 v_1$$

$$v' = 12.0 m/s: \text{ to the right}$$

Example 5.3 The Archer: A 60-kg archer stands at rest on frictionless ice and fires a 0.50-kg arrow horizontally at 50 m/s. With what velocity does the archer move across the ice after firing the arrow?

弓箭手

Solution:

The total horizontal momentum of the system before the arrow is fired is zero ($m_1v_{1i} + m_2v_{2i}=0$), where the archer is particle 1 and the arrow is particle 2. Therefore, the total horizontal momentum after the arrow is fired must be zero; that is,

$$m_1 v_{1f} + m_2 v_{2f} = 0$$

We choose the direction of firing of the arrow as the positive x direction. With m_1=60 kg, m_2 = 0.50 kg, and $\mathbf{V_{2f}}$ =50 **i** m/s, solving for $\mathbf{V_{1f}}$, we find the recoil velocity of the archer to be

$$m_1 v_{1f} + m_2 v_{2f} = 0$$

$$v_{1f} = -\frac{m_2 v_{2f}}{m_1} = -0.42\text{m/s}$$

The negative sign for $\mathbf{V_{1f}}$ indicates that the archer is moving to the left after the arrow is fired, in the direction opposite the direction of motion of the arrow.

5.4 Collisions

5.4 碰撞

When two particles of masses m_1 and m_2 collide the impulsive forces may vary in time in complicated ways. Regardless of the complexity of the time behavior of the force of interaction, however, this force is internal to the system of two particles. The total momentum just before a collision equals the total momentum of the system just after the collision.

物体相互作用时间很短

碰撞前系统总动量等于碰撞后系统总动量。

$\mathbf{P}_{\text{before}}=\mathbf{P}_{\text{after}}$

In contrast, the total kinetic energy of the system of particles may or may not be conserved, some or all of the energy is stored momentarily in the form of elastic potential energy, depending on the type of collision. In fact, whether or not kinetic energy is conserved is used to classify collisions as either *elastic* or *inelastic*.

系统的总动能可能守恒可能不守恒，与碰撞类型有关。

5.4.1 Elastic Collisions

5.4.1 弹性碰撞

An elastic collision between two objects is that in which **the total kinetic energy (as well as total momentum) of the system is the same before and after the collision.**

两物体弹性碰撞：动量守恒，总动能也守恒。

Collisions between certain objects in the **macroscopic world**, such as billiard balls, are only ***approximately*** elastic because some **deformation** and loss of kinetic energy take place. For example, you can hear a billiard ball collision, so you know that some of the energy is being transferred away from the system by sound. An elastic collision must be perfectly silent! *Truly* elastic collisions occur between atomic and subatomic particles.

宏观世界
近似的
形变

Consider two particles of masses m_1 and m_2 moving with initial velocities v_{1i} and v_{2i} along the same straight line, as shown in Figure 5-2. The two particles collide head-on and then leave the collision site with different velocities, v_{1f} and v_{2f}. If the collision is elastic, both the momentum and kinetic energy of the system are conserved. Therefore, considering velocities along the horizontal direction，we have

两物体一维弹性碰撞动
量和能量守恒方程:

$$m_1 v_{1i} + m_2 v_{2i} = m_1 v_{1f} + m_2 v_{2f} \qquad (1)$$

$$\frac{1}{2} m_1 v_{1i}^2 + \frac{1}{2} m_2 v_{2i}^2 = \frac{1}{2} m_1 v_{1f}^2 + \frac{1}{2} m_2 v_{2f}^2 \qquad (2)$$

Because all velocities in Figure 5-2 are either to the left or the right, they can be represented by the corresponding speeds along with algebraic signs indicating direction.

We shall indicate v as positive if a particle moves to the right and negative if it moves to the left. Rewrite equation above, it is obtained:

$$m_1 (v_{1i}^2 - v_{1f}^2) = m_2 (v_{2f}^2 - v_{2i}^2)$$

$$m_1 (v_{1i} - v_{1f})(v_{1i} + v_{1f}) = m_2 (v_{2f} - v_{2i})(v_{2f} + v_{2i})$$

From equation (1) we have $m_1 (v_{1i} - v_{1f}) = m_2 (v_{2f} - v_{2i})$

So $v_{1i} + v_{1f} = v_{2f} + v_{2i}$

We get the result $v_{1i} - v_{2i} = -(v_{1f} - v_{2f})$

This is an interesting result: **For any elastic head-on collision, the relative speed of the two objects after the collision has the same**

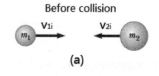

Before collision

(a)

After collision

(b)

Figure 5-2 Elastic collision

$$m_1 v_{1i} + m_2 v_{2i} = m_1 v_{1f} + m_2 v_{2f}$$

$$\frac{1}{2} m_1 v_{1i}^2 + \frac{1}{2} m_2 v_{2i}^2$$

$$= \frac{1}{2} m_1 v_{1f}^2 + \frac{1}{2} m_2 v_{2f}^2$$

解动量、能量守恒方程
得:

$$v_{1i} - v_{2i} = -(v_{1f} - v_{2f})：$$

任意两物体弹性碰撞前

magnitude as before but in opposite direction, no matter what the masses are.

The final velocities of the two particles are:

$$v_{1f} = \left(\frac{m_1 - m_2}{m_1 + m_2}\right)v_{1i} + \left(\frac{2m_2}{m_1 + m_2}\right)v_{2i}$$

$$v_{2f} = \left(\frac{2m_1}{m_1 + m_2}\right)v_{1i} + \left(\frac{m_2 - m_1}{m_1 + m_2}\right)v_{2i}$$

If particle 2 is initially at rest, then $v_{2i}= 0$,

$$v_{1f} = \left(\frac{m_1 - m_2}{m_1 + m_2}\right)v_{1i}$$

$$v_{2f} = \left(\frac{2m_1}{m_1 + m_2}\right)v_{1i}$$

If $m_1=m_2$, then we have $v_{1f}= v_{2i}$ and $v_{2f} =v_{1i}$.

That is, the particles exchange velocities if they have equal masses.

If m_1 is much greater than m_2 and $v_{2i} =0$, we see that $v_{1f} = v_{1i}$ and $v_{2f} = 2v_{1i}$.

That is, when a very heavy particle collides head-on with a very light one which is initially at rest, the heavy particle continues its motion unaltered after the collision and the light particle rebounds with a speed equal to about twice the initial speed of the heavy particle.

If m_2 is much greater than m_1 and particle 2 is initially at rest, then $v_{1f} = -v_{1i}$ and $v_{2f} = 0$.

That is, when a very light particle collides head-on with a very heavy particle which is initially at rest, the light particle has its velocity reversed and the heavy one remains approximately at rest.

5.4.2 Inelastic Collision

An inelastic collision is one in which the total kinetic energy of the system is not the same before and after the collision (even though the momentum of the system is conserved). Inelastic collisions have two types. When the colliding objects stick together after the collision, it is called perfectly inelastic. When the colliding objects do not stick together, but some kinetic energy is lost, the collision is called inelastic.

速度差值等于碰撞后两物体速度差值的负数。

第二个物体静止不动时弹性碰撞后两物体速度：

$$v_{1f} = \left(\frac{m_1 - m_2}{m_1 + m_2}\right)v_{1i}$$

$$v_{2f} = \left(\frac{2m_1}{m_1 + m_2}\right)v_{1i}$$

$m_1 = m_2$，且 $v_{2i}= 0$：

$v_{1f}= v_{2i}$，　$v_{2f} =v_{1i}$. 即两物体碰撞后交换速度

$m_1 \gg m_2$，且 $v_{2i} =0$（重物体撞击轻物体）：

$v_{1f} = v_{1i}$，$v_{2f} = 2v_{1i}$.

$m_1 \ll m_2$，且 $v_{2i} =0$（轻物体反弹）：

$v_{1f} = -v_{1i}$ and $v_{2f} = 0$.

5.4.2 非弹性碰撞

非弹性碰撞动量守恒，动能不守恒。有两种情况：完全非弹性：两物体粘到一起，碰后动能损失最大，两物体以共同速度运动。

In most collisions, the kinetic energy of the system is *not* conserved because some of the energy is converted to internal energy and some of it is transferred away by means of sound. Elastic and perfectly inelastic collisions are limiting cases; most collisions fall somewhere between them.

$$m_1 v_1 + m_2 v_2 = (m_1 + m_2)v$$

非弹性碰撞：碰撞后物体分开，有动能损失

$$m_1 v_{1i} + m_2 v_{2i} = m_1 v_{1f} + m_2 v_{2f}$$

冲击摆装置

Example 5.4 The Ballistic Pendulum: The ballistic pendulum (Fig.5-3) is an **apparatus** used to measure the speed of a fast-moving projectile, such as a bullet. A bullet of mass m_1 is fired into a large block of wood of mass m_2 suspended from some light wires. As a result of the collision, the bullet embeds in the block, and the entire system swings up to through a maximum height h. Determine the speed of the bullet from a measurement of h.

Solution:

Figure 5-3 helps to conceptualize the situation. The collision is perfectly inelastic.

$$m_1 v_{1A} = (m_1 + m_2)v_B$$

$$v_B = \frac{m_1 v_{1A}}{m_1 + m_2}$$

动量守恒

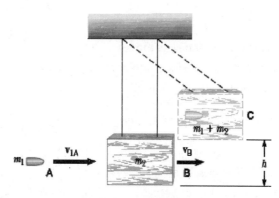

Figure 5-3 A ballistic pendulum

For the process during which the bullet-block combination swings upward to height h, this part of the motion is a conservation of mechanical energy problem:

$$K_B + U_B = K_C + U_C$$

机械能守恒

The total kinetic energy of the system right after the collision:

$$K_B = \frac{m_1^2 v_{1A}^2}{2(m_1 + m_2)}$$

We define the gravitational potential energy of the system for configuration B to be zero

So $\quad \dfrac{m_1^2 v_{1A}^2}{2(m_1 + m_2)} + 0 = 0 + (m_1 + m_2)gh$

We obtain:

$$v_{1A} = \left(\frac{m_1 + m_2}{m_1} \right)\sqrt{2gh}$$

5.4.3 Two Dimensional Collision

We showed that the momentum of a system of two particles is conserved when the system is isolated. For any collision of two particles, this result implies that the momentum in each of the directions x, y is conserved. The game of billiards is a familiar example involving multiple collisions of objects moving on a two-dimensional surface. For such two dimensional collisions, we obtain two component equations for conservation of momentum:

$$m_1 v_{1ix} + m_2 v_{2ix} = m_1 v_{1fx} + m_2 v_{2fx}$$
$$m_1 v_{1iy} + m_2 v_{2iy} = m_1 v_{1fy} + m_2 v_{2fy}$$

5.4.3 二维碰撞

平面运动的二维碰撞，在各个坐标分量方向上动量守恒。

$$m_1 v_{1ix} + m_2 v_{2ix} = m_1 v_{1fx} + m_2 v_{2fx}$$
$$m_1 v_{1iy} + m_2 v_{2iy} = m_1 v_{1fy} + m_2 v_{2fy}$$

(a) Before the collision   (b) After the collision

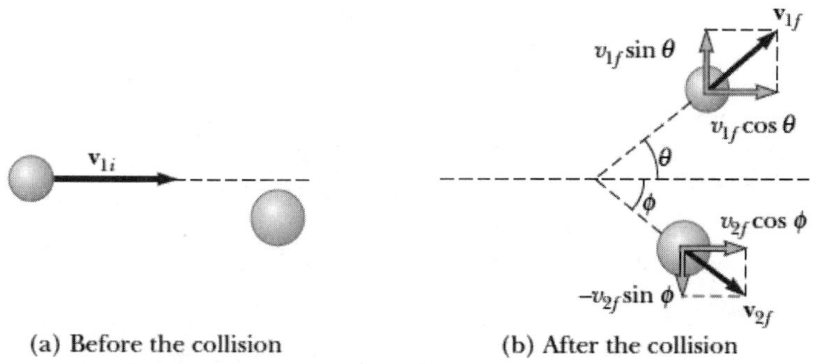

Figure 5-4 A glancing collision between two particles

Let us consider a two-dimensional problem in which particle 1 of mass $m1$ collides with particle 2 of mass m_2, where particle 2 is initially at rest, as in Figure 5-4. After the collision, particle 1 moves at an angle θ with respect to the horizontal and particle 2 moves at an angle ϕ with respect to the horizontal. This is called a *glancing* collision.

Applying the law of conservation of momentum in component form and noting that the initial *y* component of the momentum of the two-particle system is zero, we obtain

$$m_1 v_{1i} = m_1 v_{1f} \cos\theta + m_2 v_{2f} \cos\phi$$
$$0 = m_1 v_{1f} \sin\theta + m_2 v_{2f} \sin\phi$$

如果两个碰撞物体碰前 y 方向动量为零：$P_y=0$

x，y 方向动量守恒：

$$m_1 v_{1i} = m_1 v_{1f} \cos\theta + m_2 v_{2f} \cos\phi$$
$$0 = m_1 v_{1f} \sin\theta + m_2 v_{2f} \sin\phi$$

If the collision is elastic, we can also use conservation of kinetic energy with v_{2i} =0 to give

$$\frac{1}{2} m_1 v_{1i}^2 = \frac{1}{2} m_1 v_{1f}^2 + \frac{1}{2} m_2 v_{2f}^2$$

弹性碰撞动能守恒方程：

$$\frac{1}{2} m_1 v_{1i}^2 = \frac{1}{2} m_1 v_{1f}^2 + \frac{1}{2} m_2 v_{2f}^2$$

Knowing the initial speed of particle 1 and both masses, we are left with four unknowns (v_{1f}, v_{2f}, θ, and ϕ). Because we have only three equations, one of the four remaining quantities must be given if we are to determine the motion after the collision from conservation principles alone.

If the collision is inelastic, kinetic energy is *not* conserved.

Tip: always use conservation of momentum when solving a collision problem, and conservation of energy if the collision is elastic.

一般碰撞问题中动量总是守恒，动能不一定守恒。

Example 5.5: A glancing collision with two particles is shown in Figure 5-4. m_1=m_2, V_1=10m/s, θ=30^0, find out how fast the two particles are moving after collision.

Solution:

Solving the two equations above, we get

$$v_{1f} =8.66\text{m/s}, \quad v_{2f} =5\text{m/s}, \quad \phi = 60^0$$

5.5 Center of Mass and its Motion

5.5 质心及其运动

5.5.1 Center of Mass

5.5.1 质心

The center of mass is the point where all of the mass of an object

可认为物体所有质量集

can be considered to be concentrated; it is the point that represents the object of interest in a free body diagram.

中在质心上。

For an object which has uniform density, the center of mass is at the geometric center. The center of mass of any symmetric object lies on an axis of symmetry and on any plane of symmetry.

密度均匀的物体，其几何中心是它的质心。

For a collection of discrete particles, the center of mass of the particle system is defined to be:

$$x_{cm} = \frac{m_1 x_1 + m_2 x_2 + \cdots + m_n x_n}{m_1 + m_2 + \cdots + m_n} = \frac{\sum_i m_i x_i}{\sum_i m_i} = \frac{\sum_i m_i x_i}{M}$$

离散分布的质点系统，其质心的定义及计算公式：

$$y_{cm} = \frac{\sum_i m_i y_i}{M} \quad \text{and} \quad z_{cm} = \frac{\sum_i m_i z_i}{M}$$

$$x_{cm} = \frac{\sum_i m_i x_i}{M}$$

Computing the center of mass of a continuous mass distribution, we imagine dividing the object into infinitesimally pieces and then apply our center of mass equation to all these pointlike pieces.

$$x_{cm} = \lim_{\Delta m_i \to 0} \frac{\sum_i m_i x_i}{M} = \frac{1}{M} \int x dm$$

质量连续分布的物体的质心计算。

$$y_{cm} = \frac{1}{M} \int y dm$$

$$z_{cm} = \frac{1}{M} \int z dm$$

$$x_{cm} = \frac{1}{M} \int x dm$$

Center of mass in vector form:

$$\vec{r}_{cm} = \frac{1}{M} \int \vec{r} dm$$

质心的向量表达：

$$\vec{r}_{cm} = \frac{1}{M} \int \vec{r} dm$$

Example 5.6 Three particles in 2-dimension: Three particles, each with mass 2.50 kg, are located at the corner of a right triangle whose sides are 2.00 m and 1.5 m long shown in Figure 5-5. Locate the center of mass.

Solution:

Choose a coordinate system as shown (to simplify calculation) with m_1 at the origin and m_2 on the x axis.

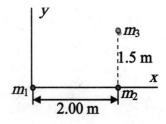

Figure 5-5 Example 5.6

$$x_{cm} = \frac{x_1 m_1 + x_2 m_2 + x_3 m_3}{M}$$

$$= \frac{0 + 2 \times 2.5 + 2 \times 2.5}{3 \times 2.5} = 1.33 \text{m}$$

$$y_{cm} = \frac{y_1 m_1 + y_2 m_2 + y_3 m_3}{M}$$

$$= \frac{0 + 0 + 2 \times 1.5}{3 \times 2.5} = 0.50 \text{m}$$

Example 5.7: A straight rod AB of length *L* has non-uniform linear density, *λ* = *Kx,* where *K* is a constant and *x* is the distance from one end A. The distance of the center of mass of the rod from the end A is

a. $\frac{1}{3}L$ b. $\frac{1}{2}L$ c. $\frac{3}{5}L$ d. $\frac{2}{3}L$ e. $\frac{3}{4}L$

Solution: d

Consider an element of very small length *dx* of the rod at distance *x* from the end A. The mass of this element is *dm* = *λdx* = (*Kx*) *dx*

We have

$$x_c = \frac{\int_0^L x dm}{\int_0^L dm} = \frac{\int_0^L kx^2 dx}{\int_0^L kx dx} = \frac{\frac{L^3}{3}}{\frac{L^2}{2}} = \frac{2}{3}L$$

5.5.2 Newton's Laws for a System of Particles

5.5.2 物体系统牛顿定律

We can begin to understand the physical significance and utility of the center of mass concept by taking the time derivative of the position vector given by the vector equation above, we obtain the following expression for the velocity of the center of mass of the system:

对质心位置向量求导，求得系统质心速度表达式。

$$\vec{v}_{cm} = \frac{d\vec{r}_{cm}}{dt} = \frac{1}{M} \sum_i M_i \frac{d\vec{r}_i}{dt} = \frac{\sum_i m_i \vec{v}_i}{M}$$

$$\vec{v}_{cm} = \frac{\sum_i m_i \vec{v}_i}{M}$$

where v*i* is the velocity of the *i* th particle.

$$Mv\vec{}_{cm} = \sum_i m_i \vec{v}_i = \sum_i \vec{P}_i = \vec{P}_{tot}$$

$$M\vec{v}_{cm} = \vec{P}_{tot}$$

系统总动量等于系统总质量乘以质心的速度。

Therefore, we conclude that the **total linear momentum of the system equals the total mass multiplied by the velocity of the center of mass.** In other words, the total linear momentum of the system is equal to that of a single particle of mass M moving with a velocity v_{cm}.

If we now differentiate the velocity of the center of mass with respect to time, we obtain the acceleration of the center of mass of the system:

对质心速度表达式求导，得到质心加速度表达式。

$$\vec{a}_{cm} = \frac{d\vec{v}_{cm}}{dt} = \frac{1}{M}\sum_i m_i \frac{d\vec{v}_i}{dt} = \frac{1}{M}\sum_i m_i \vec{a}_i$$

And we obtain

质心运动动力学方程：

$$M\vec{a}_{cm} = \sum_i m_i \vec{a}_i = \sum_i \vec{F}_i$$

$$M\vec{a}_{cm} = \sum_i \vec{F}_i$$

That is, **the net external force on a system of particles equals the total mass of the system multiplied by the acceleration of the center of mass.**

质心运动方程：作用在系统上的合外力等于系统总质量乘以质心加速度。

This is Newton's second law of motion for a system of particles.

质点系统运动牛顿定律。

We conclude that:

The center of mass of system of particles (or bodies) with total mass M moves like a single particle of mass M acted upon by the same net external force.

质心运动等效于质量全部集中在质心处的单个物体的运动。

We can treat the translational motion of any body or system of bodies as the motion of a particle.

Example 5.8: A radioactive nucleus of mass M moving along the positive x-direction with speed v emits an α-particle of mass m. If the α-particle proceeds along the positive y-direction, the center of mass of the system (made of the daughter nucleus and the α-particle) will

a.   remain at rest

b.   move along the positive x-direction with speed less than v

c.   move along the positive x-direction with speed greater than v

d.   move in a direction inclined to the positive x-direction

e.   move along the positive x-direction with speed equal to v

Solution: e

The state of rest or of uniform motion of the center of mass of a system of particles can be changed by *external* forces only. Since the α-emission is produced by *internal* forces, the center of mass is unchanged and it will continue to move along the positive x-direction with speed equal to v.

第五章总结　动量和碰撞

1. 动量： $P = mv$，机械运动的量度。

2. 冲量： $I = F * \Delta t$，当 F 为恒力时。

$I = \int F(t) \, dt$，冲量是力对时间的累积。F-t 曲线下的面积

3. 动量定理： $I = \Delta P$　合外力的冲量等于质点或系统的动量的增量。

质点　　$\int F(t) \, dt = mv_2 - mv_1$

质点组　$\int F(t) \, dt = \sum_{1}^{n} m_i v_i - \sum_{1}^{n} m_i v_{i0}$

4. 动量守恒： 当没有外力作用在系统上时，任一时刻系统动量守恒，$\Delta P = 0$。

动量守恒条件： $F_{net} = 0$，或 $F_{net} \ll$ 内力

合外力不为零，但某一方向的合外力为零，那么在这个方向的动量守恒。

动量守恒是基本普适定律之一。

5. 碰撞： 动量 $P =$ 常数（碰撞时间很短）

弹性碰撞： 动量守恒，动能也守恒。

非弹性碰撞： 只有动量守恒，动能减少。当碰撞后的两物体粘在一起时动能损失为最大，称之为完全非弹性，碰撞后的物体有相同的速度。

爆炸或内力使两物体分开：动量守恒，动能增加。

6. 质量中心

质量均匀分布、对称的几何体：质心在物体的几何中心。

质点系：$r_c = \dfrac{\sum_i m_i r_i}{\sum_i m_i}$

连续质量分布的物体：$r_c = \dfrac{\int r \, dm}{\int dm}$

质量线密度 $\lambda = \dfrac{dm}{dl}$，所以 $dm = \lambda \, dl$

7. 质心的运动

$$V_c = \frac{\sum m_i v_i}{\sum m_i}$$

$\mathbf{P}_{net} = M\mathbf{v_c}$

$\mathbf{F}_{net} = M\mathbf{a_c}$ 　　等效于质量全部集中在质心上的单个物体的运动。

Chapter 5 Linear Momentum and Collisions Practice

Multiple Choice Questions

1. A rocket engine acquires motion by ejecting hot gases in the opposite direction. This is an example of the law of

   A. Conservation of heat
   B. Conservation of energy
   C. Conservation of linear momentum
   D. Conservation of mass
   E. Conservation of angular momentum

2. A golfer swings a golf club and hits a ball. Which of the following best explains why the effects of the collision on the club are difficult to observe?

   I. The club's mass is large compared to that of the ball.

   II. The club's initial momentum is large compared to the impulse imparted to it by the collision.

   III. The collision causes only the ball to accelerate, not the club.

   A. I only
   B. III only
   C. I and II only
   D. II and III only
   E. I, II, and III

3. Two particles of masses 2 kg and 6 kg are separated by a distance of 6 m. The distance of their center of mass from the heavier particle is

   A. 1.5 m
   B. 2 m
   C. 3 m
   D. 4 m
   E. 4.5 m

4. The impulse experienced by a body is equivalent to its change in

   A. velocity
   B. kinetic energy
   C. momentum
   D. potential energy
   E. None of the above choices are valid

5. A moderate force will break an egg. An egg dropped on the road usually breaks, while one dropped on the grass usually doesn't break. This is because for the egg dropped on the grass

   A. the change in momentum is greater.
   B. the change in momentum is less.
   C. the time interval for stopping is greater.
   D. the time interval for stopping is less.
   E. Both choices A and C are valid.

6. An object at rest splits into 3 particles, each with mass m, traveling with velocity v. The angle between the velocity vectors of any two of these particles is

   A. 30^0
   B. 60^0
   C. 90^0
   D. 120^0
   E. 150^0

7. A billiard ball collides in an elastic head-on collision with a second identical ball. What is the kinetic energy of the system after the collision compared to that before collision?

   A. the same as
   B. one fourth
   C. twice
   D. four times
   E. None of the above choices are valid.

8. A railroad freight car, mass 15 000 kg, is allowed to coast along a level track at a speed of 2.0 m/s. It collides and couples with a 50 000 kg loaded second car, initially at rest and with brakes released.

What percentage of the initial kinetic energy of the 15 000-kg car is preserved in the two-coupled cars after collision?

A. 14%

B. 23%

C. 86%

D. 92%

E. 100%

9. A 7.0kg bowling ball strikes a 2.0kg pin. The pin flies forward with a velocity of 6.0 m/s; the ball continues forward at 4.0 m/s. What was the original velocity of the ball?

A. 4.0 m/s

B. 5.7 m/s

C. 6.6 m/s

D. 3.3 m/s

E. 2.8 m/s

10. Two skaters, both of mass 75 kg, are on skates on a frictionless ice pond. One skater throws a 0.3kg ball at 5 m/s to his friend, who catches it and throws it back at 5 m/s. When the first skater has caught the returned ball, what is the velocity of each of the two skaters?

A. 0.02 m/s, moving apart

B. 0.04 m/s, moving apart

C. 0.02 m/s, moving towards each other

D. 0.04 m/s, moving towards each other

E. 0.05 m/s, moving apart

11. A ball of mass m_1 travels along the x-axis in the positive direction with an initial speed of v_0. It collides with a ball of mass m_2 that is originally at rest. After the collision, the ball of mass m_1 has velocity $v_{1x}i + v_{1y}j$ and the ball of mass m_2 has

velocity $v_{2x}i + v_{2y}j$. Consider the following five statements:

I. $m_1 v_{1x} + m_2 v_{2x} = 0$

II. $m_1 v_0 = m_1 v_{1y} + m_2 v_{2y}$

III. $m_1 v_{1y} + m_2 v_{2y} = 0$

IV. $m_1 v_0 = m_1 v_{1x} + m_1 v_{1y}$

V. $m_1 v_0 = m_1 v_{1x} + m_2 v_{2x}$

Of these five statements, the system must satisfy

A. I and II.

B. III and V.

C. II and V.

D. III and IV.

E. I and III.

Questions 12 and 13

An object is throwing toward a wall. During the collision with the wall lasting from t=0 to t=0.2s, the force acting on the 2kg object is given by the equation F=300t(0.2-t) i (N)

12. The impulse that the force acts on the object during the collision is

A. 0.4 kg.m/s

B. 0.8 kg.m/s

C. 1.2 kg.m/s

D. 2.6 kg.m/s

E. 5.2 kg.m/s

13. The average force on the object is

A. 2N

B. 4N

C. 6N

D. 13N

E. 26N

Base your answers to questions 14 and 15 on

the force-time graph below, which is for a 3.5 kg object, starting from rest, moving in a straight line.

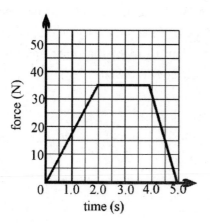

14. What is the object's momentum at 3.0 seconds?

    A. 35 kg·m/s
    B. 50 kg·m/s
    C. 70 kg·m/s
    D. 100 kg·m/s
    E. 105 kg·m/s

15. What is the kinetic energy of the particle after 2.0 seconds?

    A. 35 J
    B. 70 J
    C. 140 J
    D. 175 J
    E. 210 J

16. Two skaters are on ice with negligible friction. One skater has a mass m, the other, a mass M where $M > m$. The skaters are at rest when they simultaneously push each other horizontally. Which is true about their subsequent motion?

    A. The center of mass of the two-skater system will move in the direction of the less massive skater.
    B. The more massive person will have a greater initial acceleration than the less massive.
    C. The velocities of both skaters will be equal.

D. The speeds of both skaters will be equal.
E. The momenta of the two skaters are equal in magnitude.

17. A uniform wire with mass m is bent into a semicircle of radius R, as shown below. The coordinates of its center of mass with respect to an origin of coordinates at the center of full circle is

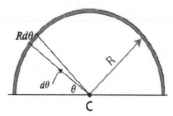

C

    A. $(0, \dfrac{R}{2})$

    B. $(0, \dfrac{2R}{\pi})$

    C. $(0, \dfrac{R}{2\pi})$

    D. $(0, \dfrac{R}{\pi})$

    E. $(0, \dfrac{2R}{3})$

18. A straight rod AB of length L has non-uniform linear density, $\lambda = Cx^2$, where C is a constant and x is the distance from end A. The distance of the center of mass of the rod from the end A is

    A. L/3
    B. L/2
    C. 3L/5
    D. 2L/3
    E. 3L/4

19. Mass m_1 is moving with speed v toward stationary mass m_2. The speed of the center of mass of the system is

    A. $(\dfrac{m_1}{m_2})v$

B. $(1+\dfrac{m_1}{m_2})v$

C. $(1-\dfrac{m_1}{m_2})v$

D. $(1+\dfrac{m_2}{m_1})v$

E. $(\dfrac{m_1}{m_1+m_2})v$

20. A 200kg flatcar with 30m long is moving

with a speed of 5.0m/s along horizontal frictionless rails. A 50kg man then starts walking from one end of the car to the other in the direction of motion, with speed 2.0m/s with respect to the car. In the time it takes for him to reach the other end, the flatcar has moved a distance

A. 45m

B. 50m

C. 69m

D. 75m

E. 105m

Free Response Questions

1. A bullet of mass m_1 is fired into a pendulum of a wood block mass m_2 and length L. The speed of the bullet as it enters the mass m_2 is V_1, see figure below.

First, assume that the collision is elastic and $m_1 \ll m_2$

A. If the pendulum is initially at rest, what is the speed of the bullet after the collision?

B. Now suppose that when the collision occurs, the pendulum, at the bottom of its swing, is moving to the left with velocity V_2. What is the speed of the bullet after the elastic collision?

Now assume that the collision is completely inelastic. The pendulum is at rest before the collision, $m_1 < m_2$, but the speed V_1 of the bullet is unknown.

C. After the collision the pendulum moves to the right and it comes to a halt when the string makes an angle θ_{max} with the vertical. What was the speed of the bullet?

D. Could θ_{max} be 90^0? Explain your answer.

2. A particle of mass m_1 and speed v_1 (in the +x direction) collides with another particle of mass m_2. m_2 is at rest before the collision occurs, thus $v_2=0$. After the collisions, the particles have velocities v_1' and v_2' in the x-y plane in the directions of θ_1 and θ_2 with the x-axis, shown in figure below. There are no external forces. Express all your answers in terms of m_1, m_2, v_1, θ_1 and θ_2.

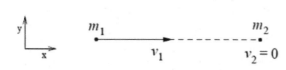 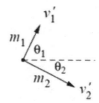

A. What is the total momentum before the collision?

B. What is the total momentum after the collision?

C. What is the total kinetic energy before the collision?

D. What is the ratio of the speeds v_2' / v_1' ?

E. What is the magnitude of v_1' ?

3. The two blocks I and II have masses m and 2m respectively. Block II has an ideal massless spring which has the spring constant k attached to one side. The two blocks are on a frictionless, horizontal surface. Block II is at rest and block I approaches with a speed v_o, as shown below. Express your answer to all parts of the question in terms of the given quantities and physical constants.

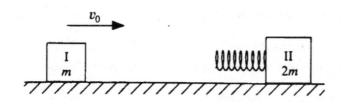

A. Determine the maximum compression of the spring during the collision.

B. Determine the velocity of block II after the collision when block I has again separated from the spring.

4. An open-top railroad car (initially empty and of mass m_o) rolls with negligible friction along a straight horizontal track and passes under the spout of a sand conveyor. When the car is under the conveyor, sand is dispensed from the conveyor in a narrow stream at a steady rate dm/dt = C and falls vertically from an average height h above the floor of the railroad car. The car has initial speed v_o and sand is filling it from time t = 0 to t=T.

A. Calculate the mass m of the car plus the sand that it catches as a function of time t for 0 < t < T.

B. Determine the speed v of the car as a function of time t for 0 < t < T.

C. Is kinetic energy conserved? Explain why or why not.

D. If you want to keep the velocity of the car constant, what kind of force needs to act on the car?

5. A bullet of mass m and velocity v_o is fired toward a block of thickness L_o and mass M. The block is initially at rest on a frictionless surface. The bullet emerges from the block with velocity $v_o/3$.

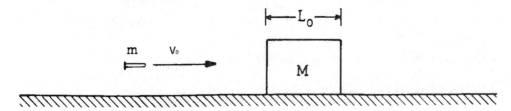

A. Determine the final speed of block M.

B. If the block is held fixed and not allowed to slide, the bullet emerges from the block with a speed $v_o/2$. Determine the loss of kinetic energy of the bullet.

C. Assume that the retarding force that the block material exerts on the bullet is constant. In terms of L_o, what minimum thickness L should a fixed block of similar material have in order to stop the bullet?

D. When the block is held fixed, the bullet emerges from the block with a greater speed than when the block is free to move. Why?

6. A bullet shoots out of a gun at V_0 m/s. While the bullet accelerates in the barrel of the gun, the total force that is applied on it is F= (a-bt), (t is in s):

A. Suppose the total force that the bullet is subjected to is zero upon the exit of the gun, calculate the total time that the bullet takes to run through the barrel.

B. Calculate the momentum of the bullet.

C. Calculate the mass of the bullet.

Answers and Explanations

Multiple Choice Answers

1. C 2. C 3. A 4. C 5. C 6. D 7. A 8. B 9. B 10. B 11. B 12. A 13. A 14. C
15. D 16. E 17. B 18. E 19. E 20. C

Multiple Choice Explanations

1. C。动量守恒。

2. C。球杆的质量远大于球的质量，球杆的部分动量转化成球的动量。

3. A。将 6kg 的物体放在原点（0,0），2kg 的物体放在 x 轴上（6,0） $x_c = \dfrac{6*0+2*6}{6+2} = 1.5m$

4. C。冲量定理：物体所受的冲量等于其动量的增量。

5. C 鸡蛋落到地面或草地上的动量改变相同，由冲量定理 $F\Delta t = \Delta P$，落到草地上的鸡蛋，力 F 作用在其上的时间长，所以作用力小。

6. D。爆炸后系统的总动量 $P=P_1+P_2+P_3=0$，因为三个物体的动量大小相等 $P_1=P_2=P_3$, 所以三个动量方向的夹角应相等为 120^0。

7. A。弹性碰撞，动能守恒。

8. B。两车连在一起后的速度 v= $\dfrac{m_1}{m_1 + m_2} v_0 = \dfrac{15}{65} v_0$，动能与碰撞前的动能比为：

$$\frac{\frac{1}{2}(m_1 + m_2)v^2}{\frac{1}{2}m_1 v_0^2} = 23\%$$

9. B。由动量守恒 $m_1 v_1 = m_1 v_1' + m_2 v_2'$，求得 v_1 =5.7m/s

10. B。两个人都获得 2mv 的动量 MV=2mv，每个人的速度都为 V=2mv/M=0.04m/s

11. B。两物体水平方向的动量和 $P_x = m_1 v_0 = m_1 v_{1x} + m_2 v_{2x}$，竖直方向的动量和 P_y=0

12. A。墙给小球的冲量 J= $\displaystyle\int_0^{0.2} 300t(0.2-t)dt$ =0.4kg m/s

13. A。小球受到的平均冲力为 $F = \dfrac{J}{\Delta t}$ =2N

14. C。由冲量定理，t=3s 时，物体的动量 P=J= $\displaystyle\int_0^3 Fdt$ =70kg m/s

15. D。t=2s 时，v=($\int_0^2 Fdt$)/m=10m/s；此时动能 KE=$\frac{1}{2}mv^2$=175J

16. E。动量守恒。两物体将具有大小相等方向相反的动量，质量小的物体的速度大于质量大的物体的运动速度，质心位置不变。

17. B。由对称性分析可知，x 方向坐标为零。$y_c = \frac{\int y dm}{m} = \frac{\int_0^\pi R\sin\theta \lambda R d\theta}{m} = \frac{2R}{\pi}$

18. E。$x_c = \frac{\int_0^L x\lambda dx}{\int_0^L \lambda dx} = \frac{3}{4}L$

19. E。设两物体相距为 x，令 m_2 为坐标原点，质心位置 $x_c = \frac{m_1 x + m_2 0}{m_1 + m_2} = \frac{m_1 x}{m_1 + m_2}$，质心的

运动速度 $v = \frac{dx_c}{dt} = \frac{m_1}{m_1 + m_2}v$

20. C。（1）用动量守恒：设人从左向右运动。由于人的运动，平板车对地面运动速度为 5-V，人的运动时间 t=15s，平板车向右运动的距离 L=（5-V）15 m。系统动量守恒：50（2-V）=200V，解得 V=0.4m/s。L=69m。

（2）由质心运动计算：设人从左向右运动，以平板车中心为原点，开始时质心坐标为

$x_c = \frac{50(-15)}{200+50}$ =-3.0m。人从左走到右面所用时间 t=15m/s。平板车向右运动的距离是：
L=vt-2*3.0=5*15-2*3.0=69m。

Free Response Explanations

1. A. 因为 $m_1 \ll m_2$，子弹离开木块时的速度大小 $v_1' = v_1$，方向沿入射方向的反方向。

   B. 碰撞之后子弹相对于木块的速度是 $v_1 + v_2$。子弹对地面的速度是

   $v_1' = (v_1 + v_2) + v_2 = v_1 + 2v_2$。

   C. 由动量守恒求得碰撞后子弹、木块系统的共同速度 $v' = \frac{m_1}{m_1 + m_2}v_1$

   由 $\frac{1}{2}(m_1 + m_2)v'^2 = (m_1 + m_2)gh \rightarrow v_1 = \frac{m_1 + m_2}{m_1}\sqrt{2gL(1 - \cos\theta_{max})}$

D. 如果 $\theta_{max} = 90^0$，那么 $v_1 = \dfrac{m_1 + m_2}{m_1}\sqrt{2gL}$，这是可能的。

2. A. 碰撞前系统总动量：$\mathbf{P} = m_1 v_1 \mathbf{i}$，沿 x 轴正向。

B. 碰撞后系统总动量：$\mathbf{P}' = m_1 v_1 \mathbf{i}$，沿 x 轴正向。

C. 系统的总能量：$\dfrac{1}{2}m_1 v_1^2$

D. 竖直方向动量守恒：$m_1 v_1' \sin\theta_1 = m_2 v_2' \sin\theta_2 \rightarrow \dfrac{v_2'}{v_1'} = \dfrac{m_1 \sin\theta_1}{m_2 \sin\theta_2}$

E. 水平方向动量守恒：$m_1 v_1' \cos\theta_1 + m_2 v_2' \cos\theta_2 = m_1 v_1$

$$\rightarrow v_1' = \dfrac{\sin\theta_2}{\cos\theta_1 \sin\theta_2 + \sin\theta_1 \cos\theta_2} v_1$$

3. A. 弹簧最大压缩 x 时，两个物体以共同的速度 v 运动，由动量守恒：$v = v_0/3$

第一个物体的能量损失转化成弹簧的弹性势能：有 $\dfrac{1}{2}mv_0^2 - \dfrac{1}{2}3mv^2 = \dfrac{1}{2}kx^2$

弹簧最大压缩量 $x = \sqrt{\dfrac{2m}{3k}}v_0$

B. 当两个物体弹开时，弹性势能转化成两物体的动能，此碰撞过程是弹性的。

动量守恒：$mv_0 = mv_1 + 2mv_2$

动能守恒：$\dfrac{1}{2}mv_0^2 = \dfrac{1}{2}mv_1^2 + \dfrac{1}{2}2mv_2^2$

求得：$v_1 = -\dfrac{1}{3}v_0$，$v_2 = \dfrac{2}{3}v_0$

4. A. 任意时刻 t，落到车上的沙子的质量为 $\Delta m = \int_0^t dm = ct$，总质量 $m = m_0 + \Delta m = m_0 + ct$

B. 由动量守恒：$m_0 v_0 = mv$ 求得 $v = \dfrac{m_0 v_0}{m_0 + ct}$

C. 任意时刻车的动能为 K=$\dfrac{1}{2}\dfrac{m_0{}^2 v_0{}^2}{m_0+ct}$，小于起始时刻的动能 $K_i=\dfrac{1}{2}m_0 v_0^2$，所以动能随时间减小。

D. 应施加以向右的水平牵引力 F。由冲量定理：$Fdt=d(mv)\rightarrow F=cv$

5. A. 由动量守恒：$mv_0=Mv+m\dfrac{v_0}{3}\rightarrow v=\dfrac{2m}{3M}v_0$

   B. 动能改变 $\Delta K=\dfrac{1}{2}mv_0^2-\dfrac{1}{2}m(\dfrac{v_0}{2})^2=\dfrac{3}{4}(\dfrac{1}{2}mv_0^2)$

   C. 子弹穿过长度为 L_0 的物体阻力的功 W=$FL_0=\Delta K=\dfrac{3}{4}(\dfrac{1}{2}mv_0^2)$

   D. 若要子弹不能从物体中穿出，物体长度应为 L，阻力的功大小为 W=FL=$\dfrac{1}{2}mv_0^2$

   解得 L 长度应为：L=$\dfrac{4}{3}L_0$

6. A. 子弹到枪口时，有 F=（a- bt）=0，得 t=a/b

   B. 子弹所受的冲量 $I=\int_0^t(a-bt)dt=at-\dfrac{1}{2}bt^2$，$\rightarrow I=\dfrac{a^2}{2b}$

   C. 由动量定理可求得子弹的质量：m=$\dfrac{I}{v_0}=\dfrac{a^2}{2bv_0}$

Rotation of Rigid Bodies
刚体转动

Chapter 6

Introduction: Until now, we have been explored the translational motion. In this chapter, we will mainly deal with the rotation of **rigid bodies about fixed axes**. A **rigid body**, an ideal model for any real body, is a body with a definite shape that doesn't change. The motion of a rigid body can be analyzed as the translational motion of its center of mass plus rotational motion about its center of mass. By purely rotational motion we mean that all points in the body move in circles, and the centers of these circles all lie on a line called **the axis of rotation**. A fixed axis **means that the rotation occurs about an axis that does not move.**

本章介绍刚体定轴转动。刚体是理想物理模型，在运动中物体形状不发生改变。

6.1 Rotational kinematics
6.1 转动运动学

6.1.1 Angular Quantities for Rotational Rigid Body
6.1.1 刚体转动的角量描述

For three dimensional rigid bodies rotational about a fixed axis, every point in a body rotating about a fixed axis moves in a circle whose center is on the axis and whose radius is r, the distance of that point from the axis of rotation. A straight line drawn from the axis to any point sweeps out the same angle (same angular displacement Δθ) in the same time, so all points in a rigid body rotate with the same angular velocity ω and same angular acceleration α. But each particle or point of a rotating rigid body has, at any moment, a different linear velocity v and a linear acceleration a. Using these quantities, we can greatly simplify the analysis of rigid-object rotation.

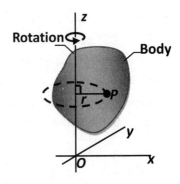

Figure 6-1 A rigid body rotating about a fixed axis

Any point in the body which rotates about a fixed axis can represent the rotation of whole body in angular quantities.

The tangential speed of a point on the rotating object increases as the point moves outward from the center of rotation according to the equation

$$v = r\omega$$

Although every point on the rigid object has the same *angular* speed, not every point has the same *tangential* speed because *r* is not the same for all points on the object.

We can relate the angular acceleration of the rotating rigid object to the tangential acceleration of the point *P by equation*

$$a_t = ra$$

This is the tangential component of the linear acceleration of a point on a rotating rigid object. We can express the centripetal acceleration at that point in terms of angular speed as

$$a_c = \frac{v^2}{r} = r\omega^2$$

Because **a=a_t+a_c** is a vector having a radial and a tangential component, the magnitude of **a** at the point *P* on the rotating rigid object is

$$a = \sqrt{a_c^2 + a_t^2} = r\sqrt{\alpha^2 + \omega^4}$$

We can relate the angular velocity ω to the frequency of rotation, f, where by frequency we mean the number of complete revolutions per second, 1 rev/s=2π rad/s.

$$f = \frac{\omega}{2\pi} \quad \text{or} \quad \omega = 2\pi f$$

The time required for on complete revolution is the period, T, and it is related to the frequency by

$$T = \frac{1}{f}$$

定轴转动刚体每个质点都以各自转动半径 r 做圆周运动

刚体上每一点有相同角位移 Δθ，角速度 ω，角加速度 α。任意一点可代表整个刚体。

但每一点速度和加速度不同，速度沿切向，大小随 r 而变。

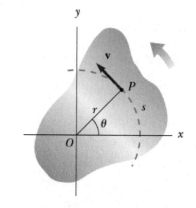

Figure 6-2 Velocity and acceleration of a rotational rigid body

P 点切向加速度和法向加速度也随转动半径 r 而变化。

每点加速度等于切向加速度与法向加速度向量和。

转动频率 f 是每秒钟转数。

$$f = \frac{\omega}{2\pi}$$

转动一周所用的时间是周期

$$T = \frac{1}{f}$$

Example 6.1 Hard drive: The platter of the hard disk of a computer rotates at 5400rpm (revolutions per minutes—rpm).

硬盘驱动
rpm：每分钟转数

a.   What is the angular velocity of the disk?

b.   If the reading head of the drive is located 3.0cm from the rotation axis, what is the speed of the point?

c.   What is the linear acceleration of this point?

d.   If the disk took 3.6s to spin up to 5400rpm from rest, what was the average acceleration?

Solution:

a.   Frequency $f = 5400/60 = 90\text{rev}/\text{s} = 90\text{Hz}$

then the angular velocity is $\omega = 2\pi f = 570\text{rad}/\text{s}$

b.   The speed of a point 3.0cm out from the axis is

$$v = R\omega = 0.030 \times 570 = 17\text{m/s}$$

c.   **a=a$_t$+a$_c$**, ω = constant so angular acceleration $\alpha = 0$

we have tangential acceleration a$_t$ = rα =0, the centripetal acceleration.

$$a_c = \omega^2 R = 570^2 \times 0.030 = 9700\text{m}/\text{s}^2$$

d.   The average angular acceleration was

$$\bar{\alpha} = \frac{\Delta\omega}{\Delta t} = \frac{570-0}{3.6} = 160\text{rad}/\text{s}^2$$

6.1.2 Kinematic Equations for Uniformly Accelerated Rotational motion

6.1.2 匀角加速度运动方程

Kinematic expressions for rotational motion under constant angular acceleration are of the same mathematical form as those for linear motion under constant linear acceleration. They can be generated from the equations for linear motion by making the substitutions $x \rightarrow \theta$, $v \rightarrow \omega$, and $a \rightarrow \alpha$

匀角加速运动与匀加速运动方程有相同形式。

Angular	Linear
$\omega = \omega_0 + \alpha t$	$v = v_0 + at$
$\theta - \theta_0 = \omega_0 t + \frac{1}{2}\alpha t^2$	$x - x_0 = v_0 t + \frac{1}{2}at^2$
$\omega^2 - \omega_0^2 = 2\alpha(\theta - \theta_0)$	$v^2 - v_0^2 = 2a(x - x_0)$
$\omega_{avg} = \dfrac{\omega + \omega_0}{2}$	$v_{avg} = \dfrac{v + v_0}{2}$

匀角加速度和匀加速运动方程对照表

Example 6.2 Rotating Wheel: A wheel rotates with a constant angular acceleration of 3.50 rad/s^2.

a.   If the angular speed of the wheel is 2.00 rad/s at t_i =0, through what angular displacement does the wheel rotate in 2.00 s?

b.   Through how many revolutions has the wheel turned during this time interval?

c.   What is the angular speed of the wheel at t = 2.00 s?

Solution:

a.
$$\Delta\theta = \theta_f - \theta_i = \omega_i t + \frac{1}{2}\alpha t^2$$
$$= (2.00)(2.00) + \frac{1}{2}(3.50)(2.00)^2 = 11.0\,\text{rad} = 630^0$$

b. $\Delta\theta = 630^0\left(\dfrac{1\text{rev}}{360^0}\right) = 1.75\text{rev}$

c. $\omega_f = \omega_i + \alpha t = 2.00 + (3.50)(2.00) = 9.00\text{rad}/\text{s}$

6.1.3 Vector Nature of Angular Quantities

6.1.3 角加速度和角速度都是向量

Both ω and α can be treated as vectors as the only unique direction in space associated with the rotation is along the axis of rotation. The convention we use, called the **right hand rule**, is the following: when the fingers of the right hand are wrapped in the direction of rotation, the extended right thumb points in the direction of ω.

If the axis of rotation is fixed in direction, then ω can change only in magnitude. Thus α=dω/dt must also point along the axis of rotation.

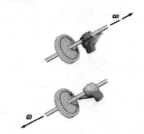

Figure 6-3 The right-hand rule

It is in the same direction as ω if the angular speed is increasing in time, and it is antiparallel to if the angular speed is decreasing in time. In this situation both ω and α can use positive or negative sign to represent their direction. Usually the direction in counterclockwise is positive and negative in clockwise.

定轴转动中 ω 方向沿转轴，由右手法则确定方向。

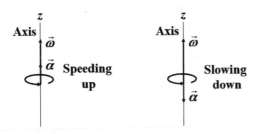

角加速度也沿转轴方向。

ω, α 可用正负表示方向。

通常规定逆时针方向的 ω, α 为正，顺时针为负。

Figure 6-4 Both ω and α are in same direction, the rotation motion is speeding up, otherwise slowing down.

6.2 Torque and Rotational Dynamics　　6.2 力矩和转动动力学

6.2.1 Definition of Torque

6.2.1 力矩定义

When a force is exerted on a rigid object pivoted about an axis, the object tends to rotate about that axis. To make an object start rotating about an axis clearly requires a force. But the direction of this force, and where it is applied, are also important. The angular acceleration of the rotating object is proportional not only to the magnitude of the force, but is also directly proportional to the perpendicular distance from the axis of rotation to the line along which the force acts. The tendency of a force to rotate an object about some axis is measured by a vector quantity called **torque τ** (Greek tau). **Torque is a vector and its direction is the same with angular acceleration α, also along the rotating axis.**

转动物体所获得的角加速度与作用力的大小有关，也与力的作用线到转轴的垂直距离相关。

改变转动状态的物理量定义为力矩。力矩是向量，方向与角加速度一致。

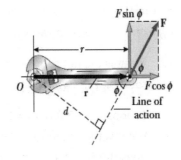

Consider the wrench pivoted on the axis through O in Figure 6-5. The applied force F acts at an angle φ to the horizontal. We define the magnitude of the torque associated with the force F by the expression

Figure 6-5 Torque acting on a wrench

力**F**对不同转轴有不同力矩。

$$\tau = rF\sin\phi = Fd = rF_\perp$$
$$F_\perp = F\sin\phi$$

d : called the lever arm or moment arm

力矩向量定义式：$\vec{\tau} = \vec{r} \times \vec{F}$

The torque about a given axis can be written as a vector cross product

$$\vec{\tau} = \vec{r} \times \vec{F}$$

Since torque is a distance times a force, it is measured in units of $m \cdot N$ in SI units.

If two or more forces are acting on a rigid object, each tends to produce rotation about the axis at O. We use the convention that the sign of the torque resulting from a force is positive if the turning tendency of the force is counterclockwise and is negative if the turning tendency is clockwise. Net torque is the reason why an object changes its rotational motion.

From related experiment we know that the angular acceleration α of object is directly proportional to the net applied torque, τ:

$$\alpha \propto \tau$$

Torque should not be confused with force. Forces can cause a change in linear motion, as described by Newton's second law. Net torque can cause a change in rotational motion, as described by Newton's second law for rotation.

Example 6.3 Net torque on a cylinder

A cylinder is shaped as shown in Figure 6-6, with a core section protruding from the larger drum. The cylinder is free to rotate about the central axis shown in the drawing. A rope wrapped around the drum, which has radius R_1, exerts a force T_1 to the right on the cylinder. A rope wrapped around the core, which has radius R_2, exerts a force T_2 downward on the cylinder.

a. What is the net torque acting on the cylinder about the rotation axis (which is the z axis in Figure 6-6)?

b. Suppose T_1 = 5.0 N, R_1 = 1.0 m, T_2 = 15.0 N, and R_2 = 0.50 m. What is the net torque about the rotation axis, and which way does the cylinder rotate starting from rest?

Solution:

a. The torque due to T_1 is $- R_1T_1$. (The sign is negative because the torque tends to produce clockwise rotation.) The torque due to T_2 is $+R_2T_2$. (The sign is positive because the torque tends to

力矩大小:

$$\tau = rF\sin\phi = Fd = rF_\perp$$

d: 力臂

力矩方向:由向量叉乘给出,沿转轴方向。使物体逆时针转动的力矩为正,顺时针转动的力矩为负。
合外力矩是物体转动状态改变的原因。

力矩的单位: $N \cdot m$

力改变物体直线运动状态,力矩改变物体转动状态。

作用在柱体上的力矩

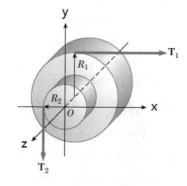

Figure 6-6 A cylinder with a core section

produce counterclockwise rotation.) Therefore, the net torque about the rotation axis is

$$\tau_{net} = -R_1 T_1 + R_2 T_2$$

b. Evaluating the net torque,

$$\tau_{net} = 2.5 \text{mN}$$

Because this torque is positive, the cylinder will begin to rotate in the counterclockwise direction.

Example 6.4 Rotating rod: A uniform rod of length L and mass M can pivot about a horizontal axis through the fixed end O in the vertical plane due to the downward force of gravity. Find the torque due to the gravity when the angle with the horizontal is θ.

Solution:

The magnitude of the torque acting on the element dm due to the gravity is

$$d\tau = xdmg$$

so the magnitude of the total torque due to the gravity should be integrated as

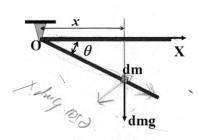

Figure 6-7 Example 6.4

$$\tau = \int g x dm = g \int x dm$$

According to the formula of the center of mass

$$\int x dm = m x_c = \frac{1}{2} mL \cos\theta$$

So $$\tau = \frac{1}{2} mgL \cos\theta$$

The direction of the torque is parallel to the rotated axis, pointing into the page. In fact, the resultant torque on the body due to the gravity equals the torque that would be produced by the single force mg acting at the center of mass of the body. If the density of the body is uniform, the center of mass is at its geometric center.

此力矩平行于转轴，垂直纸面向里。

Example 6.5 The Torque Vector: A force of **F** = (2 **i**+3 **j**) N is applied to an object that is pivoted about a fixed axis aligned along the z

力矩的向量形式

coordinate axis. If the force is applied at a point located at **r** = (4**i**+ 5**j**) m, find the torque vector τ .

Solution:

The torque vector is defined by means of a cross product

$$\tau = \mathbf{r} \times \mathbf{F} = \det \begin{pmatrix} i & j & k \\ 4 & 5 & 0 \\ 2 & 3 & 0 \end{pmatrix} = 2\mathbf{k} \text{ Nm}$$

Both r and F are in the *xy* plane. As expected, the torque vector is perpendicular to this plane, having only a *z (K)* component.

6.2.2 Rotational Dynamics-Newton's Second Law for Rotation

6.2.2 转动动力学

Suppose that there is a external force $\mathbf{F_i}$ and an internal force $\mathbf{f_i}$ acting on an element Δm_i of the rigid body. Apply Newton's second law to the element Δm_i

$$\vec{F} + \vec{f} = \Delta m_i \vec{a}_i$$

对质元 Δm_i 应用牛顿定律

切向分量式有：

$$\vec{F}_i r_i \sin \theta_i + \vec{f}_i r_i \sin \theta \varphi_i = \Delta m_i r_i^2 \vec{\alpha}$$

Consider the tangential component

$$\vec{F}_i \sin \theta_i + \vec{f}_i \sin \theta \varphi_i = \Delta m_i \vec{a}_i$$

Multiplying this equation by r_i

$$\vec{F}_i r_i \sin \theta_i + \vec{f}_i r_i \sin \theta \varphi_i = \Delta m_i r_i^2 \vec{\alpha}$$

For all elements within the rigid body we can write the equations.

Summing all these equations we have

$$\sum_i \vec{F}_i r_i \sin \theta_i + \sum_i \vec{f}_i r_i \sin \theta \varphi_i = (\sum_i \Delta m_i r_i^2) \vec{\alpha}$$

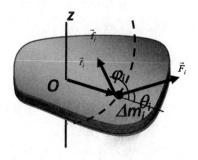

Figure 6-8 Newton's second law for rotation

The first part of the equation's left side is the net torque of the external forces on all the mass points of the rigid body about the rotational axis, the second part is the net torque of the internal forces between the mass points about the rotational axis and should be equal to zero, so the equation above becomes

$$\vec{\tau}_{net} = \sum_i (\Delta m_i r_i^2) \vec{\alpha}$$

对整个刚体所有质元求和

$$\sum_i \vec{F}_i r_i \sin \theta_i : 合外力矩$$

$$\sum_i \vec{f}_i r_i \sin \theta \varphi_i : 合内力矩=0$$

Where $\sum_i(\Delta m_i r_i^2)$ is constant value for a rigid body about a fixed axis and is called the moment of inertia or **rotational inertial**.

$$I = \sum_i(\Delta m_i r_i^2)$$

and $\tau_{net} = I\alpha$

The moment of inertia, I , is a measure of the rotational inertia of body, plays the same role for rotational motion that mass does for translational motion. We can see from the above equation that the rotational inertia of an object depends not only on its mass, but also on how that mass is distributed with respect to the axis.

Example 6.6 Rotating rod (continue to example 6.4): Find the angular acceleration and angular velocity, the rod moves down due to gravity when the angle with the horizontal is θ. Known the rotational inertia of the rod is $I = \dfrac{1}{3}mL^2$.

Solution:

According to the Newton's law of rotating $\tau_{net} = I\alpha$

$$\alpha = \frac{\tau}{I} = \frac{\dfrac{1}{2}mgL\cos\theta}{\dfrac{1}{3}mL^2} = \frac{3g\cos\theta}{2L}$$

From the definition of angular acceleration

$$\alpha = \frac{d\omega}{dt} = \frac{d\omega}{d\theta}\frac{d\theta}{dt} = \frac{d\omega}{d\theta}\omega$$

We have

$$\alpha d\theta = \omega d\omega \qquad \frac{3g}{2l}\cos\theta d\theta = \omega d\omega$$

$$\int_0^\theta \frac{3g}{2l}\cos\theta d\theta = \int_0^\omega \omega d\omega \qquad \frac{3g}{2l}\sin\theta = \frac{1}{2}\omega^2$$

$$\omega = \sqrt{\frac{3g\sin\theta}{l}}$$

$$\vec{\tau}_{net} = \sum_i(\Delta m_i r_i^2)\vec{\alpha}$$

转动惯量：$I = \sum_i(\Delta m_i r_i^2)$

刚体转动惯量只与其质量、质量分布和转轴位置有关。

转动定律—转动动力学方程：刚体获得的角加速度与合外力矩成正比。

$$\tau_{net} = I\alpha$$

合外力矩是物体转动状态发生改变的原因。

6.3.1 By Experiement

The moments of inertia of any body about any axis can be determined experimentally by measuring the net torque τ required to give the body an angular acceleration α. Then, from equation of rotational second law, $I = \dfrac{\tau}{\alpha}$.

6.3.2 Using the definition of the moment of inertia

a.   A particle of mass m rotating in a circle of radius r at the end of a string or rod whose mass can be ignored

$$I = mr^2$$

b.   Systems of particles

$$I = \sum_{i=1}^{n} m_i r_i^2$$

c.   A continuous uniform distribution of mass

$$I = \int_m r^2 dm$$

Where dm represents the mass of any infinitesimal particle of the body and r is the perpendicular distance of this particle from the axis of rotation.

For linear distribution of a mass: dm= λ dL

$$\lambda = \frac{m}{L}$$

λ : *linear mass density*, L : the length of the mass

For plane distribution of a mass: dm= σ dA

$$\sigma = \frac{m}{A}$$

σ : surface mass density, A : the area of the mass

6.3.1 通过实验方法测转动惯量

待测刚体施加合外力矩 τ ，测得刚体获得的角加速度 α ，刚体的转动惯量：

$$I = \frac{\tau}{\alpha}$$

6.3.2 由定义计算转动惯量

质点转动惯量 $I = mr^2$

质点系转动惯量

$$I = \sum_{i=1}^{n} m_i r_i^2$$

密度均匀质量连续分布物体

$$I = \int_m r^2 dm$$

质量线密度 $\lambda = \dfrac{m}{L}$

dm= λ dL

$$I = \int_L r^2 \lambda dl$$

质量面密度 $\sigma = \dfrac{m}{A}$

dm= σ dA ， $I = \int_A r^2 \sigma dA$

For solid distribution of a mass: dm= ρ dv

$$\rho = \frac{m}{v}$$

ρ : volumetric mass density, v : the volume of the mass

d. If the mass distribution is not uniform, λ, σ, ρ will be the

function of position.

Example 6.7 Uniform thin hoop and circular disk: Find the moment of inertia of a uniform thin hoop (or circular disk) of mass m and radius R about an axis perpendicular to the plane of the hoop (or circular disk) and passing through its center (Figure 6-9)

Solution:

Thin hoop: $I_z = \int R^2 dm = mR^2$

Circular disk: $\sigma = \dfrac{m}{\pi R^2}$

$$dI = r^2 dm = r^2 \sigma 2\pi r dr$$

$$I_o = \int_0^R dI = \frac{1}{2} mR^2$$

Example 6.8 Uniform Rigid Rod: Calculate the moment of inertia of a uniform rigid rod of length L and mass m (Figure 6-11a) about an axis perpendicular to the rod (the $y, y^{'}$ axis) and passing through its center of mass and one end.

Solution:

For y axis: $dm = \lambda dx = \dfrac{M}{L} dx$

$$I_y = \int r^2 dm = \int_{-L/2}^{L/2} x^2 \frac{M}{L} dx = \frac{M}{L} \int_{-L/2}^{L/2} x^2 dx$$

$$= \frac{M}{L} \left[\frac{x^3}{3} \right]_{-L/2}^{L/2} = \frac{1}{12} ML^2$$

The same calculation for $y^{'}$ axis

質量体密度 $\rho = \dfrac{m}{v}$

dm= ρ dv, $I = \int_V r^2 \rho dV$

質量分布不均勻，質量密度
是位置的函数： $I = \int_m r^2 dm$

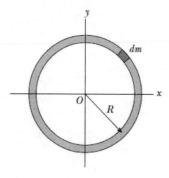

Figure 6-9 The mass elements *dm* of a uniform hoop are all the same distance from O.

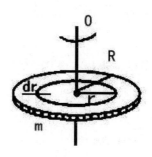

Figure 6-10 Circular disk

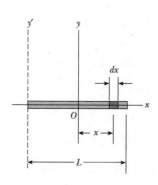

Figure 6-11 a: Example 6.8

$$I_{y'} = \frac{M}{L}\left[\frac{x^3}{3}\right]_0^L = \frac{1}{3}mL^2$$

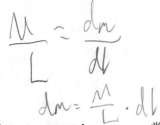

$$\frac{M}{L} = \frac{dm}{dl}$$

$$dm = \frac{M}{L}\cdot dl$$

Moment of inertia of rigid objects with different geometries　常见刚体的转动惯量

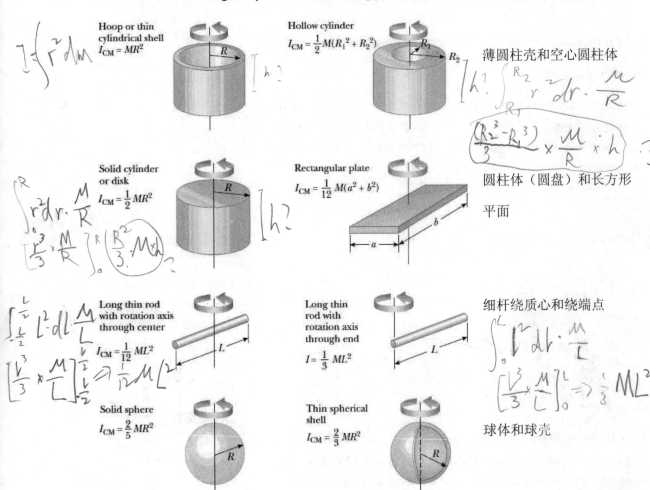

薄圆柱壳和空心圆柱体

圆柱体（圆盘）和长方形

平面

细杆绕质心和绕端点

球体和球壳

6.3.3 The Parallel-axis Theorem

6.3.3 平行轴定理

Parallel-axis theorem is helpful in obtaining moments of inertia. It states that if I is the moment of inertia of a body of total mass m about any axis, and I_{cm} is the moment of inertia about an axis passing through the center of mass and parallel to the first axis but a distance h away, then

用于计算刚体绕任意平行于质心轴转轴的转动惯量：

$$I = I_{cm} + mh^2$$

$$I = I_{cm} + mh^2$$

Thus, if the moment of inertia about an axis through the cm is known, the moment of inertia about any axis parallel to this axis is easily obtained.

I_{cm}：通过质心转轴转动惯量

h：两平行轴之间的距离

6.4.1 Work Done by a Torque

Consider the rigid object pivoted at O in Figure 6-11 b. Suppose a single external force **F** is applied at P, where **F** lies in the plane of the page. The work done by F on the object as it rotates through an infinitesimal distance $ds = r\, d\theta$ is

$$dW = \vec{F} ds = (F \sin \phi) r d\theta$$

Note that *the radial component of* **F** *does no work because it is perpendicular to the displacement.*

The magnitude of the torque due to **F** about O is defined as $rF \sin \phi$

So, $dw = \tau d\theta$

The rate of work is power

$$P = \frac{dw}{dt} = \tau \frac{d\theta}{dt} = \tau \omega$$

For a rotation from angle θ_1 to θ_2 the work is

$$W = \int_{\theta_1}^{\theta_2} \tau d\theta$$

6.4.2 Rotational Kinetic Energy

A body rotating about an axis is said to have rotational kinetic energy. An infinitesimal particle dm has kinetic energy

$$dK = \frac{1}{2} dm r_i^2 \omega^2$$

The total kinetic energy of the rigid body's rotation is the sum of all the kinetic energies associated with all of its mass points, we have

$$K = \int dK = \frac{1}{2} (\int r^2 dm) \omega^2$$

So, $K = \frac{1}{2} I \omega^2$

Rotational kinetic energy is not a new form of energy. It is ordinary kinetic energy because it is derived from a sum over individual kinetic energies of the particles contained in the rigid object.

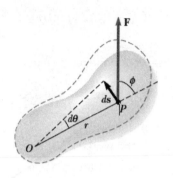

6.4.1 力矩的功

Figure 6-11 b: Work done by a Torque

力的径向分量垂直于位移—不做功。

功率 $P = \tau \omega$

力矩功： $W = \int_{\theta_1}^{\theta_2} \tau d\theta$

6.4.2 转动动能

质量微元 dm 的动能：

$$dK = \frac{1}{2} dm r_i^2 \omega^2$$

刚体转动总动能：

$$K = \frac{1}{2} I \omega^2$$

6.4.3 Theorem of Kinetic Energy of a Rigid Body Rotating about a Fixed Axis

$$dw = \tau d\theta = I\alpha d\theta = I\frac{d\omega}{dt}d\theta = I\omega d\omega$$

The work done by the external torque on the rigid body is

$$W = \int_{\omega_1}^{\omega_2} I\omega d\omega = \frac{1}{2}I\omega_2^2 - \frac{1}{2}I\omega_1^2$$

This is the work-kinetic energy theorem for a body rotating about a fixed axis. It states that the work done in rotating a body through an angle, $\theta_2 - \theta_1$ is equal to the change in rotational kinetic energy of the body.

Example 6.9 Energy and the Atwood Machine: Consider two cylinders having different masses m_1 and m_2, connected by a string passing over a pulley, as shown in Figure 6-12. The pulley has a radius R and moment of inertia about its axis of rotation. The string does not slip on the pulley, and the system is released from rest. Find the linear speeds of the cylinders after cylinder 2 descends through a distance h, the angular speed of the pulley at this time and tension of the string.

Solution:

We define the zero gravitational potential energy at the position when the system is released.

The mechanical energy of the system is conserved. $K_i=0$ and $U_i=0$

$$K_f + U_f = K_i + U_i$$
$$\left(\frac{1}{2}m_1v_f^2 + \frac{1}{2}m_2v_f^2 + \frac{1}{2}I\omega_f^2\right) + \left(m_1gh - m_2gh\right) = 0 + 0$$

Where v_f is the same for both blocks, and $v_f = R\omega_f$, solving for v_f we find

$$v_f = \left(\frac{2(m_2 - m_1)gh}{(m_1 + m_2 + (I/R^2))}\right)^{\frac{1}{2}}$$

6.4.3 定轴转动动能定理

外力矩对刚体所做功等于刚体转动动能增量。

$$\int_{\theta_1}^{\theta_2} \tau d\theta = \frac{1}{2}I\omega_2^2 - \frac{1}{2}I\omega_1^2$$

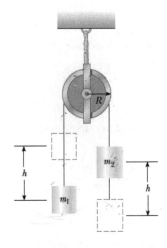

Figure 6-12 An Atwood machine
阿特伍德机

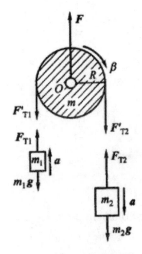

Figure 6-13 受力分析图

The angular speed of the pulley at this instant is

$$\omega_f = \frac{v_f}{R} = \frac{1}{R}\left(\frac{2(m_2 - m_1)gh}{(m_1 + m_2 + (I/R^2))}\right)^{\frac{1}{2}}$$

Example 6.10 Rotating rod: A uniform rod of length L and mass M is attached at one end to a frictionless pivot and is free to rotate about the pivot in the vertical plane, as in Figure 6-14. The rod is released from rest in the horizontal position. Determine the angular velocity of the rod when it reaches the vertical position and the speed of the rod's tip at this moment.

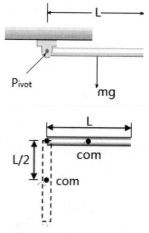

Figure 6-14 Example 6.10

Solution:

Work done by gravity is

$$W = Mg\frac{L}{2}$$

From the work-energy principle

$$Mg\frac{L}{2} = \frac{1}{2}I\omega^2$$

Since $I = \frac{1}{3}ML^2$, we can solve for ω

$$\omega = \sqrt{\frac{3g}{L}}$$

The tip of the rod will have a linear speed

$$v = L\omega = \sqrt{3gL}$$

Example 6.11: A sphere of mass m_1 and a block of mass m_2 are connected by a light cord that passes over a pulley, as shown in Figure 6-15. The radius of the pulley is R, and the mass of the rim is M. The spokes of the pulley have negligible mass. The block slides on a frictionless, horizontal surface. Find an expression for the linear acceleration of the two objects, using the concepts of angular momentum and torque.

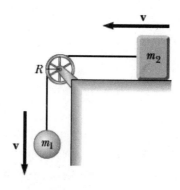

Figure 6-15 When the system is released, the sphere moves downward and the block moves to the left.

Solution:

Assume the tension on m_1 is T_1 and tension on m_2 is T_2. we have

$$m_1 g - T_1 = m_1 a$$
$$T_2 = m_2 a$$
$$a = MR^2 \alpha$$

Solving the equations above, we can get the acceleration of the system is

$$a = \frac{m_1}{m_1 + m_2 + M} g$$

6.5 Angular Momentum and its Conservation   6.5 角动量及守恒

6.5.1 Angular Momentum of a Mass Point

6.5.1 质点角动量

We have found momentum to be useful in dealing with the translational motion of a mass point or a system of mass points. In rotational motion, angular momentum (**L**) is a concept as useful as momentum in translation motion.

Consider a mass point of mass m with velocity **V** at a position **r** relative to the origin O of an inertial reference frame. We define the angular momentum of mass point with respect to the origin O to be the cross product of the particle's instantaneous position vector **r** and its instantaneous linear momentum **p**:

质点角动量定义：**L = r × p**

角动量大小：$L = rmv\sin\phi$

$$\mathbf{L} = \mathbf{r} \times \mathbf{p}$$

Angular momentum is a vector. Its magnitude is given by

角动量方向：由定义给出

$$L = rmv\sin\phi$$

Its direction is perpendicular to the plane formed by **r** and **v**. We can find that the angular momentum of the mass point depends on the selection of the reference point O. Therefore, when speaking of an angular momentum of a particle we must specify which point the angular momentum is with respect to.

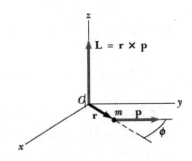

Figure 6-16 Definition of angular momentum of a mass point

If a particle moves on a circle with radius r, and its speed is v at some moment, the magnitude of the angular momentum of the particle with respect to the center of the circle O is

质点的角动量与参考点 O 的选择有关。

$$L = rmv = mr^2\omega$$

L should be parallel to the rotational axis and be same as that of **ω**.

A particle in uniform circular motion has a constant angular momentum about an axis through the center of its path.

Example 6.12: A particle moves with uniform velocity parallel to the y axis in the xy-plane. The path is described by **r**=x₀**i**+v.**j**. Find the angular momentum of the particle about the origin.

Solution:

To find the angular momentum, we use the equation

   L = **r** × **p**

First of all, we need to find the momentum **p**=m**v**

We have $\mathbf{v}=\dfrac{d\vec{r}}{dt}$ =v

Then   **L**= **r**×**p**=m(**r**×**v**)= m(x₀**i**+v.**j**)×(v**j**)=x₀mv**k**

The angular momentum is constant.

6.5.2 Angular Momentum of a Rigid Body Rotating about a Fixed Axis

The total angular momentum of a system of particles about some points is defined as the vector sum of the angular momentum of the individual particles:

$$\mathbf{L}_{tot} = \mathbf{L}_1 + \mathbf{L}_2 + \cdots + \mathbf{L}_n = \sum_i \mathbf{L}_i$$

A rigid body rotates about a fixed axis oz with angular velocity ω. Since every mass point of the rigid body does a circular motion with the same angular velocity about the axis, therefore, the angular momentum of the rigid body with respect to the oz axis is

$$L = \int dm r^2 \omega = \left(\int r^2 dm \right)\omega = I\omega$$

Example 6.13: Four identical particles of mass m are mounted at equal intervals on the thin rod of length L and mass M, with one

圆周运动角动量：

$$L = rmv = mr^2\omega$$

角动量是向量，方向与角速度方向一致。

6.5.2 刚体角动量

质点系的总角动量等于各个物体的角动量的和：

$$\vec{L}_{tot} = \sum_i \vec{L}_i$$

刚体角动量等于刚体转动惯量与角速度的乘积：

$$L = I\omega$$

$$r = mJ$$

mass at each end of the rod. Calculate the <u>kinetic energy</u> and <u>angular momentum of</u> the system if the system rotates with angular velocity ω

a. about an axis perpendicular to the rod through one of the end masses.

b. about the center of the thin rod.

Solution:

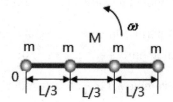

Figure 6-17 Example 6.13

a.   The rotational inertia of the system is

$$I_o = \frac{1}{3}ML^2 + m(\frac{L}{3})^2 + m(\frac{2L}{3})^2 + mL^2 = (\frac{3M+14m}{9})L^2$$

The kinetic energy of this system is

$$K = \frac{1}{2}I_o\omega^2 = (\frac{3M+14m}{18})L^2\omega^2$$

The angular momentum of the rigid body rotating about O is

$$L = I_o\omega = (\frac{3M+14m}{9})L^2\,\omega$$

b.   rotating about the center of the system

$$I_{cm} = I_o - (M+4m)(\frac{L}{2})^2 = \frac{1}{12}ML^2 + \frac{5}{9}mL^2$$

$$K = \frac{1}{2}I_{cm}\omega^2 = \frac{1}{2}(\frac{1}{12}ML^2 + \frac{5}{9}mL^2)\omega^2 \qquad \text{应用平行轴定理}$$

$$L = I_{cm}\omega = (\frac{1}{12}ML^2 + \frac{5}{9}mL^2)\omega$$

6.5.3 Theorem of Angular Momentum of a Rigid Body Rotating about a Fixed Axis

6.5.3 角动量定理

Newton's second law for rotation is

$$\tau_{net} = I\alpha = I\frac{d\omega}{dt} = \frac{dL}{dt}$$

由转动定律推出角动量定理

转动定律：$\tau_{net} = \frac{dL}{dt}$

It is the theorem of angular momentum of a rigid body rotating about a fixed axis. It states that the torque acting on an object is equal to the time rate of change of the object's angular momentum.

Changing the form of the equation we have another form of this theorem.

$$\int_{t_0}^{t} \tau_{net}dt = \int_{L_0}^{L} dL = L - L_0 = \Delta L$$

角动量定理： $\int_{t_0}^{t} \tau_{net}dt = \Delta L$

$\int_{t_0}^{t} \tau_{net}dt$ ：冲量矩

6.5.4 Law of Angular Momentum Conservation

6.5.4 角动量守恒

When the net torque τ_{net} is 0, we see from above equation that

守恒条件： τ_{net} =0

$\dfrac{dL}{dt}$ =0, or ΔL =0. Therefore, the angular momentum remains constant in time. That is

合外力矩为零，总角动量守恒： ΔL =0

L = constant or **L**$_i$ = **L**$_f$ if τ_{net} = 0

The total angular momentum of a system is constant in both magnitude and direction if the resultant external torque acting on the system is zero, that is, if the system is isolated.

合外力矩为零，刚体系统角动量不变。

For an isolated system consisting of a number of particles, we write this conservation law as $L_{total} = \sum L_n$ =constant, where the index *n* denotes the *n*th particle in the system.

If the mass of an isolated rotating system undergoes redistribution in some way, the system's moment of inertia changes. Because the magnitude of the angular momentum of the system is *L* = *I*ω, conservation of angular momentum requires that the product of *I* and ω must remain constant. Thus, a change in *I* for an isolated system requires a change in ω. In this case, we can express the principle of conservation of angular momentum as

如果系统质量分布发生改变，转动惯量随之变化，引起系统角速度改变：

$I_i\omega_i = I_f\omega_f$

$$I_i\omega_i = I_f\omega_f =constant$$

This expression is valid both for rotation about a fixed axis and for rotation about an axis through the center of mass of a moving system as long as that axis remains fixed in direction. We require only that the net external torque be zero. For example, when divers wish to double their angular speed, they must reduce their moment of inertia to half its initial value.

Until now, we have a third conservation law to add to our list. We

孤立系统遵循三大守恒定

can now state that **the energy, linear momentum, and angular momentum of an isolated system all remain constant:**

律：能量守恒、动量守恒、角动量守恒。

$$\left.\begin{array}{l} E_i = E_f \\ \vec{P}_i = \vec{P}_f \\ \vec{L}_i = \vec{L}_f \end{array}\right\} \text{For an isolated system}$$

Example 6.14: A student sits on a pivoted stool while holding a pair of objects. The stool is free to rotate about a vertical axis with negligible friction. The moment of inertia of student, objects, and stool is 2.6 kg m^2. The student is set in rotation with an initial angular speed of 5rad/s, with arms outstretched. As he rotates, he polls the objects inward so that the new moment of inertia of the system becomes 2.0kg m^2. What is the new angular speed of the system?

Solution:

Because the net external torque on the system is zero, angular momentum is conserved. Thus,

$$L = I_i \omega_i = I_f \omega_f$$

We have $\omega_f = \dfrac{I_i \omega_i}{I_f} = \dfrac{2.6 * 5}{2.0} = 6.5\text{rad/s}$

Example 6.15: A bullet of mass m with velocity v collides with a cylinder with mass M and radius R. The bullet is embarked on the edge of the cylinder. What is the angular velocity of the cylinder after this collision? Is kinetic energy conserved?

Solution:

Angular momentum is conserved for this situation.

$$mvR = (mR^2 + \frac{1}{2}MR^2)\omega$$

And after collision the angular momentum of the system is

$$I = (mR^2 + \frac{1}{2}MR^2)$$

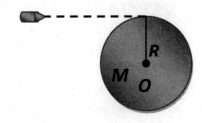

Figure 6-18 Example 6.15

so $\omega = \dfrac{mvR}{mR^2 + \dfrac{1}{2}MR^2}$

Before collision the kinetic energy of the system is

$$K_i = \frac{1}{2}mv^2$$

After collision the kinetic energy of the system is

$$K_f = \frac{1}{2}I\omega^2 \neq K_i$$

Example 6.16 Disk and Stick: A 2.00kg disk traveling at 3.00 m/s strikes a 1.00kg stick of length 4.00 m that is lying flat on nearly frictionless ice, as shown in Figure 6-19. Assume that the collision is elastic and that the disk does not deviate from its original line of motion. Find the translational speed of the disk, the translational speed of the stick, and the angular speed of the stick after the collision. The moment of inertia of the stick about its center of mass is 1.33 kg ·m^2.

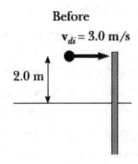

Solution:

Known m_d=2,00kg, V_{di}=3.0m/s, m_s=1.00kg, I =1.33kgm^2. Because the disk and stick form an isolated system, we can assume that total energy, linear momentum, and angular momentum are all conserved. After the collision, the stick has a velocity Vs and angular velocity ω . The disk has a velocity V$_{df}$. The first equation we have is conversation of linear momentum. P$_i$=P$_f$

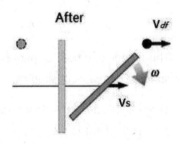

Figure 6-19 Overhead view of a disk striking a stick in an elastic collision, which causes the stick to rotate and move to the right

$$m_d v_{di} = m_d v_{df} + m_s v_s \qquad (1)$$

Applying conservation of angular momentum to the system gives L$_i$=L$_f$

$$-rm_d v_{di} = -rm_{df} + I\omega \qquad (2)$$

Finally, the elastic nature of the collision tells us that kinetic energy is conserved; in this case, the kinetic energy consists of translational and rotational forms: K$_i$=K$_f$

$$\frac{1}{2}m_d V_{di}^2 = \frac{1}{2}m_d V_{df}^2 + \frac{1}{2}m_s V_s^2 + \frac{1}{2}I\omega^2 \qquad (3)$$

In solving Equation (1), (2), and (3)simultaneously, we find that

$$v_{df} = 2.3\mathrm{m/s}$$

$$v_{s} = 1.3\mathrm{m/s}$$

$$\omega = -2.0\mathrm{rad/s}$$

6.6 Rolling—Rotational plus Translational Motion 6.6 滚动—平动加转动

So far we have discussed pure rotational motion about a fixed axis and pure translational motion. What about combined translational and rotational motion?

6.1.1 Rolling without Slipping

6.1.1 纯滚动

Consider a uniform cylinder of radius R rolling without slipping on a horizontal surface, Figure 6-20. As the cylinder rotates through an angle θ, its center of mass moves a linear distance $s = R\theta$. Therefore, the linear speed of the center of mass for pure rolling motion is given by

$$v_{cm} = \frac{ds}{dt} = \frac{Rd\theta}{dt} = R\omega$$

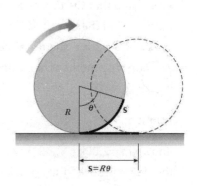

Figure 6-20 Pure rolling motion

纯滚动条件：$v_{cm}=R\omega$

纯滚动质心加速度：

This is the condition for pure rolling motion whenever a cylinder or sphere rolls without slipping.

The magnitude of the linear acceleration of the center of mass for pure rolling motion is

$$a_{cm} = \frac{dv}{dt} = \frac{Rd\omega}{dt} = R\alpha$$

$$a_{cm} = R\alpha$$

The linear velocities of the center of mass and of various points on and within the cylinder are illustrated in Figure 6-21. Note that the linear velocity of any point is in a direction perpendicular to the line from that point to the contact point P. At any instant, the part of the rim that is at point P is at rest relative to the surface because slipping does not occur.

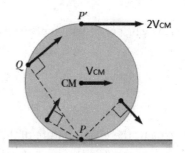

Figure 6-21 All points rotate about P

圆柱上的每一点有相同角速度。

All points on the cylinder have the same angular speed. The center of mass moves with linear speed V_{cm} while the contact point between the surface and cylinder has a linear speed of zero. We can express the total kinetic energy of the rolling cylinder as

$$K = \frac{1}{2} I_p \omega^2$$

Where I_p is the moment of inertia about a rotation axis through P. Applying the parallel-axis theorem, we can substitute $I_p = I_{CM} + MR^2$ to obtain

$$K = \frac{1}{2} I_{cm} \omega^2 + \frac{1}{2} MR^2 \omega^2$$

So $\quad K = \frac{1}{2} I_{cm} \omega^2 + \frac{1}{2} M v_{cm}^2$

The term $\frac{1}{2} I_{cm} \omega^2$ represents the rotational kinetic energy of the cylinder about its center of mass, and the term $\frac{1}{2} M v_{cm}^2$ represents the kinetic energy the cylinder would have if it were just translating through space without rotating. Thus, we can say that the total kinetic energy of a rolling object is the sum of the rotational kinetic energy about the center of mass and the translational kinetic energy of the center of mass.

纯滚动的动能：

$$K = \frac{1}{2} I_{cm} \omega^2 + \frac{1}{2} MR^2 \omega^2$$

绕质心转动动能加上质心平动动能

$\frac{1}{2} I_{cm} \omega^2$：圆柱体绕质心转动的转动动能

$\frac{1}{2} M v_{cm}^2$：圆柱体的质心平动动能

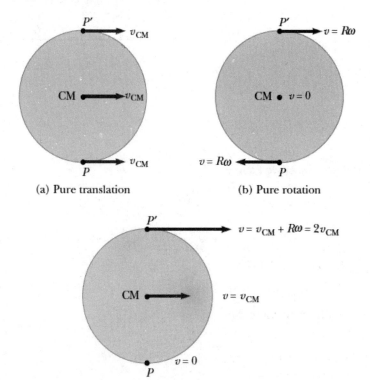

(a) Pure translation

(b) Pure rotation

(c) Combination of translation and rotation

Figure 6-22 The motion of a rolling object can be modeled as a combination of pure translation and pure rotation.

Example 6.17 Sphere Rolling Down an Incline

For the solid sphere of mass M and radius R rolls (without slipping) down an incline whose incline angle with the horizontal is θ, shown in Figure 6-23. Calculate:

a. the linear speed of the center of mass at the bottom of the incline.

b. the magnitude of the linear acceleration of the center of mass.

c. the minimum coefficient of friction that will allow the sphere to roll without slipping on this incline.

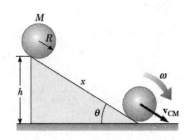

Solution:

a. We use the law of conservation of energy. The total energy at the position of height h is equal to total energy at the bottom of the incline.

Figure 6-23 A sphere rolling down an incline

$$Mgh = \frac{1}{2}Mv^2 + \frac{1}{2}(\frac{2}{5}MR^2)(\frac{v}{R})^2$$

So $v = \sqrt{\frac{10}{7}gh}$

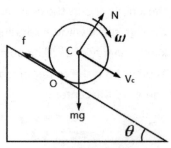

Figure 6-24 Example 6.17

b. $v^2 = 2ax,$ and $x = h/\sin\theta$

$$a = \frac{5}{7}g\sin\theta$$

c. For translation in x direction (incline surface) we have

$$Mg\sin\theta - f = Ma \qquad (1)$$

沿斜面平动

f is due to static friction and $f \le \mu_s N$, N: normal force

$$N - Mg\cos\theta = 0 \qquad (2) \quad \text{net force in y direction}$$

垂直斜面方向合外力为零

For the rotational motion about center, we use $\tau = I\alpha$

$$fR = \frac{2}{5}MR^2\alpha \qquad (3)$$

转动定律

So we obtain $f = \dfrac{2}{5}Ma = \dfrac{2}{7}Mg\sin\theta$

let $f = \mu_s N$ then $\mu_s = \dfrac{2}{7}\tan\theta$

This is the minimum coefficient of friction that will allow the sphere to roll without slipping on this incline.

Example 6.18 A falling yo-yo: Thread is wrapped around a uniform solid cylinder (something like a yo-yo) of mass M and radius R, and the cylinder starts falling from rest. As the cylinder falls, find

a. its acceleration and

b. the tension in the thread

Solution:

a. The hand holding the thread has a tension T upward acting on the cylinder

$$Mg - T = Ma \quad (1)$$

And $TR = \dfrac{1}{2}mR^2\alpha \quad (2)$

$$a = R\alpha$$

solving for a, we find that

$$a = \dfrac{2}{3}g$$

b. $T = \dfrac{1}{3}g$

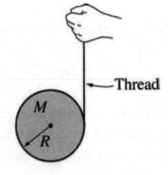

Figure 6-25 Example 6.18

6.7 Static Equilibrium

6.7 静平衡

The term *static equilibrium* implies that the object is at rest. An object is said to be in **translational equilibrium** if the sum of the forces acting on it is zero. That is, F_{net} = 0, a =0 but v may be zero or constant. If the object is modeled as a particle, then this is the only condition that must be satisfied for equilibrium. Similarly, an object is said to be in **rotational equilibrium** if the sum of the torques acting on it is zero. That is, τ_{net} = 0, α =0 but ω maybe zero or

合外力为零物体处于平动平衡，但物体可能匀速运动。

合外力矩为零物体处于转动平衡，但物体可能做匀角速度转动。

constant. For an extended object to be in static equilibrium, we have two necessary conditions:

物体静平衡的条件：

1. The resultant external force must equal zero:

1. 合外力为零 $F_{net} = 0$

$$F_{net} = 0 \quad (v_{cm} = 0 \text{ or } v_{cm} = \text{constant}) \quad \begin{cases} F_{net,x} = 0 \\ F_{net,y} = 0 \\ F_{net,z} = 0 \end{cases}$$

2. 合外力矩为零 $\tau_{net} = 0$

2. The resultant external torque about *any* axis must be zero:

$$\tau_{net} = 0 \quad (\omega_0 = 0 \text{ or } \omega_0 = \text{constant})$$

When working static equilibrium problems, you must recognize all the external forces acting on the object. Failure to do so results in an incorrect analysis.

Example 6.19 The Leaning Ladder: A uniform ladder of length l rests against a smooth, vertical wall (Figure 6-26). If the mass of the ladder is m and the coefficient of static friction between the ladder and the ground is $\mu_s = 0.40$, find the minimum angle θ_{min} at which the ladder does not slip.

Solution:

Applying the first condition for equilibrium to the ladder, we have

$$F_{net,x} = f_s - P = 0 \rightarrow P = f_s$$
$$F_{net,y} = n - mg = 0 \rightarrow n = mg$$

When the ladder is on the verge of slipping, the force of friction must be a maximum, which is given by

$$f_{s,max} = \mu_s n = \mu_s mg$$

Thus, we must have

$$P = f_s = \mu_s n = \mu_s mg$$

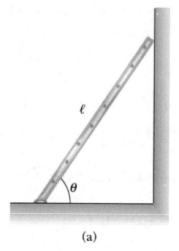

(a)

Figure 6-26 (a) A uniform ladder at rest, leaning against a smooth wall. The ground is rough.

To find θ_{min}, we must use the second condition for equilibrium. When we take the torques about an axis through the origin O at the bottom of the ladder, $\tau_{net,O} = 0$, we have

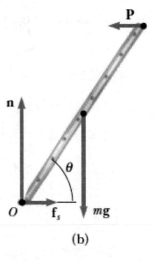

$$Pl\sin\theta - mg\frac{l}{2}\cos\theta = 0$$

This expression gives

$$\tan\theta_{min} = \frac{mg}{2P} = \frac{mg}{2\mu_s mg} = \frac{1}{2\mu_s} = 1.25$$

$$\theta_{min} = 51^0$$

If you choose a different axis of rotation (as long as it is perpendicular to the plane), you will still obtain the correct answer.

Figure 6-26 (b) The free-body diagram for the ladder

第六章总结　刚体转动

1. **刚体运动学**

   1）刚体的运动特点：刚体上所有质元都绕同一直线做圆周运动。

   2）描述刚体转动的物理量：角位置 θ、角位移 $\Delta\theta$、角速度 $\omega = \dfrac{d\theta}{dt}$、角加速度 $\alpha = \dfrac{d\omega}{dt}$。

   刚体上每一点都有相同的角位移、角速度、角加速度。

   3）线量和角量之间的关系：路程 $s = r\Delta\theta$

   速率 $v = r\omega$

   切向加速度 $a_t = r\alpha$

   法向加速度 $a_n = \omega^2 r$

   4）匀角加速度和匀加速运动公式对比：

Angular	Linear
$\omega = \omega_0 + \alpha t$	$v = v_0 + at$
$\theta - \theta_0 = \omega_0 t + \frac{1}{2}\alpha t^2$	$x - x_0 = v_0 t + \frac{1}{2}at^2$
$\omega^2 - \omega_0^2 = 2\alpha(\theta - \theta_0)$	$v^2 - v_0^2 = 2a(x - x_0)$
$\omega_{avg} = \dfrac{\omega + \omega_0}{2}$	$v_{avg} = \dfrac{v + v_0}{2}$

2. **力矩**：是物体转动状态发生改变的原因，单位是 N·m。

   $\tau = \mathbf{r} \times \mathbf{F}$，$\mathbf{r}$ 是力的作用点到转轴的距离。

   大小为：$\tau = rF\sin\theta$，θ 是 $\mathbf{r}$、$\mathbf{F}$ 的夹角。

   方向：由右旋法则确定。

   力矩为零：1）向心力对力心的力矩为零。

   　　　　　2）力的作用线与转轴平行或相交。

3. **转动惯量 I** —描述物体转动状态改变的难易程度，对应于平动状态的质量 m。

   1）定义

   质点：$I = mr^2$，r 是质点到转轴的距离。

   质点组（n 个质点）：$I = \displaystyle\sum_{i=1}^{n} m_i r_i^2$

质量连续分布的刚体：$I = \int r^2 dm$，I 与刚体的质量、质量分布和转轴的位置相关。

2）几个常见物体的转动惯量（绕质心转动，质量均匀分布）：

细棒：$I = \dfrac{1}{12} ml^2$

圆环：$I = mR^2$

圆盘：$I = \dfrac{1}{2} mR^2$

圆柱：$I = \dfrac{1}{2} mR^2$

球体：$I = \dfrac{2}{5} mR^2$

3）平行轴定理：$I = I_c + md^2$，绕任意转轴的转动惯量。

I_c 是绕质心转动的转动惯量，d 是转轴到质心轴的矩离。

4. **转动定律**：$\tau_{net} = I\alpha$

5. **转动时的能量**

1）转动动能：$K = \dfrac{1}{2} I\omega^2$

2）滚动动能：$K = \dfrac{1}{2} I_c \omega^2 + \dfrac{1}{2} mv_c^2$

3）势能：$U = mgd$，d 是质心到转点的距离

6. **角动量及守恒**

1）角动量：质点 **L = r × p**
刚体 $L = I\omega$

2）角动量定理：$\int_{t_1}^{t_2} \tau dt = \Delta L$

3）角动量守恒：$\tau = 0$，那么 $\Delta L = 0$

7. **静平衡**：$F_{net} = 0$，并且 $\tau_{net} = 0$

8. **纯滚动**：等效于平动+转动
接地点 $v = 0$

质心 $v_c = r\omega$，$a_c = r\alpha$

质点运动规律与刚体定轴转动规律对照

质点运动规律	刚体定轴转动
运动定律 $\quad \vec{F} = m\vec{a}$	转动定律 $\quad \vec{\tau} = I\vec{\alpha}$
动量定理 $\quad \int_0^t \vec{F}dt = m\vec{v} - m\vec{v}_0$	角动量定理 $\quad \int_0^t \vec{\tau}dt = \vec{L} - \vec{L}_0$
动量守恒定律 $\quad \sum \vec{F}_i = 0$，$\sum m_i\vec{v}_i =$ 恒量	角动量守恒定律 $\quad \vec{\tau} = 0$，$\sum I_i\vec{\omega}_i =$ 恒量
力做的功 $\quad W = \int_a^b \vec{F}d\vec{r}$	力矩做的功 $\quad W = \int_{\theta_0}^{\theta} \tau d\theta$
动能 $\quad E_k = \dfrac{1}{2}mv^2$	转动动能 $\quad E_k = \dfrac{1}{2}I\omega^2$

Chapter 6 Rotation of Rigid Bodies Practice

Multiple Choice Questions

1. A horizontal turntable rotates with a constant rate. As viewed from above shown below, an object on the turntable moves clockwise in a circle. Which of the following best describes the direction of the frictional force on the object?

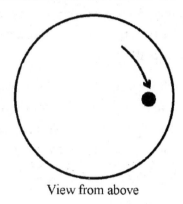

View from above

   A. To the Left

   B. To the right

   C. Down

   D. Up

   E. Up and to the left

2. Torque is the rotational analogue of

   A. kinetic energy

   B. linear momentum

   C. acceleration

   D. force

   E. mass

3. The net torque on the wheel in Figure below about the axle through O if a = 10.0 cm and b = 25.0 cm is

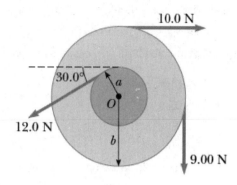

   A. 3.55N.m

   B. 3.71N.m

   C. -3.55N.m

   D. -3.71N.m

   E. 4.15N.m

4. A 100N uniform ladder, 8.0 m long, rests against a smooth vertical wall. The coefficient of static friction between ladder and floor is 0.29. What minimum angle (in degree) can the ladder make with the floor before it slips?

   A. 51

   B. 60

   C. 65

   D. 30

   E. 25

5. A uniform, horizontal beam of length 6.0 m and weight 120 N is attached at one end to a wall by a pin connection (so that it may rotate). A cable attached to the wall above the pin supports the opposite end. The cable makes an angle of 60^0 with the horizontal. What is the tension in the cable needed to maintain the beam in equilibrium?

A. 35 N

B. 69 N

C. 60 N

D. 120 N

E. 150 N

6. A 2.0 kg mass is placed at (3.0, 4.0) m. Where can a 4.0 kg mass be placed so that the moment of inertia about the z-axis is zero?

A. (-3.0, -4.0) m

B. (-6.0, -8.0) m

C. (-1.5, -2.0) m

D. (-0.75, -1.0) m

E. There is no position giving this result.

7. A bowling ball ($I = \dfrac{2}{5}mr^2$) has a uniform distributed mass of m=5.0 kg and a radius of r=0.10 m. If it rolls down the lane without slipping at a linear speed of 4.0 m/s, what is its kinetic energy?

A. 16J

B. 40J

C. 50J

D. 60J

E. 75J

8. A solid cylinder ($I = MR^2/2$) has a string wrapped around it many times. When I release the cylinder, holding on to the string, the cylinder falls and spins as the string unwinds. What is the downward acceleration of the cylinder as it falls?

A. 0

B. 4.9 m/s2

C. 6.5 m/s2

D. 9.8 m/s2

E. 11 m/s2

9. A boy with mass m is standing on the edge of a stationary platform with mass M that is free to rotate. The boy tries to walk around

the platform in a counterclockwise direction. As he does

A. the platform doesn't rotate.

B. the platform rotates in a clockwise direction just fast enough so that the boy remains stationary relative to the ground.

C. the platform rotates in a clockwise direction while the boy goes around in a counterclockwise direction relative to the ground.

D. both go around with equal angular velocities but in opposite directions.

E. none of the above.

10. A length L rod with a mass of m is hinged at one end and is held in a horizontal position. The rod is released as the free end is allowed to fall. What is the angular acceleration as it is released?

A. $\alpha = \dfrac{g}{L}$

B. $\alpha = \dfrac{3g}{2L}$

C. $\alpha = \dfrac{2g}{L}$

D. $\alpha = \dfrac{2g}{3L}$

E. $\alpha = \dfrac{3g}{L}$

11. A ventilation fan with a moment of inertia of 0.10kgm^2 has a net torque of 0.10 Nm applied to it. If it starts from rest, what kinetic energy will it have 10 s later?

A. 1.0 J

B. 2.5 J

C. 5.0 J

D. 7.5 J

E. 10 J

12. The total kinetic energy of a baseball thrown with a spinning motion is a function of

   A. its linear speed but not rotational speed.
   B. its rotational speed but not linear speed.
   C. both linear and rotational speeds.
   D. neither linear nor rotational speed.
   E. none of the above.

13. A ceiling fan is turned on and reaches an angular speed of 120 rev/min in 20 s. It is then turned off and coasts to a stop in an additional 40 s. The ratio of the average angular acceleration for the first 20s to that for the last 40 s is

   A. 2
   B. 0.5
   C. -0.5
   D. -2
   E. 1.5

14. The rod in the figure is uniform, and the tension in the string is T. The mass of the rod is

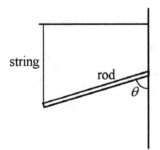

   A. 2Tg
   B. 2T/g
   C. T/g
   D. T/2g
   E. 2g/T

15. The diagram below shows a massless rod of length L that supports a mass m being held horizontally against a tower by a wire that makes an angle θ with the horizontal rod.

The wire is connected to the rod at a distance x from the free end of the rod. The mass is attached by a massless string at the free end of the rod. For the rod to remain horizontal, the tension in the wire must be

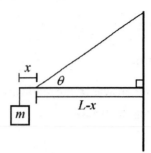

   A. mgL/2xcosθ
   B. mgx/2Lsinθ
   C. mgx/2(L−x)sinθ
   D. mgL/(L−x)sinθ
   E. mgL/2(L−x)cosθ

16. Three objects of uniform density, a solid sphere, a solid cylinder, and a hollow cylinder, are placed at the top of an incline. They are all released from rest at the same elevation and roll without slipping.

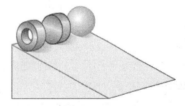

Which of the following objects has the greatest rotational kinetic energy at the bottom of the incline?

   A. cylinder
   B. sphere
   C. hoop
   D. all have the same
   E. not enough information

17. A solid cylinder of radius 0.2 m and mass 2 kg is at rest at a height H=1.2 m at the top of an inclined plane making an angle 60° with

the horizontal. Assuming no slipping, what is the speed of the cylinder at the bottom of the incline?

A. Zero
B. 2 m/s
C. 4 m/s
D. 6 m/s
E. 10 m/s

18. Base your answer to the following question on the diagram below.

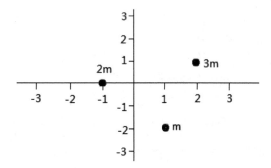

What is the total rotational inertia of the system when it is rotated about the origin?

A. 6m
B. 11m
C. 16m
D. 22m
E. 26m

19. A rod has non uniform mass distribution, a length l, and a mass m. If it is rotated around an axis that is perpendicular to its length, at what location of this axis will the rod have the smallest moment of inertia?

A. one of the ends
B. at its center, $l/2$
C. at its center of mass
D. at the point with the highest density
E. the moment of inertia is the same for any location

20. The rod of moment of inertia I is initially at rest. A ball of mass m falls onto the rod such that all of its kinetic energy is imparted to the rod. What is the rotational velocity of the rod around point P immediately after the collision?

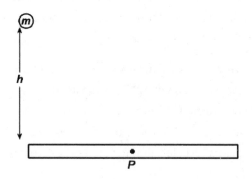

A. mg/I
B. $(mgh/2I)^{1/2}$
C. $(mgh/I)^{1/2}$
D. $(2mgh/I)^{1/2}$
E. 2mg/I

21. The angular position of a sphere is given by the equation $\theta(t) = 2t^2 + 3t + 6$, where θ is in radians and t is in seconds. If the moment of inertia for the sphere is 4 kgm^2, then what is its angular momentum at t = 3s?

A. 15 kgm^2/s
B. 27 kgm^2/s
C. 30 kgm^2/s
D. 45 kgm^2/s
E. 60 kgm^2/s

22. A figure skater of moment of inertia 40 kg•m^2 is initially spinning at a speed of 6 rad/s. If she moves her arms outward, her new moment of inertia is 60 kg•m^2. How much work does the skater do in order to move her hands outward to this position?

A. 120 J
B. 180 J
C. 240 J

D. 360 J

E. 480 J

23. A rod of length L is rotated about its center which has a moment of inertia $(1/12)ML^2$. What is the moment of inertia at a point L/4 away from the center?

A. $(1/12)ML2$

B. $(3/4)ML2$

C. $(7/48)ML2$

D. $(15/29)ML2$

E. $ML2$

24. The system below rotates with a speed ω. If the mass of the rod supports is negligible, the upper and lower crossbars' masses are 4m and 2m, respectively. What is the angular

momentum of the system?

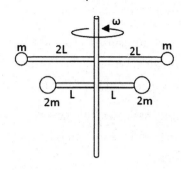

A. $\dfrac{14}{3}mL^2\omega$

B. $\dfrac{40}{3}mL^2\omega$

C. $12mL^2\omega$

D. $15mL^2\omega$

E. $18mL^2\omega$

Free Response Questions

1. An unknown mass, m_1, hangs from a massless string and descends with an acceleration g/2. The other end is attached to a mass m_2 which slides on a frictionless horizontal table. The string goes over a uniform cylinder of mass m/2 and radius R (see figure). The cylinder rotates about a horizontal axis without friction and the string does not slip on the cylinder Express your answers in parts b, c and d in terms of g, m and R.

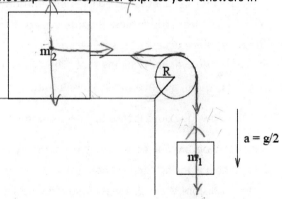

A. Draw free body diagrams for the cylinder and the two masses.

B. What is the tension in the horizontal section of the string?

C. What is the tension in the vertical section of the string?

D. What is the value of the unknown mass m_1?

2. A solid, uniform disk of mass M and radius R is oscillating about an axis through P. The axis is perpendicular to the plane of the disk. Friction at P is negligibly small and can be ignored. The distance from P to the center, C, of the disk is b (see figure). The gravitational acceleration is g.

A. When the displacement angle is θ what then is the torque relative to point P?

B. What is the moment of inertia for rotation about the axis through P?

C. The torque causes an angular acceleration about the axis through P. Write down the equation of motion in terms of the angle θ and the angular acceleration.

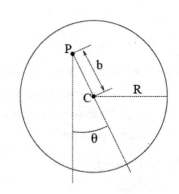

As the disk oscillates, the maximum displacement angle, θ_{max}, is very small, and the motion is a near perfect simple harmonic oscillation.

D. What is the period of oscillation?

E. As the disk oscillates, is there any force that the axis at P exerts on the disk? Explain your answer.

3. String is wrapped around a uniform solid cylinder of mass M and radius R (its momentum of inertia is $I = \dfrac{1}{2}MR^2$). The cylinder starts falling from rest at a height $I = \frac{1}{2}MR^2$

$R = \sqrt{2IM}$

h above the floor, and the thread unwinds as it falls. As the cylinder falls, find

$a = dR$

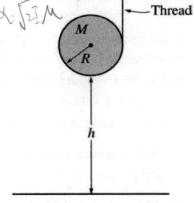

Thread

A. The linear acceleration of the spool $F = ma$ $a = \sqrt{2IM}$

$a = \dfrac{E}{m}$

B. The angular velocity of the spool just before it strikes the floor. $V = wR = w \cdot \sqrt{2IM}$

The spinning cylinder lands on the floor without bouncing and comes free from the thread. It continues to spin, but slips on the floor's surface while doing so. The coefficient of kinetic friction because the cylinder is sliding is μ . The cylinder rolls and slides on the ground, and eventually rolls without slipping.

C. How long does it take to cease slipping between the cylinder and floor?

4. A l.0 kilogram object is moving horizontally with a velocity of 10 m/s, as shown below, when it makes a glancing collision with the lower end of a bar that was hanging vertically at rest before the collision. The collision is elastic for the system. The bar, which has a length of 1.2 meters and a mass m of 3.0 kilograms, is pivoted about the upper end. Immediately after the collision the object moves with speed v at an angle θ relative to its original direction. The bar swings freely, and after the collision reaches a maximum angle of 90° with respect to the vertical. The moment of inertia of the bar about the pivot is $I_{bar} = ml^2/3$, ignoring all friction. You may use g=10m/s².

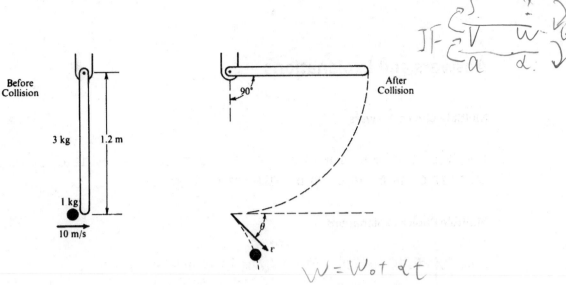

Before Collision

3 kg   1.2 m

1 kg

10 m/s

After Collision

90°

θ

r

$W = W_o + \alpha t$

$IF \frac{\varepsilon^j}{\varepsilon_a} \frac{V}{a} \frac{\dot{u}}{\alpha} \frac{\dot{\omega}}{\dot{\omega}}$

A. What is the angular velocity of the bar immediately after the collision?

B. What is the speed v of the I kilogram object immediately after the collision? $V = V_o + at$

C. Determine the magnitude of the angular momentum of the object about the pivot just after the collision.

D. Determine the angle θ. θ

5. The diagram above shows a solid uniform cylinder of mass M and radius R rolling without slipping down an incline plane of inclined angle θ. A thread wraps around the cylinder as it rolls down the plane and pulls a block of mass m upward.
Ignore the rotational inertia of the pulley.

A. What is the relationship between the magnitude of the acceleration of the block and the linear acceleration of the cylinder?

B. What is the acceleration of the cylinder?

C. What is the minimum coefficient of friction that will allow the cylinder to roll without slipping on this incline?

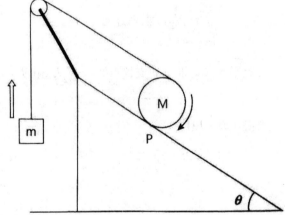

m

M

P

θ

Answers and Explanations

Multiple Choice Answers

1. A   2. D   3. C   4. B   5. B   6. E   7. D   8. C   9. C   10. B   11. C   12. C   13. D   14. B   15. D
16. C   17. C   18. D   19. C   20. D   21. E   22. C   23. C   24. E

Multiple Choice Explanations

1. A。物体受到指向转动中心的向心力，此向心力由摩擦力提供。

2. D。合外力矩改变物体的转动状态，合外力改变物体的平动状态。

3. C。合外力矩 $\tau_{net} = 12*0.14 - (10+9)*0.25 = -3.55 N*m$，负号：$\tau_{net}$ 使物体做顺时针转动。

4. B。光滑竖直墙面施加水平方向支持力作用于梯子上 N_2；水平地面施加于梯子竖直向上的支持力 N_1 和指向光滑竖直墙的静摩擦力 f= μN_1。梯子不滑动处于平衡状态，有力平衡：

$$mg = N_1，竖直方向$$

$$f = N_2，水平方向$$

力矩平衡（地面上的支撑点）：$N_2 L \sin\theta - mg\frac{L}{2}\cos\theta = 0$

求得：$\theta \approx 60^0$

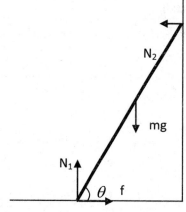

5. B。对墙面上的连接点，力矩平衡：$Tl\sin 60^0 = 120\frac{l}{2} \rightarrow T$ =69N

6. E。$I = \sum_i m_i r_i^2$，转动惯量不会被抵消。

7. D。保龄球纯滚动：$v = \omega R$，$\omega = 40$ rad/s. $E_k = \frac{1}{2}mv^2 + \frac{1}{2}I\omega^2 = 56$J

8. C。平动：mg−T=ma

转动：TR=I$\dfrac{a}{R}$

求得：$a = \frac{2}{3}g = 6.5 m/s^2$

9. C。系统角动量守恒，人和平台转动方向相反，角速度不同。

10. B。$\tau = mg\frac{L}{2} = \frac{1}{3}mL^2\alpha$，$\rightarrow \alpha = \frac{3g}{2L}$

11. C。$\tau = I\alpha$，$\omega = \alpha t$，$E_k = \frac{1}{2}I\omega^2 = 5.0$J

12. C。动能 $E_k = \frac{1}{2}mv^2 + \frac{1}{2}I\omega^2$，与物体速度和角速度都相关。

13. D。$\omega = \alpha_1 t_1$，$0 = \omega + \alpha_2 t_2 \rightarrow \dfrac{\alpha_1}{\alpha_2} = \dfrac{t_2}{t_1} = -2$

14. B。$mg\frac{l}{2}\sin\theta = Tl\sin\theta$，$\rightarrow m = \frac{2T}{g}$

15. D。$T(L-x)\sin\theta = mgL$，$\rightarrow T = \dfrac{mgL}{(L-x)\sin\theta}$

16. C。机械能 mgh=$\frac{1}{2}mv^2 + \frac{1}{2}I\omega^2 = \frac{1}{2}(mR^2 + I)\omega^2$ 为常量，转动惯量大的物体，转动动能大，即空心圆柱的转动动能最大。

17. C。mgh=$\frac{1}{2}mv^2 + \frac{1}{2}(\frac{1}{2}mR^2)\dfrac{v^2}{R^2}$，$\rightarrow$v=$\sqrt{\dfrac{4}{3}gh} = 4 m/s$

18. D。I=$m(\sqrt{5})^2 + 3m(\sqrt{5})^2 + 2m(1)^2 = 22m$

19. C。绕质心的转动惯量为最小。

20. D。 $mgh = \dfrac{1}{2}I\omega^2$, $\quad \to \omega = \sqrt{\dfrac{2mgh}{I}}$

21. E。 角速度 $\omega = \dfrac{d\theta}{dt} = 4t + 3$，当 t=3s 时：$\omega = 15$rad/s, 角动量 L=I$\omega$ =60kgm²/s

22. C。 $\Delta E = \dfrac{1}{2}I_0\omega_0^2 - \dfrac{1}{2}I\omega^2$ =240 J

23. C。 平行轴定理：$I = I_{cm} + Md^2 = \dfrac{1}{12}ML^2 + M(\dfrac{L}{4})^2 = \dfrac{7}{48}ML^2$

24. E。 系统的转动惯量 $I = 2m(2L)^2 + \dfrac{1}{12}4m(4L)^2 + 4mL^2 + \dfrac{1}{12}2m(2L)^2 = 18mL^2$

系统的角动量为 $I\omega = 18mL^2\omega$

Free Response Explanations

1. A.

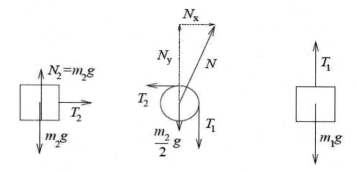

滑轮与绳的接触力 N 的分量：$N_x = T_2$ 和 $N_y = m_2g/2 + T_1$

B. $T_2 = m_2a = m_2\left(\dfrac{g}{2}\right)$

C.

$$R(T_1 - T_2) = I\alpha \quad I = \dfrac{1}{2}\dfrac{m_2}{2}R^2 \quad \alpha = \dfrac{a}{R}$$

$$R\left(T_1 - m_2\dfrac{g}{2}\right) = I\dfrac{a}{R} = \dfrac{Ig}{2R} = \dfrac{m_2gR}{8}$$

$$\Rightarrow T_1 = \dfrac{m_2g}{8} + \dfrac{m_2g}{2} = \dfrac{5}{8}m_2g$$

D.

$$m_1 g - T_1 = m_1 a = m_1 \frac{g}{2}$$

$$m_1 \frac{g}{2} = T_1 = \frac{5}{8} m_2 g \Rightarrow m_1 = \frac{5}{4} m_2$$

2. A. $\tau_p = \left| \vec{\tau}_p \times F \right| = -bMg \sin \theta$

B. $I_p = I_c + Mb^2 = \frac{1}{2} MR^2 + Mb^2$

C.

$$\sum \tau_p = I_p \alpha$$

$$-bMg \sin \theta = \left(\frac{1}{2} MR^2 + Mb^2 \right) \alpha$$

$$\Rightarrow \frac{d^2 \theta}{dt^2} + \frac{bg}{\frac{1}{2} R^2 + b^2} \sin \theta = 0$$

D. （本问题解答需学习完第八章内容）对小角度近似情况：$\sin \theta \approx \theta$，上述动力学方程

$\frac{d^2 \theta}{dt^2} + \frac{bg}{\frac{1}{2} R^2 + b^2} \theta = 0$ 表明物体做简谐运动。

角频率： $\omega = \sqrt{\dfrac{bg}{\frac{1}{2} R^2 + b^2}}$. 周期： $T = \dfrac{2\pi}{\omega} = 2\pi \sqrt{\dfrac{\frac{1}{2} R^2 + b^2}{bg}}$.

E. 一定有力作用在 P 点。否则质心将加速下落，不会转动。

3. A. 细绳作用于圆柱体上的作用力为T，对圆柱体在竖直平动方向上应用牛顿第二定律，有：

Mg-T=Ma   (1)

且圆柱体同时在绳子的作用力下发生转动，应用转动第二定律，有：

TR=$\frac{1}{2} mR^2 \alpha$ (2)

平动加速度和转动加速度的关系：

a=Rα (3)

解方程（1）、（2）、（3）得：

$$a = \frac{2}{3}g$$

B. 应用能量守恒定律，且有 $v = \omega R$：

$$Mgh = \frac{1}{2}Mv^2 + \frac{1}{2}I\omega^2$$

求得：$\omega = \sqrt{\dfrac{4gh}{3R^2}}$

C. 令圆柱体落地瞬间，时间 t=0。在停止滑动前任意时刻 t：

圆柱体受到摩擦力矩 $\tau = I\alpha = -\mu MgR \rightarrow \alpha = -\dfrac{2\mu g}{R}$

$\rightarrow \omega = \omega_0 + \alpha t = \sqrt{\dfrac{4gh}{3R^2}} - \dfrac{2\mu g}{R}t$ （角速度随时间变化规律）

圆柱体受摩擦力作用，方向与物体运动方向相同：

$F = \mu Mg = Ma \rightarrow a = \mu g \rightarrow v = at = \mu gt$ （速度随时间变化规律）

圆柱体无滑动的条件是：$v = \omega R$

求得：t= $\sqrt{\dfrac{4h}{27\mu^2 g}}$

4. A. 与物体碰撞后的棒获得动能后，运动到水平位置，在此过程中机械能守恒：

$$\frac{1}{2}I\omega^2 = Mg\frac{l}{2}, \quad \rightarrow \omega = \sqrt{\frac{3g}{l}} = 5\,rad/s$$

B. 物体和棒发生弹性碰撞，碰撞前后动能守恒：

$$\frac{1}{2}mv_0^2 = \frac{1}{2}mv^2 + \frac{1}{2}I\omega^2, \quad 求得：v = \sqrt{v_0^2 - \frac{M}{m}gl} = 8\,m/s$$

C. 物体和棒发生碰撞，角动量守恒：

$$mv_0 l = mvl\cos\theta + I\omega,$$

求得碰撞后物体的角动量 L=$mv_0l - I\omega$ =4.8 kgm²/s

D. L=$mvl\cos\theta$=4.8 kgm²/s，得 $\theta = 60^0$

5. A. 物体 m 的上升速度等于绕圆柱体的绳子的速度,而绳子的速度等于绳子与圆柱体的切点的圆柱体的速度，这个速度等于圆柱质心运动的速度的 2 倍，$v_B = 2v_{cm} = 2\omega R$（$v_{cm} = \omega R$ 是圆柱体无滑动滚动的条件）；所以物体 m 的加速度等于圆柱体质心加速度的 2 倍，$a_B = 2a_{cm}$。

B. 设绳子中的张力为 T，圆柱与斜面的摩擦力为 f，斜面给圆柱体的支持力为 N。

T-mg=2ma_{cm}，　　　　　　(1)牛顿第二定律应用于物体 m。

Mgsinθ-T-f=Ma_{cm}，　　　　　(2)牛顿第二定律应用于圆柱体平动。

fR-TR=$I\alpha = \frac{1}{2}MR^2\frac{a_{cm}}{R}$，(3) 转动定律应用于圆柱体的转动。

解方程（1）、（2）、（3）得 $a_{cm} = \dfrac{M\sin\theta - 2m}{\frac{3}{2}M + 4m}$

C. f是静摩擦力有f≤$\mu_s N$，N=Mgcosθ

从上述方程可解得：f=Mgsinθ-mg-（2m+M）a_{cm}

令f=$\mu_s N$ then μ_s=f/N

这是允许圆柱体无滑动滚动的最小摩擦系数。

Introduction: In this chapter we study the law of universal gravitation. We emphasize a description of planetary motion because astronomical data provide an important test of this law's validity. We then show that the laws of planetary motion developed by Johannes Kepler follow from the law of universal gravitation and the concept of conservation of angular momentum. We conclude by deriving a general expression for gravitational potential energy and examining the energy of planetary and satellite motion.

7.1 Newton's Law of Universal Gravitation
7.1 牛顿万有引力定律

7.1.1 Law of Universal Gravitation
7.1.1 万有引力定律

If the force of gravity is being exerted on objects on Earth, what is the origin of that force? In 1687 Newton published his work on the law of gravity in his treatise *Mathematical Principles of Natural Philosophy*. Newton's law of universal gravitation states that:

Every particle in the universe attracts every other particle with a force that is proportional to the product of their masses and inversely proportional to the square of the distance between them. This force acts along the line joining the two particles.

$$F = G\frac{m_1 m_2}{r^2}$$

Where G=$6.67\times10^{-11}\,\mathrm{N\cdot m^2/kg^2}$

The magnitude of the gravitational constant G can be measured in the laboratory by the Cavendish experiment. The law of universal gravitation can be written in full **vector form:**

牛顿在自然哲学的数学原理一书中给出万有引力定律：

$$F = G\frac{m_1 m_2}{r^2}$$

引力常数 G 由 Cavendish 实验测定。

万有引力定律向量形式：

$$\vec{F}_{1on2} = -G\frac{m_1 m_2}{r^2}\vec{r}_{0\,1to2}$$

$$\vec{F}_{1on2} = -G\frac{m_1m_2}{r^2}\vec{r}_{0\,1to2}$$

$\vec{r}_{0\,1to2}$ is a unit vector pointing from m_1 to m_2. Thus, the two masses attract each other along a line joining them.

$\vec{r}_{0\,1to2}$：由 1 指向 2 方向的单位向量。两物体相互吸引。

From the equation above, we can see that the gravitational force exerted by a finite-size, spherically symmetric mass distribution on a particle outside the distribution is the same as if the entire mass of the distribution were concentrated at the center.

球体（球壳）对外部物体的引力，球体（球壳）可看作质量集中在质心的质点。

For example, the magnitude of the force exerted by the Earth on a particle of mass m near the Earth's surface is:

$$F_g = G\frac{mM_E}{R_E^2} = ma_g$$

$$a_g = \frac{GM_E}{R_E^2} = g = 9.8\,\text{m}/\text{s}^2$$

The acceleration due to gravity varies over the Earth's surface due to altitude, local geology, and the shape of the Earth, which is not quite spherical.

The gravitational force of a hollow sphere which has mass M and radius R exerts on a point mass m inside the sphere is Zero. For solid sphere, the gravitational force exerted on an object inside any spherically symmetric mass distribution a distance r from the center is the same as if all the mass located inside an imaginary sphere of radius r (the enclosed mass) were concentrated at its center and all the mass distributed outside this imaginary sphere did not exist.

空心球壳（半径为 R，质量为 M）对质点 m 引力：

$$F = G\frac{mM}{r^2} \qquad \text{r>R}$$

$$F = 0 \qquad\qquad \text{r<R}$$

Example 7.1: A sphere which has mass M and radius R has a constant mass density ρ. Calculate the gravitational force on a point mass m as a function of distance r from the center of M.

实心球 M 对质点 m 引力。

Solution:

The force has different forms inside and outside the sphere, so we have to treat these situations separately.

a. For the force experienced by the point mass m inside the sphere r <R:

Mass enclosed within a sphere of radius r,

质点 m 位于球面内，r<R：只有半径为 r 的球面内的质量对质点 m 有引力作用，半径为 r 的球面之外的质量对质点 m 无引力作用。

$$m_r = \rho v = \frac{M}{(4/3)\pi R^3} \cdot \frac{4}{3}\pi r^3 = \frac{r^3}{R^3}M$$

this mass acts as if it is all located at the center of the sphere.

$$F = G\frac{m_1 m_2}{r^2} = G\frac{mm_r}{r^2} = G\frac{mM}{R^3}r \qquad r < R$$

The force function is a linear function inside the sphere. Because of symmetry, when m is located at the center, the force is zero.

b. For the force experienced by the point mass m outside the sphere r ≥ R

All the mass of the sphere acts as if it is at the center of the sphere outside the sphere

$$F = G\frac{m_1 m_2}{r^2} = G\frac{mM}{r^2} \qquad r \ge R$$

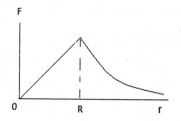

Figure 7-1 Gravitational force inside and outside a sphere

7.1.2 Gravitational Field

How is it possible for two objects to interact when they were not in contact with each other? The concept of field that exists at every point in space tells that when a particle of mass *m* is placed at a point where the gravitational field is g, the particle experiences a force $F_g = mg$. In other words, *the field exerts a force on the particle*.

If we want to measure the gravitational field at any point, we place a small "test" mass m at the point and measure the force F exerted on it, then the gravitational field, g, at the point is defined as:

$$\vec{g} = \frac{\vec{F}_g}{m}$$

The unit of g is N/kg (which is equivalent with unit m/s²).

At the example 7.1, the gravitational field strength created by sphere M is:

$$g = \frac{F_g}{m} = G\frac{M}{R^3}r \qquad r<R$$

7.1.2 引力场g

引力场对处于其中的物体 m 施加力的作用。

引力场强定义：$\vec{g} = \frac{\vec{F}_g}{m}$

单位质量物体所受到引力，方向与引力方向一致。
引力场强单位：N/kg
实心球体引力场强分布：
类同图 7-1

$$g = \frac{F_g}{m} = G\frac{M}{R^3}r \qquad r<R$$

$$g = \frac{F_g}{m} = G\frac{M}{r^2} \qquad r \geq R:$$

Vector form of gravitational strength:

$$\vec{g} = \frac{\vec{F_g}}{m} = -\frac{GM_E}{r^2}\hat{r}$$

The gravitational field strength g at any point in space does not depend on the value of our test mass, m, placed at that point, g depends only on the masses and locations of the bodies that create the field there.

Figure 7-2 (a) shows that the gravitational field vectors near a uniform spherical mass such as the Earth vary in both direction and magnitude. The vectors point in the direction of the acceleration a particle would experience if it were placed in the field. The magnitude of the field vector at any location is the magnitude of the free-fall acceleration at that location. Figure 7-2 (b) shows that the gravitational field vectors in a small region near the Earth's surface are regarded as uniform in both direction and magnitude.

Actually, the acceleration due to gravity varies slightly over the Earth's surface due to altitude, local geology, and the shape of the Earth, which is not quite spherical.

$$g = \frac{F_g}{m} = G\frac{M}{r^2} \qquad r \geq R$$

引力场强向量形式：

$$\vec{g} = \frac{\vec{F_g}}{m} = -\frac{GM_E}{r^2}\vec{r}$$

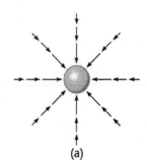

(a)

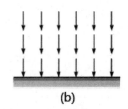

(b)

Figure 7-2 Gravitational field

地球表面附近是近似的匀强引力场，场强大小是重力加速度。

7.2 Gravitation Potential Energy

7.2 引力势能

Before we calculate this general form for the gravitational potential energy function, let us verify that *the gravitational force is conservative.* To do this, we first note that the gravitational force is a central force. By definition, a central force is always directed along one of the radial segments; Figure 7-3, therefore, the work done by **F** along any radial segment is

$$dW = \mathbf{F} \cdot d\mathbf{r} = F(r)\, dr$$

The work done by the universal gravitational force on a body that moves along an arbitrary path from the initial position to the final position is given by

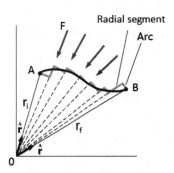

Figure 7-3 Work done by a central force

$$W = \int_{r_i}^{r_f} \left(-G\frac{Mm}{r^2} \right) dr = GMm \left(\frac{1}{r_f} - \frac{1}{r_i} \right)$$

$$W = GMm \left(\frac{1}{r_f} - \frac{1}{r_i} \right)$$

This indicates that the universal gravitational force is a conservative force. We can define the work as the negative value of increment of the universal gravitational potential energy during the process, that is:

万有引力做功与路径无关，是保守力。

$$W = -\left(\left(-\frac{GMm}{r_f} \right) - \left(-\frac{GMm}{r_i} \right) \right) = -\left(U_f - U_i \right)$$

保守力的功等于与其相应的势能增量的负值。

可引入相应的势能函数。

If we take U =0 at r=∞ as the reference of zero potential, the mutual gravitational potential energy of the system(m and M) is equal to the work done by the force when it moves from position r to infinity, that is

引力势能：$U = -\dfrac{GMm}{r}$

势能零点在无限远 U(0)=0

$$U_r = \int_r^\infty (-\frac{GMm}{r^2}) dr = -\frac{GMm}{r}$$

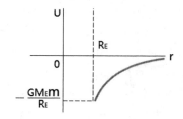

Figure 7-4 引力势能函数

Although the equation above was derived for the particle-Earth system, it can be applied to any two particles. That is, the gravitational potential energy associated with any pair of particles separated by a distance *r*. We will find that the potential energy of weight can be treated as a special case of universal gravitational potential energy as we have already got

重力势能是引力势能的特殊形式：$U = mgh$

$$U = mgh$$

When two particles are at rest and separated by a distance *r*, an external agent has to supply an energy at least equal to +Gm_1m_2/r in order to separate the particles to an infinite distance. It is therefore convenient to think of the absolute value of the potential energy as the *binding energy* of the system. If the external agent supplies energy greater than the binding energy, the excess energy of the system will be in the form of kinetic energy of the particles when the particles are at an infinite separation.

势能是系统结合能。

We can extend this concept to three or more particles. In this case, the total potential energy of the system is the sum over all pairs of particles. Each pair contributes a term of the form given by

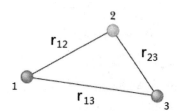

Figure 7-5 三个物体组成的系统的势能

equation above. For example, if the system contains three particles we find that

$$U_{total} = U_{12} + U_{13} + U_{23} = -G\left(\frac{m_1 m_2}{r_{12}} + \frac{m_1 m_3}{r_{13}} + \frac{m_2 m_3}{r_{23}}\right)$$

The absolute value of U_{total} represents the work needed to separate the particles by an infinite distance.

势能的绝对值是分开这些物体为无限远时，外力所做功。

Example 7.2: Three masses of magnitude m are located at the vertices of an equilateral triangle with sides of lengths s. How much energy is required to separate these masses an infinite distance apart from each other?

Solution:

Energy stored in the three pairs of masses is

$$U = -3\frac{Gmm}{s}$$

When the masses are separated, the minimum energy they can have is U=0. Therefore, the minimum amount of energy required to separate the masses is $3\frac{Gmm}{s}$.

If more energy is added, the masses can still be infinitely separated but will be left with some kinetic energy.

7.3 Kepler's Laws

7.3 开普勒定律

People have observed the movements of the planets, stars, and other celestial objects for thousands of years. After 20 years of work on Tycho Brahe's data, Johannes Kepler, the German theorist , completed analysis of planetary motion and summarized in three statements known as Kepler's laws:

1. The path of each planet about the Sun is an ellipse with the Sun at one focus.

The semimajor axis has length a, and the semiminor axis has length b，shown in Figure7-6. Each focus is located at a distance c from the center on each side of the center.

2. The radius vector drawn from the Sun to a planet sweeps out

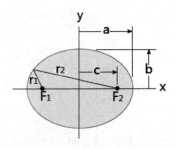

Figure 7-6 Kepler's First law

1. 行星绕太阳的轨道是以太阳为一个焦点的椭圆轨道运动。

2. 太阳到行星的连线矢量

equal areas in equal time intervals (Figure 7-7).

$$\frac{dA}{dt} = \text{constant}$$

It is important to recognize that this result is a consequence of the fact that the gravitational force is a central force, which in turn implies that angular momentum of the planet is constant.

3. The square of the orbital period of any planet is proportional to the cube of the semimajor axis of the elliptical orbit (or radius, for circular orbits).

$$\frac{T_1^2}{r_1^3} = \frac{T_2^2}{r_2^3} = \text{constant}$$

A planet of mass m is moving about the Sun M in a circular orbit with radius r. Newton's second law gives:

$$G\frac{mM}{r^2} = m\frac{v^2}{r}$$

The speed v = 2πr/T, with T is the period of the planet.

$$G\frac{mM}{r^2} = m\frac{v^2}{r} \Rightarrow G\frac{M}{r} = \left(\frac{2\pi r}{T}\right)^2 \Rightarrow$$

$$T^2 = \frac{4\pi^2}{GM}r^3 = K_s r^3$$

Kepler's third law gives us a method for measuring the mass of the Sun.

$$M_s = \frac{4\pi^2}{GK_s} = \frac{4\pi^2 r^3}{GT^2}$$

The orbits of all planets except Mercury and Pluto are nearly circular in our solar system.

Example 7.3: Mars, the planet farther than the Earth from the Sun, has an orbital period that is

a. greater than a year.

单位时间扫过相同面积：

$$\frac{dA}{dt} = \text{constant}$$

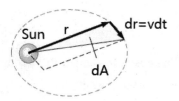

Figure7-7 Kepler's second law

3. 转动周期平方正比于椭圆长半轴（或圆半径）立方：

$$\frac{T_1^2}{r_1^3} = \frac{T_2^2}{r_2^3} = \text{constant}$$

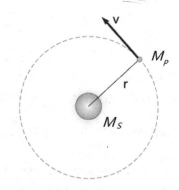

Figure 7-8 A planet of mass m moving in a circular orbit around the Sun.

开普勒第三定律可测太阳的质量： $M_s = \frac{4\pi^2 r^3}{GT^2}$

太阳系行星除了水星和冥王星外的其他行星都是近似的圆周轨道。

b. less than a year.

c. equal to a year.

Solution:

According to Kepler's third law, the answer is a.

Example 7.4: A satellite moves in an elliptical orbit about the Earth such that, at *perigee and apogee* positions, its distances from the Earth's center are respectively D and $4D$. The relationship between the speeds at these two positions is

近地点和远地点

a. $v_p = v_a$

b. $v_p = 4v_a$

c. $v_a = 4v_p$

d. $v_p = 2v_a$

e. $v_a = 2v_p$

Solution:

b. Conservation of angular momentum.

7.4 Orbits of Planets and Satellites   7.4 行星和卫星运动

If an isolated system consists of an object of mass m moving with a speed v in the *vicinity* of a massive object of mass M, the total energy E of the system is the sum of the kinetic and potential energies. The expression for the total energy of a satellite in an orbit of radius r can be derived as follow.

附近

The centripetal force on the satellite is provided by the gravitational attraction of the earth.

卫星圆周运动向心力由万有引力提供:

$$G\frac{mM}{r^2} = m\frac{v^2}{r} \quad \Rightarrow$$

$$K = \frac{1}{2}mv^2 = \frac{GmM}{2r}$$

$$G\frac{mM}{r^2} = m\frac{v^2}{r}$$

卫星轨道运动动能:

$$K = \frac{GmM}{2r}$$

Gravitational potential energy is

$$U = -\frac{GmM}{r}$$

The total energy of the satellite is

$$E = K + U = -\frac{GmM}{2r} \qquad \text{circular orbit}$$

The total energy is negative and a constant for the motion. If the object moves in an elliptical orbit of semimajor axis a around the massive object and if $M \gg m$, the total energy of the system is

$$E = -\frac{GmM}{2a} \qquad \text{elliptical orbit}$$

The escape speed for an object projected from the surface of a planet of mass M and radius R is happened when the total mechanical energy is zero E=0.

$$E = \frac{1}{2}mv^2 - G\frac{mM}{R} = 0$$

so we have escape speed $\quad v = \sqrt{\frac{2GM}{R}}$

The escape speed from the surface of the Earth is V=11.2km/s. This explains why the Earth doesn't retain the lighter molecules, like Hydrogen and Helium, which have a higher speed than heavier molecules at the same temperature.

When one body orbits another, both bodies (m_1 and m_2) orbit around their center of mass (a point called the barycenter) with same angular velocity and period. Kapler's third law for the orbiting

system is: $\quad \dfrac{T^2}{(R_1 + R_2)^3} = \dfrac{4\pi^2}{G(m_1 + m_2)}$

R_1 and R_2 are radius of circular motion respectively about the barycenter.

Example 7.5 A Geosynchronous Satellite: Consider a satellite of mass m moving in a circular orbit around the Earth at a constant speed v and at an altitude h above the Earth's surface.

势能：$U = -\dfrac{GmM}{r}$

卫星总能量：$E = -\dfrac{GmM}{2r}$

椭圆轨道运动卫星总能量：

$$E = -\frac{GmM}{2a}$$

a：椭圆长半轴

物体脱离地球的引力 E=0

地球表面物体逃逸速度：

$$v = \sqrt{\frac{2GM}{R}} = 11.2\text{km/s}$$

双星运动：两物体都绕着他们的质心在运动，具有相同的角速度和周期。

同步卫星

a. Determine the speed of the satellite in terms of G, h, R_E (the radius of the Earth), and M_E (the mass of the Earth).

b. If the satellite is to be *geosynchronous* (that is, appearing to remain over a fixed position on the Earth), how fast is it moving through space?

Solution:

a. The gravitational force of the satellite and the Earth acts as the centripetal force of the satellite:

$$G\frac{mM}{r^2} = m\frac{v^2}{r} \implies v = \sqrt{\frac{GM}{r}} = \sqrt{\frac{GM}{r_e + h}}$$

b. In order to appear to remain over a fixed position on the Earth, the period of the satellite must be 24 h and the satellite must be in orbit directly over the equator. From Kepler's third law we find the radius of the orbit:

$$T^2 = \frac{4\pi^2}{GM}r^3 \implies r = \sqrt[3]{\frac{GMT^2}{4\pi^2}} = 4.23 \times 10^7 \text{m}$$

And $v = \sqrt{\frac{GM}{r}} = \sqrt{\frac{GM}{r_e + h}} = 3.07 \times 10^3 \text{m/s}$

The value of r calculated here translates to a height of the satellite above the surface of the Earth of almost h=36 000 km.

Example 7.6 Changing the Orbit of a Satellite
The space shuttle releases a 470kg communications satellite while in an orbit 280 km above the surface of the Earth. A rocket engine on the satellite boosts it into a geosynchronous orbit, which is an orbit in which the satellite stays directly over a single location on the Earth. How much energy does the engine have to provide?
Solution:

The space shuttle at initial position

$$r_i = h + r_e = 6.65 \times 10^6 \text{m}$$

And the geosynchronous satellite's energy is

$$E = -\frac{GmM}{2r_i};$$

The satellite's finial position given at previous example

$$r_f = 4.23 * 10^7 m$$

And its total energy is

$$E = -\frac{GmM}{2r_f};$$

The energy required from the engine to boost the satellite is

$$\Delta E = E_f - E_i = -\frac{GmM}{2}(\frac{1}{r_f} - \frac{1}{r_i}) = 1.19 * 10^{10} J$$

Example 7.7 Escape Speed of a Rocket: Calculate the escape speed from the Earth for a 5000kg spacecraft, and determine the kinetic energy it must have at the Earth's surface in order to move infinitely far away from the Earth.

Solution:

a. The escape speed $v = \sqrt{\frac{2GM}{R}}$ =11.2km/s

b. The kinetic energy of the spacecraft is $K = \frac{1}{2}mv^2$ =3.14*10^{11}J

第七章总结 万有引力定律

1. 万有引力定律

1）相距为 r、质量为 m 和 M 的两个质点之间的作用引力为

$$F = G\frac{mM}{r^2}$$

引力场强 $g = \dfrac{F}{m} = G\dfrac{M}{r^2}$

2）球体和球壳（质量为 M，半径为 R）

质量为 m 的物体和球壳之间的引力为：$F = G\dfrac{mM}{r^2}$　$r > R$

$$F = 0 \qquad r < R$$

质量为 m 的物体和球体之间的引力为：$F = G\dfrac{mM}{r^2}$　$r > R$

$$F = G\frac{mM}{R^3}r \quad r < R$$

2. 引力势能 $U = -G\dfrac{mM}{r}$

3. 圆周轨道运动： $F_g = F_c$，万有引力作为圆周运动的向心力，机械能和角动量守恒。

由　$G\dfrac{mM}{r^2} = m\dfrac{v^2}{r}$，有 $v = \sqrt{\dfrac{GM}{r}}$，$V = \dfrac{2\pi r}{T}$，　T 是轨道运动周期

$K = \dfrac{1}{2}mv^2 = G\dfrac{mM}{2r}$，$E_m = K + U = -G\dfrac{mM}{2r}$

4. 一般轨道运动

系统的总能量小于零。两个物体若想脱离相互的吸引，$K \geq |U|$

若 $E_m = 0$　那么 $v_{escape} = \sqrt{\dfrac{2GM}{r}}$，m 脱离 M 的束缚。

双星系统：万有引力作为行星轨道运动的向心力。

5. 开普勒定律

第一定律：所有行星都做椭圆轨道运动

第二定律：行星轨道运动的角动量守恒

第三定律：$\dfrac{T^2}{r^3} = \dfrac{4\pi^2}{GM} =$ 常数

Chapter 7 Newton's Law of Gravity Practice

Multiple Choice Questions

1. Two planets have the same mass, but different radii, and no atmospheres. Which of the following would be the same for objects of equal mass and size on the surfaces of the two planets? Ignore any friction force.

   I. The rate of free fall
   II. The escape speed
   III. The amount of momentum each would acquire when given a certain impulse.

   A. I only
   B. III only
   C. I and III only
   D. II and III only
   E. I, II, and III

2. An object has a weight W when it is on the surface of the Earth (radius = R). When the same object is a distance $2R$ from the center of the Earth, its weight will be

   A. $4W$
   B. $2W$
   C. W
   D. $W/2$
   E. $W/4$

3. What is the total energy of a satellite of mass m that orbits a planet of mass M in an elliptical orbit with semi-major axis a?

   A. $-GMm/2a$
   B. $-GMm/a$
   C. $GMm/4a$
   D. $GMm/2a$
   E. GMm/a

4. A satellite in orbit around the Earth has a period of one hour. An identical satellite is placed in an orbit having a radius which is nine times the first satellite's radius. What is the period of the second satellite?

   A. 1/9 hr
   B. 1/3 hr
   C. 3 hr
   D. 9 hr
   E. 27 hr

5. A satellite moves in a circular orbit around a planet at a constant speed. Which of the following must be true?

   I. The net force on the satellite is always radially inward.
   II. The net work done on the satellite in the interval of half an orbit is zero.
   III. The angular momentum of the satellite is constant.

   A. I only
   B. III only
   C. I and III, only
   D. II and III, only
   E. I, II, and III

6. The gravitational potential energy of an object is -12.0 J when it is on the surface of a planet. How much work does it take to move it at a constant speed to a location one planet diameter above the surface of the planet?

   A. 12.0J
   B. 4.00J
   C. − 4.00J

D. 15.0J

E. 8.00J

7.

A large, massive, satellite is hollow, with all of its mass M located at radius R from its center, as shown above. Which graph best represents the force of gravity experienced by an astronaut at a distance r from the center of the satellite, where r goes from 0 to ∞?

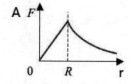

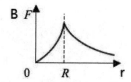

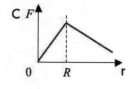

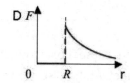

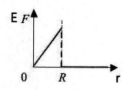

8. The escape speed for a rocket at Earth's surface is v_e. For that same rocket to launch from Saturn, with a radius approximately 10 times that of the Earth, and a mass approximately 100 times that of the Earth, what escape velocity is required?

A. $\dfrac{\sqrt{10}}{v_e}$

B. $\sqrt{10}\,v_e$

C. $10\,v_e$

D. $\dfrac{v_e}{10}$

E. $1000\,v_e$

9. In order for a satellite to be geosynchronous, its orbit must

A. go over the North and South Poles.

B. be over the equator.

C. be over a single longitude.

D. emit television signals.

E. be none of the above.

10. A satellite following an elliptical path around a planet has a velocity v_{far} when at its maximum distance d units from the planet's center. At its closest point, the distance between the satellite and planet's center is d/3. The satellite's velocity at that closest point is

A. $v_{far}/3$

B. v_{far}

C. $\sqrt{3}v_{far}$

D. $3v_{far}$

E. $9v_{far}$

11. A planet has a mass that is double mass of the Earth. The radius of the Earth is R. The gravitational field strength at the surface of the planet is equal to that at the surface of the Earth. The radius of the planet is equal to

A. R/2

B. R

C. $\sqrt{2}$ R

D. 2R

E. 4R

12. The moon has mass M and radius R. A small object is dropped from a height of R/2 from the Moon's surface. The object's impact speed when it strikes the surface of the Moon is

A. $\dfrac{2}{3}\sqrt{\dfrac{GM}{R}}$

B. $\sqrt{\dfrac{2GM}{3R}}$

C. $\sqrt{\dfrac{2GM}{R}}$

D. $\sqrt{\dfrac{GM}{R}}$

E. $\sqrt{\dfrac{GM}{3R}}$

Free Response Questions

1. Imagine a spherical, non-rotating planet of mass M and radius R. The planet has no atmosphere. A spacecraft of mass m (m $\ll$ M) is launched from the surface of the planet with speed v_0 at an angle of 30^0 to the local vertical.

   A. The speed v_0 is so high that the orbit is not bound. What is the minimum speed for which this is the case?

   Now imagine that the orbit is bound and that in its subsequent orbit the spacecraft reaches a maximum distance of 15R from the center of the planet. At this distance the speed is V.

   B. What is the ratio of v_0 / V ?

   C. What is the total energy of the spacecraft immediately after launch?

   D. What is the total energy of the spacecraft when it is farthest away from the planet?

   E. Write down one equation which would allow you to solve for v_0 in terms of M、G、and R.

2. A spacecraft of mass m kg is in an elliptical orbit about the Earth, as shown below. At point A the spacecraft is at a distance r_A from the center of the Earth and its velocity, of magnitude V_A, is perpendicular to the line connecting the center of the Earth to the spacecraft. The mass and radius of the Earth are M_E and r_E, respectively. Later the spacecraft is at point B on the exact opposite side of the orbit at a distance r_B from the center of the Earth. Assume that the gravitational potential energy is zero at an infinite distance from the Earth.

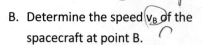

$$F = G\frac{Mm}{r^2} = mg$$
$$g = G\frac{M}{r^2}$$

$$\frac{mV_A^2}{2} + m\frac{GM}{r_A^2}\cdot r_A = \frac{mV_A^2}{2} + \frac{GMm}{r_A}$$

A. Determine the total mechanical energy of the spacecraft when it is at point A.

$$\frac{mV^2}{2} + mgh$$

B. Determine the speed v_B of the spacecraft at point B.

Suppose that a different spacecraft is at point A, a distance r_A from the center of the Earth. Determine each of the following.

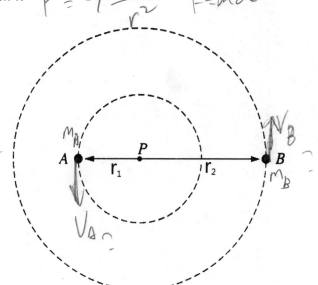

$$V = \sqrt{\frac{GM}{r}}$$

C. The speed of the spacecraft if it is in a circular orbit around the Earth

$$G\frac{Mm}{r^2} = \frac{mV^2}{r} \qquad mV^2 r^2 = GMmr.$$

D. The minimum speed of the spacecraft at point A if it is to escape completely from the Earth

3. A binary star system consists of two stars of mass m_1 and m_2 orbiting about each other. The orbits of the stars are circles of radii r_1 and r_2 centered on the center of mass of the system. Each star has the same period of revolution T.

$$F = G\frac{Mm}{r^2} \qquad F = ma$$

A. Make a drawing of the two orbits. Indicate the positions of the center of mass, and of the stars m_1 and m_2. Indicate the direction of motion for each star.

B. What is the magnitude of the gravitational force that m_1 exerts on m_2?

$$F = G\frac{Mm}{r^2}$$

C. What is the magnitude of the acceleration of m_1 and of m_2?

$$a = G\frac{M}{r^2} = \frac{F}{m}$$

D. Derive the orbital period of this binary system.

E. The angular momentum of the system about the center of mass.

F. Find the ratio of the speeds, v_2/v_1.

Suppose instead, the two star masses are equal $m_1 = m_2 = M$.

G. On the following diagram, show circular orbits for this star system.

4. The Mars Global Surveyor (GS) was in its orbit about Mars, sending data back to Earth. Assume a circular orbit with a period of $T = 7.08 \times 10^3$ s and orbital speed of $v = 3.40 \times 10^3$ m/s. The mass of the GS is $m = 930$ kg and the radius of Mars is $R = 3.43 \times 10^6$ m.

A. Determine the radius of the GS orbit.

B. Calculate the mass of Mars.

C. Determine the total mechanical energy of the GS in this orbit.

D. If the GS was to be placed in a lower circular orbit (closer to the surface of Mars), would the new orbital period of the GS be greater than or less than the given period? Justify your answer.

E. Actually, the orbit the GS entered was slightly elliptical with its closest approach to Mars at 3.71×10^5 m above the surface and its furthest distance at 4.36×10^5 m above the surface. If the speed of the GS at closest approach is 3.40×10^3 m/s, calculate the speed at the furthest point of the orbit.

Answers and Explanations

Multiple Choice Answers

1. B   2. E   3. A   4. E   5. E   6. E   7. D   8. B   9. B   10. D   11. C   12. B

Multiple Choice Explanations

1. B。两行星表面处的引力场强 $g = G\dfrac{M}{r^2}$，半径 r 不同，g 也不同。

2. E。距离 2R 处的重力$= G\dfrac{Mm}{r^2} = G\dfrac{Mm}{4R^2}$ =W/4

3. A。卫星的总机械能 $E = \dfrac{1}{2}mv^2 + \left(-G\dfrac{mM}{r}\right)$，万有引力作为卫星的向心力有：$G\dfrac{mM}{r^2} = m\dfrac{v^2}{r}$，

   得 $\dfrac{1}{2}mv^2 = G\dfrac{mM}{2r}$，$\rightarrow E = -G\dfrac{mM}{2r}$

4. E。开普勒第三定律：$\dfrac{T^2}{r^3} = \dfrac{T_0{}^2}{r_0{}^3}$，且 $r = 9r_0$，得 T=27Hr

5. E。卫星做圆周轨道运动，角动量守恒、向心力指向圆心且与速度垂直，即引力对卫星不做功。三个选项都对。

6. E。引力势能 $U = -G\dfrac{mM}{r}$，W$= \Delta U = -G\dfrac{mM}{3r} - \left(-G\dfrac{mM}{r}\right)$ =8J

7. D。宇航员进入卫星后，相互间引力为零。

8. B。$\dfrac{1}{2}mv_e^2 + \left(-G\dfrac{mM}{r}\right)$ =0, $v_e = \sqrt{\dfrac{2GM}{r}}$; $v_e' = \sqrt{\dfrac{2G100M}{10r}} = \sqrt{10}v_e$

9. B。同步卫星万有引力作为卫星绕地球的向心力，此力必须指向地球中心。

10. D。角动量守恒：$mv_{far}d = mvd/3$，$v = 3v_{far}$

11. C。$g = G\dfrac{M}{R} = G\dfrac{2M}{r^2}$，r=$\sqrt{2}$ R

12. B。物体在高度为 R/2 处和月球表面处的机械能守恒：$-G\dfrac{mM}{3R/2} = \dfrac{1}{2}mv^2 + (-G\dfrac{mM}{R})$，求

得 $v = \sqrt{\dfrac{2GM}{3R}}$

Free Response Explanations

1. A. $\dfrac{1}{2}mv^2 = G\dfrac{mM}{R} \rightarrow v = \sqrt{\dfrac{2MG}{R}}$

B. $mv_0 R\sin 30^0 = mV(15R) \rightarrow \dfrac{v_0}{V} = \dfrac{15}{\sin 30^0} = 30$

C. $\dfrac{1}{2}mv_0^2 - \dfrac{mMG}{R}$

D. same as in C or $\dfrac{1}{2}mV^2 - \dfrac{mMG}{15R} = \dfrac{1}{2}m\dfrac{v_0^2}{900} - \dfrac{mMG}{15R}$

E.
$\dfrac{1}{2}mv_0^2 - \dfrac{mMG}{R} = \dfrac{1}{2}m\dfrac{v_0^2}{900} - \dfrac{mMG}{15R}$

$\dfrac{1}{2}v_0^2 - \dfrac{MG}{R} = \dfrac{1}{2}\dfrac{v_0^2}{900} - \dfrac{MG}{15R}$

2. A. 飞船在 A 点的机械能 $E = \dfrac{1}{2}mv_A^2 + (-G\dfrac{mM_E}{r_A})$

B. 飞船椭圆轨道运动中角动量守恒：$mr_A v_A = mr_B v_B$，$\rightarrow v_B = \dfrac{r_A}{r_B}v_A$

C. 圆周轨道运动的向心力是万有引力：$G\dfrac{mM_E}{r_A^2} = m\dfrac{v_A^2}{r_A}$，得 $v_A = \sqrt{\dfrac{GM_E}{r_A}}$

D. 飞船逃逸最小速度 $v_{\min}$：$E = \dfrac{1}{2}mv_{\min}^2 + (-G\dfrac{mM_E}{r_A}) = 0$，求得 $v_{\min} = \sqrt{\dfrac{2GM_E}{r_A}}$

3. A.

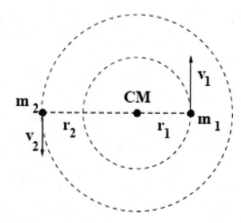

B. $F = \dfrac{Gm_1m_2}{(r_1+r_2)^2}$

C. $a_1 = \dfrac{F}{m_1} = \dfrac{Gm_2}{(r_1+r_2)^2}$, $a_2 = \dfrac{F}{m_2} = \dfrac{Gm_1}{(r_1+r_2)^2}$

D. 双星系统两星的角速度必相同，令其为 ω ，有 $a_1 = \dfrac{Gm_2}{(r_1+r_2)^2} = \omega^2 r_1$,

$a_2 = \dfrac{Gm_1}{(r_1+r_2)^2} = \omega^2 r_2$ $\rightarrow \omega^2 = \dfrac{G(m_1+m_2)}{(r_1+r_2)^3}$;

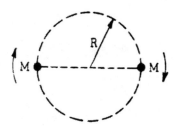

$\rightarrow T = \dfrac{2\pi}{\omega} = 2\pi\sqrt{\dfrac{(r_1+r_2)^3}{G(m_1+m_2)}}$

E. 双星系统的转动惯量 $I = m_1r_1^2 + m_2r_2^2$

双星系统的角动量 L$= I\omega = (m_1r_1^2 + m_2r_2^2)\sqrt{\dfrac{G(m_1+m_2)}{(r_1+r_2)^3}}$

F. 由 $m_1\dfrac{v_1^2}{r_1} = G\dfrac{m_1m_2}{(r_1+r_2)^2}$ 和 $m_2\dfrac{v_2^2}{r_2} = G\dfrac{m_1m_2}{(r_1+r_2)^2}$ ，得出

$\dfrac{v_2}{v_1} = \sqrt{\dfrac{m_1r_2}{m_2r_1}}$

G. $r_1 = r_2 = R$，双星系统的质心在两星连线的中点。

4. A. $T = \dfrac{2\pi r}{v}$，r：GS 的轨道半径。可知 $r = \dfrac{Tv}{2\pi}$ =3.83*10^6 m

   B. 火星的质量 M：$G\dfrac{mM}{r^2} = m\dfrac{v^2}{r}$，$M = \dfrac{v^2 r}{G}$ =6.64*10^{23} kg

   C. GS 的总机械能 E= $\dfrac{1}{2}mv^2 + (-G\dfrac{mM}{r}) = -G\dfrac{mM}{2r}$

   D. 由开普勒第三定律，$\dfrac{T^2}{r^3} = $ 常数；可知轨道半径减小，周期亦减小

   E. 由角动量守恒定律，$mr_A v_A = mr_B v_B$，近点为 A，远点为 B，可知：

   3.4*10^3(3.43*10^6+3.71*10^5)= v_B (3.43*10^6+4.36*10^5) $\rightarrow$ v_B =3.3 * 10^{3}m/s

Chapter 8

Oscillations
振动

Introduction: In this chapter we study a special type of motion called periodic motion. ***Periodic motion*** is motion of an object that regularly repeats—the object returns to a given position after a fixed time interval, actually describes many real life system. The back and forth movements of such an object are called ***oscillations***. A special case of periodic motion is called *simple harmonic motion* which is any oscillation that is governed by a ***linear restoring force*** or restoring torque such that the displacement from equilibrium can be described using sine or cosine functions. We shall find that all periodic motions can be modeled as combinations of simple harmonic motions. Thus, simple harmonic motion forms a basic building block for more complicated periodic motion.

周期运动

振动

线性回复力

任何复杂周期运动都是简谐运动的合成

8.1 Oscillations of a Spring

8.1 弹簧振子

A body of mass m is attached to an ideal spring with force constant k and free to move over a frictionless horizontal surface. Spring exerts the only force for the block. Note x=0 is the equilibrium position where the spring exerts no force on the body. Consider the oscillating system in one dimension, consisting of a particle subject to a force

$$F_s = -kx$$

Where: F_s : net force acting on an object

k : a constant (a positive value in the above equation)

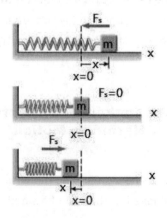

Figure 8-1 A block attached to a spring moving on a frictionless surface

x : position of the object relative to equilibrium

$$F_s = -kx$$

And we apply Newton's second law $F_x = ma_x$ to the motion of the block, so

$$a_x = -\frac{k}{m}x$$

$$a_x = -\frac{k}{m}x$$

That is, the net force F_{net} or the acceleration is proportional to the position of the block, and its direction is opposite the direction of the displacement from equilibrium. Systems that behave in this way are said to exhibit simple harmonic motion (SHM).

物体所受合外力正比于位移并与其符号相反，此物体做简谐振动。

The maximum displacement where the position x=A and x= -A is called the *amplitude*, A. One cycle refers to the complete motion from initial point back to the same point. The period, T, is defined as the time required for one complete cycle. The frequency, f, is the number of complete cycles per second, in hertz (Hz). 1Hz=1cycle per second (s^{-1}). Frequency and period are inversely related:

振幅 A：最大位移
周期 T：完成一次全振动所需要的时间
频率 f：单位时间完成全振动的次数

弹簧振子竖直方向振动：

$$T = 1/f \quad \text{and} \quad f = 1/T$$

The oscillation of a spring hung vertically is essentially the same as that of a horizontal spring. Because of the force of gravity, the length of the vertical spring at equilibrium (point O) will be longer than when it is horizontal. Now, the spring is in equilibrium when $F_{net}=0 = kx_0 - mg$, so the spring stretches an extra amount $x_0 = mg/k$ to be in equilibrium. Position x is measured from O, F=mg. The magnitude of the net force on the object is then $F_{net}=Fs - mg = -kx$. The net force on the object is the same as that on a block connected to a horizontal spring so the same simple harmonic motion results. Hooke's law can be used directly with the same value of k.

以系统的新平衡位置为原点。具有与水平方向振动相同的频率和周期，以及相同的振动方程。

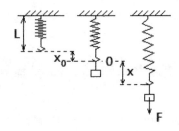

Figure 8-2 Spring hung vertically

8.2 Mathematical Representation of Simple Harmonic Motion

8.2 简谐振动方程

Let us now determine the position x as a function of time for a mass attached to the end of a simple spring with spring constant k. since

the acceleration $a = d^2x / dt^2$, we have

$$d^2x / dt^2 = -\frac{k}{m}x$$

$$\frac{d^2x}{dt^2} + \frac{k}{m}x = 0$$

This differential equation is the equation of motion for the simple harmonic oscillator. Let $\frac{k}{m} = \omega^2$, we have

$$\frac{d^2x}{dt^2} + \omega^2 x = 0$$

The solutions of the equation above, x (t), represent of the position of the particle as a function of time. The trigonometric functions sine or cosine satisfies this equation, so we can build a solution around one or both of these. The following cosine function is a solution to the differential equation:

$$x(t) = A\cos(\omega t + \phi)$$

Where A, ω, and ϕ are constants.

A, called the amplitude of the motion, is simply the maximum value of the position of the particle in either the positive or negative x direction.

The constant ω is called the angular frequency, and has units of rad s^{-1}. It is a measure of how rapidly the oscillations are occurring—the more oscillations per unit time, the higher is the value of ω. The angular frequency is

$$\omega = \sqrt{\frac{k}{m}}$$

The constant angle ϕ is called the phase constant (or initial phase angle), and it tells us how long after t=0 the peak at x=A is reached. If the particle is at its maximum position $x = A$ at $t = 0$, the phase constant is $\phi = 0$. The quantity $(\omega t + \phi)$ is called the phase of the

X(t): 弹簧振子的运动方程。

简谐振动微分方程：

$$\frac{d^2x}{dt^2} + \frac{k}{m}x = 0$$

$\omega = \sqrt{\frac{k}{m}}$ ：系统固有属性

简谐振动动力学方程：

$$\frac{d^2x}{dt^2} + \omega^2 x = 0$$

求解上面的动力学方程得到简谐振动运动学方程：

$x(t) = A\cos(\omega t + \phi)$

A：振幅是振子的最大位移

ω：圆频率，固有角频率

单位：rad/s

ϕ：初始相位。初始时刻物体所处的状态。

$\omega t + \phi$：t 时刻相位。表示

motion.

The SHM is a periodic motion and its period is

$$T = 2\pi / \omega = 2\pi\sqrt{\frac{m}{k}}$$

$$f = \frac{1}{2\pi}\sqrt{\frac{k}{m}}$$

So $\omega = \dfrac{2\pi}{T} = 2\pi f$

We can rewrite the position function as

$$X(t) = A\cos\left(\frac{2\pi t}{T} + \phi\right) \quad \text{or}$$

$$X(t) = A\cos\left(2\pi f + \phi\right)$$

Note that the frequency and period do not depend on the amplitude. Changing the amplitude of a SHM does not affect its frequency. T and f are called natural period and frequency.

The SHO is important in physics because whenever we have a net restoring force proportional to the displacement (F= -kx), which is at least a good approximation for a variety of systems, then the motion is simple harmonic—that is , *sinusoidal*.

According to the definition of velocity and acceleration of motion, it is obtained

$$v = \frac{dx}{dt} = -\omega A\sin(\omega t + \phi)$$

$$a = \frac{d^2 x}{dt^2} = \frac{dv}{dt} = -\omega^2 A\cos(\omega t + \phi) = -\omega^2 x$$

The velocity and acceleration also oscillate harmonically.

$$v_{max} = \omega A = \sqrt{\frac{k}{m}}A ,$$

The speed occurs maximum value at equilibrium point, x=0. And the

t 时刻物体运动状态。

简谐运动的周期 T 和频率：由系统固有属性决定，与振幅无关。

$$T = 2\pi\sqrt{\frac{m}{k}} , \quad f = \frac{1}{2\pi}\sqrt{\frac{k}{m}}$$

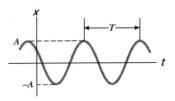

Figure 8-3 Position function, T, A

改变振幅不影响振动频率。

T 和 f 称为固有周期和频率。

振动物体速度方程和加速度方程随时间周期性变化。

$$v = -\omega A\sin(\omega t + \phi)$$

$$a = -\omega^2 A\cos(\omega t + \phi) = -\omega^2 x$$

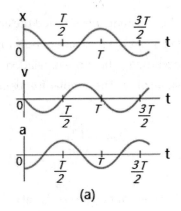

(a)

Figure 8-4 (a) Graph of the displacement, velocity, and acceleration versus time of a SHM at *t* = 0, *x*(0) = *A* and *v*(0) = 0

speed is zero at points, x=± A.

$$a_{max} = \omega^2 A = \frac{k}{m}A$$

The acceleration has its maximum value at x=± A, and a is zero at x=0.

A and ϕ can be determined uniquely by initial conditions, the position and velocity of the particle at $t = 0$, v_0 and x_0. When t=0, we have

$$x_0 = A\cos\phi \quad \text{and} \quad v_0 = -\omega A\sin\phi$$

So, $$A = \sqrt{x_0^2 + \frac{v_0^2}{\omega^2}}$$

$$\tan\phi = -\frac{v_0}{x_0\omega}$$

平衡位置处 V=V$_{max}$= ωA ,
最大位移处 V=0

最大位移处 a=a$_{max}$= $\omega^2 A$

平衡位置处 a=0

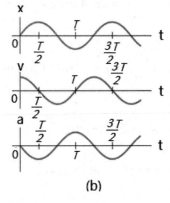

(b)

Figure 8.4 (b) SHM at $t = 0$, $x(0) = 0$ and $v(0) = vi$

A 和 ϕ 由初始条件决定：

$$A = \sqrt{x_0^2 + \frac{v_0^2}{\omega^2}}$$

$$\tan\phi = -\frac{v_0}{x_0\omega}$$

Example 8.1 An Oscillating Object: An object oscillates with simple harmonic motion along the x axis. Its position varies with time according to the equation $x = 4.00\cos(\pi t + \frac{\pi}{4})$ (m), where t is in seconds and the angles in radians.

a. Determine the amplitude, frequency, and period of the motion.

b. Calculate the velocity and acceleration of the object at any time t.

c. Determine the position, velocity, and acceleration of the object at $t = 1.00$ s.

d. Determine the maximum speed and maximum acceleration of the object.

e. Find the displacement of the object between $t = 0$ and $t = 1.00$ s.

Solution:

a. By comparing this equation $x = 4.00\cos(\pi t + \frac{\pi}{4})$ with $x(t) = A$

$\cos(\omega t + \phi)$, we see that A=4.00m, $\omega = \pi$ rad/s. So

$$T = \frac{2\pi}{\omega} = 2 \text{ s}, \quad f = \frac{1}{T} = 0.5 \text{ Hz}$$

b. $v = \dfrac{dx}{dt} = -\omega A \sin(\omega t + \phi) = -4.00\pi \sin(\pi t + \dfrac{\pi}{4})$ (m/s)

$$a = \frac{d^2 x}{dt^2} = \frac{dv}{dt} = -\omega^2 A \cos(\omega t + \phi)$$

$$= -\pi^2\, 4.00 \cos(\pi t + \frac{\pi}{4}) \ \ (\text{m/s}^2)$$

c. We obtain, at $t = 1.00$ s

$$x = 4.00 \cos(\pi + \frac{\pi}{4}) = \text{-2.83 m}$$

V= $-4.00\pi \sin(\pi + \dfrac{\pi}{4})$ = 8.89 m/s

a= $= -\pi^2\, 4.00 \cos(\pi + \dfrac{\pi}{4}) = 27.9$ m/s^2

d. $v_{max} = \omega A = 4.00\,\pi = 12.6$ m/s

$a_{max} = \omega^2 A = 4.00\,\pi^2 = 39.5$ m/s^2

e. The position at $t = 0$ is x(0)=4.00cos($\dfrac{\pi}{4}$)=2.86 m

The position at t=1.00s is x(1)= -2.83 m

Therefore, the displacement between $t = 0$ and $t = 1.00$ s is

$\Delta x = x(1)$- x(0)= -2.83 m - 2.83 m = -5.66 m

Because the object's velocity changes sign during the first second, the magnitude of Δx is not the same as the distance traveled in the first second.

Example 8.2 Spring is started with a push: A spring stretches x_0=0.150m when a 0.300kg mass m is hung from it, Figure 8-5. Suppose the spring is stretched 0.100m from equilibrium (t=0, x(0)= -0.100m) and the same time it is given an upward shove of v(0)=0.40m/s. Determine

a. the phase angle ϕ,

b. the amplitude A,

c. the displacement x as a function of time, x(t),

d. the velocity at t=2 s.

Solution:

Figure 8-5 Example 8.2

a. when t=o the position x(0)= Acos ϕ = -0.10m,

$$v(0)=-\omega A \sin \phi =0.40\text{m/s}$$

so, $\tan \phi = -\dfrac{v(0)}{\omega x(0)}$ =0.495

Our angle is in the third quadrant for both the sine and cosine are negative. Hence

$$\phi = 26.3° +180° = 206.3° = 3.60 rad$$

b. A=x(0)/cos ϕ =0.112m

c. First, we find k from mg=kx$_0$

$$k=\dfrac{mg}{x_0} =19.6 \text{ N/m}$$

Then, $\omega = \sqrt{\dfrac{k}{m}} =8.08 \text{ s}^{-1}$

x(t)=0.112cos(8.08t+3.60) m

d. The velocity at any time t is

$$v(t) = \dfrac{dx}{dt} = -A\omega \sin(\omega t +\phi) = \text{-0.905sin (8.08t+3.60) m/s}$$

209

When t=2s, v(2)= -0.715m/s

Example 8.3 The effective spring constant k_eff

Two springs with spring constant k_1 and k_2 are arranged in parallel and series. Determine the effective spring constant, k_{eff}.

Solution:

a. The two springs are in parallel.

The two strings have the same position at any time, the net force exerted by the spring would be

$$F = F_1 + F_2 = -(k_1 x + k_2 x) = -(k_1 + k_2)x = -k_{eff}x$$

So $k_{eff} = k_1 + k_2$

b. The two springs are in series.

Imagine that the block was displaced a distance x to the right of its equilibrium position. Then $x = x_1 + x_2$ and $x_1 = -\dfrac{F}{k_1}, x_2 = -\dfrac{F}{k_2},$

so $x = -F\left(\dfrac{1}{k_1} + \dfrac{1}{k_2}\right),$

$F = -k_{eff}x,$

$k_{eff} = \dfrac{k_1 k_2}{k_1 + k_2}$

Or $\dfrac{1}{k_{eff}} = \dfrac{1}{k_1} + \dfrac{1}{k_2}$

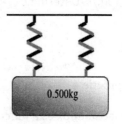

Figure 8-6 a: Two springs are in parallel

Figure 8-6 b: The two springs are also in parallel.

弹簧并联：$k_{eff} = k_1 + k_2$

k_{eff}：等效弹性系数

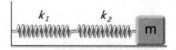

Figure 8-7 The two springs are in series.

弹簧串联：$\dfrac{1}{k_{eff}} = \dfrac{1}{k_1} + \dfrac{1}{k_2}$

For simple harmonic motion of the spring oscillator, the potential energy U at any instant is given by

$$U = \frac{1}{2}kx^2 = \frac{1}{2}kA^2\cos^2(\omega t + \phi)$$

The kinetic energy K at any instant is

$$K = \frac{1}{2}mv^2 = \frac{1}{2}kA^2\sin^2(\omega t + \phi)$$

The total mechanical energy is the sum of the kinetic energy and the potential energy. We obtain

$$E = K + U = \frac{1}{2}kA^2$$

That is, the total mechanical energy of a simple harmonic oscillator is a constant of the motion and is proportional to the square of the amplitude.

Plots of the kinetic and potential energies versus time and position appear in Figure 8-8.

In either plot, note that $K + U = \frac{1}{2}kA^2 = \frac{1}{2}mv_{max}^2$ is constant.

Example 8.4 Energy calculation: For the SHO of Example 8.2, determine

a. the total energy,

b. the kinetic and potential energies as a function of time,

c. the velocity when the mass is 0.050m from equilibrium,

d. the kinetic and potential energies at half amplitude (x=± A/2).

Solution:

a. Since k=19.6N/m and A=0.100m, the total energy E is

$$E = \frac{1}{2}kA^2 = 0.123 \text{ J}$$

b. For x(t)=0.112cos(8.08t+3.60) m, and v(t)= -0.905sin (8.08t+3.60)

简谐振动的势能和动能：

$$U = \frac{1}{2}kA^2\cos^2(\omega t + \phi)$$

$$K = \frac{1}{2}kA^2\sin^2(\omega t + \phi)$$

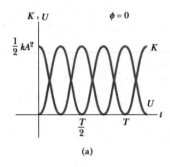

Figure 8-8 (a) Kinetic energy and potential energy versus time for a SHM with $\phi = 0$

总机械能 $E = U + K = \frac{1}{2}kA^2$

等于常数，由振幅决定。

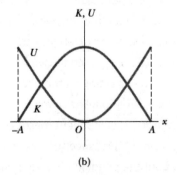

Figure 8-8 (b) Kinetic energy and potential energy versus position for a simple harmonic oscillator

m/s, so

$$U = \frac{1}{2}kx^2 = \frac{1}{2}kA^2 \cos^2(\omega t + \phi) = 0.123\cos^2(8.08t+3.60) \text{ J}$$

$$K = \frac{1}{2}mv^2 = \frac{1}{2}kA^2 \sin^2(\omega t + \phi) = 0.123\sin^2(8.08t+3.60)$$

c. Using the conservation of mechanical energy

$$\frac{1}{2}kA^2 = \frac{1}{2}kx^2 + \frac{1}{2}mv^2$$

we have $v = \omega\sqrt{A^2 - x^2}$

When x=0.050 m, v=0.81m/s

d. At x= ± A/2=0.056 m, we have

$$U = \frac{1}{2}kx^2 = E/4 = 0.0308 \text{ J}$$

$$K = \frac{1}{2}mv^2 = E - U = \frac{3E}{4} = 0.0922 \text{ J}$$

8.4 Pendulum and Other Oscillations　　8.4 摆动和其他振动

8.4.1 Simple Pendulum

8.4.1 单摆

A simple pendulum consists of a particle of mass m (called the bob of the pendulum) suspended from one end of an unstretchable, massless string of length L that is fixed at the other end, as in Figure 8-9. The bob is free to swing back and forth in the plane of the page. The forces acting on the bob are the tension T from the string and the gravitational force mg as shown in Figure 8-9. We resolve mg into radial component mgcos θ and a tangential component mgsin θ. This tangential component produces a restoring torque about the pendulum's pivot point, because it always acts opposite the displacement of the bob so as to bring the bob toward its equilibrium position (θ =0). We can write this restoring torque as

$$\tau = -Lmg\sin\theta$$

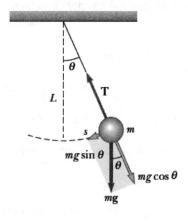

Figure 8-9 The simple pendulum

力矩：$\tau = -Lmg\sin\theta$

And using $\tau = I\alpha$, we obtain

$$\alpha = -\frac{mgL\sin\theta}{I}$$

where I is the pendulum's rotational inertia about the pivot point,

$I = mL^2$, and α is its angular acceleration about that point.

If the angle θ is small ($\theta \leq 5° =0.0873$rad), then $\sin\theta \approx \theta$ (in radian measure). We can have

$$\tau = -Lmg\theta$$

$$\alpha = -\frac{mgL}{I}\theta = -\frac{g}{L}\theta$$

When θ is small, a simple pendulum oscillates in simple harmonic motion about the equilibrium position $\theta = 0$.

$$\frac{d^2\theta}{dt^2} + \omega^2\theta = 0$$

where $\omega = \sqrt{\dfrac{g}{L}}$ is angular frequency, $\theta \leq \theta_m$, and θ_m is called the angular amplitude of the motion.

The general solution for this differential equation is

$$\theta(t) = \theta_m \cos(\omega t + \phi)$$

The period of the pendulum is given by

$$T = 2\pi\sqrt{\frac{L}{g}}$$

In other words, the period and frequency of a simple pendulum depend only on the length of the string and the acceleration due to gravity.

The simple pendulum can be used as a *timekeeper* because its period depends only on its length and the local value of *g*. It is also a

摆角很小时：$\tau = -Lmg\theta$

所以，单摆做简谐振动。

$$\alpha = -\frac{mgL}{I}\theta = -\frac{g}{L}\theta$$

动力学微分方程：

$$\frac{d^2\theta}{dt^2} + \omega^2\theta = 0$$

θ：角位移

θ_m：角振幅

角运动方程：

$$\theta(t) = \theta_m \cos(\omega t + \phi)$$

固有周期和频率由摆长和重力加速度确定：

$$T = 2\pi\sqrt{\frac{L}{g}}$$

单摆可做计时器使用。

用单摆可精确测重力加速度。

convenient device for making precise measurements of the free-fall acceleration. Such measurements are important because variations in local values of g can provide information on the location of oil and of other valuable underground resources.

Example 8.5: A simple pendulum has a period of 1s on Earth.

a. What would its period be on the moon (where g is one-sixth of its value here)?

b. If we cut the length of the pendulum half, how does the period change into on Earth?

Solution:

a. The period of the pendulum on the Moon is

$$T = 2\pi\sqrt{\frac{L}{g_{moon}}} = 2\pi\sqrt{\frac{L}{\frac{1}{6}g_{earth}}} = \sqrt{6}\, T_{earth} = 2.4s$$

b. $T = 2\pi\sqrt{\frac{L/2}{g_{moon}}} = \frac{1}{\sqrt{2}} = 0.71\ s$

8.4.2 Physical Pendulum

8.4.2 物理摆

If a hanging object oscillates about a fixed axis that does not pass through its center of mass and the object cannot be approximated as a point mass, we cannot treat the system as a simple pendulum. In this case the system is called a *physical pendulum*.

Figure 8-10 shows an arbitrary physical pendulum displaced to one side by angle θ. The gravitational force mg acts at its center of mass CM, at a distance d from the pivot point O. The restoring torque on a physical pendulum, about point O, is

$$\tau = -mgd\sin\theta$$

And using $\tau = I\alpha$, we obtain

$$\alpha = -\frac{mgd\sin\theta}{I}$$

where I is the pendulum's rotational inertia about the pivot point O,

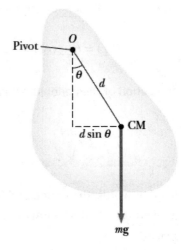

Figure 8-10 A physical pendulum pivoted at O

and α is its angular acceleration about that point.

力矩： $\tau = -mgd \sin \theta$

If the angle θ is small ($\theta \leq 5° = 0.0873\text{rad}$), then $\sin \theta \approx \theta$ (in radian measure). We can have

摆角很小时： $\tau = -mgd\theta$

$$\tau = -mgd\theta$$

此时物理摆做简谐运动。

$$\alpha = -\frac{mgd}{I}\theta$$

$$\alpha = -\frac{mgd}{I}\theta$$

When θ is small, a physical pendulum oscillates in simple harmonic motion about the equilibrium position $\theta = 0$.

$$\frac{d^2\theta}{dt^2} + \omega^2\theta = 0$$

$$\frac{d^2\theta}{dt^2} + \omega^2\theta = 0$$

$$\theta(t) = \theta_m \cos(\omega t + \phi)$$

Where $\omega = \sqrt{\dfrac{mgd}{I}}$ is angular frequency, $\theta \leq \theta_m$, and θ_m is

$$\omega = \sqrt{\frac{mgd}{I}}$$

called the angular amplitude of the motion.

The general solution for this differential equation is

$$\theta(t) = \theta_m \cos(\omega t + \phi)$$

The period of the pendulum is given by

$$T = 2\pi\sqrt{\frac{I}{mgd}}$$

固有周期： $T = 2\pi\sqrt{\dfrac{I}{mgd}}$

We can use this result to measure the moment of inertia of a flat rigid object. If the location of the center of mass—and hence the value of d—is known, the moment of inertia can be obtained by measuring the period.

可用其来测量刚体的转动惯量。

Example 8.6 A Swinging Rod: A uniform rod of mass M and length L is pivoted about one end and oscillates in a vertical plane. Find

a. the period of oscillation if the amplitude of the motion is small.

b. the length l of the simple pendulum that has the same period as the swinging rod.

Solution:

a. We know that the moment of inertia of a uniform rod about an axis through one end is $I_o = \dfrac{1}{3}ML^2$, and d=L/2, so

$$T = 2\pi\sqrt{\frac{I}{Mgd}} = 2\pi\sqrt{\frac{2L}{3g}}$$

b. The length l of a simple pendulum of the same period is determined by

$$2\pi\sqrt{\frac{l}{g}} = 2\pi\sqrt{\frac{2L}{3g}}$$

$$l = \frac{2}{3}L$$

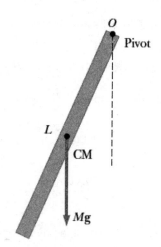

Figure 8-11 Example 8.6

8.4.3 Torsion Pendulum

Figure 8-12 shows a rigid object suspended by a wire attached at the top to a fixed support. When the object is twisted through some angle θ , the twisted wire exerts on the object a restoring torque that is proportional to the angular position. That is,

$$\tau = -\kappa\theta$$

where κ (Greek kappa) is constant, called the torsion constant, which depends on the length, diameter, and material of the suspension wire.

$$\frac{d^2\theta}{dt^2} + \frac{\kappa}{I}\theta = 0$$

where $\omega = \sqrt{\dfrac{\kappa}{I}}$, then $T = 2\pi\sqrt{\dfrac{I}{\kappa}}$

Comparison of $\tau = -\kappa\theta$ with $F = -kx$ indicates that $\tau = -\kappa\theta$ is the angular form of Hook's law, and we can transform

$T = 2\pi\sqrt{\dfrac{m}{k}}$ into an equation of angular SHM: $m \to I$, $k \to \kappa$. These

8.4.3 扭摆

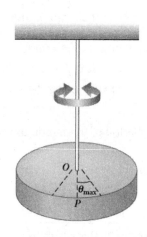

Figure 8-12 Torsion pendulum

力矩：$\tau = -\kappa\theta$

κ：扭转常数

摆角 θ 正比于扭矩，扭摆做简谐振动。

$$\frac{d^2\theta}{dt^2} + \frac{\kappa}{I}\theta = 0$$

$\tau = -\kappa\theta$ 是胡克定律角量形式。称之为回复力矩。

replacements also lead to

$$T = 2\pi\sqrt{\frac{I}{\kappa}}$$

摆动周期：$T = 2\pi\sqrt{\dfrac{I}{\kappa}}$

This system is called a *torsional pendulum.* There is no small-angle restriction in this situation as long as the elastic limit of the wire is not exceeded.

弹性限度内扭摆和单摆不同，扭角没有小角度限制。

8.4.4 Identifying SHM

SHM occur whenever there is a linear restoring force.

$$F = -k_{effective}x \rightarrow k_{effective} = -\frac{dF}{dx} \rightarrow \omega = \sqrt{\frac{k_{effective}}{m}}$$

$$\tau = -k_{effective}\theta \rightarrow k_{effective} = -\frac{d\tau}{d\theta} \rightarrow \omega = \sqrt{\frac{k_{effective}}{I}}$$

So, if you can recognize that $k_{effective}$ is some constant expression

for some oscillation, then the oscillation is a SHM.

8.4.4 简谐振动的判断

出现线性回复作用

$F = -k_{effective}x$ 或

$\tau = -k_{effective}\theta$

8.5 Forced Vibrations, Resonance

8.5 受迫振动、共振

All oscillators we talk above are ideal system. The amplitude of any real oscillating spring or pendulum slowly decreases in time until the oscillations stop altogether. The mechanical energy of a *damped oscillator* decreases in time as a result of the resistive force. It is possible to compensate for this energy decrease by applying an external force that does positive work on the system. At any instant, energy can be transferred into the system by an applied force that acts in the direction of motion of the oscillator. So, a sinusoidal external force is needed in response to this situation.

When a vibrating system is set into motion, it vibrates at its natural frequency. A system has an external force applied to it that has its own particular frequency and then we have a forced vibration. The

frequency f , $\omega = 2\pi f$, of the external force may be different

实际的振动都是减幅运动，直至最后振动停止。称之为阻尼振动。

周期性的策动外力作用于振动系统使振动持续下去。振动系统以策动力的频率 f 运动。

from the natural frequency of the vibrating system, f_0.

固有频率

$$\omega_0 = 2\pi f_0 = \sqrt{\frac{k}{m}}$$

$$\omega_0 = 2\pi f_0 = \sqrt{\frac{k}{m}}$$

In a forced vibration, the amplitude A of vibration, and hence the energy transferred to the vibrating system, is found to depend on the difference between ω and ω_0 as well as on the amount of damping. And A reaches a maximum when the driving frequency equals the nature frequency of the system, that is

当策动力的频率 f 与系统的固有频率相同时，振动达到最大振幅—共振。

$$f = f_0$$

$$f = f_0$$

When the damping is small, the increase in amplitude near f=f₀ is very large. This effect is known as **resonance**. The natural vibrating frequency f₀ of a system is called its **resonant frequency**. It clearly illustrates that at resonance, relatively little effort is required to obtain a large amplitude. Whenever any real physical system is driven near its resonance frequency, you can expect oscillations of very large amplitudes.

f_0：共振频率，固有频率

第八章总结 振动

1. 简谐振动

1）当物体受到与位移成正比的回复力作用时将做简谐振动。

$$F = -kx$$

2）振动微分方程为 $\dfrac{d^2x}{dt^2} = -\omega^2 x$

弹簧质点振动系统 $\omega = \sqrt{\dfrac{k}{m}}$

微分方程的解即使物体遵循的运动规律。

3）运动方程将遵循正弦或余弦规律。

$$x(t) = A\cos(\omega t + \phi) \quad 或 \quad x(t) = A\sin(\omega t + \phi)$$

所以，速度方程 $v(t) = -A\omega\sin(\omega t + \phi)$

加速度方程 $a(t) = -A\omega^2\cos(\omega t + \phi) = -\omega^2 x(t)$

4）周期及频率

周期 $T = \dfrac{2\pi}{\omega} = 2\pi\sqrt{\dfrac{m}{k}}$

频率 $f = \dfrac{1}{T} = \dfrac{1}{2\pi}\sqrt{\dfrac{k}{m}}$

5）简谐振动的能量

动能 $K = \dfrac{1}{2}mv^2 = \dfrac{1}{2}kA^2\sin^2(\omega t + \phi)$

势能 $U = \dfrac{1}{2}kx^2 = \dfrac{1}{2}kA^2\cos^2(\omega t + \phi)$

总机械能：$E = K + U = \dfrac{1}{2}kA^2$，振幅 A 决定系统的能量大小。

6）阻尼振动：由于阻力作用，物体振动周期变慢的减幅振动。

7）共振：当策动力的频率接近或等于系统的固有频率时，外界对系统的能量输入达到最

佳状态。

2. 弹簧物体系统无论弹簧是水平放置、竖直放置都做相同频率的简谐振动。

3. 单摆、物理摆和扭摆

1）单摆：$\omega = \sqrt{\dfrac{g}{L}}$，$T = 2\pi \sqrt{\dfrac{L}{g}}$

2）物理摆（刚体）：$\omega = \sqrt{\dfrac{mgd}{I}}$，$T = 2\pi \sqrt{\dfrac{I}{mgd}}$

d 是质心到转点的距离，I 是刚体的转动惯量。

3）扭摆：$\omega = \sqrt{\dfrac{\kappa}{I}}$，$T = 2\pi \sqrt{\dfrac{I}{\kappa}}$

κ 是有转动系统决定的常数。

其中单摆和复摆做准简谐振动，当摆动特别小时振动为简谐振动。扭摆做简谐振动。

Chapter 8 Oscillations Practice

Multiple Choice Questions

1. A 10 kg mass suspended on the Earth by a spring oscillates with a period of 12 seconds. This mass-spring system is now moved to the moon where the gravity is one-sixth that of the Earth. What is the new period of motion?

   A. 72 s
   B. 2 s
   C. 4 s
   D. 12 s
   E. 21 s

2. A block is attached to a vertical ideal spring, and is undergoing simple harmonic motion. If this same block and spring are brought to the moon, where all conditions are the same except that the acceleration due to gravity is 1/6 that of the Earth, and are undergoing simple harmonic motion of the same amplitude as on the Earth, which of the following will change?

   A. Period
   B. Frequency
   C. Maximum kinetic energy
   D. Equilibrium position
   E. The total energy of the system

3. A certain spring-mass system initially has a period of T. If the mass remains the same, what must happen to the spring in order for the period to become 2T?

   A. The spring must be double in length.
   B. The acceleration due to gravity must be doubled.
   C. The acceleration due to gravity must be halved.

   D. The spring constant must decrease by a factor of 2.
   E. The spring constant must decrease by a factor of 4.

Questions **4** and **5**

Two blocks are attached by a stretched spring and held on a frictionless surface as shown below. The blocks are then released simultaneously. Block I has one-fourth the mass of block II.

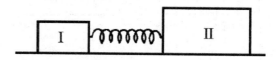

4. What is the ratio of the maximum acceleration of block I to the maximum acceleration of block II?

   A. 1/16
   B. 1/4
   C. 1
   D. 4
   E. 16

5. What is the ratio of the maximum kinetic energy of block I to the maximum kinetic energy of block II?

   A. 1/4
   B. 1/2
   C. 1
   D. 2
   E. 4

Questions **6** and **7**

A block oscillates without friction on the end of

a spring. The minimum and maximum lengths of the spring as it oscillates are, respectively, x_{min} and x_{max}. The graphs below can represent quantities associated with the oscillation as functions of the length x of the spring. Graph C and D are parabolic.

A
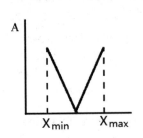

B
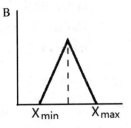

C
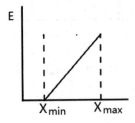

D
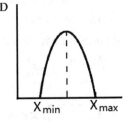

E
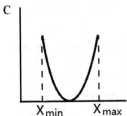

6. Which graph can represent the magnitude of the acceleration of the block as a function of x?

7. Which graph can represent the potential energy stored in the spring as a function of x?

8. A graph of the position (in centimeter) functions for a body oscillating with a period of 24sec in *simple harmonic motion* is shown below. The equation that best describes the motion is

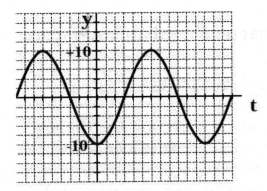

A. $y = 20 \sin \left(\dfrac{\pi}{12} t - \dfrac{\pi}{2} \right)$.

B. $y = 10 \sin \left(\dfrac{\pi}{4} t - \dfrac{\pi}{2} \right)$.

C. $y = 10 \sin \left(\dfrac{\pi}{12} t + \dfrac{3\pi}{2} \right)$.

D. $y = 20 \sin \left(\dfrac{\pi}{4} t - \dfrac{\pi}{2} \right)$.

E. $y = 10 \sin \left(\dfrac{\pi}{12} t + \dfrac{\pi}{2} \right)$

9. Which of the following is true of an oscillating spring-mass system?

A. The velocity is greatest when the potential energy is greatest.

B. The force is greatest when the velocity is greatest.

C. The kinetic energy is greatest when the force is greatest.

D. The potential energy is greatest when the acceleration is greatest.

E. The potential energy is greatest when the displacement is least.

10. The velocity of a simple harmonic oscillator is given by the equation $v = 3\cos(2t + \pi/4)$, where v is in meters per second and t is in seconds. What is its position at $t = \dfrac{5}{8}\pi$ if its position is $x = \dfrac{3}{2}$ m at $t = \dfrac{\pi}{8}$ s?

A. -3 m

B. $-\dfrac{2}{3}$ m

C. 0

D. $-\dfrac{3}{2}$ m

E. 3 m

11. A simple harmonic oscillator has the position given by $x(t) = A\sin(2t)$, where x is in meters and t is in seconds. What is its acceleration at $t = \pi/12$ s?

  A. $-2A$

  B. $-A$

  C. 0

  D. A

  E. $2A$

12. Which of the following is true of a damped simple pendulum in which the amplitude of motion decreases exponentially?

  A. Its period decreases through time.

  B. The total energy of the pendulum remains the same.

  C. The maximum kinetic energy decreases through time.

  D. The maximum potential energy increases through time.

  E. It is not influenced by external forces.

13. An ideal spring with natural length 10 cm and spring constant 100 N/m is kept at its natural length as a 2 kg mass is hung from it. When the spring is released, how far will the mass fall before its velocity becomes 0?

  A. 10 cm

  B. 20 cm

  C. 40 cm

  D. 80 cm

  E. 100 cm

14. A simple pendulum in simple harmonic motion on the Earth's surface has a period of

1 s. If the same pendulum is undergoing simple harmonic motion on the Moon, under which of the following modifications would the pendulum have the same period T=1s?

  A. Increase the length of the pendulum by a factor of 6.

  B. Decrease the length of the pendulum by a factor of 6.

  C. Increase the length of the pendulum by a factor of $\sqrt{6}$.

  D. Decrease the length of the pendulum by a factor of $\sqrt{6}$.

  E. No change would be necessary.

15. A pendulum is released from a height h. At the equilibrium position, it strikes an object of mass m and the mass sticks together with the pendulum bob. Which of the following describes the pendulum object system after the collision?

I. The kinetic energy of the system increases.
II. The period of the pendulum remains constant.
III. The maximum height the pendulum reaches decreases.

  A. I only

  B. II only

  C. III only

  D. II and III only

  E. I, II, and III only

16. A pendulum of length L swings in simple harmonic motion with period T and angular displacement θ about the equilibrium point $\theta = 0$. What is the maximum velocity of the pendulum?

  A. $\sqrt{gL(\sin\theta - \cos\theta)}$

223

B. $\sqrt{2gL(1-\cos\theta)}$

C. $\sqrt{2gL\cos\theta}$

D. $\sqrt{1gL(1-\sin\theta)}$

E. $\sqrt{2gL\sin\theta}$

17. Which is not an example of approximate

simple harmonic motion?

A. A ball bouncing on the floor.

B. A child swinging on a swing.

C. A piano string that has been struck.

D. A car's radio antenna as it waves back and forth.

E. A heavy irregular rod with mass m and length L swinging about one end of the rod.

Free Response Questions

1. A particle of mass 0.1kg moves in one dimension as a function of time $x = -0.3\sin(2t + \pi/4)$. x is in meters and t is in sec.

    A. What is the frequency (in Hz) of this simple harmonic oscillation?

    B. What are the times (in sec) at which the speed of the particle is maximum?

    C. Determine the total energy of the system.

2. The graph below shows the variation with time t of the displacement x of a system executing SHM. Use the graph to determine

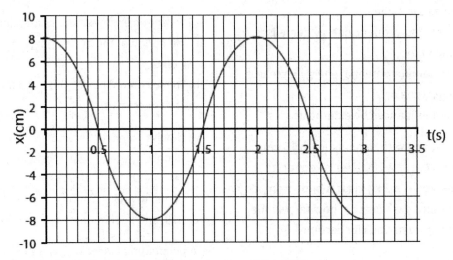

    A. the function with time t of the displacement x of the SHM

    B. maximum speed

    C. the speed at t = 1.3 s

    D. maximum acceleration

3. A ball of mass m is attached to a light but rigid rod of length L. The rod is pivoted at the top and is free to rotate in a circle in the plane of the page, as shown on the right.

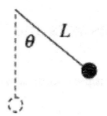

   A. The mass oscillates to a maximum angle θ (θ is angular position). Draw a vector representing the direction of the net force on the mass while it is at angle θ. And show the expression of the net force.
   B. Derive an expression for the ball's potential energy U as a function of the angle θ. Assume that a negative angle represents displacement from the vertical in the clockwise direction.
   C. The pendulum is considered a classic example of simple harmonic motion when it undergoes small amplitude oscillation. Explain why the assumption of simple harmonic motion is valid.
   D. Determine the function of angular position with time when the ball is undergoing a SHM.

   Suppose the ball is dropped at the maximum angular position θ_{max}.

4. A spherical, non-rotating planet has a radius R and a uniform density ρ throughout its volume. Suppose a narrow tunnel was drilled through the planet along one of its diameters, as shown in the figure below. A small ball of mass m could move freely under the influence of gravity. Let r be the distance of the ball from the center of the planet.

   A. Determine the magnitude of the force on the ball at a distance r < R from the center of the planet.
   B. Let the potential energy of the ball to be zero at the planet's center. Calculate the ball's potential energy as a function of distance from the center of the planet, U(r), for r<R.
   C. If the ball is dropped into the tunnel from rest at point P at the planet's surface, determine the speed of the ball when it reaches the center of the planet.

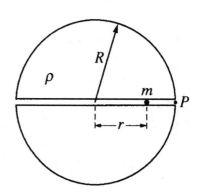

   D. How long will it take the ball to move from point P to the center of the planet?
   E. Describe the subsequent motion of the ball from the time it reaches the center of the planet.

5. Two blocks with mass m_1 and m_2 lying on a frictionless horizontal surface are attached by a spring of spring constant k as shown below. The spring is compressed a distance d, and the two blocks are then released from rest simultaneously.

   A. Determine the maximum speed of mass m_2.
   B. What is the period of oscillation of each mass?

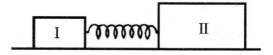

Answers and Explanations

Multiple Choice Answers

1. D   2. D   3. E   4. D   5. E   6. A   7. C   8. C   9. D   10. D   11. A   12. C   13. C   14. B   15. D
16. B   17. A

Multiple Choice Explanations

1. D。弹簧振子系统的固有周期 T=$2\pi\sqrt{\dfrac{m}{k}}$ ，与 **g** 无关。

2. D。竖直放置的弹簧振子平衡位置在 $x_0 = \dfrac{m}{k}g$ ，与 **g** 相关。其他物理量与 **g** 无关。

3. E。T=$2\pi\sqrt{\dfrac{m}{k}}$ ，当 $k^{'} = \dfrac{k}{4}$ 时，$T^{'} = 2T$

4. D。$ma_1 = 4ma_2$, $\rightarrow a_1 / a_2 = 4$

5. E。$mv_1 = 4mv_2$, $\rightarrow v_1 / v_2 = 4$ ，有 $\dfrac{1}{2}mv_1^2 / \dfrac{1}{2}4mv_2^2 = 4$

6. A。$a = -\omega^2 x$

7. C。$U = \dfrac{1}{2}kx^2$

8. C。周期 T=24s，角频率 $\omega = \dfrac{2\pi}{T} = \dfrac{\pi}{12}$ ，振幅 A=10cm，初相为 $\dfrac{3\pi}{2}$ or $-\dfrac{\pi}{2}$

y = $10\sin(\dfrac{\pi}{12}t + \dfrac{3\pi}{2})$

9. D。$U = \dfrac{1}{2}kx^2, E_k = \dfrac{1}{2}mv^2$

10. D。x=$\dfrac{3}{2} + \int_{\frac{\pi}{8}}^{\frac{5\pi}{8}} 3\cos(2t + \dfrac{\pi}{4})dt = -\dfrac{3}{2}$ m

11. A。$a = \dfrac{d^2 x}{dt^2} = -4A\sin 2t$, t=$\dfrac{\pi}{12}$ 时，$a = -2A$

12. C。阻尼振动的周期变长，总能量减少。

13. C。振幅 A=$\dfrac{mg}{k}$ =0.2m，当 v=0 时，物体运动到 2A=0.4m 处。

14. B。$T=2\pi\sqrt{\dfrac{L}{g}}$，当 $g'=\dfrac{g}{6}$ 时，$T'=T$，有 $L'=\dfrac{L}{6}$

15. D。单摆的周期与质量无关；摆锤与 m 完全非弹性碰撞，系统能量减少，单摆能达到的高度降低。

16. B。mgL（1-$\cos\theta$）$=\dfrac{1}{2}mv^2$，$\rightarrow v=\sqrt{2gL(1-\cos\theta)}$

17. A。弹力球在往复运动中受到恒定的重力 mg 的作用，不是简谐运动。

Free Response Explanations

1. A. $\omega=2\pi f=2$，$f=\dfrac{1}{\pi}$（Hz）

   B. $v=\dfrac{dx}{dt}=-0.6\cos(2t+\dfrac{\pi}{4})$，速度取极大值时，$2t+\dfrac{\pi}{4}=k\pi$

   $\rightarrow t=(k-\dfrac{1}{4})\dfrac{\pi}{2}$，K=0，$\pm1,\pm2\cdots$

   C. $v_{\max}=0.6m/s$，$E=E_{k,\max}=\dfrac{1}{2}mv_{\max}^2$=0.018J

2. A. x=Acosωt =8cosπt (cm)

   B. $v=\dfrac{dx}{dt}=-8\pi\sin\pi t(cm/s)$，$v_{\max}=8\pi$=25 cm/s

   C. t=1.3s 时，$v=-8\pi\sin(\pi*1.3)$=20 cm/s

   D. $a=\dfrac{dv}{dt}=-8\pi^2\cos\pi t$，$a_{\max}=8\pi^2=79cm/s^2$

3. A. 在 $\theta=\theta_{\max}$ 处，$v=0$，沿细杆方向的合外力为零，细杆张力 $T=mg\cos\theta$；所以合外力

   $F_{net}=-mg\sin\theta$，指向平衡位置且垂直于细杆。

   B. 小球在最低处为系统的平衡位置（θ=0），设此处的势能 U=0；在任意位置 θ 处

   U=mgL（1-$\cos\theta$）

C. 在任意时刻 t: 力矩 $\tau = -mgL\sin\theta$，当 θ 很小时 $\sin\theta \approx \theta$，有 $\tau = -mgL\theta = -k\theta$，所以

小球做简谐运动。

D. $\tau = -mgL\theta = I\alpha = mL^2\dfrac{d^2\theta}{dt^2}$，得微分方程 $\dfrac{d^2\theta}{dt^2} + \dfrac{g}{L}\theta = 0$，t=0 时 $\theta = \theta_{max}$，解之得

$\theta = \theta_{max}\cos\sqrt{\dfrac{g}{L}}t$，其中角频率 $\omega = \sqrt{\dfrac{g}{L}}$，周期 T=$2\pi\sqrt{\dfrac{L}{g}}$

4. A. F=$-G\dfrac{mM(r)}{r^2} = -\dfrac{4}{3}G\pi\rho mr$

B. U(r)=$U(r) - U(0) = -\int_0^r F(r)dr = \dfrac{2}{3}G\pi\rho mr^2$

C. 由机械能守恒：$\dfrac{2}{3}G\pi\rho mR^2 = \dfrac{1}{2}mv^2$，$\rightarrow v = \sqrt{\dfrac{4}{3}G\pi\rho}R$

D. F=-kr, k=$\dfrac{4}{3}G\pi\rho m$，周期 T=$2\pi\sqrt{\dfrac{m}{k}} = 2\pi\sqrt{\dfrac{3}{4G\pi\rho}}$，

小球运动到中心所用时间 t=$\dfrac{T}{4} = \dfrac{\pi}{2}\sqrt{\dfrac{3}{4G\pi\rho}}$

E. 小球将会在隧道中做往复的周期性简谐振动，周期 T=$2\pi\sqrt{\dfrac{3}{4G\pi\rho}}$。

5. A. 最大速度发生在弹簧处于平衡位置，弹簧的弹性势能全部转化为两个物体的动能，

$\dfrac{1}{2}kd^2 = \dfrac{1}{2}m_1v_1^2 + \dfrac{1}{2}m_2v_2^2$；

此时系统无外力作用，动量守恒，$m_1v_1 = m_2v_2$；

求得 $v_2 = \sqrt{\dfrac{kd^2}{m_2(1 + \dfrac{m_2}{m_1})}}$

B. 系统无外力作用，质心保持不变，设此位置坐标为零：$\dfrac{m_2x_2 - m_1x_1}{m_1 + m_2} = 0$。

在振动的任意时刻 t，m_2 与质心的距离为 x_2，向右；m_1 与质心的距离为 x_1，向左。此时弹簧的总伸长量为 $x_1 + x_2$，m_2 受到作用力的大小为 $F = k（x_1 + x_2）= k(1 + \dfrac{m_2}{m_1})x_2$，对 m_2 物体

等效弹簧的弹性系数为 $k' = k(1 + \dfrac{m_2}{m_1})$，

振动周期 $T = 2\pi\sqrt{\dfrac{m}{k}} = 2\pi\sqrt{\dfrac{m_2}{k(1 + \dfrac{m_2}{m_1})}} = 2\pi\sqrt{\dfrac{m_1 m_2}{k(m_1 + m_2)}}$。

与 m_1 的振动周期相同。

PART TWO

电磁学
Electromagnetism

Electrostatics
静电场

Introduction：The *electromagnetic force* between charged particles is one of the fundamental forces of nature. We begin this chapter by the electric force and then we discuss Coulomb's law. Next, we introduce the concept of an electric field associated with a charge distribution and describe its effect on other charged particles. We showed how to calculate the electric field generated by a given charge distribution and described **Gauss's law**—an alternative procedure for calculating electric fields. The *electrostatic force* is conservative, electrostatic phenomena can be conveniently described in terms of an electric potential energy. This idea enables us to define a scalar quantity known as *electric potential.*

电磁力是四种基本力之一

静电力是保守力

电势

9.1 Charge and Coulomb's Law
9.1 电荷和库仑定律

Electric **charge** is a fundamental quantity like mass, distance, or time. Charge is observable and measurable by the force it exerts on other charges.

电荷是基本物理量

9.1.1 Properties of Electric Charge
9.1.1 电荷

There are two types of charges: positive and negative. Like charges repel one another: Opposite charges attract one another: The variable q or Q is used to represent an amount of charge (may be positive or negative).

两种电荷：正、负电荷

同号相斥，异号相吸

The SI unit of charge is the **Coulomb**, abbreviated C.

电荷单位：库仑，C

Since all matter contains **protons and electrons**, there is charge present (often in great quantities) in every object. Typically, however, the number of protons in an object essentially equals the

质子和电子

number of electrons—adding the amounts of charge gives a total of zero—the object is said to have no net charge and to be neutral. An object is charged or has a net charge when there are unequal numbers of protons and electrons. This occurs almost always as a result of electrons being transferred to or from an object.

The smallest possible amount of charge is that on an electron or proton. This amount is called the fundamental or elementary charge, *e*.

$e = 1.602 \times 10^{-19}$ C

An electron has charge: $q = -e = -1.602 \times 10^{-19}$ C

A proton has charge: $q = +e = 1.602 \times 10^{-19}$ C

基本电荷电量 e=1.6×10^{-19}C

Furthermore, any amount of charge greater than the elementary charge is an exact integer multiple of the elementary charge!

$q = ne$, where *n* is an integer.

电荷量子化：q=ne

For this reason, charge is said to be "quantized". It comes in quantities of 1.602×10^{-19} C.

In all processes, the total charge of the universe remains unchanged. This is called the law of conservation of electric charge: **The net charge in an isolated system is always conserved, or total charge is constant in any process.**

电荷守恒定律：孤立系统的总电荷保持不变。

9.1.2 Electric Charge in the Atom

9.1.2 原子中的电荷

Materials through which electric charge is easily transported are called ***conductors***. Materials through which it is very difficult for charge to transport through are called ***insulators***. An intermediate class of materials is called ***semiconductors***.

电荷在导体中可以自由移动，在绝缘体中不能自由移动。

半导体

We can use two ways to charge an object. First one is ***conduction***. It is the transfer of charge from one object to another, usually as a result of contact. Another one is ***induction*** which involves the rearrangement of charge within an object due to the presence of an external charge (or electric field). There is no contact.

物体带电有两种方式：接触导电、静电感应。

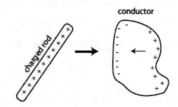

Both insulators and conductors can possess charge. Their key difference is charges can travel freely through conductors. Charges can't travel freely through insulators, but rather tends to be "locked" in place.

Figure 9-1 Induction of a conductor, induced charge

导体中感应电荷是自由电荷。

When a charged object is brought near a conductor, the electrons in the conductor are free to move. When a charged object is brought near an insulator, the electrons are not free to move, but they may spend a little more time on one side of their orbit than another, creating a net separation of charge in a process known as polarization. The charge of the conductor on the near side of the charged rod is called **induced charge**. The charge of the insulator on the near side of the charged rod is called **polarized charge**.

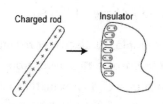

Figure 9-2 Polarization of an insulator and polarized charge

绝缘体极化电荷是束缚电荷

9.1.3 Coulomb's Law

9.1.3 库仑定律

We will use the term point charge to mean a particle of zero size that carries an electric charge. From experimental observations on the electric force, we can express Coulomb's law as equation

库仑定律：距离为 r 的两个点电荷之间相互作用力。

$$F_{12} = k\frac{q_1 q_2}{r^2}\hat{r}$$

$\hat{r}$: unit vector along the line joining the two charges.

The magnitude of force between two point charges at rest was inversely proportional to the square of the distance between them and proportional to the product of the charges and the direction of interaction force is along the line connected them, like charges repel each other, and unlike charges attract each other.

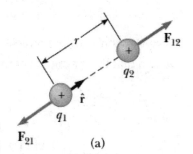

Where K is a constant called the Coulomb constant.

K=8.987 5 * 10^9 Nm^2/C^2

This constant is also written in the form

$$K=\frac{1}{4\pi\varepsilon_0}$$

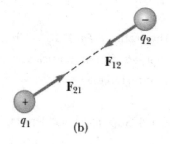

Figure 9-3 Coulomb's law

Where the constant ε_0 is known as the **permittivity of free space** and has the value

ε_0：真空中的介电常数

$$\varepsilon_0 = 8.854\ 2 * 10^{-12}\ C^2/Nm^2$$

库仑定律向量公式：

So $F_{12}=\dfrac{1}{4\pi\varepsilon_0}\dfrac{q_1 q_2}{r^2}\hat{r}$

$F_{12}=\dfrac{1}{4\pi\varepsilon_0}\dfrac{q_1 q_2}{r^2}\hat{r}$

And we have $\mathbf{F}_{12} = -\mathbf{F}_{21}$

作用力等于反作用力

Example 9.1 Electric Force on Electron by Proton: The electron and proton of a hydrogen atom are separated (on the average) by a distance of approximately $5.3 *10^{-11}$ m. Assume the electron orbits the proton. Find the magnitudes of the electric force and the gravitational force between the two particles.

质子对电子的作用力

Solution:

From Coulomb's law, we find that the magnitude of the electric force is

$$F = k\frac{e^2}{r^2} = 9*10^9 \frac{(1.6*10^{-19})^2}{(5.3*10^{-11})^2} = 8.2*10^{-8}\,\mathrm{N}$$

Using Newton's law of universal gravitation for the particle masses, we find that the magnitude of the gravitational force is

$$F_g = G\frac{mM}{r^2}$$

$$= 6.67*10^{-11}\frac{9.11*10^{-31}*1.67*10^{-27}}{(5.3*10^{-11})^2} = 3.6*10^{-47}\,\mathrm{N}$$

The ratio $F/Fg = 2*10^{39}$. Thus, the gravitational force between charged atomic particles is negligible when compared with the electric force.

电荷间的静电力远远大于它们之间的万有引力。

9.1.4 Superposition Principle

9.1.4 电场力叠加原理

If several charges are present, ***the net force on any one of them will be the vector sum of the forces due to each of the others***. This principle of superposition is based on experiment, and tells us that electric force vectors as like any other vector.

多个电荷的系统，一电荷受到的作用力等于所有其他电荷作用在其上的力的向量和。

$$\vec{F}_{net} = \sum_i \vec{F}_i$$

点电荷系统：$\vec{F}_{net} = \sum_i \vec{F}_i$

For continuous distributions of charge Q, the sum of the force on a charge q_0 becomes an integral.

$$\vec{F}_{net} = \int d\vec{F}$$

连续带电体：$\vec{F}_{net} = \int d\vec{F}$

Example 9.2 Find the Resultant Force: Calculate the net

electrostatic force on charge $q_3 = 5\mu$ C shown in Figure 9-4 due to the charge $q_1 = 5\mu$ C and $q_2 = -2.0\mu$ C. $a = 0.10$m.

Solution:

The magnitude of F_{23} is

$$F_{23} = K\frac{q_2 q_3}{a^2} = 9.0\text{N} \qquad \text{Pointing to the charge } q_2.$$

So in vector form $\qquad$ **F_{23} = -9.0 i N**

The magnitude of the force F_{13} exerted by q_1 on q_3 is

$$F_{13} = K\frac{q_1 q_3}{(\sqrt{2}a)^2} = 11\text{N} \qquad \text{Pointing away from } q_2.$$

In vector form $\qquad$ **F_{13}**=(7.9i +7.9j) N

The net force on q_3 is **F_3**=**F_{13}**+**F_{23}**=(-1.1i +7.9j) N

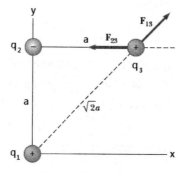

Figure 9-4 Example 9.2

9.2 Electric Field (E)

9.2 电场强度

The concept of a field was developed by *Michael Faraday* (1791–1867), an electric field extends outward from every charge and permeates all of space. When a second charge is placed near the first charge, it feels a force because of the electric field that is there. *It is similar to gravitational field* !

电荷在空间产生电场，电场对处于其中的电荷有力的作用。

9.2.1 Definition of Electric Field

9.2.1 电场强度定义

An electric field is said to exist in the region of space around a charged object—the *source charge*. When another charged object—the *test charge*—enters this electric field, an electric force acts on it.

场源电荷 Q：产生电场 **E**

Figure 9-5 Definition of E

A *test charge* is used to measure the force and thus detect the existence of the field and evaluate its strength. It should be a point charge whose electric quantity is smaller far than the source charge in order to decrease the disturbance as much as possible to the source charge and its electrostatic field. Usually test charge is positive.

试验电荷 q_0：正电荷且足够小，对原电场几乎无影响。

At a point in the given electrostatic field the ratio of the electric field force **F** on the test point charge q_0 is defined by electric field intensity, **E**.

$$E=F/q_0$$

The electric field describes the amount of electrostatic force observed by a charge placed at a point in the field per unit charge. The electric field vector points in the direction a positive test charge would feel a force. Electric field strength is measured in N/C, which is equivalent to V/m.

Note:

1. The electric field depends only on the "field charges" and their distribution. The presence of test charge does also not alter the electric field.

2. Electric field is a vector function of space, **E**=**E**(r).

3. A charge q will feel a force at any point of the field, **F**=q**E**.

9.2.2 Electric Field of a Single Point Charge

To find the electric field due to a point charge q, we put a positive test charge q_0 at that point. From Coulomb's law:

$$E=F/q_0=\frac{1}{4\pi\varepsilon_0}\frac{Q}{r^2}\hat{r}$$

Q>0 **E** has same direction with **r**.
Q<0 **E** has opposite direction with **r**.

9.2.3 Superposition of Electric Fields

To find the net electric field due to more than one point charge, we place a positive test charge q_0 near n point charges. From the principle of superposition of electric force we have:

$$E=\frac{\sum_i \vec{F}_i}{q_0}=\sum_i \frac{\vec{F}_i}{q_0}=\sum_i \vec{E}_i=\frac{1}{4\pi\varepsilon_0}\sum_i \frac{q_i}{r_i^2}\hat{r}_i$$

场强定义：**E**=F/q_0

空间任意一点场强：单位正试验电荷在该点所受电场力。

E 与试验电荷 q_0 无关，是空间场点位置的函数。

场强单位：1N/C=1V/m

关于电场强度 **E**：

1. 场源电荷决定电场分布状态，与试验电荷无关

2. 场强是空间位置向量函数

3. 电荷 q 在电场中受到作用力。

9.2.2 点电荷场强

Figure 9-6 E of point charge Q

$$E=\frac{1}{4\pi\varepsilon_0}\frac{Q}{r^2}\hat{r}$$

Figure 9-7 Graph of E

9.2.3 电场强度叠加原理

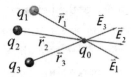

Figure 9-8 Superposition of **E** for system of point charges

That is at any point *P*, the total electric field due to a group of source charges equals the **vector sum** of the electric fields of all the charges.

If the electric charge Q can be treated as being distributed continuously, we can divide up a charge distribution into infinitesimal charges dq, each of which will act as a tiny point charge.

$$d\vec{E} = \frac{1}{4\pi\varepsilon_0}\frac{dq}{r^2}\hat{r}$$

Then the electric field E, at any point, is obtained by summing over all the infinitesimal contributions, which is the integral

$$\vec{E} = \int_{(Q)} d\vec{E} = \int_{(Q)} \frac{dq}{4\pi\varepsilon_0 r^2}\hat{r}$$

where $dq = \begin{cases} \lambda dl \\ \sigma ds \\ \rho dv \end{cases}$

λ —linear charge density

σ —surface charge density

ρ —volume charge density

When the charge is uniformly distributed on a line, on a surface, or throughout a volume, then

$$\lambda = \frac{Q}{L}, \quad \sigma = \frac{Q}{S}, \rho = \frac{Q}{V}$$

L—length, S—area, V—volume

In three dimensions, **E** can be component form

$$E = \int dE_x i + \int dE_y j + \int dE_z k = \vec{E}_x + \vec{E}_y + \vec{E}_z$$

magnitude and direction of **E**.

点电荷系统：$E = \sum_i \vec{E}_i$

各个点电荷在 P 点 **E** 的向量和

Figure 9-9 Electric field due to two point charge systems

电荷连续分布的带电体 Q：

电荷微元 dq 在 p 点产生电场

$$d\vec{E} = \frac{1}{4\pi\varepsilon_0}\frac{dq}{r^2}\hat{r}$$

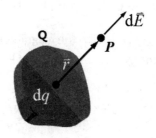

Figure 9-10 Superpositions for a distributed charge, Q

P 点总场强：$E = \int_Q d\vec{E}$

电荷线分布：线密度 $\lambda = \frac{dq}{dl}$

面分布：面密度 $\sigma = \frac{dq}{dA}$

体分布：体密度 $\rho = \frac{dq}{dV}$

质量均匀分布时：$\lambda = \frac{Q}{L}$,

$\sigma = \frac{Q}{S}, \rho = \frac{Q}{V}$

$$\vec{E} = \vec{E}_x + \vec{E}_y + \vec{E}_z$$

$$E = \sqrt{E_x^2 + E_y^2 + E_z^2},$$

$$\cos\alpha = \frac{E_x}{E}, \quad \cos\beta = \frac{E_y}{E}, \quad \cos\gamma = \frac{E_z}{E}.$$

α, β, γ are angles of **E** with three axis x, y, z.

Example 9.3 Electric Field Due to Two Charges: A charge q_1 = 7.0 μC is located at the origin, and a second charge q_2 = - 5.0 μC is located on the x axis, 0.30 m from the origin (Figure 9-11). Find

a. the electric field at the point P, which has coordinates (0, 0.40) m.

b. if an electron is placed at rest at P, what will its acceleration be initially?

c. the point at which the electric field equal to zero

Solution:

a. First, to find the magnitude of the electric field at P due to each charge. The magnitude of E$_1$ and E$_2$ are

$$E_1 = K\frac{q_1}{r_1^2} = 3.9*10^5 \text{ N/C}$$

$$E_2 = K\frac{q_2}{r_2^2} = 1.8*10^5 \text{ N/C}$$

The vector **E$_1$** has only a y component. The vector **E$_2$** has both x and y components. Hence, we can express the vectors as

E$_1$=3.9*10^5 **j** N/C

E$_2$=(1.1*10^5 **i** -1.4*10^5 **j**)N/C

The resultant field E at P is the superposition of E1 and E2:

E =**E$_1$** +**E$_2$** = (1.1 * 10^5 **i** + 2.5 * 10^5 **j**) N/C

From this result, we find that **E** makes an angle ϕ =66° with the

positive x axis and has a magnitude of 2.7 * 10^5 N/C.

b. The electron will feel a force **F** to opposite direction of **E** at point P.

场强大小：

$$E = \sqrt{E_x^2 + E_y^2 + E_z^2},$$

场强方向与 x, y, z 轴夹角：

α, β, γ

两个电荷产生的电场

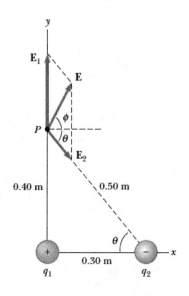

Figure 9-11 Example 9.3

P 点的场强为两电荷产生场强的向量叠加

F= -eE

So $\quad \mathbf{a} = \dfrac{\vec{F}}{m_e} = \dfrac{1.6*10^{-19}}{9.1*10^{-31}}(1.1*10^5\,\mathbf{i}+2.5*10^5\,\mathbf{j})$

$\qquad = (1.9*10^{16}\mathbf{i}+4.4*10^{16}\mathbf{j})$ m/s^2

c. $q_1 > |q_2|$, so the point E=0 must be at the position x from the origin, the right side of q_2,

$$K\frac{q_1}{x^2}+K\frac{q_2}{(x-0.30)^2}=0$$

Solve the equation, we have

$\quad x = 1.94$m

Example 9.4 The Electric Field Due to a Long Charged Rod: Find the 带电长直线场强
electric field some distance a from a long straight insulating rod of
uniformly distributed charge at a point P which is perpendicular to
the wire. Let λ be the charge per unit length (C/m).

Solution：

We set up a coordinate system so the wire is on the x axis with
origin at O. A segment of wire dx has charge dq= λ dx and is at the
position x. The field dE at P due to dq at x has magnitude

$$dE = \frac{\lambda dx}{4\pi\varepsilon_0 r^2}$$

and from geometry, we have

$$x = a\tan\left(\theta-\frac{\pi}{2}\right) = -a\cot\theta$$

$$dx = a\csc^2\theta d\theta$$

$$r^2 = a^2 + x^2 = a^2\csc^2\theta$$

$$dE_x = dE\cos\theta = \frac{\lambda}{4\pi\varepsilon_0 a}\cos\theta d\theta$$

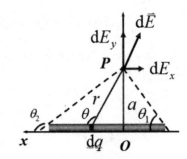

Figure 9-12 Example 9.4

长直带电线：$\theta_1 = 0, \theta_2 = \pi$

241

$$dE_y = dE\sin\theta = \frac{\lambda}{4\pi\varepsilon_0 a}\sin\theta d\theta$$

$$E = \frac{\lambda}{2\pi\varepsilon_0 a}$$

So $E_x = \int dE_x = \int_0^\pi \frac{\lambda}{4\pi\varepsilon_0 a}\cos\theta d\theta = 0$

$$E = E_y = \int dE_y = \int_0^\pi \frac{\lambda}{4\pi\varepsilon_0 a}\sin\theta d\theta = \frac{\lambda}{2\pi\varepsilon_0 a}$$

场强具有柱面对称性，方向垂直直线向外或向内，与到带电线的距离成反比。

Thus the field of a long straight line of charge decreases inversely as the distance from the wire.

Example 9.5 A Ring of Charge: A ring of radius *a* carries a uniformly distributed positive total charge *Q*. Calculate the electric field due to the ring at a point *P* lying a distance *x* from its center along the central axis perpendicular to the plane of the ring, Figure 9-13.

带电圆环中轴线上场强

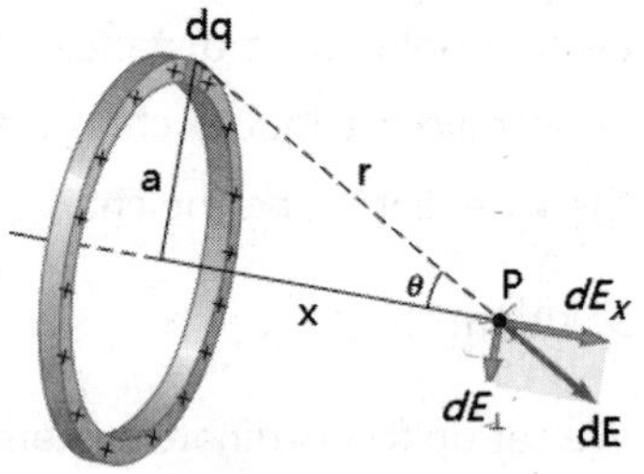

Solution:

Let $\lambda = \frac{Q}{2\pi a}$ be the charge per unit length. The electric field, d**E**, due to a particular segment of the ring of length dl , dq= λdl , has magnitude

Figure 9-13 **E** of a charge ring

$$dE = \frac{dq}{4\pi\varepsilon_0 r^2}$$

and $dE_\perp = dE\sin\theta$ $dE_x = dE\cos\theta$

By symmetry the only net electric field will be in x-direction, $E_\perp = 0$

So $E = E_x = \int \frac{dq}{4\pi\varepsilon_0 r^2}\cos\theta = \frac{Q}{4\pi\varepsilon_0 r^2}\cos\theta$

$$= \frac{Qx}{4\pi\varepsilon_0 (x^2+a^2)^{3/2}}$$

$$E = \frac{Qx}{4\pi\varepsilon_0 (x^2+a^2)^{3/2}}$$

沿轴线方向

If x=0, then E=0;

圆环中心处的场强为零

If x>>R, then E= $\dfrac{Q}{4\pi\varepsilon_0 x^2}$; the ring would appear to be a point

charge.

And how about if the charge is distributed uniformly over the thin circular disk of radius R;

$$dE_X = \frac{x}{4\pi\varepsilon_0(x^2+r^2)^{3/2}}\sigma 2\pi r dr$$

$$E = E_x = \frac{\sigma}{2\varepsilon_0}(1-\frac{x}{(x^2+R^2)^{1/2}})$$

When $x \ll R$ (a large plane), we can obtain a very useful result

$$E = \frac{\sigma}{2\varepsilon_0}$$

Thus the field near a large uniformly charged plane is uniform, and directed outward if the plane is positively charged.

For two large parallel planes

$$E_{\mathrm{I}} = E_{\mathrm{III}} = E_1 - E_2 = 0$$

$$E_{\mathrm{II}} = E_1 + E_2 = \frac{\sigma}{\varepsilon_0}$$

Example 9.6 A Circular Arc of Charge: A thin insulating semicircle of charge Q with radius R is centered at point C. Determine the electric field at point C due to the semicircle of charge.

Solution:

Because of the vertical symmetry (y axis) of the semicircle, horizontal component will cancel out since the charge is uniformly distributed $\lambda = \dfrac{Q}{\pi R}$, so we only need to calculate the vertical component of the electric field, E=E_y

x>>R 时，圆环可看做点电荷

均匀带电圆盘轴线场强：

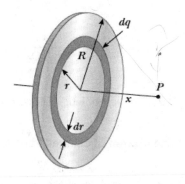

Figure 9-14 **E** of circular disk

无限大平面电场： $E = \dfrac{\sigma}{2\varepsilon_0}$

匀强电场，具有平面对称性。

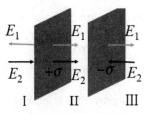

Figure 9-15 Electric field for two large parallel plates

两无限大平行平板带等量异

号电荷，板间场强 $E = \dfrac{\sigma}{\varepsilon_0}$

带电圆弧在曲率中心场强

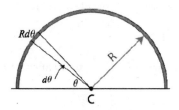

Figure 9-16 Example 9.6

$$dE_y = \frac{dq}{4\pi\varepsilon_0 R^2}\sin\theta, \quad dq = \lambda R d\theta$$

$$E = E_y = \frac{\lambda}{4\pi\varepsilon_0 R}\int_0^\pi \sin\theta d\theta = \frac{\lambda}{2\pi\varepsilon_0 R}$$

Q>0, direction of **E** points downward, away from the semicircle.

9.2.4 Motion of Charged Particles in a Uniform Electric Field

When a particle of charge q and mass m is placed in an electric field E, the electric force exerted on the charge is F=q E. If this is the only force exerted on the particle, it must be the net force and causes the particle to accelerate according to Newton's second law. Thus,

F=qE=ma

The acceleration of the particle is

$$a = \frac{qE}{m}$$

If E is uniform (that is, constant in magnitude and direction), then the acceleration is constant. If the particle has a positive charge, its acceleration is in the direction of the electric field. If the particle has a negative charge, its acceleration is in the direction opposite the electric field.

Example 9.7 Electric Force: Positively charge is distributed uniformly over a large, horizontal plane. An object of mass 5g is placed at a distance of 5cm above the plate. If the strength of the electric field at this location is E=10^6N/C, how much charge would the object need to have in order for the electrical repulsion to balance the gravitational pull?

Solution:

In order for F=qE to balance W=mg, we must have

$$qE = mg$$

so $\quad q = \dfrac{mg}{E}$ =50 nC

Apparently the object would have to carry a positive charge.

9.2.4 带点粒子在匀强电场中运动

带电粒子受到电场力作用获得加速度：

F=qE=ma

带电粒子在匀强电场中做匀加速度运动：

$$a = \frac{qE}{m}$$

Example 9.8 Acceleration a Positive Charge: A positive point charge *q* of mass *m* is released from rest in a uniform electric field **E** directed along the *x* axis, shown in Figure 9-17. Describe its motion.

Solution:

The acceleration is constant and is given by a=qE/m. The motion is simple linear motion along the *x* axis. Therefore, we can apply the equations of kinematics in one dimension

$$v = at = \frac{qE}{m}t$$

$$x = \frac{1}{2}at^2 = \frac{qE}{2m}t^2$$

$$W = Fx = qEx$$

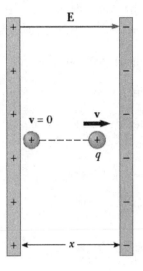

Figure 9-17 Example 9.8

9.3 Gauss's Law   ## 9.3 高斯定理

9.3.1 Electric Field Lines   ### 9.3.1 电场线

A convenient specialized pictorial representation for visualizing electric field patterns is created by drawing lines which are called electric field lines.

用电场线形象化表示电场

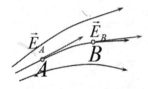

Figure 9-18 Electric field line

The electric field lines are related to the electric field in any region of space in the following manner:

电场线特征：

1. The electric field vector **E** is tangent to the electric field line at each point.

1. 电场线切线方向：**E** 方向

2. The number of lines per unit area through a surface perpendicular to the lines is proportional to the magnitude of the electric field in that region. Thus, the field lines are close together where the electric field is strong and far apart where the field is weak.

2. 电场线的疏密：**E** 大小。电场线密表示电场强，电场线疏表示电场弱。$E_A > E_B$

3. The electric field lines start on positive charges and terminate on negative charges, and never intersect each other. It is never interrupted in region without charge; this is called the continuity of electric field line.

3. 电场线始于正电荷或无限远，终止于负电荷或无限远。不会再没有电荷的地方中断。电场线是连续的。

4. Keep in mind: electric field lines do not actually exist. Electric field lines are shown in Figure 9-7, Figure 9-9 and Figure 9-19.

4. 电场线是假想线，用来形象化描述电场。

Example 9.9: Which of the following statements about electric field lines associated with electric charges is false?

a. Electric field lines can be either straight or curved.

b. Electric field lines can form closed loops.

c. Electric field lines begin on positive charges and end on negative charges.

d. Electric field lines can never intersect with one another.

Solution：b.

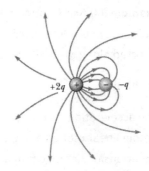

Figure 9-19 The electric field lines for a point charge +2q and a second point charge –q

9.3.2 Electric Flux

Electric Flux (Φ_E) is the amount of electric field lines penetrating a surface. Consider an electric field that is uniform in both magnitude and direction, as shown in Figure 9-20. The field lines penetrate a rectangular surface of area A, whose plane is oriented perpendicular to the field. The electric flux Φ_E through this surface is defined as the product

$$\Phi_E = EA$$

From the SI units of E and A, we see that Φ_E has units of **Nm^2/C**.

If the area A is not perpendicular to E, but rather makes an angle θ as shown in Figure 9-21, fewer field lines will pass through the area. In this case we define Φ_E

$$\Phi_E = E\,A_\perp = EA\cos\theta$$

The angle θ is the angle between **E** and **A** (A**n**)**,** so the electric flux can be written

$$\Phi_E = \mathbf{E}\cdot\mathbf{A}$$

Now let us consider the more general case—nonuniform electric field, arbitrary surface S, Figure 9-22.

For an infinite small area, the area d**A** can be treated as a flat and the electric field can be considered uniform over this tiny area. d**A** is a vector which direction is the normal direction of the area, d**A**=dA**n**. The flux through the area d**A** is

$$d\Phi_E = \mathbf{E}\cdot d\mathbf{A}$$

9.3.2 电场强度通量—电通量

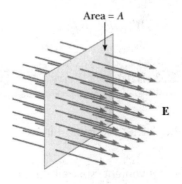

Figure 9-20 $\Phi_E = EA$

电通量 Φ_E：穿过某一面积的电力线数量。单位：**Nm^2/C**

匀强电场通过任意平面通量：

$$\Phi_E = \mathbf{E}\cdot\mathbf{A} = EA\cos\theta$$

电通量可以是正值、负值或零

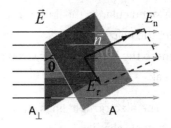

Figure 9-21 $\Phi_E = \mathbf{E}\cdot\mathbf{A}$

电场通过任意曲面的通量：

$$\Phi_E = \int \mathbf{E}\cdot d\mathbf{A}$$

then the electric flux through the entire surface is an integral

$$\Phi_E = \int \mathbf{E} \cdot d\mathbf{A}$$

We are often interested in evaluating the flux through a *closed surface*, which is defined as one that divides space into an inside and an outside region, so that one cannot move from one region to the other without crossing the surface. Flux through the total closed area is

$$\Phi_E = \oint_A \mathbf{E} \cdot d\mathbf{A}$$

Convention: Normal to closed surfaces point from the inside to the outside.

For a closed surface, we define the direction of d**A** to point outward from the enclosed volume, Figure 9-23. For a field line leaving the enclosed volume, the angle θ between **E** and d**A** must be less than $\frac{\pi}{2}$, so $\cos\theta > 0$ (Figure 9-23 ①). For a line entering the enclosed volume, Figure 9-23 ③, $\theta > \frac{\pi}{2}$, so $\cos\theta < 0$. Hence, flux entering the enclosed volume is negative, whereas flux leaving the volume is positive. Anywhere if d**A** is perpendicular to E, then $d\Phi_E = 0$ (Figure 9-23 ②).

Total flux through the closed surface is positive if there is more flux from inside to outside than outside to inside, and negative if there is more flux from outside to inside than inside to outside.

Example 9.10 Electric Flux Through a Sphere: What is the electric flux through a sphere that has a radius of 1.00 m and carries a charge of +1.00 μ C at its center?

Solution:

The magnitude of the electric field 1.00 m from this charge is

$$E = \frac{1}{4\pi\varepsilon_0}\frac{Q}{r^2} = 8.99*10^3 \text{ N/C}$$

The field radiates outward and is therefore everywhere perpendicular to the surface of the sphere. The flux through the sphere is thus

d**A** 表示微元面积，是向量

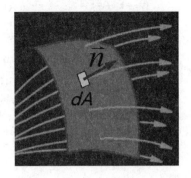

Figure 9-22 $\Phi_E = \int \mathbf{E} \cdot d\mathbf{A}$. 通过任意曲面的电通量

闭合曲面正法向：由内向外

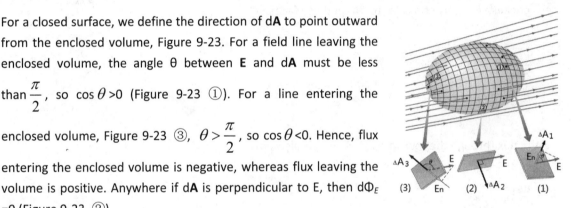

Figure 9-23 $\Phi_E = \oint_A \mathbf{E} \cdot d\mathbf{A}$

通过任意闭合曲面的电通量

通过球面的电通量计算

穿过球面的电通量，与半径无关，只与球面所包围电荷有关。

$$\Phi_E = \mathbf{E} \cdot \mathbf{A} = E\,4\pi r^2 = \frac{Q}{\varepsilon_0} = 1.13 * 10^5 \text{ N m}^2/\text{C}$$

$$\Phi_E = \frac{Q}{\varepsilon_0}$$

Example 9.11 Electric Flux Through a Cube: Find the net electric flux through the surface of a cube of edge length L, oriented as shown in Figure 9-24.

a. A uniform electric field **E** oriented in the *x* direction.

b. $E_x = 2x + L$, $E_y = 0$, $E_z = 0$

Solution:

The net flux is the sum of the fluxes through all faces of the cube.

a. First, note that the flux through four of the faces (3, 4, 5, 6) is zero because **E** is perpendicular to *d***A** on these faces.

and $\Phi_{E1} = -E\,l^2$, $\Phi_{E2} = E\,l^2$, so

$$\Phi_E = \oint_A \mathbf{E} \cdot d\mathbf{A} = 0$$

通过立方体的通量

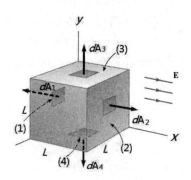

Figure 9-24 Example 9.11

b. the flux through the four faces (3, 4, 5, 6) is also zero.

$$\Phi_{E1} = -l * l^2 = -l^3$$

$$\Phi_{E2} = (2\,l + l)\,l^2 = 3\,l^3$$

$$\Phi_E = \Phi_{E1} + \Phi_{E2} + 0 = 2\,l^3 \text{ Nm}^2/\text{C}$$

9.3.3 Gauss's Law

In this section we describe a general relationship between the net electric flux through a closed surface (called a ***Gaussian surface***) and the charge enclosed by the surface. This relationship, known as *Gauss's law*, is of fundamental importance in the study of electric fields.

According to example 9.10, we conclude that the net flux through any closed surface surrounding a point charge q is given by q/ε_0 and is independent of the shape of that surface. From example

9.3.3 高斯定理

高斯面：电场中任意闭合曲面

9.11(a), we conclude that the net electric flux through a closed surface that surrounds no charge is zero. And according to the superposition of electric field we get the precise relation between the electric flux through a closed surface and the net charge enclosed within that surface—Gauss's law: **The net electric flux** Φ_E **of an arbitrary closed surface in the vacuum is equal to the net charge inside the surface divided by** ε_0

通过任意高斯面的电通量与高斯面所包围电荷的代数和成正比。表明电场源于电荷，是有源场。

$$\Phi_E = \oint_A \mathbf{E} \cdot d\mathbf{A} = \frac{Q_{encl}}{\varepsilon_0}$$

$$\Phi_E = \oint_A \mathbf{E} \cdot d\mathbf{A} = \frac{Q_{encl}}{\varepsilon_0}$$

Q_{encl}：高斯面内的总电荷量。

Where Q_{encl} represents the net charge inside the surface and **E** represents the electric field at any point on the surface.

Φ_E：由高斯面内的电荷决定。

Note: **E** represents the *total electric field,* which includes contributions from charges both inside and outside the surface.

E：高斯面上的电场强度，由空间所有电荷产生，即高斯面内、外所有电荷共同产生。

$$Q_{encl} = \sum_i q_i \quad \text{system of charge particles}$$

点电荷系统，高斯面内所包含电荷的代数和：$Q_{encl} = \sum_i q_i$

$$Q_{encl} = \int dq \quad \text{continuous distributed charge}$$

$$dq = \lambda dl, \quad dq = \sigma ds, \quad dq = \rho dv$$

电荷连续分布系统，高斯面内包含总电荷：$Q_{encl} = \int dq$

Gauss's law gives a simple way to calculate the distribution of electric field for a given charge distribution with sufficient symmetry. Useful for finding the electric field due to charge distributions for cases of:

用高斯定理可方便计算具有对称性的电场强度：

1) Spherical symmetry

2) Cylindrical symmetry

3) Planar symmetry

1）球面对称

2）柱面对称

3）平面对称

The Gaussian surface had better satisfy one or more of the following conditions:

高斯面的选择最好满足如下条件，使高斯面上的场强：

The value of the electric field is E = constant.

a. E 的大小为常数

E and d**A** are parallel, so **E** · d**A**=EdA

b. E 的方向与高斯面法向平行

E and d**A** are perpendicular, so **E** · d**A**=0

E is equal to zero everywhere on the surface.

c. E 的方向与高斯面法向垂直

d. E 为零

Note: The surface integral in Guass's law is taken over the entire Gaussian surface.

Example 9.12 A Sphere Shell: A thin spherical shell of radius R possesses a total net charge Q that is uniformly distributed on it. Determine the electric field at points

均匀带电球壳内外场强分布

a. outside the shell

b. inside the shell

Solution:

Because the charge is distributed symmetrically, the electric field must also be symmetric.

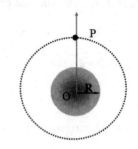

Figure 9-25 a: E outside a sphere

a. r>R. at point P, we chose the surface, radius is r, as Gaussian surface

$$\Phi_E = \oint_A \mathbf{E} \cdot d\mathbf{A} = E \, 4\pi r^2 = \frac{Q}{\varepsilon_0}$$

$$E = \frac{1}{4\pi\varepsilon_0} \frac{Q}{r^2}, r>R; \quad E=0, r<R$$

So $\quad E = \frac{1}{4\pi\varepsilon_0} \frac{Q}{r^2} \quad$ r>R

Direction of E is outward along radial.

b. we chose a sphere surface r<R as Gaussian surface

$$\Phi_E = \oint_A \mathbf{E} \cdot d\mathbf{A} = E \, 4\pi r^2 = 0$$

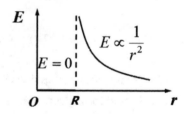

Figure 9-25 b: Electric field distribution of a sphere shell

So $\quad E=0 \quad$ r<R

The electric field shown in Figure 9-25 b.

场强方向沿半径向外（球壳带正电荷）或向内（负电荷）

Example 9.13 Solid Sphere of Charge: An insulating solid sphere of radius R has a uniform volume charge density ρ and carries a total positive charge Q (Figure 9-26). Determine the electric field

均匀带电球体场强分布：

a. outside the sphere

b. inside the sphere

$$E = \frac{1}{4\pi\varepsilon_0} \frac{Q}{r^2} \quad r>R$$

Solution:

$$E = \frac{1}{4\pi\varepsilon_0} \frac{Q}{R^3} r \quad r<R$$

a. The field outside a spherically symmetric distribution of charge is the same as that for a point charge of the same magnitude located at the center of the sphere, so

$$E = \frac{1}{4\pi\varepsilon_0} \frac{Q}{r^2} \qquad r>R$$

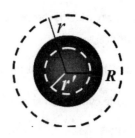

b. In this case we select a spherical Gaussian surface having radius r <R,

$$Q_{encl} = \int dq = \rho \frac{4}{3}\pi r^3, \quad \rho = \frac{Q}{\frac{4}{3}\pi R^3}$$

$$\Phi_E = \oint_A \mathbf{E} \cdot d\mathbf{A} = E\, 4\pi r^2 = \frac{Q_{encl}}{\varepsilon_0}$$

$$E = \frac{1}{4\pi\varepsilon_0} \frac{Q}{R^3} r \qquad r<R$$

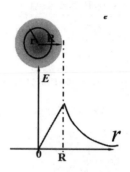

Figure 9-26 b: Electric field of a solid sphere

E 的方向沿半径向外

Thus the field increases linearly with r, until r=R. it then decreases as 1/r, as plotted in Figure 9-26 b.

Example 9.14 The Electric Field Due to a Long Uniform Line

均匀长直带电细线场强：

A very long straight wire possesses a uniform positive charge per unit length, λ. Calculate the electric field at a point near the wire.

Solution:

Because of the cylindrical symmetry we select a cylinder, for radius is r and height is l, as Gaussian surface.

Since E is parallel to the ends, there is no flux through the ends of the cylinder, $\mathbf{E} \perp d\mathbf{A}$. On the curved side of the cylinder $\mathbf{E} \parallel d\mathbf{A}$. So Gauss's law tells us

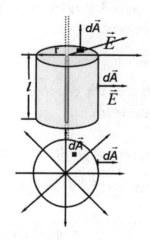

Figure 9-27 Long uniform line of charge

$$\Phi_E = \oint_A \mathbf{E} \cdot d\mathbf{A} = E * 2\pi r l = \frac{Q_{encl}}{\varepsilon_0} = \frac{\lambda l}{\varepsilon_0}$$

Hence $\quad E = \frac{1}{2\pi\varepsilon_0} \frac{\lambda}{r}$

$$E = \frac{1}{2\pi\varepsilon_0} \frac{\lambda}{r}$$

场强有柱面对称性

Direction of E is perpendicular to the curved side surface of the cylinder.

方向：垂直带电直线向外或向内（负电导线）

This is the same result as we got using Coulomb's law.

For long cylindrical shell of radius R, λ is charge per unit length

长直圆柱壳的电场：

$$E=0 \qquad\qquad r<R$$

$$E=\frac{1}{2\pi\varepsilon_0}\frac{\lambda}{r} \qquad r>R$$

$$E=0 \qquad\qquad r<R$$

$$E=\frac{1}{2\pi\varepsilon_0}\frac{\lambda}{r} \qquad r>R$$

For an infinite uniform solid charged cylinder of radius *R*. λ is charge per unit length

长直圆柱体的电场：

$$E=\frac{1}{2\pi\varepsilon_0}\frac{\lambda r}{R^2} \qquad r<R$$

$$E=\frac{1}{2\pi\varepsilon_0}\frac{\lambda}{r} \qquad r>R$$

$$E=\frac{1}{2\pi\varepsilon_0}\frac{\lambda r}{R^2} \qquad r<R$$

$$E=\frac{1}{2\pi\varepsilon_0}\frac{\lambda}{r} \qquad r>R$$

Example 9.15 Infinite Plane of Charge: Find the electric field due to a nonconducting infinite plane with uniform surface charge density σ.

无限大均匀带电平面 E：

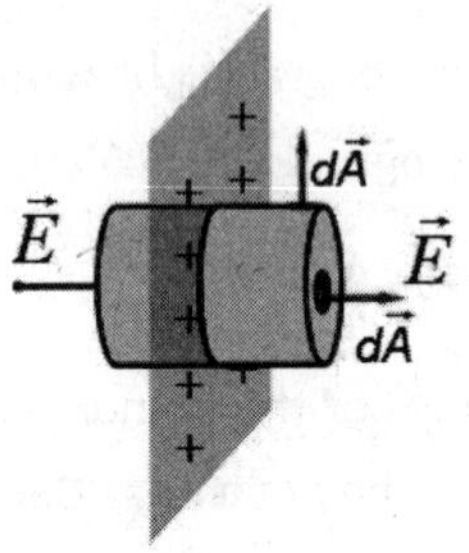

Solution:

We select a cylindrical Gaussian surface penetrating an infinite sheet of charge.

Each end of the Gaussian surface ($\triangle$A) **E**∥**A**, and on curved surface of cylinder **E**⊥**dA**. Hence

Figure 9-28 a: Example 9.15
高斯面侧柱面的电通量为零。
每一柱底面的通量是 E $\triangle$ A

$$\Phi_E=\oint_A \ \mathbf{E}\cdot\mathbf{dA}= 2\triangle A*E=\frac{\sigma\triangle A}{\varepsilon_0}$$

$$E=\frac{\sigma}{2\varepsilon_0}$$

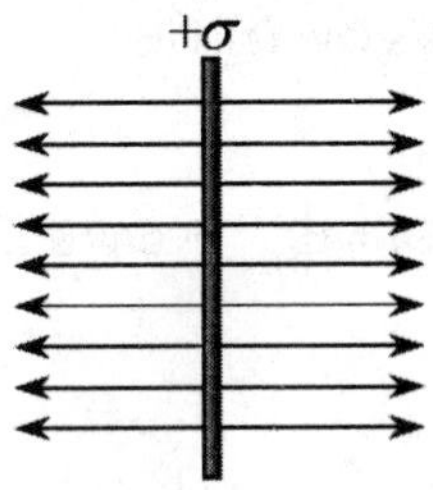

Figure 9-28 b: 无限大平面周围是匀强电场

Direction of E is perpendicular to the charge surface pointing away from the surface.

Because the distance from each flat end of the cylinder to the plane does not appear in Equation above, we conclude that the field is uniform everywhere.

场强方向垂直板面向外或向内（负电平面）：$E=\dfrac{\sigma}{2\varepsilon_0}$

9.4 Electric Potential Energy and Potential (V)　　9.4 电势能和电势

The energy point of view can be used in electricity, and it is especially useful. In many cases it is a tool in solving problems more easily than by using forces and electric field for energy is a scalar quantity.

用能量概念可方便求解问题

9.4.1 Work done by Electric Force

9.4.1 电场力的功

When a test charge q is placed in an electric field E created by some source charge distribution, the electric force acting on the test charge is qE. It is easy to see the force qE is conservative because the force between charges described by Coulomb's law is conservative.

静电力是保守力，做功与路径无关。

When analyzing electric and magnetic fields, we use the notation d**l** to represent an infinitesimal displacement vector that is oriented tangent to a path through space. This path may be straight or curved, and an integral performed along this path is called either a *path integral* or a *line integral*.

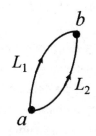

Figure 9-29 a: Path integral

For an infinitesimal displacement $d\,l$ of a charge, the work done by the electric field on the charge is

$$dW = F \cdot d\,l = qE \cdot d\,l$$

路径积分或线积分：

$$W = {}_{L_1}\!\int_a^b qE \cdot dl = {}_{L_2}\!\int_a^b qE \cdot dl$$

For a finite displacement of the charge from point a to point b along the path L_1, Figure 9-28, work done electric force is

$$W = \int_a^b qE \cdot dl$$

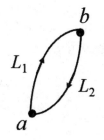

Figure 9-29 b: Circulation Theorem

It is not related with traveling path, but depends on its initial and final position. So work done by the electric force on the closed path $a \rightarrow b \rightarrow a$ is

$$W = \oint_{aba} qE \cdot dl = 0$$

$$W = \oint_{aL_1bL_2a} qE \cdot dl = 0$$

We have,

$$\oint E \cdot dl = 0$$

It is called **Circulation Theorem** of Electrostatic Field:

The work done by electrostatic field force to any test charge along a closed curve equals zero.

9.4.2 Potential Energy U

We can define electric potential energy for electric force is conservative. When a charge q moves from some point a to some point b we define the change in electric potential energy,

$\Delta U = U_b - U_a$, as the negative of the work done by the electric force to move the charge from a to b: W= $-\Delta U$

$$\Delta U = U_b - U_a = -q \int_a^b E \cdot dl$$

For a given position of the test charge in the field, a, the electric potential energy belongs to the charge-field system. To select *b* point as the reference point of electric potential energy, means U_b=0, the charge-field system has a potential energy U_a relative to position b which potential energy equals zero.

$$U_a = q \int_a^b E \cdot dl \qquad U_b = 0$$

The electric potential energy of *q* equals the work done by the electrostatic force when *q* is moved from *a* to the reference point b along an arbitrary path. Usually, we let b=∞, U(∞)=0.

For a charge q in an electric field of a point charge Q, the potential energy of q is

$$U = q \int_r^\infty \frac{1}{4\pi\varepsilon_0} \frac{Q}{r^2} \, dr = \frac{1}{4\pi\varepsilon_0} \frac{qQ}{r}$$

For a system of two charged particles, we can express the potential energy of the system as

环路定理： $\oint E \cdot dl = 0$

静电场力做功与路径无关。场强沿任意闭合路径的环量为零。静电场是保守场。

9.4.2 电势能

电场力是保守力。

电场力的功等于相应电势能增量的负值： W= $-\Delta U$

系统电势能变化：

$$\Delta U = U_b - U_a = -q \int_a^b E \cdot dl$$

选择 b 为势能零点 U(b)=0：

$$U_a = q \int_a^b E \cdot dl$$

对有限大小带电体，U(∞)=0：

$$U_a = q \int_a^\infty E \cdot dl$$

电势能定义：移动电荷 q 从 a 点到零势能点电场力所做的功。通常取无限远为零势能点。

电势能是空间位置函数，具有相对性，是标量。任意两点电势能差有确定数值。

点电荷电场： U= $\dfrac{1}{4\pi\varepsilon_0} \dfrac{qQ}{r}$

254

$$U = \frac{1}{4\pi\varepsilon_0} \frac{qQ}{r}$$

If the system consists of more than two charged particles, we can obtain the total potential energy by calculating U for every pair of charges and summing the terms algebraically. As an example, the total potential energy of the system of three charges shown in Figure 9-30 is

$$U = \frac{1}{4\pi\varepsilon_0} \left(\frac{q_1 q_2}{r_{12}} + \frac{q_1 q_3}{r_{13}} + \frac{q_2 q_3}{r_{23}} \right)$$

We can interpret this as follows: imagine that q_1 is fixed at the position shown in Figure 9-30, but that q_2 and q_3 are at infinity. The work by an external force must do to bring q_2 from infinity to its position near q_1 is $\frac{1}{4\pi\varepsilon_0} \frac{q_1 q_2}{r_{12}}$. The last two terms represent the work required to bring q_3 from infinity to its position near q_1 and q_2 is $\frac{1}{4\pi\varepsilon_0} \left(\frac{q_1 q_3}{r_{13}} + \frac{q_2 q_3}{r_{23}} \right)$.

两个电荷系统的电势能：

$$U = \frac{1}{4\pi\varepsilon_0} \frac{qQ}{r}$$

三个电荷系统的电势能：

$$U = \frac{1}{4\pi\varepsilon_0} \left(\frac{q_1 q_2}{r_{12}} + \frac{q_1 q_3}{r_{13}} + \frac{q_2 q_3}{r_{23}} \right)$$

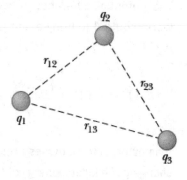

Figure 9-30 Three point charges are fixed at the positions.

9.4.3 Electric Potential V and Potential Difference

1. Potential V

The electric potential energy is related to the test charge q, not a property of the field. The potential energy per unit charge U/q is independent of the value of q and has a unique value at every point in an electric field. This quantity U/q is called the electric potential (or simply the potential) V. Thus, the electric potential V at any point P in an electric field is defined

$$V_p = \frac{U_p}{q} = \int_P^\infty E \cdot dl$$

Infinity, ∞, is a point where the potential energy equals zero, and can be chosen arbitrarily, but usually we choose infinity, ∞, as our zero potential.

The potential at a point equals the work required to bring a unit

9.4.3 电势和电势差

1. 电势 V

电势能不仅是空间位置的函数，而且与实验电荷有关。不能反映场本身的性质。

电势定义：

$$V_p = \frac{U_p}{q} = \int_P^\infty E \cdot dl$$ ，电势是标量。

∞：表示零势能点

电场中某点的电势：单位正电

positive charge from this point to the zero point of electric potential.

Electric potential is nothing to do with test charge, it is only related to the position of electric field.

Potential is a scalar same as potential energy.

Unit of potential energy is **V(volt), 1V=1 J/C.**

2. Potential Difference ΔV

The potential difference between the points *a* and *b* equals the work required to bring a unit positive charge from point *a* to point *b*.

$$\Delta V = V_b - V_a = \frac{U_b - U_a}{q} = -\int_a^b E \cdot dl$$

If an external force moves a test charge from a to *b* without changing the kinetic energy of the test charge, the agent performs work which changes the potential energy of the system:

$$W = \Delta U = q\Delta V$$

$$U_b - U_a = q(V_b - V_a) = qV_{ba}$$

A simple special case is when the field is uniform, for example, a field between two parallel plates. A path parallel the electric field lines from point a at the positive plate to point b at the negative plate gives

$$V_b - V_a = -\int_a^b E \cdot ds = -E\int_a^b ds = -Ed$$

Where d is the distance, parallel to the field lines, between points a and b.

We can see from above equation that the units for electric field intensity can be written as volts per meter (V/m) as well as Newton per Coulomb (N/C).

$$1N/C = 1V/m$$

A unit of energy commonly used in atomic and nuclear physics is the electron volt (eV), a new energy unit, which is defined as the energy a charge-field system gains or loses when a charge of

荷从这点移动到零电势能点电场力所做的功—单位电荷的电势能。

电势与试验电荷无关，由电场位置决定，电势是场点位置函数。电势是标量。
电势单位：伏特，V

2. 电势差 ΔV

单位正试验电荷从 a 移动到 b 电场力所做的功：

$$\Delta V = -\int_a^b E \cdot dl$$

外力克服电场力做的功等于电势能增量： $W = \Delta U = q\Delta V$

电势能与电势差关系：

$$\Delta U = qV_{ba}$$

匀强电场中电势差：

两带有等量异号电荷的无限大平行平板，间距为 d。a 板带正电，b 板带负电。两板间的电势差 $V_b - V_a = -Ed$。

电场强度单位：V/m，或 N/C

能量的另一个单位：电子伏特常用于原子和核物理问题中。

magnitude e (that is, an electron or a proton) is moved through a potential difference of 1 V. Because 1 V = 1 J/C and because the fundamental charge is 1.60 * 10⁻¹⁹ C, the electron volt is related to the joule as follows:

$$1 \, eV = 1.60 * 10^{-19} J$$

3. Equipotential Surfaces

Equipotentials are surfaces with constant potential, similar to altitude lines on a topographic map.

Equipotential always runs perpendicular to electric field lines. The work done in moving a particle along equipotential is zero since the electric force is conservative. The direction of electric field always points to the direction decreasing electric potential.

Electric field line and equipotential surface are perpendicular to each other everywhere.

The equipotential surfaces of a uniform electric field consist of a family of parallel planes that are all perpendicular to the field.

The surfaces are drawn so that the potential difference between successive surfaces is a constant value, ΔV. If the distance between successive surfaces is d, then

$$\Delta V = -Ed$$

So, if d is bigger, E will be weaker.

The labeled points in Figure 9-31 are on a series of equipotential surfaces associated with an electric field.

$$E_A < E_D$$

The work done by the electric field on a positively charged particle, q, that moves from *A* to *B* is *W= qΔV =0*; from *B* to *C* is *W=2q*; from *C* to *D* is *W=q*; from *D* to *E* is *W=-q*.

Example 9.16 A Proton in a Uniform E: In two parallel plates (see Example 9.8, Figure 9-17), the proton is free to move from positive to negative plate and undergoes a displacement of d=0.50 m in the direction of **E**, whose magnitude is 8.0 * 10⁴ V/m.

a. Will its electric potential energy increase or decrease?

b. If we put another charge q=+8e at the same position with the

3. 等势面

电势相等点组成的一系列面。

沿等势面移动电荷电场力不做功。电场线与等势面垂直并指向电势降落方向。

电场线垂直于等势面。

匀强电场等势面平行等间距。

等势面图：任意相邻两等势面电势差相等。等势面稀疏处场强弱，密集处场强强。

$$\Delta V = -Ed$$

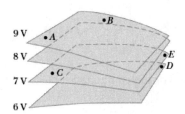

Figure 9-31 Equipotential surfaces

质子在匀强电场中运动。

proton, are their change of potential energy and change of potential the same?

c. Find the speed of the two charges after completing the 0.50 m displacement in the electric field.

Solution:

The proton will move from the positive toward the negative plate,

a. its potential energy decreases as its kinetic energy gets larger.

$\Delta U = -eEd < 0, \quad \Delta V = -Ed$

The proton moves from high potential to low potential.

b. for a charge q=8e

$\Delta U = -8eEd, \quad \Delta V = -Ed$

Two charges have the same electric potential, but the charge q=8e has more potential energy.

c. for the proton q=e, according to the work-kinetic energy theorem

$\Delta U = -eEd = -W, \text{ and } W = \Delta K = \frac{1}{2}mv^2 - 0$

$v = \sqrt{\dfrac{2eEd}{m}} = 2.8 * 10^6 \text{ m/s}$

For the charge q=8e, calculating the same way, we have

$v = \sqrt{\dfrac{8eEd}{m}} = 5.6 * 10^6 \text{ m/s}$

9.4.4 Superposition of Electric Potential

1. Electric potential due to point charges

The electric potential at a distance r form a single point charge Q can be derived from

$$V_p = \frac{U_p}{q} = \int_{P}^{\infty} E \cdot dl$$

9.4.4 电势叠加原理

1. 点电荷电势

由电势定义导出。

for a single point charge: V=0 at r=∞ and we have E=$\dfrac{1}{4\pi\varepsilon_0}\dfrac{Q}{r^2}$, so

$$V=\int_r^\infty E \cdot ds = \int_r^\infty \frac{1}{4\pi\varepsilon_0}\frac{Q}{r^2}\,dr = \frac{1}{4\pi\varepsilon_0}\frac{Q}{r}$$

We can think of V as the potential difference between r and infinity. V decreases with the first power of the distance. The potential near a positive charge is positive, and decreases toward zero at infinity. For a negative charge, the potential is negative and increases toward zero at infinity. Potential has spherically symmetry.

2. Superposition of potential

To find the electric potential due to a collection of point charges is far easier than electric fields since the electric potential is a scalar.

According to superposition principle of field intensity. The electric potential at point P is the algebraic sum of the potentials due to the individual charges.

$$V=\sum_{i=1}^n V_i = \sum_{i=1}^n \frac{1}{4\pi\varepsilon_0}\frac{Q_i}{r_i}$$

This is the Potential due to the system of point charges.

If the electric charge Q can be treated as being distributed continuously, we can divide up a charge distribution into infinitesimal charges dq, each of which will act as a point charge.

$$dV = \frac{1}{4\pi\varepsilon_0}\frac{dq}{r}$$

Then the electric potential, at any point, is obtained by summing over all the infinitesimal contributions, which is the integral

$$V = \int_Q dV = \int_Q \frac{1}{4\pi\varepsilon_0}\frac{dq}{r}$$

Example 9.17 Work Required to Establish a System of Point charges: Two point charges (5 μC and 2 μC) are placed 0.5 meters apart. How much work was required to establish the charge

令无穷远处的电势为零。

点电荷电势：V=$\dfrac{1}{4\pi\varepsilon_0}\dfrac{Q}{r}$

电势可看做场点与无穷远处电势差。正电荷电场电势为正，随距离增加而减小，直至为零。负电荷电场电势为负，随距离增加而增加，直至为零。电势呈球面对称，即等势面为球面。

2. 电势叠加原理

在点电荷系产生电场中，某点电势是各个点电荷单独存在时，在该点产生的电势代数和。

点电荷系统电势——标量叠加：

$$V=\sum_{i=1}^n \frac{1}{4\pi\varepsilon_0}\frac{Q_i}{r_i}$$

电荷连续分布的带电体电势：

$$V = \int_Q \frac{1}{4\pi\varepsilon_0}\frac{dq}{r}$$

建立点电荷系统所需的功。

system? What is the electric potential halfway between the two charges?

Solution:

$$W=U=\frac{1}{4\pi\varepsilon_0}\frac{qQ}{r}=0.18J$$

$$V=\frac{1}{4\pi\varepsilon_0}\frac{q}{r/2}+\frac{1}{4\pi\varepsilon_0}\frac{Q}{r/2}=252\ kv$$

3. The potential due to continuous charge distributions

We can calculate the electric potential due to a continuous charge distribution in two ways.

1) If the charge distribution is known, we divide the charge distribution into small charge element dq, treating this element as a point charge (Figure 9-32). The electric potential dV at some point P due to the charge element dq is

$$dV=\frac{1}{4\pi\varepsilon_0}\frac{dq}{r}$$

To obtain the total potential at point P, we integrate dV to include contributions from all elements of the charge distribution. We can express V as

$$V=\int_Q\frac{1}{4\pi\varepsilon_0}\frac{dq}{r}$$

Note that this expression for V uses a particular reference: the electric potential is taken to be zero when point P is infinitely far from the charge distribution.

The object has different charge distribution, dq expresses as

$dq=\lambda dl$ linear charge density

$dq=\sigma ds$ surface charge density

$dq=\rho dv$ volume charge density

3.电荷连续分布体电势计算

两种方法：

1）由电势叠加原理求电势。

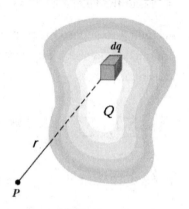

Figure 9-32 Potential of dq

dq 在 P 点电势：$dV=\frac{1}{4\pi\varepsilon_0}\frac{dq}{r}$

电势叠加原理计算电荷连续分布的带电体的电势：

$$V=\int_Q\frac{1}{4\pi\varepsilon_0}\frac{dq}{r}$$

电荷线密度：$dq=\lambda dl$

电荷面密度：$dq=\sigma ds$

电荷体密度：$dq=\rho dv$

Example 9.18 Potential Due to a Ring of Charge

A thin circular ring of radius R carries a uniformly distributed charge Q. Determine the electric potential at a point P in the axis of the ring a distance x from its center (Figure 9-33).

Solution:

Each point on the ring is equidistant from point P, and the distance r is $\sqrt{x^2 + R^2}$.

So $V = \int_Q \frac{1}{4\pi\varepsilon_0} \frac{dq}{r} = \frac{1}{4\pi\varepsilon_0} \frac{Q}{\sqrt{x^2 + R^2}}$

If $x \gg R$, then $V = \frac{1}{4\pi\varepsilon_0} \frac{Q}{x}$

This means if the point P is far from the ring, we can treat it as a point charge.

If x=0, then $V = \frac{1}{4\pi\varepsilon_0} \frac{Q}{R}$

带电细圆环轴线上的电势

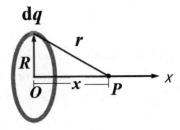

Figure 9-33 a: Potential of ring

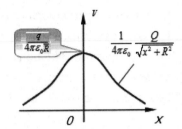

Figure 9-33 b: Potential distribution of a ring

$$V = \frac{1}{4\pi\varepsilon_0} \frac{Q}{\sqrt{x^2 + R^2}}$$

Example 9.19 Electric Potential on the Axis of a Uniformly Charged Disk:

A thin flat disk, of radius a, carries a uniformly distributed charge Q. Find the electric potential at point P on the axis of a disk, a distance x from its center (Figure 9-34).

Solution:

Divide the disk into thin rings of radius r and thickness dr. Each thin ring has area dA= $2\pi r dr$ and dq= σ dA.

So $dq = \frac{Q}{\pi a^2} 2\pi r dr = \frac{2Qr dr}{a^2}$

$dV = \frac{1}{4\pi\varepsilon_0} \frac{dq}{\sqrt{x^2 + r^2}}$

Then the potential at P is

$V = \frac{2Q}{4\pi\varepsilon_0 a^2} \int_0^a \frac{r dr}{\sqrt{x^2 + r^2}} = \frac{Q}{2\pi\varepsilon_0 a^2} \sqrt{x^2 + r^2} \Big|_{r=0}^{r=a}$

带电薄圆盘轴线上的电势

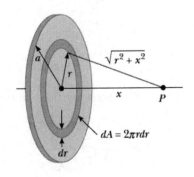

Figure 9-34 A uniformly charged disk

$$V = \frac{Q}{2\pi\varepsilon_0 a^2} (\sqrt{x^2 + r^2} - x)$$

$$= \frac{Q}{2\pi\varepsilon_0 a^2}(\sqrt{x^2 + r^2} - x)$$

2) If the electric field is already known from other considerations, we can calculate the electric potential due to a continuous charge distribution using the definition of potential.

$$\Delta V = -\int_a^b E \cdot dl$$

If the charge distribution has sufficient symmetry, we first evaluate **E** at any point using Gauss's law and then substitute the value obtained into the definition to determine the potential difference V between any two points. We then choose the electric potential V to be zero at some convenient point, for example $r=\infty$.

$$V_a = \int_a^\infty E \cdot dl$$

Example 9.20 Electric Potential of a Spherical Shell

Find the electric potential both inside and outside a uniformly charged shell of radius R and total charge Q.

Solution:

We know the electric field distribution of a spherical shell from Example 9.12 is

$$E = \frac{1}{4\pi\varepsilon_0}\frac{Q}{r^2} \qquad r>R$$

$$E = 0 \qquad r<R$$

Potential at point outside the sphere is

$$V = \int_r^\infty E \cdot dl = \frac{1}{4\pi\varepsilon_0}\frac{Q}{r} \qquad r>R$$

$$V = \int_D^\infty E \cdot dl = \int_D^C E \cdot dl + \int_C^\infty E \cdot dl = \frac{1}{4\pi\varepsilon_0}\frac{Q}{R} \qquad r<R$$

$$V_C = V_D = \frac{1}{4\pi\varepsilon_0}\frac{Q}{R}$$

2）场强分布已知，可由电势定义来求电场。

电荷分布具有对称性，可用高斯定理先求电场，再由电势定义求出电势。

$$V_a = \int_a^\infty E \cdot dl$$

均匀球壳电势分布

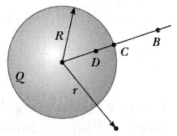

Figure 9-35 a: Example 9.20

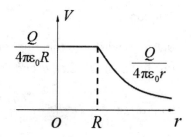

Figure 9-35 b: Potential distribution of a sphere shell

$$V = \frac{1}{4\pi\varepsilon_0}\frac{Q}{r} \qquad r>R$$

So, the whole sphere inside and surface are equipotentials, shown in Figure 9-35 b.

$$V = \frac{1}{4\pi\varepsilon_0}\frac{Q}{R} \qquad r<R$$

Example 9.21 Uniformly Charged Solid Insulating Sphere

均匀带电绝缘球体：电势分布

An insulating solid sphere of radius R has a uniform positive volume charge density and total charge Q. Find the potential inside and outside the sphere.

Solution:

According to the solution of Example 9.13, we know

$$E_1 = \frac{1}{4\pi\varepsilon_0}\frac{Q}{r^2} \qquad r>R$$

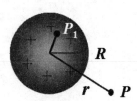

Figure 9-36 Example 9.21

$$E_2 = \frac{1}{4\pi\varepsilon_0}\frac{Q}{R^3}r \qquad r<R$$

So for r>R

$$V_p = \int_r^\infty E \cdot dr = \frac{1}{4\pi\varepsilon_0}\frac{Q}{r}$$

$$V = \frac{1}{4\pi\varepsilon_0}\frac{Q}{r}, \qquad r>R$$

$$V = \frac{1}{8\pi\varepsilon_0}\frac{Q}{R}(3-\frac{r^2}{R^2}), \quad r<R$$

For inside point of the sphere r<R

$$V_{P1} = \int_r^R E_2 \cdot dr + \int_R^\infty E_1 \cdot dr = \frac{1}{8\pi\varepsilon_0}\frac{Q}{R}(3-\frac{r^2}{R^2})$$

When r=0, $V = \frac{3}{8\pi\varepsilon_0}\frac{Q}{R}$

Example 9.22 Concentric Spheres

带电同心球电势

There are two concentric charged spherical surfaces with radius R_1 and R_2, and the charge quantity on the surfaces is Q_1 and Q_2 respectively. Find the potential difference of the two surfaces.

Solution:

We can calculate the potential difference in two ways:

a. By definition.

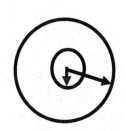

Figure 9-37 Example 9.22

We can get the electric field through Gauss's law

$E_1 = 0$ $r < R_1$

$E_2 = \dfrac{1}{4\pi\varepsilon_0}\dfrac{Q_1}{r^2}$ $R_1 < r < R_2$

$E_3 = \dfrac{1}{4\pi\varepsilon_0}\dfrac{Q_1 + Q_2}{r^2}$ $r > R$

$$\Delta V = V_2 - V_1 = -\int_{R_1}^{R_2} E_2 \cdot dr = \dfrac{Q_1}{4\pi\varepsilon_0}\left(\dfrac{1}{R_2} - \dfrac{1}{R_1}\right)$$

b. Superposition of potential

$$V_1 = \dfrac{Q_1}{4\pi\varepsilon_0}\dfrac{1}{R_1} + \dfrac{Q_2}{4\pi\varepsilon_0}\dfrac{1}{R_2}$$

$$V_2 = \dfrac{Q_1}{4\pi\varepsilon_0}\dfrac{1}{R_2} + \dfrac{Q_2}{4\pi\varepsilon_0}\dfrac{1}{R_2}$$

$$\Delta V = V_2 - V_1 = \dfrac{Q_1}{4\pi\varepsilon_0}\left(\dfrac{1}{R_2} - \dfrac{1}{R_1}\right)$$

Generally speaking, the zero point of electric potential could be selected at will, but if the source charge is an infinite charged body, cannot select infinite far point as zero point of electric potential.

a. 由电势差定义计算

$$\Delta V = \dfrac{Q_1}{4\pi\varepsilon_0}\left(\dfrac{1}{R_2} - \dfrac{1}{R_1}\right)$$

b. 由电势叠加原理计算

两球面在面 1 上的电势和

两球面在面 2 上的电势和

两球面的电势差

一般来说，有限大小的带电体电势零点选在无限远。带电体无限大时选择方便的任意一点为零电势点，不能选择无限远。

9.5 The Relationship Between E and V   9.5 场强和电势的关系

The electric field E and the electric potential *V* are related as shown in equation

$$\Delta V = V_b - V_a = -\int_a^b E \cdot dl$$

We can use it to determine the potential difference between two points if the electric field is known in the region between those two points. Now we show how to calculate the value of the electric field if the electric potential is known in a certain region.

已知场强分布可求电势差和电势：

电势差： $\Delta V = -\int_a^b E \cdot dl$

电势： $V = \int_r^\infty E \cdot dl$

已知电势分布求电场：

From equation above we can express the potential difference dV between two points a distance dl apart as

$$dV = -\mathbf{E} \cdot dl = -E_l dl$$

$dV = -E_l dl$

E_l is the component of the electric field in the direction of the infinitesimal displacement dl. We can write

$$E_l = -\frac{dV}{dl}$$

E_l：电场强度沿 l 方向分量

$$E_l = -\frac{dV}{dl}$$

So the component of the electric field in any direction is equal to the negative of the rate of change of the electric potential with distance in that direction. The quantity dV/dl is called the gradient of V in a particular direction. So we can write

$$E = -\frac{dV}{dl} \qquad \text{if} \quad dl \parallel E$$

$\dfrac{dV}{dl}$：电势梯度

任意方向的场强分量等于该方向电势梯度的负值。

If E is written as a function of x, y and z, we have

$$E_x = -\frac{\partial V}{\partial x}, \ E_y = -\frac{\partial V}{\partial y}, \ E_z = -\frac{\partial V}{\partial z}$$

知道电势分布函数，可很方便地求出场强。

Once you have a functional description of the electric potential, it is convenient to find electric field by the partial derivative.

$$\mathbf{E} = -\left(\frac{\partial V}{\partial x} i + \frac{\partial V}{\partial y} j + \frac{\partial V}{\partial x} k \right)$$

Example 9.23 Electric Field E of Ring and Disk: Determine the electric field at point P in the axis if

已知电势分布求圆环和圆盘的场强

a. a circular ring of charge (Example 9.18).

b. a uniformly charged disk(Example 9.19).

Solution:

a. From example 9.18, see Figure 9-32

$$V = \frac{1}{4\pi\varepsilon_0} \frac{Q}{\sqrt{x^2 + R^2}}$$

Then $E_x = -\dfrac{\partial V}{\partial x} = \dfrac{1}{4\pi\varepsilon_0}\dfrac{Qx}{(x^2+R^2)^{3/2}}$

$E_y = E_z = 0$

The result is the same as we got from Example 9.5, but it is easy.

b. From Example 9.19, see Figure 9-33

$$V = \dfrac{Q}{2\pi\varepsilon_0 a^2}(\sqrt{x^2+r^2}-x)$$

So $E_x = -\dfrac{\partial V}{\partial x} = \dfrac{\sigma}{2\varepsilon_0}(1-\dfrac{x}{(x^2+R^2)^{1/2}})$

From this example, we see that, as for many charge distributions, it is easier to calculate V first, and then **E** from the partial derivative, than to calculate E. This is because V is a scalar, whereas **E** is a vector.

电势是标量，场强是向量，标量叠加较向量叠加容易。先求电势，再由导数关系求场强。

266

第九章总结　静电场

1. 电荷：两种电荷，同号相斥，异号相吸。

   电荷守恒：孤立系统无论经过任何过程，电荷量保持不变。

   电荷量子化：q=ne 电荷量是基本电荷的整数倍。

   导体：电子能自由运动的物质是导体。

   点电荷：理想化的物理模型。

   试验电荷：带很小正电荷的点电荷。

2. 库仑定律：两个点电荷之间的相互作用力

   $$\mathbf{F}_{12}=\frac{1}{4\pi\varepsilon_0}\frac{q_1q_2}{r^2}\hat{r}$$

   $$\mathbf{F}_{12}=-\mathbf{F}_{21}$$

   电场力叠加原理：$\mathbf{F}_{net}=\sum_i\vec{F_i}$　　多个点电荷组成的系统

   $$\mathbf{F}_{net}=\int dF \quad \text{连续带电体}$$

3. 电场：描述电场性质的基本物理量，是空间点的向量函数，即向量场。

   定义：$\mathbf{E}=\mathbf{F}/q_0$　　单位试验电荷在空间某点所受的电场力。

   点电荷的场强：$\mathbf{E}=\mathbf{F}/q_0=\frac{1}{4\pi\varepsilon_0}\frac{Q}{r^2}\hat{r}$

4. 电场力：$\mathbf{F}=q\mathbf{E}$

   电荷在电场力的作用下的运动：$a=\frac{qE}{m}$

5. 电场强度叠加原理

点电荷系统：$\vec{E} = \sum_i \vec{E}_i = \dfrac{1}{4\pi\varepsilon_0} \sum_i \dfrac{q_i}{r_i^2} r_i$

连续带电体：$\vec{E} = \int\limits_{(Q)} d\vec{E} = \int\limits_{(Q)} \dfrac{dq}{4\pi\varepsilon_0 r^2} \hat{r}$

6. 电力线：始于正电荷或无限远，终止于负电荷或无穷远。

任意两电力线不相交。

电力线的切向是 E 的方向，电力线的疏密描述电场的强弱。

7. 电通量：通过电场中任一给定面的电场线数称为通过该面的电通量。

$$\Phi_E = \int \mathbf{E} \cdot \mathbf{dA}$$

8. 高斯定理：通过任意高斯面的电通量与高斯面所包围的电荷的代数和成正比。

$$\Phi_E = \oint\limits_A \mathbf{E} \cdot \mathbf{dA} = \dfrac{Q_{encl}}{\varepsilon_0}$$

由高斯定理计算几种常见电场的电场强度：

球壳（半径为 R，带电量 Q）：$E = \dfrac{1}{4\pi\varepsilon_0} \dfrac{Q}{r^2}$ $r \geq R$

$E = 0$ $r < R$

球体（半径 R，均匀带电 Q）：$E = \dfrac{1}{4\pi\varepsilon_0} \dfrac{Q}{r^2}$ $r \geq R$

$E = \dfrac{1}{4\pi\varepsilon_0} \dfrac{Q}{R^3} r$ $r < R$

长直导线（电荷线密度 λ）：$E = \dfrac{1}{2\pi\varepsilon_0} \dfrac{\lambda}{r}$

长直柱壳（电荷线密度 λ）：$E = 0$ $r < R$

$$E = \frac{1}{2\pi\varepsilon_0}\frac{\lambda}{r} \qquad r \geq R$$

无限大平板（电荷面密度 σ）：$E = \frac{\sigma}{2\varepsilon_0}$，匀强电场。

用高斯定理求电场强度的步骤：

1）分析电荷分布的对称性。

2）选取合适的高斯面。待求点的场强在高斯面上；场强与高斯面平行或垂直。

3）使用高斯定理求电场强度。

9. 电场力的功：$W = \int_a^b qE \cdot dl$

静电场的环流定理：$\oint E \cdot dl = 0$，电场力是保守力，电场是保守场。

10. 电势能 U：$\Delta U = U_b - U_a = -q\int_a^b E \cdot dl$

电场力的功：$W = -\Delta U$

$U_a = q\int_a^b E \cdot dl \qquad U_b = 0$

点电荷 q（在点电荷 Q 电场中）的电势能：$U = \frac{1}{4\pi\varepsilon_0}\frac{qQ}{r}$，$U(\infty) = 0$

单位：J 和 eV。$1ev = 1.6 * 10^{-19} J$

点电荷（3 个）系统的电势能：$U = \frac{1}{4\pi\varepsilon_0}(\frac{q_1q_2}{r_{12}} + \frac{q_1q_3}{r_{13}} + \frac{q_2q_3}{r_{23}})$

电势能的性质：

1）电势能属于 q 和产生电场的源电荷系统共有。

2）电荷在某点的电势能的值与零点选取有关，势能是相对量；而两点的电势能的差值与零点选取无关。

3）选势能零点的原则：

● 当电荷分布在有限范围内时，势能零点一般选择在无穷远处。

- 无限大带电体，势能零点一般选在有限远处的一点。

- 实际应用中取大地、仪器外壳为势能零点。

11. 电势 V：描述静电场性质的物理量，是空间点的标量函数，即标量场。

电势差： $\Delta V = V_b - V_a = \dfrac{U_b - U_a}{q} = -\displaystyle\int_a^b E \cdot dl$

$V_p = \dfrac{U_p}{q} = \displaystyle\int_P^0 E \cdot dl$ ，0 表示零电势点。

电势是相对量，空间任意点的电势随零电势点的选择而不同，但空间任意两点的电势差不变。

当带电体的电荷分布在有限区域之内时，一般取无限远为电势零点，此时

$V = \displaystyle\int_r^\infty E \cdot dl$

点电荷电场的电势： $V = \displaystyle\int_r^\infty \dfrac{1}{4\pi\varepsilon_0} \dfrac{Q}{r^2} \, dr = \dfrac{1}{4\pi\varepsilon_0} \dfrac{Q}{r}$

12. 电势叠加原理：

点电荷系统： $V = \displaystyle\sum_{i=1}^n V_i = \sum_{i=1}^n \dfrac{1}{4\pi\varepsilon_0} \dfrac{Q_i}{r_i}$

电荷连续分布的带电体： $V = \displaystyle\int dV = \int_Q \dfrac{1}{4\pi\varepsilon_0} \dfrac{dq}{r}$

常见带电体的电势：

均匀带电圆环： $V = \displaystyle\int_Q \dfrac{1}{4\pi\varepsilon_0} \dfrac{dq}{r} = \dfrac{1}{4\pi\varepsilon_0} \dfrac{Q}{\sqrt{x^2 + R^2}}$ ，轴线上距离圆心 x 处。

$V = \dfrac{1}{4\pi\varepsilon_0} \dfrac{Q}{R}$ ，环心处 x=0

均匀带电球壳： $V = \dfrac{1}{4\pi\varepsilon_0} \dfrac{Q}{r}$ 　　　　$r \geq R$

$$V = \frac{1}{4\pi\varepsilon_0}\frac{Q}{R} \qquad r<R$$

均匀带电球体：$V = \frac{1}{4\pi\varepsilon_0}\frac{Q}{r} \qquad r \geq R$

$$V = \frac{1}{8\pi\varepsilon_0}\frac{Q}{R}(3-\frac{r^2}{R^2}) \qquad r<R$$

$$V = \frac{3}{8\pi\varepsilon_0}\frac{Q}{R} \qquad r=0$$

13. 等势面：电势相同的所有点组成的面。相邻等势面之间电势差相同。

等势面性质：等势面下降的方向是场强方向；

等势面密集的地方场强强，稀疏的地方场强弱；

等势面与电场线垂直；

电荷沿等势面移动电场力不做功。

14. 场强和电势的关系：$dv = -E \cdot dl$

$V = \int_r^\infty E \cdot dl$，已知场强分布可求电势分布。

$E_x = -\dfrac{\partial V}{\partial x}$，$E_y = -\dfrac{\partial V}{\partial y}$，$E_z = -\dfrac{\partial V}{\partial z}$，已知电势分布可求场强分布。

Chapter 9 Electrostatics Practice

Multiple Choice Questions

1. A cube has sides L on one face of the cube. The electric field is uniform with magnitude E and has a direction pointing directly into the cube. The total charge on and within the cube is zero. Which statement is necessarily true?

   A. The electric field on the opposite face of the box has magnitude E and points directly out of the face.
   B. The total flux through the remaining five faces is out of the box and equal to EL^2.
   C. At least on other face of the cube must have an inward flux.
   D. The flux through the opposite face of the box is EL^2 out of the face.
   E. None of the above statements must be true.

2. The electric flux through a spherical surface is zero. Which condition is necessarily true?

   A. There are no charges inside the sphere.
   B. The electric field is zero everywhere within the sphere.
   C. The electric field is zero everywhere on the sphere.
   D. The sum of the charges inside the sphere is zero.
   E. None of the above statements is necessarily true.

3. An object with a total charge of 0.01C has zero acceleration in a uniform vertical downward electric field of 100N/C. The mass of this object and the charge are

   A. 0.01kg, negative charge

   B. 0.1kg, positive charge
   C. 0.1kg, negative charge
   D. 1.0kg, negative charge
   E. 1.0kg, positive charge

4. A particle has a kinetic energy of 300ev. It moves to a position where the electric potential is 350V higher. What is the kinetic energy of the particle at the new position?

   A. 0ev
   B. 300ev
   C. 600ev
   D. 900ev
   E. Not enough information is given to determine the kinetic energy.

5. An electric field is constant in magnitude and points toward the east. In which direction does the electric potential increase?

   A. East.
   B. North.
   C. West.
   D. South.
   E. The electric potential is uniform.

6. In the diagram below, what is the force a small negative test charge of magnitude q_0 would feel at point P?

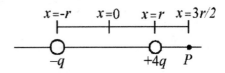

   A. $\dfrac{12}{25}\dfrac{kqq_0}{r^2}$

B. $-\dfrac{396}{25}\dfrac{kqq_0}{r^2}$

C. $\dfrac{4}{3}\dfrac{kq}{r^2}q_0$

D. $-\dfrac{4}{3}\dfrac{kqq_0}{r^2}$

E. 0

7. A charge +Q is fixed in position as a small charge +q is brought near it and released from rest. Which best describes the magnitude of the velocity of the charge +q as r, the distance between the charges increases?

   A. The magnitude of the velocity will increase, and its rate of increase will also increase.
   B. The magnitude of the velocity will increase, but its rate of increase will decrease.
   C. The magnitude of the velocity will remain constant.
   D. The magnitude of the velocity will decrease, and its rate of decrease will also decrease.
   E. The magnitude of velocity will increase, but its rate of decrease will increase.

Questions **8** and **9**

Five particles, all of the same mass and initial horizontal velocity, are sent through an uniform electric field directed upwards and follow the paths depicted by A, B, C, D, and E, respectively.

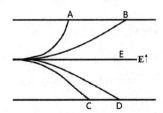

8. Which path did the particle with the greatest magnitude of charge follow?

A. Path A
B. Path B
C. Path C
D. Path D
E. Path E

9. Which of the following statements is true?

   A. All of the particles moved to a higher level of electric potential.
   B. Particles A, B, C, D and E are at equipotentials.
   C. Particle E moved to a lower electric potential.
   D. Particle A is at a higher electric potential than Particle B.
   E. Particle C and Particle D are at equipotentials.

10. The potential of a non-uniform cloud of charge is given by $V(r) = Kr^2 + Cr$ where r is the distance from the center of the cloud and k, c are both constant number. What is the electric field as a function of r?

   A. −2Kr-C
   B. 2Kr+C
   C. $(Kr^3/3) + Cr^2/2$
   D. −Kr-C
   E. −kr+C

Questions **11-13**

11. Four positive point charges of magnitude Q are placed at the corners of a square with a diagonal length of a. The potential at the center of the square is

   A. 0

   B. $\dfrac{Q}{4\pi\varepsilon_0 a}$

   C. $\dfrac{Q}{2\pi\varepsilon_0 a}$

273

D. $\dfrac{Q}{\pi\varepsilon_0 a}$

E. $\dfrac{2Q}{\pi\varepsilon_0 a}$

12. What is the magnitude of the resultant electric field at the center of the square?

A. 0

B. $\dfrac{1}{2\pi\varepsilon_0}\dfrac{Q}{a^2}$

C. $\dfrac{1}{\pi\varepsilon_0}\dfrac{Q}{a^2}$

D. $\dfrac{2}{\pi\varepsilon_0}\dfrac{Q}{a^2}$

E. $\dfrac{4}{\pi\varepsilon_0}\dfrac{Q}{a^2}$

13. With the four particles held fixed, how much work would be required to bring a fifth particle of charge Q from very far away and place it at the center of the circle?

A. 0

B. $\dfrac{Q^2}{4\pi\varepsilon_0 a}$

C. $\dfrac{Q^2}{2\pi\varepsilon_0 a}$

D. $\dfrac{Q^2}{\pi\varepsilon_0 a}$

E. $\dfrac{2Q^2}{\pi\varepsilon_0 a}$

Questions **14-15**

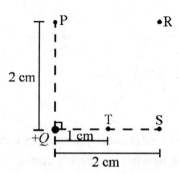

14. How much work is done on the electric field generated by the stationary charge $+Q = +1$ C to move a charge $+q = +2$ μC from P to T?

A. 900 kJ

B. $900\sqrt{5}$ kJ

C. $900\sqrt{3}$ kJ

D. 1800 kJ

E. $1800\sqrt{5}$ kJ

15. The work done on the electric field generated by the stationary charge $+Q$ to move a charge $+q$ from P to T to R is W_1. The work done to move the same charge from P to S to R is W_2. Which is necessarily true concerning W_1 and W_2?

A. $W_1 > W_2$
B. $W_2 > W_1$
C. $W_2 = W_1$
D. $W_1 > 0$, $W_2 < 0$
E. $W_1 < 0$, $W_2 > 0$

Questions **16-18**

The figure below shows two concentric, conducting, thin spherical shells of radii a and b, and charges q and Q.

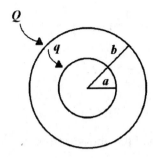

16. What is the electric field strength between the two shells, a< r<b?

A. $\dfrac{q}{4\pi\varepsilon_0 r^2}$

B. $\dfrac{Q}{4\pi\varepsilon_0 r^2}$

C. $\dfrac{q+Q}{4\pi\varepsilon_0 r^2}$

D. $\dfrac{q}{4\pi\varepsilon_0 r}$

E. $\dfrac{q}{4\pi\varepsilon_0 r^2}+\dfrac{Q}{4\pi\varepsilon_0 b^2}$

17. What is the potential between the two shells?

A. $\dfrac{q}{4\pi\varepsilon_0 r^2}$

B. $\dfrac{q+Q}{4\pi\varepsilon_0 r^2}$

C. $\dfrac{q}{4\pi\varepsilon_0 r}$

D. $\dfrac{q}{4\pi\varepsilon_0 r}+\dfrac{Q}{4\pi\varepsilon_0 b}$

E. $\dfrac{q+Q}{4\pi\varepsilon_0 r}$

18. What is the work required to bring a test charge of q_0 from the outer shell to the inner shell?

A. $\dfrac{q_0 q}{4\pi\varepsilon_0}$ (a-b)

B. $\dfrac{q_0 q}{4\pi\varepsilon_0}$ (b-a)

C. $\dfrac{q_0 q}{4\pi\varepsilon_0}$ (1/a-1/b)

D. $\dfrac{q_0 q}{4\pi\varepsilon_0}$ /(b-a)²

E. $\dfrac{q_0 q}{4\pi\varepsilon_0}$ /(b-a)

19. A point charge q is placed at a corner of a cube with side l. What is the flux through the box?

A. $\dfrac{q}{4\varepsilon_0}$

B. $\dfrac{q}{8\varepsilon_0}$

C. $\dfrac{3q}{4\pi\varepsilon_0}$

D. $\dfrac{q}{4\pi\varepsilon_0}$

E. $\dfrac{q}{\varepsilon_0}$

20. The electric potential over a certain region of space is $V(x, y) = x^2 - 2xy^2$ volts. What is the electric field over this region?

A. $\mathbf{E} = 2(x - y^2)\,\mathbf{i} - 2x\,\mathbf{j}$

B. $\mathbf{E} = 2(x - y^2)\,\mathbf{i} + 2x\,\mathbf{j}$

C. $\mathbf{E} = 2(y^2 - x)\,\mathbf{i} - 2x\,\mathbf{j}$

D. $\mathbf{E} = 2(y^2 - x)\,\mathbf{i} + 2x\,\mathbf{j}$

E. None of the above is true.

Free Response Questions

1. The nonconducting ring of radius R shown on the right lies in the yz-plane and carries a uniformly distributed positive charge Q.

A. Show that the electric field along the x-axis is given by
$$\mathbf{E} = \frac{Qx}{4\pi\varepsilon_0 \left(R^2 + x^2\right)^{\frac{3}{2}}}\,\mathbf{i}$$

B. Determine the maximum electric field E and where it happened.

C. An electron is placed at x = R/2 and released from rest. Describe its subsequent motion qualitatively.

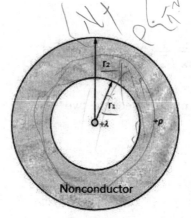

(handwritten annotations):

$E' = \frac{Q}{4\pi\varepsilon_0} x$

$\left[\left(R^2 + x^2\right)^{\frac{3}{2}} \right]'$

$= \frac{3}{2}\left(R^2+x^2\right)^{\frac{1}{2}} \cdot 2x$

$\frac{\left(R^2+x^2\right)^{\frac{3}{2}} - x \cdot \frac{3}{2}x\left(R^2+x^2\right)^{\frac{1}{2}}}{\left[\left(R^2+x^2\right)^{\frac{3}{2}}\right]^2}$

$= \frac{\left(R^2+x^2\right)^{\frac{3}{2}} - 3x^2\left(R^2+x^2\right)^{\frac{1}{2}}}{\left(R^2+x^2\right)^{3}}$

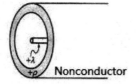

Nonconductor

$\frac{kQq}{r^2}$

Nonconductor

Cross Section

In the figure above, the left shows a hollow, infinite, cylindrical nonconducting shell of inner radius r_1 and outer radius r_2 and carries a uniform volume charge density $+\rho$. The infinite line charge of linear charge density $+\lambda$ is located at the center of the shell as shown above an enlarged cross section of the cylindrical shell is shown above on the right. Calculate the magnitude of the electric field as a function of the distance r from the center of the shell for each of the following regions.

A. $r < r_1$

B. $r_1 \le r \le r_2$

276

C. $r > r_2$

3. The square of side a below contains a positive point charge +Q fixed at the lower left corner and negative point charges -Q fixed at the other three corners of the square. Point P is located at the center of the square.

   A. Determine the electric field E and potential at center point P of the square. $k\dfrac{Q}{r^2}$ $k\dfrac{Q}{\left(\frac{\sqrt{2}}{2}a\right)^2}$

   B. A positive charge q is placed at point P. It is then moved from point P to point R, which is at the midpoint of the bottom side of the square. As the charge is moved, what is the work done on it by the electric field? $k\dfrac{Q}{r}$

   C. Describe one way to replace a single charge in this diagram such that the electric potential at the center of the square is zero but the electric field is not zero.

   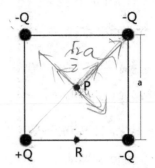

4. The figure below shows the electric field in x-y plane. Points A, B, C and D are shown in the diagram.

   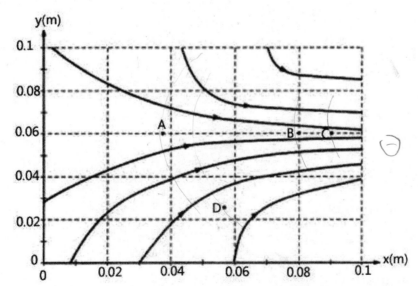

   A. Which point has the greatest magnitude of the electric field and which point has the greatest potential? C (0,8 M) 0.06 m

   B. An electron is released from rest at point B. Which point does it move towards, A, D or C? After it has moved through a potential difference of V_0, what is the electron's speed?

   C. Points B and C are separated by a potential difference of 5V. Estimate the magnitude of the electric field midway between them.

$E A \qquad E = k \dfrac{Q}{r^2} \qquad k = \dfrac{1}{4\pi\varepsilon} \qquad \dfrac{1}{4\pi r^2}$

5. In the figure below, a nonconducting solid sphere of radius a with charge $+Q$ uniformly distributed throughout its volume is concentric with a nonconducting spherical shell of inner radius $2a$ and outer radius $3a$ that has a charge $-Q$ uniformly distributed throughout its volume.

A. Determine the magnitude of the electric field as a function of radius r in the following regions.

$E A = k \dfrac{Q}{r^2} \cdot 4\pi r^2$

$= 4\pi k Q = \dfrac{1}{\varepsilon} Q$

$E A = k \dfrac{Q}{r^2} \cdot 4\pi r^2$

1) Within the solid sphere: $r < a$

2) Between the solid sphere and the spherical shell: $a < r < 2a$

$= k \dfrac{Q}{a^2} \times 4\pi r^2$

3) Within the spherical shell: $2a < r < 3a$

$E A = k \dfrac{Q}{r^2} \cdot 4\pi r^2$

$= \dfrac{Q r^2}{a^2 \varepsilon}$

4) Outside the spherical shell: $r > 3a$

$= \left(k\dfrac{Q}{a^2} + k\dfrac{Q}{r^2} \right) \cdot 4\pi r^2$

$E A = k\dfrac{Q}{r^2} \cdot 4\pi r^2$

B. Determine the electric potential as a function of radius r in the regions above.

$= \left(\dfrac{Q}{\varepsilon a^2} + \dfrac{Q r^2}{\varepsilon r^2} \right) \cdot r^2 = \dfrac{Q r^2}{\varepsilon a^2} + \dfrac{Q}{\varepsilon}$

$E A = k\dfrac{Q}{r^2} \cdot 4\pi r^2$

$= \left[k\dfrac{Q}{a^2} + k\dfrac{Q}{(3a)^2} \right] \cdot 4\pi r^2$

C. Derive an expression for the electric potential difference $V_x - V_y$ between points X and Y shown in the figure.

$= \left(k\dfrac{Q}{a^2} + k\dfrac{Q}{9a^2} \right) \cdot 4\pi r^2$

$= k\dfrac{10 Q}{9a^2} \times 4\pi r^2$

$= \dfrac{40 Q r^2}{9a^2 \varepsilon}$

$V_x - V_y = k\dfrac{Q}{r_x} - k\dfrac{Q}{r_y} = k\dfrac{Q}{a} - k\dfrac{Q}{2a} = k\dfrac{Q}{2a}$

$V = k\dfrac{Q}{r}.$

Answers and Explanations

Multiple Choice Answers

1. B   2. D   3. C   4. E   5. C   6. B   7. B   8. A   9. E   10. A   11. E   12. A   13. E   14. A   15. C
16. A   17. D   18. C   19. B   20. D

Multiple Choice Explanations

1. B。由高斯定理 $\Phi_E = \oint_A \mathbf{E} \cdot \mathbf{dA} = \dfrac{Q_{encl}}{\varepsilon_0} = 0$，有 $-El^2 + \phi_E = 0$，即 $El^2 = \phi_E$ 穿出其他 5 个面的电通量

等于 El^2。

2. D。穿过闭合曲面的电场通量为零，只能知道闭合面内电荷的代数和 Q_{encl} 为零。

3. C。电场中的点电荷受电场力作用 qE，但其加速度为零，所以电荷所受重力 $mg = qE$。

4. E。电场力所做的功等于电荷动能的增量 $q\Delta V = E_{k2} - E_{k1}$，带电粒子的电量没有给出，所以
加速后粒子的动能无法确定。

5. C。沿着电力线电势下降，逆着电力线电势升高。所以电势增加指向场强的反方向。

6. B。$F = -\dfrac{kqq_0}{(0.5r)^2} + \dfrac{kqq_0}{(2.5r)^2} = -\dfrac{396}{25}\dfrac{kqq_0}{r^2}$

7. B。$F = \dfrac{1}{4\pi\varepsilon_0}\dfrac{Qq}{r^2} = ma$，随着两个电荷距离的增加，加速度减小，速度增加。

8. A。A 点偏离水平运动方向最远，竖直方向受力 $F = qE$ 最大。

9. E。匀强电场等势面垂直于电力线，C、D 在同一等势面上。

10. A。$E = -\dfrac{dV}{dr} = -2kr$

11. E。由电势叠加原理 $V_0 = 4\dfrac{1}{4\pi\varepsilon_0}\dfrac{Q}{a/2} = \dfrac{2Q}{\pi\varepsilon_0 a}$

12. A。由场强叠加原理 $E_0 = 0$

13. E。 $w=qV_0=\dfrac{2Q^2}{\pi\varepsilon_0 a}$

14. A。 $w=q(V_T-V_p)=900$ kJ

15. C。电场力做功与路径无关，只与起点和终点的位置相关。

16. A。由高斯定理得 $E=\dfrac{q}{4\pi\varepsilon_0 r^2}$

17. D。 $V(r)=\displaystyle\int_r^b \dfrac{q}{4\pi\varepsilon_0 r^2}dr+\int_b^\infty \dfrac{q+Q}{4\pi\varepsilon_0 r^2}dr=\dfrac{q}{4\pi\varepsilon_0 r}+\dfrac{Q}{4\pi\varepsilon_0 b}$

18. C。 $W=-Q\displaystyle\int_b^a \dfrac{q}{4\pi\varepsilon_0 r^2}dr=\dfrac{Qq}{4\pi\varepsilon_0}$ $(1/a-1/b)$

19. B。点电荷 q 向外发射出总电力线的数目为 $\dfrac{q}{\varepsilon_0}$，一个点在空间可向外做出 8 个立方体，所有

这些电力线均匀穿过这 8 个立方体。

20. D。电场强度等于电势的负梯度： $E=-\left(\dfrac{\partial V}{\partial x}i+\dfrac{\partial V}{\partial y}j\right)$，　$E_x=-\dfrac{\partial V}{\partial x}=2(y^2-x)$，

$$E_y=-\dfrac{\partial V}{\partial y}=2x。$$

Free response Explanations

1. A. 圆环上任意电荷元 dq 在 p 点产生的电势相同，dq 到 p 点的距离 r

相同 r= $\sqrt{x^2+R^2}$，p 点到圆环中心的距离为 x：

所以 $V=\displaystyle\int_Q \dfrac{1}{4\pi\varepsilon_0}\dfrac{dq}{r}=\dfrac{1}{4\pi\varepsilon_0}\dfrac{Q}{\sqrt{x^2+R^2}}$

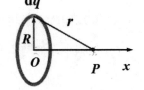

X 轴上点的电势 V 是位置 x 的函数，当 x=0 时，$V=\dfrac{1}{4\pi\varepsilon_0}\dfrac{Q}{R}$

由 V 和 E 的关系： $E_x=-\dfrac{\partial V}{\partial x}$，$E_y=-\dfrac{\partial V}{\partial y}$，$E_z=-\dfrac{\partial V}{\partial z}$

$$E_x = -\frac{\partial V}{\partial x} = \frac{Qx}{4\pi\varepsilon_0 \left(R^2+x^2\right)^{\frac{3}{2}}}\;;\quad E_y = -\frac{\partial V}{\partial y}=0;\quad E_z = -\frac{\partial V}{\partial z}=0$$

所以 $E=\dfrac{Qx}{4\pi\varepsilon_0 \left(R^2+x^2\right)^{\frac{3}{2}}}\mathbf{i}$

轴上个点的电场 E 是 x 的函数，当 x=0 时, E=0

B. 电场强度最大值位置：dE/dx=0,

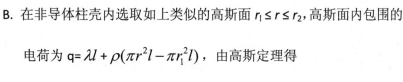

求得当 $x=\pm\dfrac{\sqrt{2}}{2}R$ 时，最大场强 $E_{max}=\dfrac{Q}{2\pi\varepsilon_0 (3)^{\frac{3}{2}}R^2}$

C. 当一个电子放置在 x = R/2 处静止释放，电子受到电场力大小为 F= eE，指向圆环中心。电子向圆心加速运动，到达原点 x=0 时，电子的速度最大，沿 x 轴反向，此时受力 F=0。电子继续沿 x 轴反向运动，受力 F=eE 指向 x 轴正向，电子减速运动直至到 x=-R/2。此时电子速度为零，受力最大。所以电子在 R/2 和-R/2 之间往复运动。

2. A. $r<r_1$：在空腔内取半径为 r 高为 l 的同心柱形球面为高斯面，面内包围电荷 $q=\lambda l$，如右图。

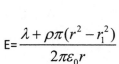

$E\,2\pi r l=\dfrac{\lambda l}{\varepsilon_0}$， $\rightarrow E=\dfrac{\lambda}{2\pi\varepsilon_0 r}$，方向垂直于中心轴向外。

B. 在非导体柱壳内选取如上类似的高斯面 $r_1 \le r \le r_2$,高斯面内包围的

电荷为 $q=\lambda l+\rho(\pi r^2 l-\pi r_1^2 l)$，由高斯定理得

$E=\dfrac{\lambda+\rho\pi(r^2-r_1^2)}{2\pi\varepsilon_0 r}$

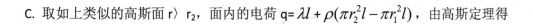

C. 取如上类似的高斯面 $r \rangle\ r_2$，面内的电荷 $q=\lambda l+\rho(\pi r_2^2 l-\pi r_1^2 l)$，由高斯定理得

$E=\dfrac{\lambda+\rho\pi(r_2^2-r_1^2)}{2\pi\varepsilon_0 r}$

3. A. 中心点场强的方向指向右上角处的负电荷，大小为 $E=2\dfrac{1}{4\pi\varepsilon_0}\dfrac{Q}{(\frac{\sqrt{2}}{2}a)^2}=\dfrac{1}{\pi\varepsilon_0}\dfrac{Q}{a^2}$

P 点电势 $V_p = -2\frac{1}{4\pi\varepsilon_0}\frac{Q}{\frac{\sqrt{2}}{2}a} = -\frac{1}{\sqrt{2}\pi\varepsilon_0}\frac{Q}{a}$

B. R 点电势 $V_R = -2\frac{1}{4\pi\varepsilon_0}\frac{Q}{\frac{\sqrt{5}}{2}a} = -\frac{1}{\sqrt{5}\pi\varepsilon_0}\frac{Q}{a}$

正电荷 q 从 p 点移动到 R 点电场力做功 $W = -q(V_R - V_p) = -\frac{1}{\pi\varepsilon_0}\frac{qQ}{a}\left(\frac{1}{\sqrt{2}} - \frac{1}{\sqrt{5}}\right)$

电势是标量 $V_R \rangle V_p$，所以电场力做负功。

C. 将右下角或左上角的负电荷换成等量异号电荷，P 点的电势 V=0 但 E≠0。

4. A. 图中电场线密度在 C 点为最大，此处 E 最强。过 A、B、C、D 这几个点做等势面，可看到过 A 点的等势面在最左端，电力线从左向右电势下降，所以 A 点电势最高。

B. 电子放到 B 点，将受到向左的电场力，逆着电力线运动，所以向 A 点移动。

$$eV_0 = \frac{1}{2}mv^2 \rightarrow v = \sqrt{\frac{2eV_0}{m}}$$

C. 题目中没有给出 E 的函数，假设在 B、C 区间是匀强电场，则此区间 E 的大小是

$E = \frac{\Delta V}{\Delta x}$，图中可知 $\Delta x = 0.01m$，所以 E=5/0.01=500v/m

5. A. 1) 在 r<a 区间：选同心球形面为高斯面，面内总电荷 $q = Q\left(\frac{r}{a}\right)^3$，由高斯定理

$$E \; 4\pi r^2 = q/\varepsilon_0 \rightarrow E_1 = \frac{Q}{4\pi\varepsilon_0 a^3}r$$

2) a<r<2a：选同心球形面为高斯面，面内总电荷 Q，由高斯定理

$$E 4\pi r^2 = Q/\varepsilon_0 \rightarrow E_2 = \frac{Q}{4\pi\varepsilon_0 r^2}$$

3) 2a<r<3a：在此区间选择同样的球形高斯面，面内总电荷为 $q = Q - \frac{r^3 - 8a^3}{19a^3}Q = \frac{27a^3 - r^3}{19a^3}Q$

由高斯定理得 $E_3 = \dfrac{Q}{4\pi\varepsilon_0 r^2} \dfrac{27a^3 - r^3}{19a^3}$

4）$r > 3a$：在此区间选同心球形高斯面，面内总电荷为 q=0，得 $E_4 = 0$。

B. 空间任意一点的电势由电势的定义求得，选择无限远处为电势零点。

1) $r < a$：$V_1 = \displaystyle\int_r^\infty E \cdot dl = \int_r^\infty E dl = \int_r^a E_1 \cdot dl + \int_a^{2a} E_2 dl + \int_{2a}^{3a} E_3 dl + \int_{3a}^\infty E_4 dl$

$$= \frac{Q}{4\pi\varepsilon_0} \left(\frac{a^2 - r^2}{2a^3} + \frac{1}{2a} + \frac{2}{19a} \right) = \frac{Q}{4\pi\varepsilon_0 a} \left(\frac{21}{19} - \frac{r^2}{2a^3} \right)$$

2) $a < r < 2a$：$V_2 = \displaystyle\int_r^\infty E dl = \int_r^{2a} E_2 dl + \int_{2a}^{3a} E_3 dl + \int_{3a}^\infty E_4 dl = \frac{Q}{4\pi\varepsilon_0} \left(\frac{1}{r} - \frac{1}{2a} + \frac{2}{19a} \right)$

3) $2a < r < 3a$：$V_3 = \displaystyle\int_r^\infty E dl = \int_r^{3a} E_3 dl + \int_{3a}^\infty E_4 dl = \frac{Q}{4\pi\varepsilon_0} \frac{1}{19a^3} \left(\frac{27a^3}{r} - \frac{r^2}{2} - \frac{9a^2}{2} \right)$

4) $r > 3a$：$V_4 = 0$

C. $V_x - V_y = \displaystyle\int_a^{2a} E_2 dl = \frac{Q}{8\pi\varepsilon_0 a}$

10

Conductor, Capacitor, and Dielectric
导体、电容器和电介质

Introduction: A conductor in electric field will be in ***electrostatic equilibrium***. A capacitor consists of two conductors separated by an ***insulator***. The capacitance of a given capacitor depends on its geometry and on the material—called a ***dielectric***—that separates the conductors. Capacitors are commonly used in a variety of electric circuits. And electrical potential energy storage in capacitors.

静电平衡

绝缘体
电介质

10.1 Electrostatics with Conductor   10.1 静电场中的导体

A *conductor* is a material in which the electrons at the outer periphery of an atom are not bound or tied to individual atoms. These so-called conduction electrons are essentially free to move about within the material.

导体中有大量自由电荷。

10.1.1 Electrostatic Equilibrium

10.1.1 静电平衡

When there are no moving charges in a conductor, the conductor is in electrostatic equilibrium.

静电场中的导体处于静电平衡：
导体中没有电荷宏观移动。

10.1.2 Electric Field of a Conductor

10.1.2 静电场中的导体

A conductor in electrostatic equilibrium has the following properties:

导体静电平衡特征：

1. The electric field is zero everywhere inside the conductor.

1. 导体内部场强处处为零。

If the field were not zero, free electrons in the conductor would experience an electric force ($F = q$E) and would accelerate due to this force.

2. Any net charge on the conductor resides entirely on its surface.

The electric field everywhere inside the conductor is zero when it is in electrostatic equilibrium. Therefore, the electric field must be zero at every point on a Gaussian surface we draw inside the conductor (Figure 10-1). Thus, the net flux through this Gaussian surface is zero. From this result and Gauss's law, we conclude that *the net charge inside the Gaussian surface is zero.*

3. The electric field just outside the conductor is perpendicular to its surface and has a magnitude σ / ε_0, where σ is the surface charge density at that point.

If the field vector **E** which is at outside the conductor had a component parallel to the conductor's surface, free electrons would experience an electric force and move along the surface; in such a case, the conductor would not be in equilibrium. Thus, the field vector must be perpendicular to the surface. We chose our Gaussian surface as a small cylinder whose height is very small and end faces are parallel to the surface of the conductor (Figure 10-2). Gauss's law gives

$$\Phi_E = \oint_A \mathbf{E} \cdot \mathbf{ds} = E\, dS = \frac{\sigma dS}{\varepsilon_0}$$

So that $\quad E = \dfrac{\sigma}{\varepsilon_0}$

4. On an irregularly shaped conductor, the surface charge density is greatest where the radius of curvature of the surface is the smallest.

Corona Discharge: observed near a conductor which has a strong electric field.

10.1.3 Electric Potential of a Conductor

The surface of any charged conductor in electrostatic equilibrium is an equipotential surface. Furthermore, because the electric field is zero inside the conductor, we conclude that the electric potential is constant everywhere inside the conductor and equal to its value at

2. 净电荷分布在导体外表面。

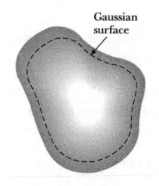

Figure 10-1 Conductor in E

3. 导体表面附近场强垂直于导体表面，大小为 σ / ε_0。

Figure 10-2 a: Electric Field near the surface of conductor

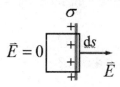

Figure 10-2 b: Applying Gauss's law

4. 导体表面电荷的分布与曲率有关。曲率大，电荷密度大，电场强度大。

尖端放电：源于强电场。

10.1.3 导体静电平衡时电势

导体是等势体，表面是等势面。整个导体 V=常数。

the surface.

$$V_b - V_a = -\int_a^b E \cdot dl = 0$$

导体中任意两点电势差为
零：$V_b - V_a = 0$

a and b are any two points on the surface of a charged conductor. V is constant everywhere in the conductor.

Example 10.1: Consider a solid metal conducting sphere of radius R and total positive charge Q. Draw a plot of the electric potential as a function of r, and show how the electric field varies with r.

导体球电场和电势

Solution:

The electric field of the sphere is

$$E = \frac{1}{4\pi\varepsilon_0}\frac{Q}{r^2} \qquad r \geq R$$

$$E = 0 \qquad r < R$$

The thing shown in Figure 9-25 b is the same as Example 9.12 and points radially outward.

导体球电场和电势与第九章
例题 9.12、9.20 均匀带电球
壳的电场和电势分布相同。

We know that the electric potential at the interior and outside of the sphere must be

$$V = \frac{1}{4\pi\varepsilon_0}\frac{Q}{R} \qquad r \leq R$$

$$V = \frac{1}{4\pi\varepsilon_0}\frac{Q}{r} \qquad r > R$$

The thing shown in Figure 9-35 b is the same as Example 9.20.

Example 10.2: Two conducting spheres, 1 and 2, are placed a large distance from each other. The radius of Sphere 1 is 20 cm, and the radius of Sphere 2 is 5 cm. A charge Q=200 nC is placed on Sphere 1, while Sphere 2 is uncharged. The spheres are then connected by a wire. Calculate

a. the charge on each sphere after the wire is connected.

b. the ratio of the magnitudes of the electric fields at the surfaces of the spheres.

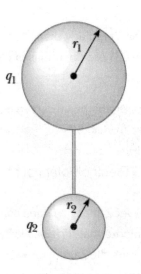

Figure 10-3 Example 10.2

Solution:

Once connected by a wire, the spheres must be at equipotential and have q_1, q_2 respectively, shown in Figure 10-3. Then the sum of the charges on each sphere must equal Q. $q_1+q_2=Q$.

静电平衡，两球等电势

a. The two spheres have the same potential $V_1=V_2$, $r_1=20cm$, $r_2=5cm$, $q_1=Q-q_2$.

So $\dfrac{1}{4\pi\varepsilon_0}\dfrac{q_1}{r_1}=\dfrac{1}{4\pi\varepsilon_0}\dfrac{q_2}{r_2}$

We obtain

$q_1=160$ nC , $q_2=40$ nC

b. Because the two spheres are separated far away, their electric fields don't affect each other. So we have

$E_1=\dfrac{1}{4\pi\varepsilon_0}\dfrac{q_1}{r_1^2}$, $E_2=\dfrac{1}{4\pi\varepsilon_0}\dfrac{q_2}{r_2^2}$

and $\dfrac{E_1}{E_2}=\dfrac{r_2}{r_1}=\dfrac{1}{4}$

10.1.4 Electrostatic Shielding

10.1.4 静电屏蔽

If there is an empty cavity inside a conductor, by Gauss's law, there can be no net charge at the surface of the cavity. Furthermore, the field in the cavity is zero even if an electric field exists outside the conductor, shown in Figure 10-4. The induced charge is on the outer surface of the conductor.

导体空腔内没有电荷，空腔内 E=0，内表面没有电荷。

导体空腔内有电荷时，空腔内外表面感应电荷相等。

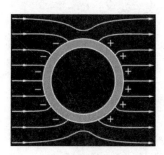

Figure 10-4 A cavity conductor at an uniform electric field

Figure 10-5 Electric field of charge inside the cavity

If a charge q is placed inside the cavity shown in Figure 10-5, the charge creates electric field both inside the cavity and outside the conductor. A net induced charge -q must exist on the inner surface of the conductor and net induced charge q exists on the outer surface. No matter where you put the –q in the cavity, the net induced charge on surfaces of the conductor never change. But the electric field inside the cavity will change and the electric field outside the conductor will not change.

If we connect the conductor to the ground, the inner and outer electric fields are separated. They don't disturb each other. We call it electrostatic shielding.

Any hollow conductor has zero electric field in its interior. This allows for hollow conductors to be utilized isolating regions completely from electric fields. In this configuration, a hollow conductor is known as a *Faraday Cage*.

导体外壳接地：

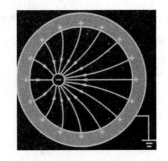

Figure 10-6 Electrostatic shielding

空腔内外电场互不影响。

法拉第笼是阻隔内外电场相互影响的金属外壳或网罩。

接地的空腔能屏蔽内外电场，使内外电场不相互影响。

10.2 Capacitors | 10.2 电容器

A capacitor is a device that can store electric charge and energy. It usually consists of two conductors (usually plates or sheets) placed near each other and widely used in electronic circuits.

电容器由两个相互靠近的导体组成，储存电荷和电能。广泛应用于电路中。

10.2.1 Definition of Capacitance

10.2.1 电容器电容定义

For a particular geometry of two conductors, the two conductors carrying charges of same magnitude Q and opposite sign will cause a potential difference V between the two conductors.

电容器：两导体带等量异号电荷 Q, 两板间的电势差为 ΔV。

The capacitance C of a capacitor is defined as the ratio of the magnitude of the charge on either conductor to the magnitude of the potential difference between the conductors:

电容定义： $C = \dfrac{Q}{\Delta V}$

$$C = \frac{Q}{\Delta V}$$

The SI unit of capacitance is the **Farad (F). 1F=1 C/V.**

电容单位：F（法拉）

Most capacitors have capacitance in the range of 1pF to $1\,\mu$F. 1pF=1*10^{-12} F, $1\,\mu$F=1*10^{-6} F.

常用单位：pF 和 μF

$$1F = 10^6\,\mu F = 10^{12}\,pF$$

Note: The capacitance C does not depend on Q or V. Its value depends only on the size, shape, and relative position of the two

电容值 C 与极板的尺寸、形状和极板的相对位置有关。

conductors, and also on the material that separates them.

C 也与两导体间电介质相关。

10.2.2 Determination of Capacitance

10.2.2 电容计算

The capacitance of a given capacitor can be determined experimentally directly from the definition by measuring the charge Q on either conductor for a given potential difference Δ V.

电容值可通过测量给定电势差的极板上电荷来测定。

For some very symmetric arrangements of conductors, we can derive an expression for the capacitance in the following manner: assume a charge of magnitude *Q on the conductor*, and calculate the potential difference. We then use the expression *C=Q/Δ V* to evaluate the capacitance. As we might expect, we can perform this calculation relatively easily if the geometry of the capacitor is simple.

对具有对称性导体，让导体上带有电荷 Q，由高斯定理可求得导体间电场强度，再由电势差定义求出两导体间的电势差，最后由电容定义 C=Q/Δ V 求出电容。

Let us work on three familiar geometries, namely, parallel plates, concentric cylinders, and concentric spheres. In these examples, we assume that the charged conductors are separated by a vacuum.

常见的具有对称性的电容器：平板、同轴柱形和同心球形电容器。

1. Parallel-plate Capacitors

1. 平行平板电容器

Two parallel metallic plates of equal area A are separated by a distance *d*, as shown in Figure 10-7. One plate carries a charge *Q*, and the other carries a charge -*Q*. We assume d is small compared to the dimensions of each plate so that the electric field E is uniform between them and we can ignore fringing at the edges. The magnitude of electric field we got before is

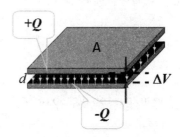

Figure 10-7 Capacitor of parallel plates

$$E=\frac{\sigma}{\varepsilon_0} = \frac{Q}{\varepsilon_0 A}$$

The relation between E and V is

平板电容器场强是常数。

$$\Delta V = V_- - V_+$$

Let V_- = 0, we have

$$\Delta V = -V_+ = -\int_+ E dl$$

电势差

So $V_+ = V = \frac{Qd}{\varepsilon_0 A}$

平板电容器 C= $\frac{\varepsilon_0 A}{d}$

Thus $C = \dfrac{Q}{\Delta V} = \dfrac{\varepsilon_0 A}{d}$

That is, the capacitance of a parallel-plate capacitor is proportional to the area of its plates and inversely proportional to the plate separation. We can get that capacitor is nothing to do with Δ V or Q.

平板电容器的电容正比于平板面积 A,反比于两平板间距 d。
电容与板面带不带电荷、有没有电势差无关。

Example 10.3 Calculate

a. The capacitance of a capacitor whose plates are 40cm*30cm and are separated by a 1.0mm.

b. The charge on the plate if the capacitor is connected to a 12v battery.

c. The electric field between the plates.

d. Estimate the area of the plates needed to achieve C= 1F.

Solution:

a. $C = \dfrac{\varepsilon_0 A}{d}$ =106 pF

b. $Q=CV=1.3*10^{-9}$ C

c. $E=V/d=1.2*10^{4}$ V/m

d. $A = \dfrac{Cd}{\varepsilon_0} \approx 10^{8}$ m^2

The area is too big! So pF or μ F is usually used as unit of capacitances.

法拉单位太大,电容单位常使用微法、皮法。

2. Cylindrical Capacitors

2. 圆柱形电容器

The concentric cylindrical capacitor is a long, length l, thin hollow conducting cylinder of radius R_1 surrounding a long solid conducting cylinder of radius R_2. Its capacitance can be determined first by assuming a charge of +Q and -Q on each of the cylinders. And then, determine the electric field between the cylinders. From the example 9.14, we obtained

$$E = \frac{1}{2\pi\varepsilon_0}\frac{\lambda}{r} = \frac{1}{2\pi\varepsilon_0}\frac{Q}{rl}$$

The potential difference of the two cylinders can be calculated by

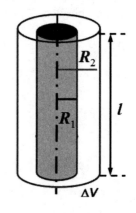

Figure 10-8 Cylindrical Capacitor

integrating the electric field.

$$\Delta V = -\int_{R_1}^{R_2} \frac{1}{2\pi\varepsilon_0} \frac{Q}{rl} dr = \frac{1}{2\pi\varepsilon_0} \frac{Q}{l} \ln\frac{R_1}{R_2}$$

由前面的例题知道两柱面间的场强，计算出电势差。

Find C using C=Q/|ΔV|:

$$C = \frac{2\pi\varepsilon_0 l}{\ln(R_2/R_1)}$$

We see that the capacitance per unit length of a combination

of concentric cylindrical conductors is

$$\frac{C}{l} = \frac{2\pi\varepsilon_0}{\ln(R_2/R_1)}$$

由电容定义求出同心柱形电

容器电容：$C = \frac{2\pi\varepsilon_0 l}{\ln(R_2/R_1)}$

单位长度电容：

$$\frac{C}{l} = \frac{2\pi\varepsilon_0}{\ln(R_2/R_1)}$$

3. Concentric Sphere Capacitor

A spherical capacitor consists of a spherical conducting shell of radius R_2 and charge -Q concentric with a smaller conducting sphere of radius R_1 and charge Q (Figure 10-9). The electric field between the two spheres is

$$E = \frac{1}{4\pi\varepsilon_0} \frac{Q}{r^2} \qquad R_1 < r < R_2$$

The potential difference is

$$\Delta V = -\int_{R_1}^{R_2} \frac{1}{4\pi\varepsilon_0} \frac{Q}{r^2} dr$$

$$|\Delta V| = \frac{Q}{4\pi\varepsilon_0}(\frac{1}{R_1} - \frac{1}{R_2})$$

$$C = \frac{4\pi\varepsilon_0 R_1 R_2}{R_2 - R_1}$$

3. 同心球形电容器

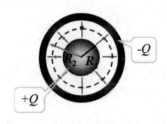

Figure 10-9 Spherical Capacitor

电容值：$C = \frac{4\pi\varepsilon_0 R_1 R_2}{R_2 - R_1}$

10.2.3 Capacitors in Series and Parallel

Two or more capacitors often are combined in electric circuits. We

10.2.3 电容器的串联和并联

can calculate the equivalent capacitance of certain combinations assuming that the capacitors to be combined are initially uncharged.

In studying electric circuits, we use a simplified pictorial representation called a circuit diagram. Such a diagram uses circuit symbols to represent various circuit elements, shown in Figure 10-10.

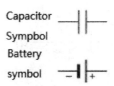

Figure 10-10 Symbols for capacitor and battery

1. Parallel Combination

Capacitors in parallel have the same voltage across their plates because the upper sides of the two capacitors have the same potential and the lower sides also have the same potential, shown in Figure 10-11. Charges on the two capacitors are Q_1, Q_2 and potential difference is V_1, V_2.

Total charge $Q=Q_1+Q_2$ and $V_1=V_2=\Delta V=V$. The equivalent capacitor of the two parallel capacitors has charge Q and potential difference V, so the equivalent capacitance C_{eq} is Q/V.

$$Q_1=C_1V, Q_2=C_2V$$

Thus, $\dfrac{Q_1}{Q_2}=\dfrac{C_1}{C_2}$

And we have

$$Q= Q_1+Q_2=(C_1+C_2)V$$

$$C_{eq}=Q/V=C_1+C_2$$

The net effect of connecting capacitors in parallel is to increase the capacitance.

If we extend this treatment to three or more capacitors (let us say n) connected in parallel, we find the equivalent capacitance to be

$$C=\sum_{i=1}^{n}C_i$$

Thus, the equivalent capacitance of a parallel combination of capacitors is the algebraic sum of the individual capacitances and is greater than any of the individual capacitances.

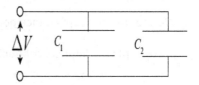

Figure 10-11 Capacitors in Parallel

并联电容器有相同电势差 V。

等效电容电势差为 V。

等效电容器极板上电荷为 Q。

电容器并联，电荷的分配与电容成正比。

1. 电容器并联

等效电容：$C_{eq}=C_1+C_2$

等效电容变大。

n 个并联电容器的电容：

$$C=\sum_{i=1}^{n}C_i$$

等效电容器的电容等于并联放置的各电容器的电容之和，比其中任意一个的电容大。

2. Series Combination

Capacitors can also be connected in series. That is, end to end, as shown in Figure 10-12. We see the charge on each capacitor is the same value Q. A single capacitor (equivalent capacitor) that could replace these two in series without affection the circuit would have a capacitance C_{eq} where

$Q=C_{eq}V$

Now the total voltage V across the two capacitors in series must equal the sum of the voltages across each capacitor

$V=V_1+V_2$

And we have $Q=C_1V_1=C_2V_2$

Thus, $\dfrac{V_1}{V_2}=\dfrac{C_2}{C_1}$

So $\dfrac{Q}{C_{eq}}=\dfrac{Q}{C_1}+\dfrac{Q}{C_2}$

Or $\dfrac{1}{C_{eq}}=\dfrac{1}{C_1}+\dfrac{1}{C_2}$

When this analysis is applied to three or more capacitors connected in series, the relationship for the equivalent capacitance is

$$\frac{1}{C_{eq}}=\sum_{i=1}^{n}\frac{1}{C_i}$$

Note that the equivalent capacitance is smaller tan the smallest contributing capacitance.

Example 10.4: Three capacitors are connected as shown in Figure 10-13. Capacitances of their capacitors are shown in the figure.

a. What is the equivalent capacitance of the circuit?

b. What is the charge on the capacitors?

Solution:

2. 电容器串联

串联电容器上的电荷 Q 相等。总电势差等于各电容器上的电压之和。

等效电容器电荷：$Q=C_{eq}V$

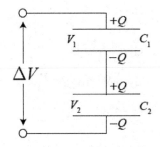

Figure 10-12 Capacitors in Series

两电容器串联，电压分配和电容成反比。等效电容 C_{eq}。

$$\frac{1}{C_{eq}}=\frac{1}{C_1}+\frac{1}{C_2}$$

电容器串联，等效电容比最小的电容还小。

n 个电容串联，等效电容：

$$\frac{1}{C_{eq}}=\sum_{i=1}^{n}\frac{1}{C_i}$$

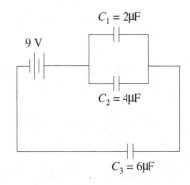

Figure 10-13 Example 10.4

a. C_1 and C_2 are parallel, their equivalent capacitance is $6 \mu F$. And this equivalent capacitor is series with C_3.

So, the equivalent capacitor of the combination of capacitor system is

$C_{eq}=3 \mu F$

b. $V_1=V_2=V_3=4.5v$

$Q_1=C_1V_1=9 \mu c$

$Q_2=C_2V_2=18 \mu c$

$Q_3=C_3V_3=27 \mu c$

10.2.4 Energy Stored in a Charged Capacitor

10.2.4 充电电容器储存能量

Work is done in charging a capacitor, allowing the capacitor to store energy. The net effect of charging a capacitor is to remove charge from one plate and add it to the other plate. This is what battery does when it connects to a capacitor. It takes some time to charge a capacitor. During the charging, at some time t the plate has a charge q(t) which is function of time and the capacitor has potential difference v(t). The work needed to add a small amount of charge dq is

移动dq 从负极板到正极板克服电场力所做的功：

$$dW = Vdq$$

$$dW = Vdq$$

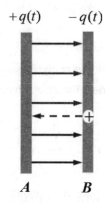

Since v=q/C at any moment, where C is the capacitance, the total work needed to store a total charge Q is

$$W = \int_0^Q Vdq = \frac{1}{C} \int_0^Q qdq = \frac{Q^2}{2C}$$

So we can say that the energy stored in a capacitor is

$$U = \frac{Q^2}{2C} = \frac{1}{2}CV^2 = \frac{1}{2}QV$$

Q=CV, V is final potential difference.

We can consider the energy stored in a capacitor as being stored in

$+q(t)$ $-q(t)$

A B

Figure 10-14 Charging a Capacitor

正极板带电 Q 时所做总功：

$$W = \int_Q dW$$

电容器储存能量：

$$U = \frac{Q^2}{2C} = \frac{1}{2}CV^2 = \frac{1}{2}QV$$

the electric field created between the plates as the capacitor is charged. Let us calculate the energy stored in a parallel-plate capacitor in terms of the electric field.

We have seen that the electric field E of a parallel-plate capacitor is uniform and its magnitude is E=V/d. And its capacitor is

$$C=\frac{\varepsilon_0 A}{d}, \text{thus}$$

$$U=\frac{1}{2}CV^2 = \frac{1}{2}\varepsilon_0 E^2 Ad$$

可认为储存在电容器中的能量就是储存在电场中的能量。

平板电容器储存能量:

$$U = \frac{1}{2}\varepsilon_0 E^2 Ad$$

The quantity Ad is the volume between the plates. We define a quantity, energy density u, as energy stored per unit volume in electric field, it is

$$u=\frac{U}{Ad}=\frac{1}{2}\varepsilon_0 E^2 \qquad Ad : \text{the volume of electric field}$$

能量密度: $u=\frac{1}{2}\varepsilon_0 E^2$

单位体积电场的能量。

We derived u for the special case of a parallel-plate capacitor. But it is true for any region of space where there is an electric field.

虽然电场能量密度公式是由平板电容器导出,但对任意电场都成立。

So energy stored in any electric field is

$$U=\int_V u dV = \int_V \frac{1}{2}\varepsilon_0 E^2 dV$$

任意电场空间电场能量计算:

$$U=\int_V \frac{1}{2}\varepsilon_0 E^2 dV$$

Example 10.5: You have two capacitors and a battery. In which of the following combinations of the two capacitors will the maximum possible energy be stored when the combination is attached to the battery?

两个电容器和电源连接储能。

a. series

b. parallel

c. Both combinations will store the same amount of energy.

Solution: b

The two capacitors are series with the battery, energy stored is

两电容器串联后和电池相连,电容器上储存总能量。

$$U_s = \frac{1}{2}C_1 V_1^2 + \frac{1}{2}C_2 V_2^2$$

When they are parallel

两电容器并联后和电源相接,电容器上储存的总能量。

$$U_p = \frac{1}{2}C_1V^2 + \frac{1}{2}C_2V^2$$

Because V=V$_1$+V$_2$ in series, U$_p$>U$_s$

Example 10.6: You charge a parallel-plate capacitor, remove it from the battery. When you pull the plates apart to a larger separation (d increases), what happens to the following quantities?

平板电容器脱离充电电源后拉大两平板间的距离。

a. Capacitance C

b. Charge Q on the plate

c. E between the plates

d. Potential difference ΔV of the capacitor

e. Energy stored in the capacitor

Solution:

a. C=$\frac{\varepsilon_0 S}{d}$ will decrease because d is increased.

电容下降。

b. Q will keep the same as before.

电荷保持不变。

c. E=$\frac{\sigma}{\varepsilon_0}$ $\sigma = \frac{Q}{S}$ doesn't change so E keeps the same.

场强不变。

d. ΔV=Ed   since d increases, ΔV will increase.

电势差增加。

e. U=$\frac{Q^2}{2C}$ C decreases and Q doesn't change, so U will increase.

电容器储存的能量增加。

Example 10.7: Repeat example 10.6, but this time answers the questions for the situation in which the battery remains connected to the capacitor while you pull the plates apart.

平板电容器充电后，电源保持和电容器连接。拉大两极板间距。

Solution:

a. C=$\frac{\varepsilon_0 S}{d}$ will decrease because d is increased.

电容下降。

b. Q= CV, for C decreases and V keeps constant, Q decreases.

极板上的电荷减少。

c. E=$\frac{\sigma}{\varepsilon_0}$ $\sigma = \frac{Q}{S}$ since Q decreases, E decreases.

场强下降。

d. $\Delta V=V$ connected to the battery so V doesn't change.

电势差不变。

e. $U=\frac{1}{2}CV^2$ C decreases and V doesn't change, so U will decrease.

电容器储存的能量减少。

10.3 Dielectrics | 10.3 电介质

Dielectrics are insulators. When the atoms or molecules of a dielectric are placed in an external electric field, the nuclei are pushed with the field resulting in an increased positive charge on one side while the electron clouds are pulled against it resulting in an increased negative charge on the other side. This process is known as polarization and a dielectric material in such a state is said to be polarized. The charges "stored" in a dielectric layer are called polarized charge and aren't available as a pool of free charges.

电介质是绝缘物质。

组成电介质的分子在电场中被极化。表面产生束缚电荷，不能自由移动。

Dielectrics in capacitors serve three purposes:

电容器中电介质的3个作用：

1. to keep the conducting plates from coming in contact, allowing for smaller plate separations and therefore with higher capacitances.

1. 避免两极板接触。可使小尺寸极板间距尽量小，且有较大电容。

2. to increase the effective capacitance by reducing the electric field strength, which means you get the same charge at a lower voltage.

2. 降低电场强度增加电容。

3. to reduce the possibility of shorting out by sparking (more formally known as dielectric breakdown) during operation at high voltage.

3. 高电压时降低短路可能性避免电介质击穿。

In most capacitors there is a dielectric between the plates. It is found experimentally that if the dielectric fills the space between the two conductors, it increases the capacitance by a factor κ which is known as the *dielectric constant*. Hence

实验给出电容器极板间充入电介质将增大电容器电容。

$$C=\kappa C_0$$

$C=\kappa C_0$

Where C_0 is the capacitance when the space between the two conductors of the capacitor is a *vacuum* and C is the capacitance when the space is filled with a material whose dielectric constant is κ.

κ is a dielectric constant of the material and varies from one material to another.

介电常数 κ：由电介质材料确定。

For a parallel-plate capacitor

$$C= \kappa \frac{\varepsilon_0 A}{d}$$

平板电容器：$C= \kappa \dfrac{\varepsilon_0 A}{d}$

We define a new quantity ε called the ***permittivity*** of a material.

$$\varepsilon = \kappa \varepsilon_0$$

$\varepsilon = \kappa \varepsilon_0$

So $\quad C= \varepsilon \dfrac{A}{d}$

电介质内的电场能量密度：

The energy density stored in an electric field E in a dielectric is given

$$u = \frac{1}{2} \varepsilon E^2$$

$u = \dfrac{1}{2} \varepsilon E^2$

Two experiments illustrate the effect of a dielectric:

电介质对电容的影响机制：

1. A battery of voltage V_0 is kept connected to a capacitor and a dielectric is inserted between the plates.

1. 电容器连接在电源上，插入电介质。V=常数：

The charge on the plates without dielectric is Q_0, then after the dielectrics inserted, it is found that the charge Q on the plates is increased by a factor of κ

电荷量变成原来的 κ 倍。

$$Q= \kappa Q_0 \qquad V=\text{constant}$$

The capacitance increases to

电容增加到没有电介质时的

$$C= Q / V_0 = \kappa C_0$$

κ 倍：$C= \kappa C_0$

2. A battery V_0 is connected to a capacitor C which holds a charge $Q_0=C_0 V_0$. Then, the battery is disconnected, leaving the capacitor isolated with charge Q_0 and still at voltage V_0. Next a dielectric is inserted between the plates of the capacitor. The charge remains Q_0 but the voltage drops by a factor of κ

2. 电容器充电后，拔掉电源，再放入电介质。Q=常数：

$$V= \frac{V_0}{\kappa}$$

电压下降为没放电介质时的 $1/\kappa$ 倍：$V= \dfrac{V_0}{\kappa}$

Now the capacitance changes to

电容增加到没有电介质时的

$$C = \frac{Q_0}{V} = \kappa C_0$$

In the two experiments, both capacitances increased by a factor of κ after inserting a dielectric, but they are different.

Example 10.8 Energy Stored Before and After

A parallel-plate capacitor is charged with a battery to a charge Q_0, as shown in Figure 10.15 a. The battery is then removed, and a slab of material that has a dielectric constant κ is inserted between the plates, as shown in Figure 10.15 b. Find the energy stored in the capacitor before and after the dielectric is inserted.

Solution:

We see that the energy stored in the capacitor before the dielectric is inserted is

$$U_0 = \frac{Q_0^2}{2C_0}$$

After the battery is removed and the dielectric is inserted, the *charge on the capacitor remains the same*. So, the energy stored in the capacitor with dielectric is

$$U = \frac{Q_0^2}{2C} = \frac{Q_0^2}{2\kappa C_0} = \frac{1}{\kappa} U_0$$

For $\kappa > 1$, the final energy is less than the initial energy U_0.

κ 倍：$C = \kappa C_0$

两种情况都会使电容增加 κ 倍，但增加机制不同。

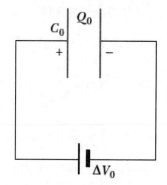

Figure 10-15 a: Example 10.8

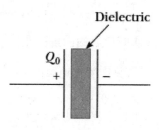

Figure 10-15 b: Insert a dielectric in the capacitor

移除电源后，电容器上电荷保持不变，放入电介质后，电场能量减少。

第十章总结　导体、电容器和电介质

1. 静电平衡：导体内部和表面没有电荷的宏观移动。

2. 导体静电平衡条件：

   电场强度：导体内部电场为零，电荷分布在外表面，表面处的场强大小正比于所在区域的电荷面密度且垂直于表面，$E=\dfrac{\sigma}{\varepsilon_0}$。

   电势：导体是等势体，表面是等势面。

3. 静电屏蔽：接地的空腔导体能够隔绝空腔内外电场，互不干扰。

4. 电容：$C=\dfrac{Q}{\Delta V}$，升高单位电势极板上的电量。

   单位：法拉 F。常用微法和皮法 $1F=10^6\,\mu F=10^{12}\,pF$。

   影响电容的因素：导体的几何尺寸，两导体的相对位置，以及导体间是否有电介质。

5. 常见电容器电容：

   平行平板：$C=\dfrac{\varepsilon_0 S}{d}$

   同心柱形：$C=\dfrac{2\pi\varepsilon_0 l}{\ln(R_2/R_1)}$

   同心球形：$C=\dfrac{4\pi\varepsilon_0 R_1 R_2}{R_2-R_1}$

6. 电容器的结合使用，等效电容：

   串联：$C_{eq}=\displaystyle\sum_{i=1}^{n}C_i$

   并联：$\dfrac{1}{C_{eq}}=\displaystyle\sum_{i=1}^{n}\dfrac{1}{C_i}$

7. 电容器储存的能量 $U = \dfrac{Q^2}{2C} = \dfrac{1}{2}CV^2 = \dfrac{1}{2}QV$

电场能量密度 $u = \dfrac{1}{2}\varepsilon_0 E^2$

8. 电介质：

增大电容：$C = \kappa C_0$

κ：电介质材料的介电常数

削弱场强、降低电压：$V = \dfrac{V_0}{\kappa}$

Chapter 10 Conductor, Capacitor and Dielectric Practice

Multiple Choice Questions

1. There is a parallel plate capacitor with air between the plates and its capacitance is C_0. You have a conductor slab which has the same area and half thickness with the capacitor. The slab inserts into the capacitor paralleling the plates of the capacitor. Now the capacitance is

   A. $C<C_0$, nothing to do with the position relative to the plates.
   B. $C<C_0$, depend on where it is between the two plates.
   C. $C>C_0$, nothing to do with the position relative to the plates.
   D. $C>C_0$, depend on where it is between the two plates.
   E. $C=C_0$.

2. Two parallel plates capacitor C_1 and C_2 in series are connected with a battery, so the two capacitors are fully charged. Then the battery is removed. And a dielectric slab is inserted into C_1. What happens to the potential differences of the two capacitors, V_1 and V_2?

   A. V_1 decreases and V_2 increases.
   B. V_1 decreases and V_2 remains unchanged.
   C. V_1 increases and V_2 decreases.
   D. V_1 increases and V_2 remains unchanged.
   E. Both V_1 and V_2 remain unchanged.

3. A parallel plate capacitor is fully charged to a potential difference of V. A charge of Q is on one plate and a charge $-Q$ is on the other. Then the capacitor is disconnected from the charging source, and a dielectric is then inserted. What happens to the potential

difference V and the stored electrical potential energy U?

   A. V decreases, and U decreases.
   B. V decreases, and U increases.
   C. V increases, and U decreases.
   D. V increases, and U increases.
   E. V decreases, and U remains unchanged.

4. When a voltage V is applied to a parallel-plate capacitor, it is able to hold a charge Q. A second parallel plate capacitor has plates with twice the area and half the separation. When a voltage V is applied to it, the amount of charge that it can hold is

   A. Q/2
   B. Q/4
   C. Q
   D. 2Q
   E. 4Q

5. All the capacitors are identical, and each has capacitance C. The equivalent capacitance of the configuration shown in Figure below is

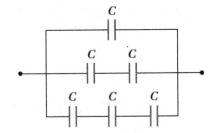

   A. 6C
   B. 3C
   C. $\dfrac{6}{11}C$

D. $\frac{11}{6}C$

E. $\frac{3}{5}C$

6. A charge Q is placed at the center of a hollow conducting solid spherical shell of inner radius 2R and outer radius 4R. If the electric field strength at a distance R from the charge is E, what is the electric field strength at a point a distance 3R from the center of the sphere?

A. 0

B. $E/3$

C. $E/9$

D. E

E. $3E$

7. Two charged conducting spheres are touched together. Charge flows between them until which of the following is the same for both spheres?

A. electric field at the surface
B. electric field at the center
C. electric potential
D. total charge
E. total energy

8. A hollow conducting sphere of a radius of 0.60 m carries a charge of 4.0 µC. A 2.0 µC charge is placed at the center of the sphere. How much work does it take to move the charge to a distance of 0.30 m from the center?

A. 0 J

B. 0.12 J

C. 0.20 J

D. 0.24 J

E. 0.8 J

9. What is the electric potential at the center of a conducting sphere with a diameter of 0.6

meters that carries a total charge of 2.0 × 10^{-8} C?

A. 0 V

B. 300 V

C. 500 V

D. 600 V

E. 2000 V

10. A capacitor is charged to a potential of 300 V and stores a charge of 4 mC in 3 s. What is the average power delivered to the capacitor in this time?

A. 0.02 W

B. 0.04 W

C. 0.20 W

D. 2.0 W

E. 10 W

11. An electric potential of V_0 is initially applied to a capacitor. If a dielectric with a dielectric constant of κ is added between the plates of the capacitor, what is the new electric potential that must be applied in order for the charge on the capacitor to stay the same?

A. V_0/κ^2

B. V_0/κ

C. V_0

D. κV_0

E. $\kappa^2 V_0$

12. Two capacitors, C_1 and C_2, are connected in parallel and charged with a power supply V. What potential difference would be required across the same two capacitors connected in series in order that the combination stores the same amount of energy as in parallel?

A. $\dfrac{C_1^2 + C_2^2}{\sqrt{C_1 C_2}} V$

D. $\dfrac{C_1 + C_2}{\sqrt{C_1 C_2}} V$

B. $\dfrac{C_1^2 + C_2^2}{C_1 C_2} V$

E. $\dfrac{C_1^2 + C_2^2}{C_1^2 C_2^2} V$

C. $\dfrac{C_1 + C_2}{C_1 C_2} V$

Free Response Questions

1. An isolated conducting sphere of radius a is at a potential of V_a.

A. What is the charge Q on the sphere?

 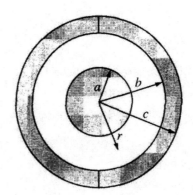

The charged sphere is then concentrically surrounded by two uncharged conducting hemispheres of inner radius b and outer radius c, which are joined together as shown above, forming a spherical capacitor. A wire is connected from the outer sphere to ground, and then removed.

B. Determine the magnitude of the electric field in the following regions as a function of the distance from the center of the inner sphere.

1. r < a

2. a < r < b

3. b < r < c

4. r > c

C. Determine the magnitude of the potential difference between the sphere and the conducting shell.

D. What is the capacitance of the spherical capacitor?

E. What is the energy stored in the capacitor?

F. An electron of mass m_e carrying a charge $-e$ is moving with a speed v_0 at a very large distance from the spheres. Derive an expression for the speed of the particle at point P which is a distance $2c$ from the center of the spheres.

2. A capacitor consisting of conducting coaxial cylinders of radii a and b, respectively, and length L is connected to a source of emf, ε, as shown below. When the capacitor is charged, the inner cylinder has a charge +Q on it. Neglect end effects and assume that the region between the cylinders is filled with air.

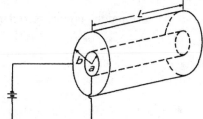

A. Determine an expression for the electric field at a distance r from the axis of the cylinder where $a < r < b$.

B. What is the potential difference between the cylinders?

C. What is the capacitance C_o of the capacitor?

D. The capacitor is then filled with a dielectric of dielectric constant κ. Determine the new capacitance C in terms of C_o.

3. A parallel plate capacitor with plate separation d is charged to a potential difference V_0 and then disconnected from battery.

A. What is the electric field inside the capacitor?

B. What is the charge density on each of the plates?

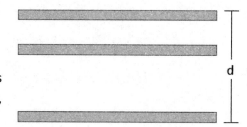

Then a third plate, a metal sheet of thickness t (t<d) is slipped inside the capacitor parallel to the two plates, as shown above.

C. What is the electric field above, within, and below the metal sheet?

D. What is the voltage between the two plates of the capacitor?

E. By what factor has the energy increased or decreased?

And then a dielectric material with dielectric constant κ is added, completely filling the space between the plates.

F. If the capacitor is not connected to a battery, are the electric field inside the capacitor and potential difference increasing or decreasing?

4. Consider the circuit shown in the diagram on the right,

where $C_1 = 6.00\ \mu$ F, $C_2 = 3.00\ \mu$ F, and $\Delta V = 20.0$ V.

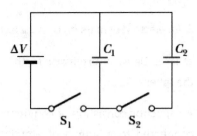

Capacitor C_1 is first charged by the closing of switch S_1.
Switch S_1 is then opened, and the charged capacitor is
connected to the uncharged capacitor by the closing of S_2.

A. Calculate the initial charge acquired by C_1 and the final charge on each capacitor.

B. Determine the energy stored in the capacitor C_2.

Answers and Explanations

Multiple Choice Answers

1. C   2. B   3. A   4. E   5. D   6. A   7. C   8. A   9. B   10. A   11. B   12. D

Multiple Choice Explanations

1. C。由 $C=\dfrac{\varepsilon_0 S}{d}$，插入金属板之后 d 变小，C 增大，但与金属板的位置无关。

2. B。充电后将电源断开，C_1 和 C_2 的电荷总量保持不变。将电介质板插入 C_1 后，C 的电容增大，因其电荷量不变，所以它的电压减小。C_2 的电荷量和电容均无变化，故其上的电势差不变。

3. A。因为电荷量不变，插入电介质后电容增加，V=Q/C 一定减小，$U=Q^2/2C$ 也减小。

4. E。极板面积增大一倍，板间距减小一半后的电容是原来电容的 4 倍，$Q=CV=4Q_0$

5. D。C=C/3+C/2+C=11C/6

6. A。静电平衡时导体内部场强处处为零。

7. C。两带电球体达到等电势时，导体球处于静电平衡，电荷停止移动。

8. A。导体球壳内部是等势体，电荷在其中移动电场力不做功。

9. B。导体球的电势 $V=k\dfrac{q}{r}$=300V。

10. A。平均功率 $P=\dfrac{U}{t}=\dfrac{QV}{2t}$=0.02W。

11. B。插入电解质后电荷量不变 $Q=C_0 V_0=\kappa C_0 V$，所以 $V=V_0/\kappa$。

12. D。$\dfrac{1}{2}(C_1+C_2)V^2=\dfrac{1}{2}(\dfrac{C_1 C_2}{C_1+C_2})V_s^2 \rightarrow V_s=\dfrac{C_1+C_2}{\sqrt{C_1 C_2}}V$

Free Response Explanations

1. A. 球形导体是等电势体：$V=\dfrac{1}{4\pi\varepsilon_0}\dfrac{q}{r}$，所以 $Q=4\pi\varepsilon_0 a V_a$。

B. 由于静电感应外导体壳内表面感应出电荷-Q，外导体表面感应电荷 Q。导线使外表面接地时，外表面电荷为零（电荷全部流入地球）；导线移除后，导体静电平衡的结果还是如此—内表面电荷-Q，外表面电荷为零。

1. $r<a$: $E_1=0$

2. $a<r<b$: $E_2=\dfrac{1}{4\pi\varepsilon_0}\dfrac{Q}{r^2}$

3. $b<r<c$: $E_3=0$

4. $r>c$: $E_4=0$

C. $V_a-V_b=\displaystyle\int_a^b \dfrac{1}{4\pi\varepsilon_0}\dfrac{Q}{r^2}dr=\dfrac{Q}{4\pi\varepsilon_0}\left(\dfrac{1}{a}-\dfrac{1}{b}\right)$

D. $C=\dfrac{Q}{V_a-V_b}=4\pi\varepsilon_0\dfrac{ab}{b-a}$

E. $U=\dfrac{1}{2}C(\Delta V)^2=\dfrac{Q^2}{8\pi\varepsilon_0}\left(\dfrac{1}{a}-\dfrac{1}{b}\right)$

F. $V_\infty=0$, $V_p=0$。电场力的功等于电子动能的增量：$eV_p=\dfrac{1}{2}m_e v^2-\dfrac{1}{2}m_e v_0^2 \rightarrow v=v_0$

2. A. $E=\dfrac{Q}{2\pi\varepsilon_0 Lr}$

B. $\Delta V=\dfrac{Q}{2\pi\varepsilon_0 L}\ln\dfrac{b}{a}$

C. $C_0=\dfrac{Q}{\Delta V}=2\pi\varepsilon_0 L/\ln\dfrac{b}{a}$

D. $C=\kappa C_0=2\pi\varepsilon_0 L\kappa/\ln\dfrac{b}{a}$

3. A. $E=V_0/d$，方向由正极板指向负极板。

B. 由高斯定理求得 $E=\dfrac{\sigma}{\varepsilon_0}$，$\sigma=\dfrac{\varepsilon_0 V_0}{d}$。两极板具有等量异号的电荷面密度。

C. 导体处于静电平衡状态，内部场强处处为零。金属导体上下表面感应出等量异号电荷面密度 $\pm\sigma$。电荷面密度没有发生改变，所以在电容器内部插入的导体之外，电场强度不变。

D. 电势差 V=E（d-t），下降为原来电势差的（d-t）/d 倍。

E. U=QV/2，Q 不变，U 下降为原来的（d-t）/d 倍。

F. 电容器中插入电解质后 E 和 V 都要下降。

4. A. $Q_1=C_1\Delta V=120\,\mu C$

开关 1 打开，2 关闭后，两电容器上的电压相同 $V_1=V_2$。由 $\dfrac{Q_1-Q_2}{C_1}=\dfrac{Q_2}{C_2}$ 解得 C_2 上的电荷

$Q_2=40\,\mu C$，C_1 上的电荷 $Q_1^{'}=Q_1-Q_2=80\,\mu C$。

B. $U=\dfrac{1}{2}\dfrac{Q_2^2}{C_2}=2.67*10^{-4}$ J

11

Direct Current Circuits
直流电路

11.1 Current, Resistance and Power

11.2 Electric Circuits

11.3 Resistance-Capacitance (RC) Circuits

11.1 电流、电阻和功率

11.2 电路

11.3 电阻-电容（RC）电路

Introduction：In this chapter we begin our study of charges in motion, and we call a flow of charge as an electric current. We can control the flow of charge using electric fields and electric potential. In order to have a current in a wire, a potential difference is needed, which can be provided by a battery. Electron flow occurs in a closed path, or **electric circuit**. Because electrons must travel through the metallic lattice of a conductive wire, the longer the distance they travel, the more collisions they have, changing their kinetic energy into radiant energy. The wire heats up and there is energy loss. RC circuits are common in everyday life.

场强和电势差控制电荷流动。

11.1 Current, Resistance and Power
11.1 电流、电阻和功率

11.1.1 Electric Current
11.1.1 电流

A useful analogy exists between electric current and flowing water. When electrons flow through a wire, the amount of electron flow or **current** is determined by the pressure forcing the electrons through the diameter or cross-sectional area of the wire and the resistance is inside the wire, which also becomes greater with increasing length.

电流是电荷的定向移动。

We define a current is the rate at which charge flows through this surface. If ΔQ is the amount of charge that passes through this area in a time interval Δt, the average current *rate* is equal to the charge that passes through *A* per unit time:

电流定义：单位时间流过某一截面的电量

$$I_{av} = \frac{\Delta Q}{\Delta t}$$

平均电流：$I_{av} = \frac{\Delta Q}{\Delta t}$

If the rate at which charge flows varies in time, then the current varies in time; we define the instantaneous current *I* as the differential limit of average current:

瞬时电流：$I = \frac{dQ}{dt}$

$$I = \frac{dQ}{dt}$$

The SI unit of current is the ampere (A), 1A=1C/s.

It is conventional to assign to the current the same direction as the flow of positive charge. When we speak of current in an ordinary conductor, the direction of the current is opposite the direction of flow of electrons. The battery sets up a potential difference between the ends of the loop, creating an electric field within the wire. The electric field exerts forces on the conduction electrons in the wire, causing them to move in the wire, thus creating a current.

In any single circuit, with only a single path for current to follow, a steady current at any instant is the same at one point as at any other point. This follows from the conservation of electric charge.

Example 11.1: An electronic scanner uses a 900 mA power supply. How many Coulombs of charge does this represent in 1 minute of use? How many electrons does this represent?

Solution:

For one minute of operation, the scanner uses

$$\Delta Q = I \Delta t = (0.9 \text{ C/s}) (60 \text{ sec}) = 54.0 \text{ C}$$

Since 1 C = $6.25 \cdot 10^{18}$ electrons, for one minute of operation the scanner uses

$$(54.0 \text{ C})(6.25 \cdot 10^{18}) = 3.38 \cdot 10^{20} \text{ electrons}$$

11.1.2 Ohm's Law: Resistance and Resistors

Georg Ohm discovered that the ratio of the potential difference or *electromotive force* (denoted by the symbol ε) to the current in a closed-loop circuit is a constant, which represents the circuit's resistance. Ohm's Law is a very important relationship in the study of electrical energy:

$$R = \frac{V}{I}$$

Where V is the potential difference in Volts, I is the current in Amperes, and R is the resistance in Ohms (Ω). One Ohm equals the resistance that will allow a current of 1 Ampere to pass between

电流的单位：安培 A

电流方向是正电荷运动方向。导体中电流是电子运动反方向。

电源建立电势差，在导线中产生电场，电场施力于导体中电子，电子运动产生电流。

单一回路稳恒电流处处相等，遵循电荷守恒定律。

11.1.2 欧姆定律：电阻

电源电动势 ε

欧姆定律： $R = \frac{V}{I}$

电阻的单位是欧姆。

two points that have a potential difference of 1 Volt between them, $1\Omega = 1V/A$.

All electric devices offer resistance to the flow of current. Generally, the connecting wires have very low resistance in comparison to the wire filaments or coil. In many circuits, particularly in electronic devices, resistors are used to control the amount of current.

导线相比于灯丝和线圈电阻很小。

11.1.3 Resistivity

11.1.3 电阻率

The resistance R of a metal wire is found experimentally that it is directly proportional to its length l and inversely proportional to its cross-sectional area A. That is

电阻与导线长度成正比，与导线的截面积成反比。

$$R = \rho \frac{l}{A}$$

导线电阻公式： $R = \rho \dfrac{l}{A}$

where ρ is a constant and called the *resistivity*. Its unit is $\Omega \cdot m$. It depends on purity, heat treatment, temperature, and other factors of the material used.

比例系数是 *电阻率* ρ ，电阻率与材料特性相关。

The reciprocal of the resistivity is called the *conductivity* σ ,

$$\sigma = \frac{1}{\rho}$$

电导率： $\sigma = \dfrac{1}{\rho}$

which has units of $(\Omega m)^{-1}$.

电导率单位： $(\Omega m)^{-1}$

Example 11.2: Calculate the resistance of an aluminum cylinder that has a length of 10.0 cm and a cross-sectional area of $2.0 * 10^{-4}$ m². Repeat the calculation for a cylinder of the same dimensions and made of glass having a resistivity of $3.0 * 10^{10}$ Ω m.

Solution:

a. We can calculate the resistance of the aluminum cylinder as follows:

$$R = \rho \frac{l}{A} = 1.4 * 10^{-5} \ \Omega$$

b. Similarly, for glass we find that

$$R = \rho \frac{l}{A} = 1.5 * 10^{13} \, \Omega$$

We can see the big difference in resistivity.

The resistivity of a material depends somewhat on temperature. In general, the resistance of metals increases with temperature. For at higher temperatures, the atoms are moving more rapidly and are arranged in a less orderly fashion. So they might be expected to interfere more with the flow of electrons. If the temperature change is not too great, the resistivity of metals usually increases nearly linearly with temperature. That is

电阻率也与温度相关，随温度升高而变大。

温度变化不太大时，电阻率与温度成线性关系。

$$\rho = \rho_0 (1 + \alpha (T - T_0))$$

where ρ_0 is the resistivity at some reference temperature T (such as $0^0 C$ or $20^0 C$), ρ is the resistivity at a temperature T and α is the *temperature coefficient of resistivity*.

温度和电阻率关系：

$$\rho = \rho_0 (1 + \alpha (T - T_0))$$

α：电阻温度系数

Note that the temperature coefficient for semiconductors can be negative. Thus, the resistance of a semiconductor can decrease with an increase in temperature.

半导体的温度系数可以是负值，所以半导体的电阻随温度升高可能下降。

Example 11.3: When does a light bulb carry more current:

a. Just after it is turned on and the glow of the metal filament is increasing, or

b. After it has been on for a few milliseconds and the glow is steady?

Solution: a

11.1.4 Electric Power

11.1.4 电功率

If a battery is used to establish an electric current in a conductor, there is a continuous transformation of chemical energy in the battery to kinetic energy of the electrons to internal energy in the conductor, resulting in an increase in the temperature of the conductor.

Electric energy is transformed into thermal energy or light in some devices, and there are many collisions between the moving

电能转化成热或光。

electrons and the atoms of the wire. In each collision, part of the electron's kinetic energy is transferred to the atom with which it collides. As a result, the kinetic energy of the wire's atoms increases and hence the temperature of the wire element increases.

运动电荷与导线中的原子碰撞，将能量传输给导线而使导线温度升高。

To find the power transformed by an electric device, we know that the energy transformed when an infinitesimal charge dq moves through a potential difference V is dU= V dq. If dt is the time required for an amount of charge dq to move through the potential difference V, the power P, which is the rate energy transformed, is

$$P = dU / dt = Vdq / dt = IV$$

电功率：P= IV

This general relation gives us the power transformed by any device, where I is the current passing through it and V is the potential difference across it. It also gives the power delivered by a source such as a battery. The SI unit of power is the watt

可用于任何电路用电装置及电源。

1 W=1J/s

The rate of energy transformation in a resistance R can be written in two other ways:

功率的单位：瓦特 W

$$P = IV = I^2R = \frac{V^2}{R}$$

$$P = IV = I^2R = \frac{V^2}{R}$$

适用于电阻电路中。

These two new expression of power can apply only to resistors, whereas P=IV applies to any device.

Example 11.4: An electric heater is constructed by applying a potential difference of 120 V to a Nichrome wire that has a total resistance of $8.00\,\Omega$. Find the current carried by the wire and the power rating of the heater. How much does it cost per month (30 days) if it operates 3 hours per day and the electric company charges 10.5 cents per kWh.

Solution:

a. $I = \dfrac{V}{R}$ =15A

b. p=IV=1.8 kW

c. To operate it for 3*30=90h would cost

1.8*90 *0.105= 17 dollar

11.1.5 Microscopic Model of Current

When a potential difference is applied to the two ends of a wire of uniform cross section, the direction of the electric field E is parallel to the walls of the wire. Charges are free to move in a conductor, and hence can move under the action of the electric field at a velocity V which is an average speed called the drift speed, v_d. The drift velocity is normally very much smaller than the electrons' average random speed.

To understand the meaning of drift speed, consider a conductor in which the charge carriers are free electrons. If the conductor is isolated—that is, the potential difference across it is zero—then these electrons undergo random motion that is analogous to the motion of gas molecules. As we discussed earlier, when a potential difference is applied across the conductor (for example, by means of a battery), an electric field is set up in the conductor; this field exerts an electric force on the electrons, producing a current. However, the electrons do not move in straight lines along the conductor. Instead, they collide repeatedly with the metal atoms, and their resultant motion is complicated and zigzag (Figure 11-1). Due to the collisions, the electrons move slowly along the conductor (in a direction opposite that of E) at the drift velocity v_d.

We can relate current to the motion of the charge carriers by describing a microscopic model of conduction in a metal. In a time Δt, the electrons will travel a distance $\Delta x = v_d \Delta t$ on average. Suppose the wire has cross sectional area A.

In time Δt, electrons in a volume $V = A\Delta x = Av_d\Delta t$ will pass through the cross section A of wire, as shown in Figure 11-2. If there are n free electrons per unit volume (n=N/V), then the total charge ΔQ that passes through the area A in a time Δt is

$\Delta Q = nV(-e) = -nAv_d\Delta t\, e$

The current I in the wire is

$$I = \frac{\Delta Q}{\Delta t} = -neAv_d$$

Now we define a new microscopic quantity, the current density, j. It is defined as the electric current per unit cross-sectional area at any

11.1.5 电流微观表示

电子漂移速度 V_d

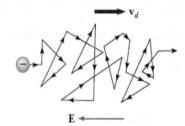

Figure 11-1 Electrons move along the conductor at a drift velocity v_d

导体中的电子宏观上以漂移速度 V_d 沿导线运动。

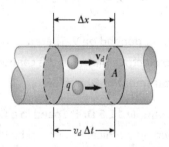

Figure 11-2 Microscopic View of Electric Current

n：单位体积内载流子数目

电流的微观表示 I = -neAV$_d$

电流密度：单位截面上流过的电流

point in space. If the current density j in a wire of cross sectional area A is uniform over the cross section, then j is related to the electric current by

$$j = \frac{I}{A} = -nev_d \quad \text{its unit is A/m}^2$$

电流密度: $j = \frac{I}{A} = -nev_d$

If the current density is not uniform, the general relation is

$$I = \int j \cdot dA$$

电流密度不均匀时电流:

$$I = \int j \cdot dA$$

j is a vector which has the same direction with E and represents the direction of flow of positive charge. In a conductor, the negative charged electrons move in the direction of –J, or –E.

电流密度是向量, 方向与场强一致。

Ohm's law, V=IR, can be written in terms of microscopic quantities.

For R= $\rho \dfrac{l}{A}$, I =JA, and V=El

El = JA $\rho \dfrac{l}{A}$

So $J = \dfrac{1}{\rho} E = \sigma E$

$J = \sigma E$

Where $\sigma = \dfrac{1}{\rho}$ is the conductivity. For a metal conductor, σ, ρ

don't depend on V. Therefore the current density j is proportional to electrical field E in the conductor. This is the microscopic statement of Ohm's law.

Example 11.5 Drift Speed in a Copper Wire: The 12-gauge copper wire in a typical residential building has a cross-sectional area of $3.31 * 10^{-6}$ m^2. If it carries a current of 10.0 A,

a. what is the drift speed of the electrons? Assume that each copper atom contributes one free electron to the current. The density of copper is 8.95 g/cm^3.

b. what is the electric field inside the wire? $\rho = 1.68 * 10^{-8} \Omega m$

for copper.

Solution:

a. The molar mass of copper is 63.5 g/mol. And 1 mol of any substance contains Avogadro's number of atoms (6.02 *10^{23}). We can calculate the volume occupied by 63.5 g (1 mol) of copper.

$$V = \frac{m}{\rho}$$

The number of electron in per unit volume is

$$n = \frac{N_A}{V} = \frac{N_A \rho}{m} = 8.49 * 10^{28} /m^3$$

So, the drift velocity is

$$V_d = \frac{I}{nqA} = 2.22 * 10^{-4} \; m/s$$

The drift velocity of electrons in a wire is clearly very slow, only about 0.22mm/s. It means it takes an electron 75min to travel 1m!

b. $E = \rho j = \rho \frac{I}{A} = 5.1 * 10^{-2} \; V/m$

We see that a modest electric field is needed for current flow in practical cases.

11.2 Electric Circuits   11.2 电路

An electric current is maintained when the terminals of a voltage source are connected by a conducting pathway, which is called a circuit. If the current always travels in the same direction through the pathway, it is called a direct current.

11.2.1 EMF and Terminal Voltage

11.2.1 电源电动势和端电压

A battery is called either a *source of electromotive force* or, more commonly, a *source of EMF*. The EMF ε of a battery is the maximum possible voltage that the battery can provide between its terminals. Or it is the electric potential difference across the two terminals when no current flows from the source. When current does flow through the device, the device may have some internal resistance that causes a voltage drop internal to the device, so that the potential difference across the terminals of the device falls below

电源端电压：外电路电压

端电压和电动势关系：

$$V_{ab} = \varepsilon - Ir$$

r：内阻，R：负载电阻

the EMF of the source. The potential difference between the two terminals of the device is called the *terminal voltage* $\Delta V = V_{ab} = V_b - V_a$, shown in Figure 11-3. When a current I flows naturally from the battery there is an internal drop in voltage equal to Ir. Thus the terminal voltage (the actual voltage delivered) is

$$V_{ab} = \varepsilon - Ir$$

The internal resistance r of a battery is usually small. We see that the terminal voltage ΔV must equal the potential difference across the external resistance R, often called the load resistance. The resistor represents a *load* on the battery because the battery must supply energy to operate the device. The potential difference across the load resistance is $\Delta V = IR$. We see that

$$\varepsilon = IR + Ir$$

So, $I = \dfrac{\varepsilon}{R+r}$

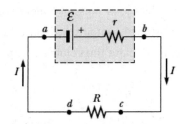

Figure 11-3 Circuit diagram of a source of EMF, of internal resistance *r*, connected to an external resistor of resistance *R*

电路中电流：$I = \dfrac{\varepsilon}{R+r}$

This equation shows that the current in this simple circuit depends on both the load resistance R external to the battery and the internal resistance r. If R is much greater than r, as it is in many real-world circuits, we can neglect r.

简单电路中电流与负载电阻和电源内阻都有关。
如果 R 远大于 r，r 可忽略。

To multiply the equation above by the current I, we obtain

$$I\varepsilon = I^2R + I^2r$$

This equation indicates that the total power output $I\varepsilon$ of the battery is delivered to the external load resistance in the amount I^2R and to the internal resistance in the amount I^2r.

电源的输出功率提供给外电路使用和内阻消耗。

Example 11.6: A battery has an EMF of 12.0 V and an internal resistance of 0.05 Ω. Its terminals are connected to a load resistance of 3.00 Ω.

a. Find the current in the circuit and the terminal voltage of the battery.

b. Calculate the power delivered to the load resistor, the power delivered to the internal resistance of the battery, and the power delivered by the battery.

Solution:

a. $I = \dfrac{\varepsilon}{R+r}$ =3.93A

$\Delta V = \varepsilon - Ir$ =11.8 v

$\Delta V = IR$ =11.8 v

b. The power delivered to the load resistor R is

$P_R = I^2 R$ =46.3 W

The power delivered to the internal resistor r is

$P_r = I^2 r$ =0.772 W

The power provided by the EMF is

P= $I\varepsilon$ =47.1 W

Hence, the power delivered by the battery is the sum of the power delivered to the load and internal resistance.

11.2.2 Resistors in Series and in Parallel

Resistors can be connected in series or parallel. Resistors are connected in series if identical currents must flow through each resistor. Resistors that are connected in series have an equivalent resistance that is the sum of the resistances in the series network, shown in Figure 11-4.

$R_{eq} = R_1 + R_2$

In general, for an arbitrary number of resistors connected in series, the equivalent resistance, R_{eq}, is

$$R_{eq} = \sum R_i$$

where R_i is the ith resistor in the network. The equivalent resistance is always greater than any individual resistance.

Figure 12-4 shows that $I_1 = I_2 = I$

And $V_1 = IR_1$, $V_2 = IR_2$

11.2.2 电阻的串联和并联

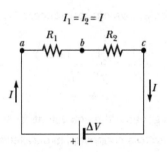

Figure 11-4 Two resistors are in series.

串联等效电阻：$R_{eq} = \sum R_i$

串联电路各处电流相同：

$I_1 = I_2 = I$

So $\dfrac{V_1}{V_2} = \dfrac{R_1}{R_2}$

电压的分配和电阻成正比：

$$\frac{V_1}{V_2} = \frac{R_1}{R_2}$$

Now consider two resistors connected in *parallel,* as shown in Figure 12-5. When charges reach point *a* in Figure 11-5 called a *junction,* they split into two parts, with some going through R_1 and the rest going through R_2. A junction is any point in a circuit where a current can split. This split results in less current in each individual resistor than the current leaving the battery. Because electric charge is conserved, the current *I* that enters point *a* must equal the total current leaving that point:

$$I = I_1 + I_2$$

电阻并联：

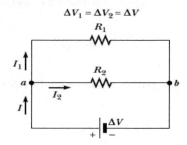

Figure 11-5 Parallel resistors

We can see from the Figure 11-5 that both resistors are connected directly across the terminals of the battery. Therefore,

$$V = V_1 = V_2 = I_1 R_1 = I_2 R_2$$

So, $\dfrac{I_1}{I_2} = \dfrac{R_2}{R_1}$

节点：$I = I_1 + I_2$

流入、流出节点电流相等。

各个电阻上的电压相同：

V=V₁=V₂

The equivalent resistance of two parallel resistors is given by

$$\frac{1}{R_{eq}} = \frac{1}{R_1} + \frac{1}{R_2}$$

电阻并联电路，电流的分配和电阻成反比。

In general, the equivalent resistance of an arbitrary number of resistors connected in parallel is given by

$$\frac{1}{R_{eq}} = \sum \frac{1}{R_i}$$

$$\frac{I_1}{I_2} = \frac{R_2}{R_1}$$

并联等效电阻公式：

$$\frac{1}{R_{eq}} = \sum \frac{1}{R_i}$$

The equivalent resistance is always less than the smallest resistance in the group.

11.2.3 Kirchhoff's Law

11.2.3 基尔霍夫定律

Simple circuits can be analyzed using the expression *V =IR* and the rules for series and parallel combinations of resistors. Very often,

通常电路很难简化成单一回路，复杂电路分析应使用

however, it is not possible to reduce a circuit to a single loop. The procedure for analyzing more complex circuits is greatly simplified if we use two principles called Kirchhoff 's rules:

1. **Junction rule**. The sum of the currents entering any junction in a circuit must equal the sum of the currents leaving that junction:

$$\sum I_{in} = \sum I_{out}$$

2. **Loop rule**. The sum of the potential differences across all elements around any closed circuit loop must be zero:

$$\sum_{\substack{closed \\ loop}} \Delta V = 0$$

You should note the following sign conventions when using the second rule:

Because charges move from the high-potential end of a resistor toward the low-potential end,

• if a resistor is traversed in the direction of the current, the potential difference "V across the resistor is –IR (Figure 11-6 a).

• if a resistor is traversed in the direction *opposite* the current, the potential difference ΔV across the resistor is +IR (Figure 11-6 b).

• if a source of EMF (assumed to have zero internal resistance) is traversed in the direction of the EMF (from – to +), the potential difference ΔV is + ε . The EMF of the battery increases the electric potential as we move through it in this direction (Figure 11-6 c).

• if a source of EMF (assumed to have zero internal resistance) is traversed in the direction opposite the EMF (from + to -), the potential difference ΔV is - ε . In this case the EMF of the battery reduces the electric potential as we move through it (Figure 11-6 d).

In general, in order to solve a particular circuit problem, the number of independent equations you need to obtain from the two rules equals the number of unknown currents.

Complex networks containing many loops and junctions generate great numbers of independent linear equations and a correspondingly great number of unknowns. Such situations can be

基尔霍夫定律：

1. 节点定律：任意节点流入和流出的电流相等。遵循电荷守恒定律。

$$\sum I_{in} = \sum I_{out}$$

2. 环路定理：任意闭合回路电势差的和为零。遵循能量守恒定律。

$$\sum_{\substack{closed \\ loop}} \Delta V = 0$$

电势差正负规定：
电阻：电流方向与回路方向相同，电势差为负，反之为正。

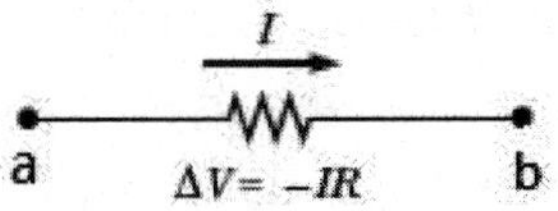

Figure 11-6 a: Resistor is traversed in the direction of the current.

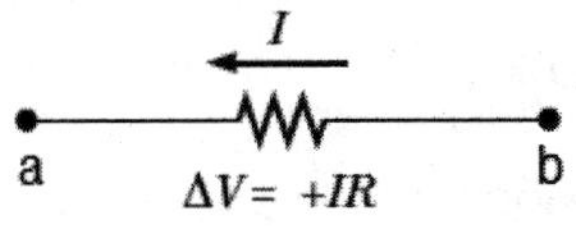

Figure 11-6 b: A resistor is traversed in the direction *opposite* the current.

电源：方向与回路方向一致电势差为正，反之为负。

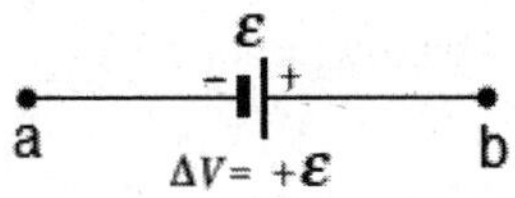

Figure 11-6 c: Battery in direction of EMF

handled formally through the use of matrix algebra.

To make use of Kirchhoff's rules, there are some details that require careful attention:

1. Each unknown current must have a direction of positive current flow defined. It is arbitrary which direction is defined as the positive direction, but consistency must be maintained throughout the solution of the problem. Put an arrow on the circuit diagram defining the direction of positive current for each current.

2. When the junction rule is used, currents are treated as positive if they flow into the node and negative if they flow out of the node.

3. When loop rule is used, make sure a complete closed path through the circuit is used and components are traversed in the same direction around a loop.

4. To obtain a complete set of equations that can be solved for the unknown currents, each unknown current must appear in at least on Kirchhoff's current rule equation and at least on Kirchhoff's voltage rule equation.

In all cases, it is assumed that the circuits have reached steady-state conditions—that is, the currents in the various branches are constant. Any capacitor acts as an open branch in a circuit; that is, the current in the branch containing the capacitor is zero under steady-state conditions.

Example 11.7: Find the currents I_1, I_2, and I_3 in the circuit shown in Figure 11-7.

Solution:

We cannot simplify the circuit by the rules of adding resistances in series and in parallel. We must use Kirchhoff's rules to analyze the circuit and arbitrarily choose the directions of the currents as labeled in Figure 11-7.

We have three unknown and three equations are needed. First of all, applying Kirchhoff's junction rule to junction c gives

$$I_3 = I_1 + I_2 \qquad (1)$$

Then applying Kirchhoff's loop rule to loops *abcda* and *befcb* and traversing these loops clockwise, we obtain the expressions:

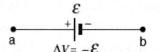

Figure 11-6 d: Battery in opposite direction of EMF

使用基尔霍夫定律时注意事项：

1. 每一未知电流要定义好正方向。正方向的定义是随意的，但定好后整个解题过程都要保持一致性。

2. 使用节点定律：电流流入为正，流出为负。

3. 环路定律：确认是电路中一个完整闭合回路。各元件电势差正负，上述已做规定。

4. 有多少个未知量就需要多少个独立的方程。

电路处于稳恒条件，各支路电流保持不变。电容可看作开路，电流 I =0。

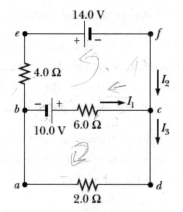

Figure 11-7 Example 11.7

10.0 V - (6.0)I_1 - (2.0)I_3 = 0   (2)   for loop *abcda*

-14.0 V + (6.0) I_1 -10.0 V - (4.0) I_2 = 0   (3)   for loop *befcb*

Solving the equations of (1), (2), and (3), we obtain

$$I_1 = 2.0A,\ \ I_2 = -3.0A,\ \ I_3 = -1.0A$$

Note that I_2 and I_3 are both negative. This indicates only that the currents are the opposite direction we chose for them. However, the numerical values are correct.

Example 11.8: Resistances, battery EMF, and capacitance are labeled on Figure 11-8. And the circuit is under steady-state conditions.

a. Find the unknown currents I_1, I_2, and I_3 in the multi-loop circuit shown in Figure 11-8.

b. What is the charge on the capacitor?

Solution:

a. Because the capacitor represents an open circuit, there is no current between *g* and *b* along path *ghab* under steady-state conditions. Applying junction rule to node *c*, we obtain

$$I_3 = I_1 + I_2 \qquad\qquad (1)$$

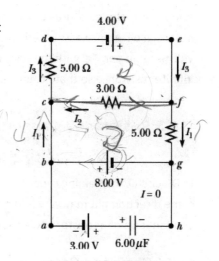

4.00 V

Figure 11-8 Example 11.8

And applying loop rule to loops *defcd* and *cfgbc,* traversed clockwise, gives

4.00 - (3.00)I_1 - (5.00)I_3 = 0   (2)   for loop *defcd*

8- (5.00) I_1 + (3.00) I_2 = 0   (3)   for loop *cfgbc*

Solving the equations of (1), (2), and (3), we obtain

$$I_1 = 1.38A,\ \ I_2 = -0.364A,\ \ I_3 = 1.02A$$

b. We can apply Kirchhoff's loop rule to loop *bghab* to find the potential difference ΔV across the capacitor.

$\Delta V = 8+3 = 11\ v$

Q=CΔV= 66.0 μC

11.2.4 Electrical Meters

An *ammeter* is used to measure current, the ammeter must be connected in series with other elements in the circuit. When using an ammeter to measure direct currents, you must connect it so that charges enter the instrument at the positive terminal and exit at the negative terminal.

Ideally, an ammeter should have zero resistance so that the current being measured is not altered. Because any ammeter always has some internal resistance, the presence of the ammeter in the circuit slightly reduces the current from the value it would have in the meter's absence.

And a *voltmeter* measures potential difference or voltage. The potential difference across resistor is measured by connecting the voltmeter in parallel with the resistor. An ideal voltmeter has infinite resistance so that no current exists in it.

11.2.4 电表

电流表测电流：
与所测电流串联使用。

理想电流表电阻趋于零。电流表对所测电流影响很小，会使电流略有下降。

电压表测电势差：
电压表电阻很大，与所测电阻并联。电压表使所测电压略有下降。

11.3 Resistance-Capacitance (RC) Circuits

11.3 电阻–电容（RC）电路

In DC circuits containing capacitors, the current is always in the same direction but may vary in time. A circuit containing a series combination of a resistor and a capacitor is called an RC circuit.

有电容存在的电路中电流可以随时间变化。

11.3.1 Charging a Capacitor

11.3.1 电容器充电

Let us examine the simple RC circuit shown in Figure 11-9. When the switch S is closed, current immediately begins to flow through the circuit. Electron will flow out from the negative terminal of the battery, through the resistor R, and accumulate on the upper plate of the capacitor. Electron will flow into the positive terminal of the battery. During charging on the capacitor, the potential difference across it increases, and the current is reduced until eventually the voltage equals the EMF of the battery. Meantime, there is no potential difference across the resistor and no current flows. Finally the charge on the capacitor is Q.

We apply Kirchhoff's loop rule to the circuit after the switch is closed, and we obtain

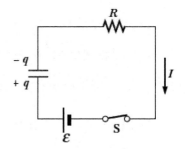

Figure 11-9 Charging a Capacitor at time t

基尔霍夫定律环路方程：

$$\varepsilon - IR - \frac{q}{C} = 0$$

$$\varepsilon - IR - \frac{q}{C} = 0$$

The resistance R includes all resistance in the circuit, including the internal resistance of the battery. I is the current in the circuit at any instant. And q is the charge on the capacitor at that same instant. I and q are functions of time. The rate at which charge flows through the resistor $I = \frac{dq}{dt}$ is equal to the rate at which charge accumulates on the capacitor. So, we have

$$\varepsilon - \frac{dq}{dt}R - \frac{q}{C} = 0$$

Solving this differential equation, first separate the two variable q and t

$$\frac{dq}{C\varepsilon - q} = \frac{dt}{RC}$$

Integral both sides, using the fact t=0, q=0. $I_0 = \varepsilon / R$

$$\int_0^q \frac{dq}{C\varepsilon - q} = \frac{1}{RC}\int_0^t dt$$

We have

$$q(t) = C\varepsilon(1 - e^{-t/RC}) = Q(1 - e^{-t/RC})$$

Where Q=Cε is the maximum charge on the capacitor, Figure 11-10 a shows that q increases from zero to maximum charge Q. And we derive the current on the resistor by derivative,

$$I = \frac{dq}{dt} = \frac{\varepsilon}{R}e^{-t/RC} = I_0 e^{-t/RC}$$

shown in Figure 11-10 b, decreasing from I_0 to zero.

The potential difference across the capacitor is

$$V_C = \varepsilon(1 - e^{-t/RC})$$

解得：$q(t) = Q(1 - e^{-t/RC})$

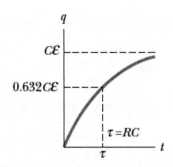

Figure 11-10 a: Charge on the capacitor increases with time.

$$I = I_0 e^{-t/RC}$$

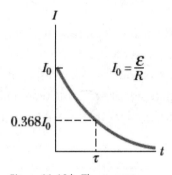

Figure 11-10 b: The current through the resistor decreases with time.

电流和电量都是时间的函数。

τ =RC：RC 电路时间常数

τ 是描述此电路充电快慢的物理量。代表电容器充电到 63%时所用的充电时间。

或电流下降到 37%时所用的时间。

$V_C = \varepsilon(1 - e^{-t/RC})$

电容器上电压-时间图同电

which has similar plot with q(t), increasing from zero to the maximum value ε.

And the potential difference across the resistor is

$$V_R=IR=\varepsilon e^{-t/RC}$$

which has similar plot with I(t), decreasing from ε to zero.

Note that the charge is zero at t = 0 and approaches the maximum value $Q = C\varepsilon$ as $t \to \infty$. The current has its maximum value I_0 = ε /R at t =0 and decays exponentially to zero as $t \to \infty$. And $V_C = \varepsilon$ after a very long time. The quantity RC that appears in the exponent is called the *time constant* τ of the circuit:

$$\tau = RC$$

The unit of RC is second (s). It represents the time required for the capacitor to reach $(1-e^{-1})$=0.63 or 63 percent of its full charge. Thus the product RC is a measure of how quickly the capacitor gets charged. Likewise, the time constant RC represents the time required for the current to drop to 1/e=0.37 of its initial value.

Table 11-1 Summary for charging a capacitor

	Capacitor C		Resistor R	
	V_C	q	V_R	I
t=0	0	0	ε	ε / R
t	$\varepsilon(1-e^{-t/RC})$	$Q(1-e^{-t/RC})$	$\varepsilon e^{-t/RC}$	$I_0 e^{-t/RC}$
$t \to \infty$	ε	Q=Cε	0	0

11.3.2 Discharging a Capacitor

Now consider the circuit shown in Figure 11-11, which consists of a capacitor carrying an initial charge Q, a resistor, and a switch. When the switch is open, a potential difference Q /C exists across the capacitor and there is zero potential difference across the resistor because I = 0. If the switch is closed at t = 0, the capacitor begins to discharge through the resistor. At some time t during the

量-时间图。

$$V_R=IR=\varepsilon e^{-t/RC}$$

电阻上电压-时间图同电流-时间图。

电容器充电总结

11.3.2 电容器放电

基尔霍夫定律环路方程

$$-IR+\frac{q}{C}=0$$

discharge, the current in the circuit is *I* and the charge on the capacitor is *q*. Thus, we obtain the appropriate loop equation for the circuit in Figure 11-11:

$$-IR + \frac{q}{C} = 0$$

Substitute I= -dq/dt into the equation, it becomes

$$\frac{dq}{dt}R + \frac{q}{C} = 0$$

Solving this differential equation, like charging problem, we have

$$q(t) = Qe^{-t/RC}$$

Thus the charge on the capacitor decreases exponentially in time with a time constant RC.

Differentiating this expression with respect to time gives the instantaneous current as a function of time:

$$I = -dq/dt = \frac{Q}{RC}e^{-t/RC} = I_0 e^{-t/RC}$$

We see that both the charge on the capacitor and the current decay exponentially at a rate characterized by the time constant $\tau = RC$.

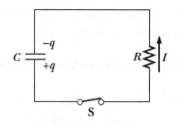

Figure 11-11 Discharging a capacitor when t>0

电流是单位时间极板上电量的减少。

$$\frac{dq}{dt}R + \frac{q}{C} = 0$$

电容器放电时极板上电荷：

$$q(t) = Qe^{-t/RC}$$

τ =RC 描述放电快慢

$$I = -dq/dt = I_0 e^{-t/RC}$$

电容器上的电荷和电阻上电流以时间常数衰减。

电容器放电总结

Table 11-2 Summary for discharging a capacitor

	Capacitor C		Resistor R	
	V_C	q	V_R	I
t=0	Q/C	Q	Q/c	Q/RC
t	$\frac{Q}{C}e^{-t/RC}$	$Qe^{-t/RC}$	$\frac{Q}{C}e^{-t/RC}$	$\frac{Q}{RC}e^{-t/RC}$
t → ∞	0	0	0	0

Example 11.9 Charging a Capacitor: An uncharged capacitor and a resistor are connected in series to a battery, as shown in Figure

11-9. If ε = 12.0 V, C=0.3 μ F, and R = 20kΩ , find

电容器充电计算

a. the time constant of the circuit,

b. the maximum charge on the capacitor,

c. the maximum current in the circuit,

d. the time it takes for the charge to reach 99 percent of the maximum charge,

e. the current I when the charge q is half its maximum, q=Q/2.

solution:

a. $\tau = RC$ =6.0*10^{-3} s

b. Q=Cε =3.6 μ C

c. $I_{max} = \dfrac{\varepsilon}{R}$ =600 μ A

d. q= $Q(1-e^{-t/RC})$ =0.99Q

    t=4.6RC=0.028s

Time constant is very short, so the circuit rapidly reaches its steady state.   时间常数很短， RC 电路迅速达到稳恒状态。

e. q= $Q(1-e^{-t/RC})$ =Q/2 $\rightarrow$ $e^{-t/RC}$ =1/2

    $I = I_{max}e^{-t/RC}$ =600/2=300 μ A

Example 11.10 Discharging RC Circuit: In the RC circuit shown in Figure 11-11, the capacitor of capacitance C that is being discharged through a resistor of resistance R,   RC 电路放电

a. after how many time constants is the charge on the capacitor one-fourth of its initial value?

b. the energy stored in the capacitor decreases with time as the capacitor discharges. After how many time constants is this stored energy one-fourth of its initial value?

Solution：

a. $q = Qe^{-t/RC}$ =Q/4 $\rightarrow$ t= RC(ln4)=1.39τ

b. Energy stored in the capacitor at any time is

$$U= \frac{1}{2}CV^2 = \frac{1}{2}C\left(\frac{Q}{C}e^{-t/RC}\right)^2 = \frac{Q^2}{2C}e^{-2t/RC} = U_{max}e^{-2t/RC}$$

电容器储存的能量

    U=U$_{max}$/4= U$_{max}e^{-2t/RC}$ $\rightarrow$ T=0.693τ

第十一章总结 直流电路

1. 电流：$I = \dfrac{dQ}{dt}$ 单位时间流过导体截面的电量。单位：安培 1A=1C/s

   电流的微观表示：$I = nqAv_d$

   电子在导体中飘移速度：v_d

   电流密度：$j = \dfrac{I}{A} = nqv_d$

   $j = \dfrac{1}{\rho} E = \sigma\, E$

2. 电源电动势 EMF （ε）和电势差。

3. 电阻 R、电阻率 ρ、电导率 σ。电阻单位：欧姆 （Ω）。

   导线上的电阻：$R = \rho \dfrac{l}{A}$ l 升高电阻变大，A 升高电阻变小。

   电阻率：ρ，电导率 $\sigma = \dfrac{1}{\rho}$ 由材料而定。

   电阻率随温度变化：$\rho = \rho_0 (1 + \alpha(T - T_0))$。

   电阻串联：等效电阻 $R_{eq} = \sum R_i$。电路中电流处处相同，电压的分配和电阻成正比。

   电阻并联：等效电阻 $\dfrac{1}{R_{eq}} = \sum \dfrac{1}{R_i}$。电路中电势差处处相同，电流的分配和电阻成反比。

4. 欧姆定律：$I = V / R$

5. 电功率 P：$P = dU/dt = IV$

电阻上的功率：$P = dU/dt = IV = I^2R = V^2/R$

6. 电动势 ε 和端电压 V：$V = \varepsilon - Ir$

ε：电源提供的最大电压

r：电源内阻

V：电源提供给外电路的电压

7. 基尔霍夫定率：解决复杂电路问题

1）节点定律：$\sum_i I_i = 0$，流入、流出任意节点的电流相等（电荷守恒）。

2）环路定律：$\sum_i V_i = 0$，任意闭合回路的总电压为零（能量守恒）。

8. 电压表和电流表：用之测量时都使待测量数值减小。

电压表：内阻大

电流表：内阻小

9. RC 电路

电路时间常数 τ =RC：是描述充电、放电快慢的物理量。

充电、放电过程中，电容器和电阻上物理量的变化规律可见 Table11-1 和 11-2。

Chapter 11 Direct Current Circuits Practice

Multiple Choice Questions

1. Kirchoff's loop rule is essentially a restatement of which of the following?

   A. Ohm's Law
   B. Faraday's Law
   C. Conservation of momentum
   D. Conservation of charge
   E. Conservation of energy

Questions **2-3** are based on the circuit below.

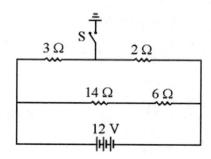

2. If the switch S opens, the current through the $3\,\Omega$ resistor will be

   A. 0.6 A
   B. 0.8 A
   C. 2.4 A
   D. 4 A
   E. 6 A

3. If the switch S is closed, the current through the $3\,\Omega$ resistor will be

   A. 0.6 A
   B. 0.8 A
   C. 2.4 A
   D. 4 A
   E. 6 A

4. A certain resistor has a resistance that is directly proportional to its temperature. If the temperature of the resistor is doubled, and the current through the resistor remains constant, the voltage drop across the resistor will

   A. increase by a factor of 4.
   B. increase by a factor of 2.
   C. remain the same.
   D. decrease by a factor of 2.
   E. decrease by a factor of 4.

5. A wire with a circular cross-sectional area has a resistance R. A circular wire of the same material has a cross-sectional radius twice that of the first wire. The resistance of the second wire is

   A. R/4
   B. R/2
   C. R
   D. 2R
   E. 4R

6. A circuit is built using three resistors of resistance R. Which of the following is a possible equivalent resistance of the circuit?

   A. *R/6*
   B. *2R/3*
   C. *R*
   D. *2R*
   E. *5R/2*

7. A circuit contains a 12 V power source, and a $3\,\Omega$, $4\,\Omega$, and $6\,\Omega$, resistor. How should the resistors be arranged for the current through the battery to be 2A?

   A. All resistors should be in series.
   B. All resistors should be in parallel.

C. The $3\,\Omega$ and $4\,\Omega$ resistors should be in parallel, and the $6\,\Omega$ resistor in series.

D. The $3\,\Omega$ and $6\,\Omega$ resistors should be in parallel, and the $4\,\Omega$ resistor in series.

E. The $4\,\Omega$ and $6\,\Omega$ resistors should be in parallel, and the $3\,\Omega$ resistor in series.

8. Drift velocity is best defined as

A. the relationship between current and current density.

B. the number of mobile electrons per volume.

C. the number of mobile electrons per length.

D. the flux of the current density through a given area.

E. the average speed of the motion of the electrons in a wire.

9. A battery requires an amount of time t_0 to charge a capacitor to 25% of its final charge, what is the time constant of the circuit, τ ?

A. $\tau = \dfrac{t_0}{\ln(4/3)}$

B. $\tau = t_0 / \ln 4$

C. $\tau = t_0 / \ln 0.25$

D. $\tau = t_0 / \ln 0.75$

E. $4 t_0$

Questions **10-11**

Consider the circuit below and assume that the battery has no internal resistance.

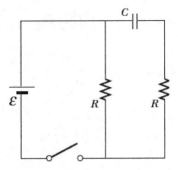

10. Just after the switch is closed, the current in the battery is

A. zero

B. $\varepsilon /2R$

C. $2\varepsilon /R$

D. ε /R

E. impossible to determine

11. After a very long time, the current in the battery is

A. zero

B. $\varepsilon /2R$

C. $2\varepsilon /R$

D. ε /R

E. impossible to determine

Questions **12-13** are based on the circuit diagram below.

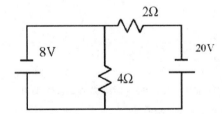

12. What is the current through the $2\,\Omega$ resistor?

A. 2 A

B. $\dfrac{10}{3}$ A

C. 6 A

D. 8 A

E. 10 A

13. What is the potential drop across the 4 Ω resistor?

A. 8 V

B. 12 V

C. 16 V

D. 18 V

E. 20 V

Questions **14-15**

The circuit in Figure below has been connected for a long time.

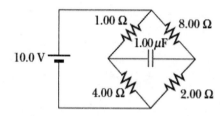

14. What is the voltage across the capacitor?

A. 2V

B. 4V

C. 6V

D. 8V

E. 10V

15. If the battery is disconnected, how long does it take the capacitor to discharge to 1/e of its initial voltage?

A. 1.8 μ s

B. 3.6 μ s

C. 8.3 μ s

D. 18 μ s

E. 36 μ s

16. In order to measure the power dissipated in a resistor of unknown value, the minimum equipment needed would be

A. a voltmeter only

B. an ammeter only

C. a voltmeter and an ammeter

D. an ammeter, a voltmeter, and a resistor of known value

E. a voltmeter and a magnet producing a known magnetic field

Free Response Questions

1. In Figure below, suppose the switch has been closed for a time sufficiently long for the capacitor to become fully charged.

    A. Calculate the steady-state current in each resistor.

    B. Find charge Q on the capacitor.

    C. The switch is now opened at t =0. Write an equation for the current through R_2 as a function of time.

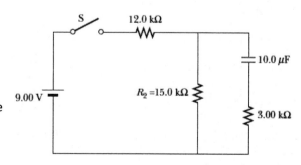

D. Calculate the time interval required for the charge on the capacitor to fall to one-fifth of its initial value.

E. Find the power dissipated in R_2 as a function of time.

F. Determine the total amount of energy dissipated as heat by R_2.

2. A dead battery is charged by connecting it to the live battery of another car with jumper cables. Determine the current in the starter and in the dead battery.

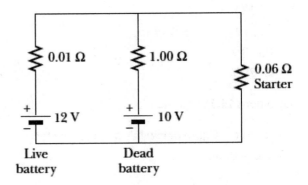

Answers and Explanations

Multiple Choice Answers

1. E   2. C   3. D   4. B   5. A   6. B   7. D   8. E   9. A   10. C   11. D   12. C   13. A   14. C   15. B
16. C

Multiple Choice Explanations

1. E。回路中总的电势降落为零，电源提供外电路能量。

2. C。串联电路电阻 R=4Ω，总电流 I=3A。并联电路电流的分配与电阻成反比 I_3=2.4A。

3. D。3Ω 电阻两端的电势差为 12V，电流 I=4A。

4. B。温度 $T \rightarrow 2T_0$，电阻 $R \rightarrow 2R_0$，且电流不变；所以 $V=IR=2V_0$。

5. A。导线电阻 $R = \rho \dfrac{l}{S}$，$S = \pi r^2$，r 增加一倍，面积变为原来的 4 倍；$R=R_0/4$。

6. B。两个电阻串联后再和第三个电阻并联。

7. D。电路中的等效电阻 R=V/I=6Ω。3Ω 和 6Ω 的电阻并联后再和 4Ω 的电阻串联。

8. E。I=nqv_DS。漂移速度是电子在导线中的平均运动速度。

9. A。$Q = Q_0(1 - e^{-\frac{t}{\tau}})$。$1 - e^{-\frac{t_0}{\tau}}$ =0.25 $\rightarrow \tau = \dfrac{t_0}{\ln(4/3)}$

10. C。电源闭合时，电容器相当于短路，电势差 ε 加在两并联电阻上，$I = \dfrac{\varepsilon}{R/2}$ =2ε/R。

11. D。电路稳定后电容器上的电压为 ε，此时电容器等效于电路开路，$I = \dfrac{\varepsilon}{R}$。

12. C。2Ω 电阻上的电势降落为 12v，I=V/R=6A。

13. A。4Ω 电阻上的电势降落为 8V。

14. C。电容器左端 V_L=8V，右端电势为 V_R=2V，$\Delta V = 6V$。

15. B。去掉电源后电路的总电阻为 R=3.6Ω，电势差降为原来的 1/e 所用时间 t=τ =RC=3.6 μs。

16. C。R=V/I，测量电阻需要电流表和电压表。

Free Response Explanations

1. A. 通过 $3\,k\Omega$ 的电流为零；$12\,k\Omega$ 和 $15\,k\Omega$ 的电流为 $333\,\mu A$。

   B. 电阻 R_2 上的电压 $V_2=5V$，电容 C 上的电量 $Q=CV_2=50.0\,\mu C$。

   C. 开关断开瞬间电流最大：$I_{max}=\dfrac{V_2}{R_2+3k\Omega}=278\,\mu A$；RC 电路的时间常数 $\tau=RC=0.18s$。

   所以电流的时间函数是：$I=278e^{-\frac{t}{0.18}}\mu A$。

   D. $Q=50e^{-\frac{t}{0.18}}\mu C=50/5$，求出 $t=290$ ms。

   E. 功率 P=$I^2R=1.16e^{-\frac{t}{0.09}}$ mW。

   F. 电阻 R_2 消耗的能量：W=$\displaystyle\int_0^\infty Pdt=\int_0^\infty 1.16e^{-\frac{t}{0.09}}dt=0.104mJ$

2. 流入 dead Battery 的电流向下，大小为 I_2；流过 starter 的电流为 I_1，向下；流出 live battery 的电流为 I_1+I_2。应用基尔霍夫环路定理有：

   12-0.01（I_1+I_2）-0.06I_1=0   (1)

   12-10-0.01（I_1+I_2）-I_2=0   (2)

   解方程求得：I_1=171A，I_2=0.283A

Chapter 12

Magnetic Fields
磁场

Introduction: This chapter explores the origin of the magnetic field—moving charges. Electric charges that move are the sources of magnetic fields, and other charges that move can experience a magnetic force in these fields. Not only do moving charges create magnetic fields, but certain materials that are called *ferromagnetic* can produce permanent magnets. And we show how to use the law of Biot and Savart to calculate the magnetic field produced at some point in space by a small current element. Using this formalism and the principle of superposition, we then calculate the total magnetic field due to various current distributions. We also introduce Ampère's law, which is useful in calculating the magnetic field of a highly symmetric configuration carrying a steady current. This chapter examines the forces that act on moving charges and on current-carrying wires in the presence of a magnetic field.

磁场源于运动电荷或电流。运动电荷或电流在磁场中受到磁场力作用。

铁磁物质

毕奥-沙伐尔定律是小段电流产生的磁场计算公式，再用叠加原理计算任意电流产生的磁场。

具有对称性的磁场可由安培环路定理求出。

12.1 Magnetic Field   12.1 磁场

12.1.1 Magnetic Field B

12.1.1 磁感应强度B

Historically, the symbol **B** has been used to represent a magnetic field, and this is the notation we use. The direction of the magnetic field **B** at any location is the direction in which a compass needle points at that location. As with the electric field, we can represent the magnetic field by means of drawings with *magnetic field lines*.

Figure 12-1 shows how the magnetic field lines of a bar magnet can be traced with the aid of a compass. Note that the magnetic field lines outside the magnet point away from north poles and toward

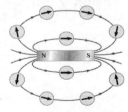

Figure 12-1 Compass needles used to trace the magnetic field lines in the region outside a bar magnet.

south poles. The north pole of compass needle points the direction of magnetic field at that point.

磁场用**B**表示，小磁针N极指向磁场的方向。

Oersted discovered in 1819 that a compass needle is deflected by a current-carrying conductor. What Oersted found was that an electric current produces a magnetic field. The direction of the magnetic field created by a current is given by the right-hand rule. If you grasp a wire carrying a current with your right hand, your thumb extends in the direction the current flows through the wire, and your fingers wrap around the wire in the same direction that the magnetic field lines wrap around the wire. The magnetic field lines due to a circular loop can be determined in a similar way.

电流或运动电荷激发磁场。电流、磁场符合右手定则。

右手定则：拇指指向电流，四指绕向磁场线方向。四指握电流，拇指指向磁场方向。

Unit of magnetic field B is Tesla, T.

磁感应强度单位：T

12.1.2 Magnetic Poles

12.1.2 磁极

As electric charges can be positive or negative, magnetic poles can be north or south. Just like electric charges repel and opposite charges attract, magnetic poles repel and opposite magnetic poles attract.

南北磁极：N、S
同号磁极相斥，异号相吸。

Although the force between two magnetic poles is otherwise similar to the force between two electric charges, electric charges can be isolated (witness the electron and proton) whereas a single magnetic pole has never been isolated. That is, magnetic poles are always found in pairs. All attempts thus far to detect an isolated magnetic pole (*monopoles*) have been unsuccessful and perhaps do not exist. Nonetheless, scientists continue the search because certain theories that are otherwise successful in explaining fundamental physical behavior suggest the possible existence of monopoles.

不存在单独的磁极，磁极都是成对出现。

磁单极子：目前还没有发现

12.2 Magnetic Flux

12.2 磁通量

12.2.1 Magnetic Field Line

12.2.1 磁场线

Like electric field line, magnetic field lines can represent the magnitude （density of lines） and direction (tangent of lines) of magnetic fields. The magnetic field line shown has no beginning and no end. It forms a closed loop. This is a major difference between magnetic field lines and electric field lines, which begin on positive

磁场线描述磁场大小（磁场线密度）和方向（切向）
磁场线是无头无尾的闭合曲线。任意两条不相交。

charges and end on negative charges.

12.2.2 Magnetic Flux

The flux associated with a magnetic field is defined in a manner similar to that used to define electric flux. Consider an element of area dA on an arbitrarily shaped surface, as shown in Figure 12-2. If the magnetic field at this element is B, the magnetic flux through the element is $\mathbf{B} \cdot d\mathbf{A}$, where $d\mathbf{A}$ is a vector that is perpendicular to the surface and has a magnitude equal to the area dA. Therefore, the total magnetic flux ϕ_m through the surface is

$$\phi_m = \int_A B \cdot dA$$

In the special case of a plane of area S in a uniform field **B** that makes an angle θ with plane A=An. The magnetic flux through the plane, shown in Figure 12-2 b, is

$$\phi_m = B \cdot A = BA\cos\theta$$

The unit of magnetic field flux is Weber. 1WB=1T m^2.

If magnetic field B is parallel to the surface A, ϕ_m =0.

Example 12.1 There is a constant magnetic field **B=5i + 3j.** A plane A is placed at the plane YOZ, shown in Figure 12-3. Find the magnetic flux through S.

Solution:

The area S has the direction in n, along x axis, An=Ai

$$\phi_m = B \cdot A =(5\mathbf{i} +3\mathbf{j}) \bullet S\mathbf{i} = 5\ S$$

Example 12.2 ϕ_m **Through a Rectangular Loop:** A rectangular loop of width a and length b is located near a long wire carrying a current I (Figure 12-4). The distance between the wire and the closest side of the loop is c. The wire is parallel to the long side of the loop. Find the total magnetic flux through the loop due to the current in the

12.2.2 磁通量

定义：$\phi_m = \int_A B \cdot dA$

与电通量定义和计算相同，磁通量可以是正、负或零。

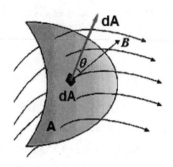

Figure 12-2 a: Magnetic Flux through a surface A

磁通量的单位：WB

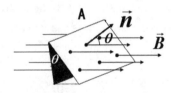

Figure12-2 b: Flux of a plane

$$\phi_m = B \cdot A = BA\cos\theta$$

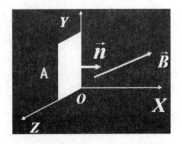

Figure 12-3 Example 12.1

wire. The magnitude of the magnetic field created by the wire at a distance r from the wire is B=$\dfrac{\mu_0 I}{2\pi r}$.

Solution:

The direction of **B** is directed into the page at the right side of the current (at the location of the loop). **B** is parallel to dA=bdr at any point within the loop, the magnetic flux through an area element dA is

$$\mathrm{d}\phi_m = \mathbf{B}\cdot \mathbf{dA} = \frac{\mu_0 I}{2\pi r}\,\mathrm{b\,dr}$$

So, $\quad \phi_m = \displaystyle\int_c^{c+a} \frac{\mu_0 I}{2\pi r}\,\mathrm{b\,dr} = \frac{\mu_0 Ib}{2\pi}\ln(\frac{c+a}{c})$

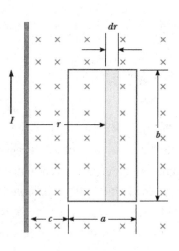

Figure 12-4 Example 12.2

12.2.3 Gauss's Law in Magnetic Field

Magnetic field lines are continuous, form closed loops, and do not begin or end at any point. Note that for any closed surface the number of lines entering the surface equals the number leaving the surface; thus, the net magnetic flux is zero. In contrast, for a closed surface surrounding charges, the net electric flux is not zero, that gives out the Gauss's law in electric field. So, Gauss's law in magnetism states that

$$\phi_m = \oint_A B\cdot dA = 0$$

the net magnetic flux through any closed surface is always zero.

12.2.3 磁场高斯定理

磁场线是无头无尾的闭合曲线。

$$\phi_m = \oint_A B\cdot dA = 0$$

A：任意闭合曲面，高斯面

通过任意闭合曲面的磁通量为零。磁场是无源场。

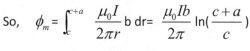

12.3 Biot-Savart Law

12.3 毕奥–沙伐尔定律

Electric currents create magnetic fields. In order to calculate the magnetic fields, a magnetic equivalent to Coullomb's law in the electric field was developed by Biot and Savart.

From their experimental results, Biot and Savart arrived at a mathematical expression that gives the magnetic field at some point in space in terms of the current that produces the field. That expression for magnetic field is based on the following experimental observations for the magnetic field d**B** at a point P associated with a length element d**l** of a wire carrying a steady current I (Figure 12-5).

电流产生磁场

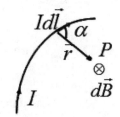

Figure 12-5 I**d**l creates d**B**

• The vector $d\mathbf{B}$ is perpendicular both to Idl (it is a vector which points in the direction of the current) and to the unit vector $\mathbf{r_0}$ directed from dl toward P.

• The magnitude of $d\mathbf{B}$ is inversely proportional to r^2, where r is the distance from dl to P.

• The magnitude of $d\mathbf{B}$ is proportional to Idl and $\sin\alpha$, where is the angle between the vector Idl and $\mathbf{r_0}$.

These observations are summarized in the mathematical expression known today as the Biot–Savart Law:

$$d\mathbf{B} = \frac{\mu_0}{4\pi} \frac{Idl \times r_0}{r^2}$$

where μ_0 is a constant called the permeability of free space:

$$\mu_0 = 4\pi \times 10^{-7} T \cdot m / A$$

$\mathbf{r_0}$ is the unit vector of $\mathbf{r}$. We can write Biot-Savart Law as

$$d\mathbf{B} = \frac{\mu_0}{4\pi} \frac{Idl \times r}{r^3}$$

The magnitude of $d\mathbf{B}$ is

$$d\mathbf{B} = \frac{\mu_0}{4\pi} \frac{Idl \sin\alpha}{r^2}$$

The direction of $d\mathbf{B}$ is decided by the cross product of Idl and $\mathbf{r}$, perpendicular to the two vectors. Hence, if the conductor lies in the plane of the page, as shown in Figure 12-2, $d\mathbf{B}$ points into the page at point P.

Magnetic field created by a Idl is different from electric field created by a point charge. If α =0, r is along the direction of Idl (parallel with Idl), then we have

dB=0

The total magnetic field at point P is then found by integrating over all current elements.

$$\mathbf{B} = \frac{\mu_0}{4\pi} \int_L \frac{Id\vec{l} \times \vec{r_0}}{r^2}$$

电流元 Idl：是向量，指向电流流向，在周围空间产生磁场 d**B**

d**B** 的方向：垂直于 Idl 和 r 组成的平面

d**B** 的大小：正比于 Idl 和 Idl 与 r 夹角的正弦 $\sin\alpha$，反比于电流元到 p 点距离的平方。

毕奥-沙伐尔定律：

$$d\mathbf{B} = \frac{\mu_0}{4\pi} \frac{Idl \times r_0}{r^2}$$

μ_0：真空中磁导率

d**B** 大小：$d\mathbf{B} = \frac{\mu_0}{4\pi} \frac{Idl \sin\alpha}{r^2}$

d**B** 方向：由 Idl 和 **r** 这两个向量叉乘确定。

α =0 或 180^0：dB=0

沿着电流元方向磁场为零。

任意一段电流产生的磁场由磁场叠加原理计算：

$$\mathbf{B} = \frac{\mu_0}{4\pi} \int_L \frac{Id\vec{l} \times \vec{r_0}}{r^2}$$

Where the integral is taken over the entire current distribution, the length of the current, L. This expression must be handled with special care because the integrand is a cross product.

It is an inverse square law, like Coulomb's law.

Example 12.3 B Due to Current in a Straight Wire: A thin, straight wire carrying a constant current I placed along the vertical axis Y as shown in Figure 12-6. Determine the magnitude and direction of the magnetic field at point P due to this current.

Solution:

θ is the angle of Idl (Y direction) and r. a is the distance from P to the current wire. And l is the poison of Idl. θ_1, θ_2 are the angles formed by the current wire and the line segments from end points to point P. From Biot-Savart Law, we know the magnetic filed created by Idl is

$$dB= \frac{\mu_0}{4\pi} \frac{Idl \times r}{r^3}$$

Direction of dB is into the page. Magnitude of dB is

$$dB= \frac{\mu_0}{4\pi} \frac{Idl \sin\theta}{r^2}$$

From Geometry of the Figure 12-6 , we have

$$-l = a\cot\theta$$

So, $dl = a\sec^2\theta d\theta$

Also we have

$$r = \frac{a}{\sin\theta} = a\csc\theta$$

and $dB= \frac{\mu_0 I}{4\pi a} \sin\theta d\theta$

This is an expression in which the only variable is θ. We now obtain the magnitude of the magnetic field at point P by integrating over all elements because all of them have the same direction. So the direction of magnetic field at p is into the page.

毕-沙定律是平方反比律,类比库仑定律。

直线电流的磁场

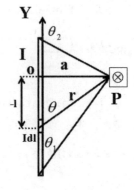

Figure 12-6 Example 12.3

各个电流元产生 dB 在 P 点方向一致，垂直纸面向里。

dB 大小： $dB= \frac{\mu_0}{4\pi} \frac{Idl \sin\theta}{r^2}$

p 点总场强： $B= \int dB$

直线电流距离为 a 处场强：

$$B= \frac{\mu_0 I}{4\pi a}(\cos\theta_1 - \cos\theta_2)$$

长直电流磁场， $\theta_1 = 0^0$ ，

$\theta_2 = \pi$ ： $B= \frac{\mu_0 I}{2\pi a}$

磁场线是垂直导线平面上的系列圆环，磁力线是闭合

$$B= \frac{\mu_0 I}{4\pi a} \int_{\theta_1}^{\theta} \sin \theta d\theta = \frac{\mu_0 I}{4\pi a} (\cos \theta_1 - \cos \theta_2)$$

This is the magnetic field of *any* straight current-carrying wire if we know the geometry.

If we let the wire in Figure 12-7 become infinitely long, we see that

$\theta_1 \rightarrow 0$ 0 and $\theta_2 \rightarrow \pi$,then

$$B= \frac{\mu_0 I}{2\pi a}$$

The result is important because a current in the form of a long, straight wire occurs often. Figure 12-7 is a perspective view of the magnetic field surrounding a long, straight current-carrying wire. Because of the symmetry of the wire, the magnetic field lines are circles concentric with the wire and lie in planes perpendicular to the wire. The magnitude of B is constant on any circle of radius *a*. A convenient rule for determining the direction of B is to grasp the wire with the **right hand**, positioning the thumb along the direction of the current. The four fingers wrap in the direction of the magnetic field.

Example 12.4 Current Loop: A circular wire loop of radius *R* located in the *yz* plane and carrying a steady current *I*, as in Figure 12.8. Calculate the magnetic field at an axial point *P* a distance *x* from the center of the loop.

Solution:

For an current element at the top of the loop, Idl is perpendicular to **r**, the magnetic field d**B** at point P on the axis has the direction shown in Figure 12-8, and the magnitude is a constant

$$dB= \frac{\mu_0}{4\pi} \frac{Idl}{r^2}$$

We can break dB down into components dB$_x$ and d$B_\perp$ which are parallel and perpendicular to the x axis. When we sum over all the elements of the loop symmetry tells us that the perpendicular components will cancel on opposite sides, so $B_\perp$ =0. So, the total B will point along the x axis, have magnitude

线，见下图。

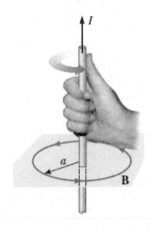

Figure 12-7 **B**'s direction around the current wire

同一圆环上 B 大小相同。磁场具有柱面对称性。

B 方向：圆环切向。由图示右手螺旋法则确定。

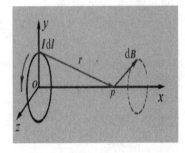

Figure 12-8 Determine B due to a current loop

各个电流元在 P 点产生的 dB 大小相同：dB= $\frac{\mu_0}{4\pi} \frac{Idl}{r^2}$ dB 分解成两个分量，一个平行于 x 轴 dB$_x$，另一个垂直于 x 轴 d$B_\perp$，电流环所有电流元的 d$B_\perp$ 分量叠加为零。

总磁场强度沿 x 轴方向：

$$B=B_x=\oint dB\cos\theta$$

Where θ is the angle formed by d**B** and x axis.

And we have $\cos\theta=\dfrac{R}{r}$, $r^2=x^2+R^2$

$$B=\frac{\mu_0}{2}\frac{IR^2}{(x^2+R^2)^{3/2}}$$

To find the magnetic field at the center of the loop, we set

$x=0$ in Equation above. At this special point,

$$B=\frac{\mu_0 I}{2R}$$

The field has its maximum value.

Example 12.5: One quarter of a circular loop of wire carries a current I, the current I enters and leaves on straight segments of wire, as shown in Figure 12-10. The straight wires are along the radial direction from the centre O of the circular portion. Find the magnetic field at point O.

Solution:

The two straight segments creating magnetic field are zeros at the center of O.

The one quarter of the circular loop carrying a current I creates magnetic field $B_L=\dfrac{\mu_0 I}{2R}\cdot\dfrac{1}{4}=\dfrac{\mu_0 I}{8R}$

Total magnetic field is

$$B=0+0+\frac{\mu_0 I}{8R}=\frac{\mu_0 I}{8R}$$

The direction of B at center O is coming out of the page.

$$B=\frac{\mu_0}{2}\frac{IR^2}{(x^2+R^2)^{3/2}}$$

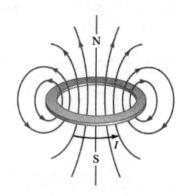

Figure 12-9 Magnetic field line of a current loop wire

圆心处 x=0：$B=\dfrac{\mu_0 I}{2R}$，为最大值。

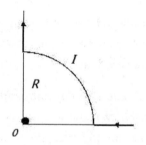

Figure 12-10 Example 12.5

O 点的磁场强度 **B** 等于三段电流在 O 点处激发的场强之和。两半无限长导线在 O 点产生场强为零。1/4 圆弧电流产生场强等于圆环电流在 O 点产生场强的 1/4。方向垂直纸面向外。

$$B_0=\frac{\mu_0 I}{8R}$$

12.4 Ampere's Law

12.4 安培环路定理

A long straight current carrying wire produces a magnetic field, B. The lines of B form circles around the wire by symmetry, and the

磁场不同于电场。
电场是保守场，**E** 环流为零。

magnitude of B is the same everywhere on a circular path centered on the wire and lying in a plane perpendicular to the wire, shown in Figure 12-11.

Electric field forces are conservative forces, we have circulation theorem of electric field.

$$\oint_L E \cdot dl = 0$$

It tells us that electric fields are conservative. Then, how about magnetic field? What will it be for a circular integration of magnetic field ($\oint_L B \cdot dl$)? L is an arbitrary closed path. Figure 12-11 shows a circular path l whose direction is the same with B along the path.

$B = \dfrac{\mu_0 I}{2\pi r}$, so

$$\oint_L B \cdot dl = \int_l \frac{\mu_0 I}{2\pi r}\, dl = \frac{\mu_0 I}{2\pi r} \oint_l dl = \mu_0 I$$

We know from above equation that magnetic fields are not conservative, so we can't introduce a quantity like potential in magnetic field.

Although this result was calculated for the special case of a circular path surrounding a wire, a great many experiments indicated that it is valid in general. It holds for a closed path of *any* shape (an *Amperian loop*) surrounding a current that exists in an unbroken circuit. The general case, known as Ampère's law, can be stated as follows:

$$\oint_L B \cdot dl = \mu_0 I_{encl}$$

The line integral of **B** *d*l around any closed path equals $\mu_0 I_{encl}$, where $I_{encl} = \sum\limits_{insideL} I_i$ is the total steady current passing through any surface bounded by the closed path. $\oint_L B \cdot dl$ is decided by sum of currents inside the Amperian loop, nothing to do with the currents outside the loop. It should be noted, that **B** in Ampere's law is the field at each point in space along the chosen path due to all sources—including the current I enclosed by the path, but

电场中可引入电势能、电势。

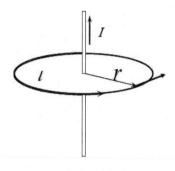

Figure 12-11 B of long straight current carrying wire

长直通电导线沿半径为 r 的圆形回路的 B 的环流:

$$\oint_L B \cdot dl = \mu_0 I$$

磁场环流不为零,所以 **B** 是非保守场,与电场相比有不同的性质,磁场中不能引入势能、势。

磁场中安培环路定理:

$$\oint_L B \cdot dl = \mu_0 I_{encl}$$

L:任意闭合回路,安培环路

$\oint_L B \cdot dl$:B 的环流或 B 的线积分,由 L 包围的电流确定,与 L 外的电流无关。

I_{encl}:L 内的所有电流的代数和。
任意一点的 **B** 由空间存在的所有电流共同确定。

also due to any other sources. Currents in Ampere's law can be positive, negative or zero. If current I and loop L are satisfied with right hand rule, the current is positive, otherwise it is negative. Currents must go through the surface formed by the loop; otherwise it is zero for the loop, zero contribution to the line integral of $\mathbf{B} \cdot \mathbf{d}l$ around the closed path. Figure 12-12 shows there are four currents in the space. For the chosen Amperian loop L, current I_4 is located outside the loop and I_1 goes through the surface twice. Hence, Ampere's law is

$$\oint_L B \cdot dl = \mu_0 (I_2 - I_3)$$

Note：**B** on any point of the loop L is the sum of the magnetic fields created by all four currents.

As Gauss's law for the electric field, we can only use Ampere's law to calculate the magnetic fields which are limited mainly to simple or symmetric situations.

Ampère's law describes the creation of magnetic fields by all continuous current configurations, but at our mathematical level it is useful only for calculating the magnetic field of current configurations having a high degree of symmetry. Its use is similar to that of Gauss's law in calculating electric fields for highly symmetric charge distributions.

The Ampere's law is considered one of the basic laws of electricity and magnetism. It is valid for any situation where the currents and fields are steady and not changing in time and no magnetic material are present.

Example 12.6 The Magnetic Field Created by a Long Current-Carrying Wire:
A long straight cylindrical wire conductor of radius R carries a current I of uniform current density in the conductor. Determine the magnetic field at

a. points outside the conductor, r>R

b. points inside the conductor, r<R

Solution:

a. Because the wire has a high degree of symmetry, let us choose for our path of integration circle 1 to analyze the problem in Figure

I 的符号规定：先确定闭合回路 L 的绕行方向。若电流方向与 L 一致，电流为正，反之为负。若一电流与环路平面平行或穿过平面两次，它对环流的贡献为零。

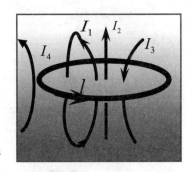

Figure 12-12 Loop L encloses some currents

$$\oint_L B \cdot dl = \mu_0 (I_2 - I_3)$$

安培环路定理对磁场中任意回路都适用。但用其计算磁场时，磁场要具有对称性。

安培定律是电磁场基本定律之一。适用于电流和磁场不随时间变化且无磁介质存在的情况。

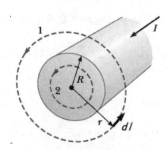

Figure 12-13 a: Example 12.6

12-13. From symmetry, B must be constant in magnitude and parallel to dl at every point on this circle. The total current passing through the plane of the circle is I, and Ampère's law gives

$$\oint_1 B \cdot dl = B 2\pi r = \mu_0 I$$

So $B = \dfrac{\mu_0 I}{2\pi r}$

This has the same result as for a thin wire.

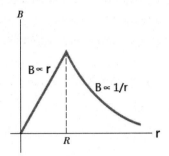

Figure 12-13 b: Magnetic field inside and outside a cylindrical conductor

b. Inside the wire (r<R), we choose a circular path 2 concentric with the cylinder. B is tangential to this path. Because of the symmetry, B will have the same magnitude at all points on the circles. The current enclosed in this case is less than I by a factor of the ration of the areas:

$$I_{encl} = \frac{I}{\pi R^2} \pi r^2 = I \frac{r^2}{R^2}$$

$$B = \frac{\mu_0 I}{2\pi r}, \qquad r > R$$

$$B = \frac{\mu_0 I}{2\pi R^2} r, \quad r < R$$

So Ampere's law gives

$$\oint_2 B \cdot dl = B\, 2\pi r = \mu_0\, I \frac{r^2}{R^2}$$

$$B = \frac{\mu_0 I}{2\pi R^2} r$$

The field is zero at the center of the conductor and increases lineally with r until r=R; beyond r=R, B decreases as 1/r. This is shown in Figure12-13 b.

Example 12.7 An Infinite Current Sheet: A thin, infinitely large sheet lying in the *yz* plane carries a current of linear current density J_s, shown in Figure 12-14. The current is in the *y* direction, and J_s represents the current per unit length measured along the *z* axis. Find the magnetic field near the sheet.

Solution:

From the symmetry of the plane current, we might expect the magnetic field does not depend on distance from the sheet. The direction of the magnetic field is shown in Figure 12-14. So We construct a rectangular path counterclockwise through the sheet.

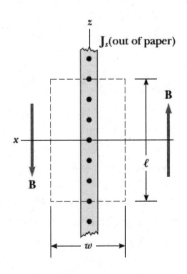

Figure 12-14 Example 12.7

The net current in the plane of the rectangle is $J_s l$. By symmetry, the magnetic field is constant over the sides of length l. Because every point on the infinitely large sheet is equivalent, we apply Ampère's law over the rectangle:

$$\oint_L B \cdot dl = 2Bl = \mu_0 J_s l$$

$$B = \frac{\mu_0 J_s}{2}$$

This result shows that the magnetic field is independent of distance from the current sheet. It is uniform B beside the plane, as we suspected.

Example 12.8 A Long Straight Current Carrying Solenoid

A long coil of wire consisting of many loops is called a solenoid. The loop's radius is much less than the length L and the number of the total loops is N. Now, a current I flows through the wire of the solenoid. What is the magnetic field created by the solenoid?

Solution:

For a long solenoid, with closely packed coils, the field is nearly uniform and parallel to the solenoid axes within the entire cross section, as shown in Figure 12-15. The field outside the solenoid is very small compared to the field inside, except near the ends.

We choose the path abcda for applying Ampere's law:

$$\oint_L B \cdot dl = \int_a^b B \cdot dl + \int_b^c B \cdot dl + \int_c^d B \cdot dl + \int_d^a B \cdot dl = B\overline{ab}$$

$$= \mu_0 I_{encl} = \mu_0 n \overline{ab} I$$

So $B = \mu_0 nI$

Where n=N/L is the number of loops per unit length.

Note that B is uniform and depends only on the number of loops per unit length and the current I.

$$B = \frac{\mu_0 J_s}{2}$$

无限大电流板周围是匀强磁场，与到板面距离无关。

方向：平行于板面

长直螺线管磁场

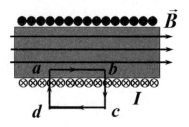

Figure 12-15 B of a solenoid

由对称性分析可知：内部是匀强磁场，方向由右手定则确定。外部磁场强度为零。

$B = \mu_0 nI$

n：单位长度的匝数

螺线管与磁铁棒等效

螺线管内部的场强只与通过的电流和单位长度匝数成正比。

We know that an electric current exerts a force on a magnet, such as compass needle. By Newton's third law, we might expect the reverse to be true as well as a magnet exerts a force on a current-carrying wire. And experiments indeed confirm this effect. The magnetic force is often called Ampere's force.

12.5.1 Ampere's Force on a Current Carrying Wire

A current carrying wire L is in a magnetic field **B** (Figure 12-16). It is found experimentally that the magnitude of the magnetic force on a current element Idl is proportional to the magnitude of Idl and B. The force also depends on the angle α between the current direction and the magnetic field. The force is proportional to $\sin \alpha$. When the current element is parallel to the magnetic field lines, there is no force at all. Thus, we have

$$dF \propto IdlB \sin \alpha$$

The direction of d**F** is given by cross product $Id\vec{l} \times \vec{B}$.

So, the vector form of magnetic force on Idl is given

$$d\mathbf{F} = Id\vec{l} \times \vec{B}$$

The total force on the wire L is then found by integrating:

$$\mathbf{F} = \int_L Id\vec{l} \times \vec{B}$$

If magnetic field is assumed to be uniform in magnitude and direction, see Figure 12-17.

$$\mathbf{F} = I(\int_L d\vec{l}) \times \vec{B}$$

The quantity $\int_l dl$ represents the *vector sum* of all the length elements from a to b. From the law of vector addition, the sum equals the vector $\vec{l}$ directed from a to b. Therefore, Equation above reduces to

$$\mathbf{F} = I\vec{l} \times \vec{B}$$

12.5.1 载流导线上安培力

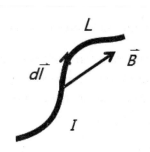

Figure 12-16 **B** acts a force on an current element $Id\vec{l}$

电流元 Idl 受磁场力：

$$d\mathbf{F} = Id\vec{l} \times \vec{B}$$

电流为 I 长度为 L 的导线在磁场 **B** 中所受磁场力：

$$\mathbf{F} = \int_L Id\vec{l} \times \vec{B}$$

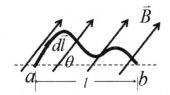

Figure 12-17 A curved current in a uniform **B**

匀强磁场中导线受力：

$$\mathbf{F} = I\vec{l} \times \vec{B}$$

l：导线等效长度

From this we conclude that the magnetic force on a curved current-carrying wire in a uniform magnetic field is equal to that on a straight wire connecting the end points and carrying the same current.

An arbitrarily shaped closed loop carrying a current *I* is placed in a uniform magnetic field, as shown in Figure 12-18. $\oint dl = 0$

F=0

That is, the net magnetic force acting on any closed current loop in a uniform magnetic field is zero.

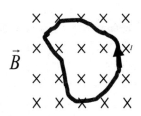

Figure 12-18 A closed current in a uniform B

匀强磁场闭合电流:

F=0

Example 12.9 Force on a Semicircular Conductor

A rigid wire, carrying a current I, is a semicircle of radius R, shown in Figure 12-19. The wire lies in a plane perpendicular to a uniform magnetic field **B**. Determine the net force on the wire due to the magnetic field **B**.

Solution:

Magnetic force acting on the curved semicircle is the same as that on a straight wire of length L=2*R* carrying current to the right, thus

F=2 IRB

The direction of F is pointing upward based on the right-hand rule for the cross product **L**×**B**.

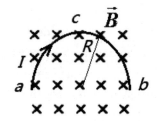

Figure 12-19 Example 12.9

F=2 IRB

12.5.2 Force Between Two Parallel Wires

We have seen that a long straight wire carrying a current produces a magnetic field, and furthermore that such a wire feels a force when placed in a magnetic field. Thus, the two current carrying wires would exert a force on each other.

Figure 12-20 shows two long parallel conductors separated by a distance d. They carry currents I_1 and I_2, respectively. Each current produces a magnetic field that is felt by the other so that each must exert a force on the other. The magnetic field B₁ produced by I_1 at the location of the second conductor is given

12.5.2 两无限长载流平行直导线间的相互作用力

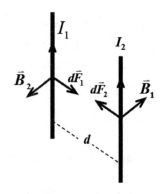

Figure 12-20 Force between two parallel wires

$$B_1 = \frac{\mu_0 I_1}{2\pi d}$$

The force dF_2 on the current element $I_2 dl_2$ is

$$dF_2 = I_2 dl_2 B_1 = \frac{\mu_0 I_1 I_2}{2\pi d} dl_2$$

$I_2 dl_2$ is on the wire 2 and has a distant d to $I_1 dl_1$ which is on the wire 1. The direction of the force on I_2 is pointing to I_1.

$$\frac{dF_2}{dl_2} = \frac{\mu_0 I_1 I_2}{2\pi d}$$

I_2 also produces a field, exerts a force on I_1, pointing to I_2, and has opposite direction with dF_2

$$\frac{dF_1}{dl_1} = \frac{\mu_0 I_1 I_2}{2\pi d}$$

$$\frac{dF_1}{dl_1} = \frac{dF_2}{dl_2} = \frac{F}{l} = \frac{\mu_0 I_1 I_2}{2\pi d}$$

This is the force per unit length felt by the two wires.

Hence, parallel conductors carrying currents in the same direction attract each other, and parallel conductors carrying currents in opposite directions repel each other.

The force between two parallel wires is used to precisely define the Ampere as follows:

One ampere is defined as that current flowing in each of two long parallel conductors 1 m apart, which results in a force of exactly $2 * 10^{-7}$ N/m of length of each conductor.

Example 12.10 See Figure 12-20

For $I_1 = 2A$ and $I_2 = 6$ A , which one is true for the magnitude of the interacting force？

电流 I_1 在电流 $I_2 dl_2$ 处磁场：

$$B_1 = \frac{\mu_0 I_1}{2\pi d}$$

对电流元 $I_2 dl_2$ 的作用力：

$$dF_2 = \frac{\mu_0 I_1 I_2}{2\pi d} dl_2$$

$\dfrac{dF_2}{dl_2}$：导线 2 上单位长度所

受到的作用力，方向指向 I_1

$\dfrac{dF_1}{dl_1}$：导线 1 上单位长度所

受到的作用力，方向指向 I_2

单位长度导线受力大小相同：

$$\frac{dF_1}{dl_1} = \frac{dF_2}{dl_2} = \frac{F}{l} = \frac{\mu_0 I_1 I_2}{2\pi d}$$

安培单位的定义：

如果 $I_1 = I_2$，d=1m，单位

长度上的相互作用力是
f=2*10^{-7} N/m，那么

$I_1 = I_2$ =1A。

a. $F_1 = 3F_2$,

b. $F_1 = F_2/3$,

c. $F_1 = F_2$

Solution: c

12.5.3 Torque on a Rectangular Current Loop

When a current flows in a closed loop of wire placed in a magnetic field, as shown in Figure 12-21 a, the magnetic force on the current can produce a torque. The torque tends to rotate the loop about its vertical axis. This is the basic principle behind a number of important practical devices, such as voltmeters, ammeters, and motors.

Let us calculate the net torque on the loop. If the loop makes an angle θ with the magnetic field, as shown in Figure 12-21 b, the forces on the four sides are

$$\mathbf{F_3} = -\mathbf{F_4}$$

And both of them are along the axis of the rectangular wire. They will cancel out.

$$\mathbf{F_1} = -\mathbf{F_2}$$

These two forces are also in the opposite direction, $\mathbf{F_2}$ is into the page and $\mathbf{F_1}$ is out of the page (in Figure 12-21 a), but they give rise to a net torque that tends to rotate the loop about its axis.

$$F_1 = F_2 = Il_2B$$

The total torque is

$$\tau = Il_2B \cdot l_1 \sin\theta = IAB\sin\theta$$

where A=l_1l_2 is the area of the rectangular loop. If the coil consists of N loops of wire, the torque on N wires becomes

$$\tau = NIAB\sin\theta$$

Its direction is along the loop axis, upward, making the loop to rotate counterclockwise.

12.5.3 矩形载流线圈的磁力矩

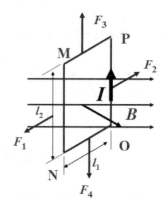

Figure 12-21 a: Torque on a loop

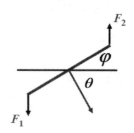

Figure 12-21 b: Top view of the figure above

线圈所受合外力：$F_{net}=0$

线圈所受力矩大小：

$$\tau = IAB\sin\theta$$

A=l_1l_2

N 匝线圈力矩大小：

$$\tau = NIAB\sin\theta$$

This formula, derived here for a rectangular coil, is valid for any shape of flat coil.

The quantity NIA is called the *magnetic dipole moment* of the coil and is considered a vector:

$$\vec{\mu} = NI\vec{A}$$

where the direction of **A** is perpendicular to the plane of the coil consistent with the right hand rule. We rewrite the torque in vector form

$$\vec{\tau} = \vec{\mu} \times \vec{B}$$

which gives the correct magnitude and direction for $\vec{\tau}$.

Although we derive the torque expression for a rectangular loop, the result is valid for a loop of any shape.

线圈磁矩定义：$\vec{\mu} = NI\vec{A}$

面积向量 **A**：绕电流方向由右手法则确定面积正法向。

磁场力作用于闭合线圈力矩：$\vec{\tau} = \vec{\mu} \times \vec{B}$

力矩公式表述虽由矩形线圈推出，此表述适用于任意线圈。

Example 12.11 Torque on a Coil

A circular coil of wire has a diameter of 20cm and contains 20 loops. The current in each loop is 3.00 A, and the coil is placed in a 2.0 T magnetic field. Determine the maximum and minimum torque exerted on the coil by the field.

Solution:

The torque formula is valid for a circular coil.

$$S = \pi r^2 = 3.14 \times 10^{-2} \text{ m}^2$$

The maximum torque occurs when the coil's face is parallel to the magnetic field, so $\theta = 90^o$,

$$\tau = NISB\sin\theta = 3.76 \text{ m N}$$

The minimum torque occurs if $\theta = 0^o$, $\sin\theta = 0$, and then $\tau = 0$

12.6 Magnetic Force on a Moving Charge

12.6 运动电荷所受磁场力

A current carrying wire experiences a force when placed in a magnetic field. Since a current in a wire consists of moving electric charges, we might expect that freely moving charged particles (not in a wire) would also experience a force when passing through a magnetic field.

If N such particles of charge q pass by a given point in time t, they constitute a current I=Nq/t. We let t be the time for a charge q to travel a distance L in a magnetic field B, then **L=vt** where v is the velocity of the particle. Thus, the force on these N particles is

F= I **L×B=Nq/t vt×B=Nqv×B**

The force on one of the N particles is

F=qv×B

Notice that the direction of the force is perpendicular to the direction of v and direction of B and is given by the right hand rule if the charge is positive, as shown in Figure 12-22. For negatively charged particles, the force is in exactly the opposite direction, downward in Figure12-22. The magnitude of the force is

$$F = qvB\sin\theta$$

θ is the angle between **v** and **B**. The force is greatest when the particle moves perpendicular to **B, v ⊥ B,** $\theta = 90^{o}$,

$$F_{max} = qvB$$

The force is zero if the particle moves parallel to the field lines, $\theta = 0^{o}$ or $\theta = 180^{o}$.

We found that the magnetic force acting on a charged particle moving in a magnetic field is perpendicular to the velocity of the particle and that the work done by the magnetic force on the particle is zero. Now consider the special case of a positively charged particle moving in a uniform magnetic field with the initial velocity perpendicular to the field. Let us assume that the direction of the magnetic field is into the page, as in Figure 12-23. As the particle changes the direction of its velocity in response to the magnetic force, the magnetic force (F=qvB) remains perpendicular to the velocity. If the force is always perpendicular to the velocity,

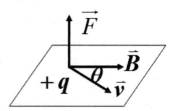

Figure 12-22 Magnetic Force on a moving charge

运动电荷受磁场力：

F=qv×B

F 大小： $F = qvB\sin\theta$

F 方向： **V,B** 的叉乘

如果电荷速度方向与磁场方向垂直，电荷受力最大：

$\theta = 90^{o}, F_{max} = qvB$,

如果电荷速度方向与磁场方向平行，电荷不受力：

$\theta = 0^{o}$ 或 $\theta = 180^{o}$， **F=0**

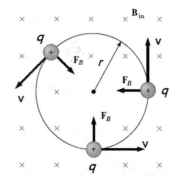

Figure 12-23 运动电荷在匀强磁场做圆周运动，磁场力为向心力

the path of the particle is a circle! The rotation is counterclockwise for a positive charge. If q were negative, the rotation would be clockwise. The magnetic force F is centripetal force of the circular motion, from Newton's second law, F=ma, we have

$$qvB = m\frac{v^2}{r}$$

where r is the radius of the circle, m is the mass of the particle.

$$r = \frac{mv}{qB}$$

That is, the radius of the path is proportional to the velocity of the particle and inversely proportional to the magnitude of the charge on the particle and to the magnitude of the magnetic field.

The period of the motion (the time interval the particle requires to complete one revolution) is equal to:

$$T = \frac{2\pi r}{v} = \frac{2\pi m}{qB}$$

The result shows that the period of the circular motion do not depend on the linear speed of the particle or on the radius of the orbit. The frequency of the circular motion is called the cyclotron frequency because charged particles circulate at this frequency in the type of accelerator called a *cyclotron*.

If a charged particle moves in a uniform magnetic field with its velocity at some arbitrary angle with respect to B, as shown in Figure 12-24 a, its path is a helix (shown in Figure 12-24 b). For example, if the field is directed in the *x* direction, as shown in Figure 12-24 a, there is no component of force in the *x* direction. As a result, a_x= 0, and the x component of velocity remains constant.

However, the magnetic force F= $qv_\perp B$ causes the resulting motion is

a helix whose axis is parallel to the magnetic field. The projection of the path onto the *yz* plane (viewed along the *x* axis) is a circle. (The projections of the path onto the *xy* and *xz* planes are sinusoids!)

There are several important differences between electric and magnetic forces:

磁场力垂直带电粒子速度 V

$$qvB = m\frac{v^2}{r}$$

圆周运动轨道半径：

$$r = \frac{mv}{qB}$$

质量为 m 的带电粒子圆周运动轨道半径与速度相关。

圆周运动周期：

$$T = \frac{2\pi r}{v} = \frac{2\pi m}{qB}$$

带电粒子圆周运动周期，与速度无关。
速度与磁场夹角为 θ：粒子做螺旋曲线运动。

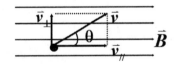

Figure 12-24 a: Velocity of a particle has an angle with B.

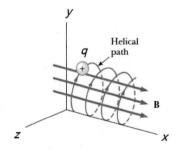

Figure 12-24 b: A particle moves in a helical path.

电场力和磁场力的区别：

• The electric force acts along the direction of the electric field, whereas the magnetic force acts perpendicular to the magnetic field.

1. 电场力沿着场强方向，磁场力垂直于磁场。

• The electric force acts on a charged particle regardless of whether the particle is moving, whereas the magnetic force acts on a charged particle only when the particle is in motion.

2. 电场中的电子无论运动与否，都受到电场力；而磁场力只作用于运动电荷。

• The electric force does work in displacing a charged particle, whereas the magnetic force associated with a steady magnetic field does no work when a particle is displaced because the force is perpendicular to the displacement.

3. 电场力移动电荷做功，而磁场力不做功，因为磁场力垂直于位移。

A charge moving with a velocity **v** in the presence of both an electric field **E** and a magnetic field **B** experiences both an electric force q**E** and a magnetic force q **v** × **B**. The total force (called the **Lorentz force**) acting on the charge is

运动电荷在电磁场中受力—洛伦兹力：

$$F= q\mathbf{E} +q\ \mathbf{v} \times \mathbf{B}$$

F= q**E** +q **v** × **B**

Example 12.12 Electron's Path in a Uniform Magnetic Field

An electron travels at v=4*10^7 m/s in a plane perpendicular to a 0.02 T magnetic field. What is its radius of the circular path?

Solution:

The electron moves at speed v in a circle whose radius is

$$r = \frac{mv}{qB} = 1.1 \text{ cm}$$

Example 12.13 Velocity Selector: Crossed E and B Fields

Some electronic devices and experiments need a beam of charged particles all moving at nearly the same velocity. This can be achieved using both a uniform electric field and a uniform magnetic field. Arranged so they are at right angles to each other. As shown in Figure 12-25 a, particles of charge q with different velocities pass through the slit and enter the region where B points into the page and E points from the positive plate toward to negative plate. For this system, what is selected velocity with which the particles will go through directly from the magnetic and electric field region?

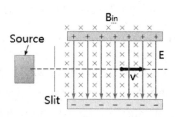

Figure 12-25 a: A velocity selector

Solution:

When entering the region of magnetic and electric field, each particle is subject to two forces as shown in Figure 12-25 b. If q is positive, the magnetic force is upwards and the electric force downwards (Vice versa if q is negative). Depending on the magnitude of v, some particles will be bent upwards and some downwards. The only ones to make it through the region directly will be those for which the net force is zero.

Figure 12-25 b: Forces on the charge

$$F = qvB - qE = 0$$

Hence this device selects particles whose velocity is

$$V = \frac{E}{B}$$

The result doesn't depend on the sign of the charge q on the particle.

Example 12.14: A particular ion has had two electrons removed. The ion is accelerated form rest by a 300v potential difference. It then enters a magnetic field perpendicular to its velocity with a magnitude 2.00T in which it travels along a trajectory with a radius of curvature equal to 13.0cm. What is the mass of the ion?

Solution:

We know the charge of the ion is q=2e. The velocity of the ion entering the magnetic field is

$$\Delta K + \Delta U = 0 \text{, or } \frac{1}{2}mv^2 + q\Delta V = 0$$

So $$v = \sqrt{\frac{-2q\Delta V}{m}}$$

And we know the moving charge experiences a magnetic force when it enters the field, and this force is the centripetal force for the ion to move in a circular path.

$$qvB = m\frac{v^2}{r}$$

$$m = -\frac{qB^2 r^2}{2\Delta V} = 2.15*10^{-23} \text{ kg}$$

第十二章总结　磁场

1. 磁力线：描述磁场。磁力线疏密表示场强强弱，切向是磁场方向。磁力线是闭合曲线。

2. 磁通量：$\phi_m = \int_S B \cdot ds$

   匀强磁场通过某平面 S 的通量：$\phi_m = B \cdot S = BS\cos\theta$

3. 高斯定理：$\phi_m = \oint_S B \cdot dS = 0$。穿过闭合曲面的磁通量为零，磁场是无源场。

4. 毕奥-沙伐尔定律：电流元 Idl 在周围产生磁场 d**B**。电流元延长线方向的磁场为零。

   $$d\mathbf{B} = \frac{\mu_0}{4\pi}\frac{Idl \times r_0}{r^2} = \frac{\mu_0}{4\pi}\frac{Idl \times r}{r^3}$$

   磁场叠加原理：$\mathbf{B} = \int_L d\mathbf{B} = \frac{\mu_0}{4\pi}\int_L \frac{Idl \times r}{r^3}$

   长直通电导线：$B = \frac{\mu_0 I}{2\pi a}$

   电流圆环：$B = \frac{\mu_0}{2}\frac{IR^2}{(x^2 + R^2)^{3/2}}$，圆环轴线上距离环心 x 处。

   圆心处 x=0；$B = \frac{\mu_0 I}{2R}$

   应用毕-沙定律解题步骤：

   1）用对称性分析确定磁场方向，写出任意电流元产生的 d**B**。

   2）由叠加原理计算整个电流的磁场 $\mathbf{B} = \int_L d\mathbf{B}$

   3）计算各方向的合成磁场。

5. 安培环路定理：$\oint_L B \cdot dl = \mu_0 I_{encl}$，磁场是非保守场。

   电流正负规定：环路取向和电流若呈右螺旋，电流为正，反之为负。

   圆柱电流：$B = \frac{\mu_0 I}{2\pi R^2}r$　　r<R

   $\quad\quad\quad\quad B = \frac{\mu_0 I}{2\pi r}$　　　　r>R

无限大平面电流：B=$\frac{\mu_0 J_s}{2}$，J_s：单位长度上流过的电流

长直螺线管：B=$\mu_0 nI$，n：单位长度上缠绕的线圈数目。

应用安培环路定理求磁感应强度步骤：

1）根据磁场的对称性选择合适的环路。待求点在环路上；环路上每点的 **B** 和 **dl** 要么平行，

要么垂直，使 **B·dl** 为常数或零；回路必须包围有不为零的电流。

2）计算回路所包围的电流。

3）应用安培环路定理求出磁感应强度。

6. 载流导线在磁场中受力：**F**=$\int Idl \times B$

等效直导线：**F**=$Il \times B$，任意通电曲线所受磁场力等于将电流两端点连成的直线电流所受的

磁场力。

7. 两平行直导线相互作用力：$\frac{F}{l} = \frac{\mu_0 I_1 I_2}{2\pi d}$

电流单位安培的定义：如果 $I_1 = I_2$，d=1m，单位长度上的相互作用力是 f=2*10^{-7} N/m，那么

$$I_1 = I_2 = 1A$$

8. 载流线圈所受磁力矩：$\vec{\tau} = \vec{\mu} \times \vec{B}$，

$$\vec{\mu} = NI\vec{A} \quad 磁矩$$

载流线圈在磁场中受到的合外力为零，合外力矩不为零。线圈转动状态将发生改变。

9. 运动电荷在磁场中受力：**F**=q**v**×**B**

运动电荷在磁场中做圆周运动：半径 r=$\frac{mv}{qB}$

周期 T=$\frac{2\pi r}{v} = \frac{2\pi m}{qB}$

磁场力垂直于电荷的运动速度，所以磁场力对运动电荷不做功。

应用：速度选择器、质谱仪、回旋加速器

Chapter 12 Magnetic Fields Practice

Multiple Choice Questions

1. A current-carrying wire 3.0 m long is positioned perpendicular to a uniform magnetic field. If the current is 10 A and there is a resultant force of 30 N on the wire due to the interaction of the current and field, The magnetic field strength is

   A. 15 T
   B. $1.8 * 10^3$ T
   C. $6.7 * 10^3$ T
   D. 0.67 T
   E. 1.0 T

2. Under which of the following conditions is the net magnetic force on a charged particle equal to zero?

   A. When the particle is not charged
   B. When the particle is moving parallel to the magnetic field
   C. When the particle is stationary
   D. When the particle is charged and stationary
   E. All of the above

3. The magnetic field due to a long straight wire at a distance d from it has a magnitude B. If the current in the wire is tripled, the magnetic field at a distance d would be

   A. $B/3$
   B. $B/9$
   C. B
   D. $3B$
   E. $9B$

4. Two parallel, straight, long wires a distance d apart each carry a current I in the same direction. A particle with charge $+q$ is traveling midway between and parallel to the wires at velocity v. The force on the particle is equal to

   A. $\dfrac{2\mu_0 Iqv}{\pi d}$ upward, in the plane of the page
   B. $\dfrac{2\mu_0 Iqv}{\pi d}$ downward, in the plane of the page
   C. 0
   D. $\dfrac{\mu_0 Iqv}{\pi d}$ upward in the plane of the page
   E. $\dfrac{\mu_0 Iqv}{\pi d}$ downward in the plane of the page

5. A charged particle is a certain distance away from a current carrying wire. The particle is moving at a constant velocity, perpendicular to the magnetic field produced by the wire. If the distance from the wire is doubled and the velocity of the particle is halved, the force on the particle

   A. increases by a factor of 4
   B. increases by a factor of 2
   C. remains the same
   D. decreases by a factor of 2
   E. decreases by a factor of 4

6. A current carrying wire is bent into a square loop and is placed perpendicular to a magnetic field coming out of the page. The motion of the wire will be

   A. into the page and to the left
   B. out of the page
   C. downward and into the page

D. no motion as the forces are in equilibrium

E. upward, to the left, and out of the page

7. Two wire loops are in a plane perpendicular to a magnetic field and are completely within the magnetic field. If one loop has a radius r and the other loop has a radius $3r$, the ratio of the flux through the loop of radius r to the flux through the loop of radius $3r$ is

A. 1:9

B. 1:3

C. 1:1

D. 3:1

E. 9:1

8. In the figure below, what is the direction of the magnetic force vector?

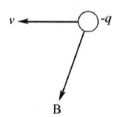

A. To the right

B. To the left

C. Downward, in the plane of the page

D. Out of the page

E. Into the page

9. A positron executes uniform circular motion due to the influence of a magnetic force within a uniform magnetic field B. If the positron's charge is q, and the linear momentum of the positron is p, find an expression for the radius of the positron's path.

A. p/qB

B. p^2/qB

C. $2p/qB$

D. qB/p

E. qB/p^2

10. Two long parallel wires are fixed at a distance d apart and each carries a current of I. The force of attraction between them is F. If the distance between the wires is doubled and the current in each of the wires is doubled, what is the new force of attraction between the wires?

A. $F/4$

B. $F/2$

C. F

D. $2F$

E. $4F$

11. The Biot-Savart Law is used to

A. determine the electric field created by individual point charges

B. determine the electric field created by an electric current

C. determine the magnetic field created by individual point charges

D. determine the magnetic field created by an electric current

E. determine the force field created by an electric current

12. A wire carrying a current I is bending into an arc with radius R and center angle 60^0. The magnitude of magnetic field due to the arc at the center point is

A. $\dfrac{\mu_0 I}{2\pi R}$

B. $\dfrac{\mu_0 I}{12R}$

C. $\dfrac{\mu_0 I}{8\pi R}$

D. $\dfrac{\mu_0 I}{2R}$

E. $\dfrac{\mu_0 I}{8R}$

361

13. Two long wires carry current in opposite directions in the paper plane. The wires are 10 cm apart. The upper wire carries a current of 6A flowing to right and the lower wire carries a current of 4 A flowing to left. Where is the magnetic field equal to zero?

   A. 30 cm above the upper wire

   B. 30 cm below the upper wire

   C. 30 cm above the lower wire

   D. 30 cm below the lower wire

   E. None of the above

14. Two charged particles moving with same speed are projected into a region with a uniform magnetic field and take circular paths with the same radius, but opposite direction, as shown below. These particles are most likely

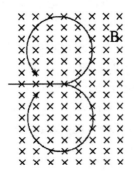

   A. an electron and a proton

   B. an alpha particle and a beta particle

   C. a proton and a neutron

   D. an electron and a positron

   E. a neutron and a neutrino

15. A 4 mA beam of electrons enters a 2 T magnetic field and moves in a circle with a radius of 3 m. The plane of this circle is perpendicular to the magnetic field. Which of the following is the most nearly work done by the magnetic field on the particle during 5 s?

   A. 0 J

B. 20 J

C. 30 J

D. 104 J

E. 1022 J

16. A cube of edge length l is positioned as shown in Figure below. A uniform magnetic field given by B = (5i +4j + 3k) T exists throughout the region. The flux through the shaded face and the total flux through the six faces will be

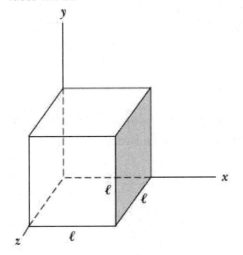

A. $12\,l^2$; 0

B. $5\,l^2$; 0

C. $5\,l^2$; $60\,l^2$

D. $12\,l^2$; $60\,l^2$

E. $5\,l^2$; $12\,l^2$

17. Four long, parallel conductors carry equal currents of I . The figure below is an end view of the conductors. The current direction is into the page at points A and B and out of the page at C and D. The magnitude and direction of the magnetic field at point P, located at the center of the square of edge length L=0.200 m, are

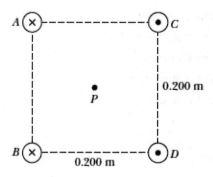

A. 0

B. $\dfrac{2\mu_0 I}{\pi L}$, toward upper of the page

C. $\dfrac{2\mu_0 I}{\pi L}$, toward bottom of the page

D. $\dfrac{\mu_0 I}{2\pi L}$, toward upper of the page

E. $\dfrac{\sqrt{2}\mu_0 I}{\pi L}$, toward bottom of the page

18. An infinitely long straight wire carrying a current I_1 is partially surrounded by a loop as shown in Figure below. The loop has a length L, radius R, and carries a current I_2.

The axis of the loop coincides with the wire. Calculate the force exerted on the loop.

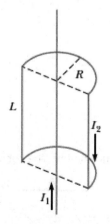

A. 0

B. $\dfrac{\mu_0 I_1 I_2 L}{\pi R}$, to the right of I_1

C. $\dfrac{\mu_0 I_1 I_2 L}{\pi R}$, to the left of I_1

D. $\dfrac{\mu_0 I_1 I_2 L}{\pi R}$ into the plane consisting

Of I_1 and L

E. $\dfrac{\mu_0 I_1 I_2 L}{\pi R}$ out of the plane of I_1 and L

19. A conductor consists of a circular loop of radius R and two straight, long sections, as shown in Figure below. The wire lies in the plane of the paper and carries a current I =7A. Find an expression for the vector magnetic field at the center of the loop.

I=7.00A

A. $\dfrac{7\mu_0}{2\pi R}$, out of the page

B. $\dfrac{7\mu_0}{2R}$, out of the page

C. 0

D. $\dfrac{7\mu_0}{2R} + \dfrac{7\mu_0}{2\pi R}$, into the page

E. $\dfrac{7\mu_0}{2R} - \dfrac{7\mu_0}{2\pi R}$, into the page

20. A rectangular coil consists of N = 50 closely wrapped turns and has dimensions a =0.400 m and b =0.300 m. The coil is hinged along the y axis, and its plane makes an angle $\theta = 30.0°$ with the x axis (shown in Figure below). What is the magnitude of the torque exerted on the coil by a uniform magnetic field B =1.00T directed along the x axis when

the current is I =1.20 A in the direction shown? What is the expected direction of rotation of the coil as seen looking down from above (top view)?

A. 3.60 N.m, Clockwise
B. 3.60 N.m, Counterclockwise
C. 6.24 N.m, Clockwise
D. 6.24 N.m, Counterclockwise
E. None of the above

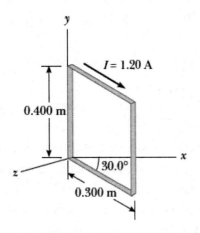

Free Response Questions

1. A very long, thin strip of metal of width w carries a current I along its length as shown in Figure below. Find the magnetic field at the point P in the diagram. The point P is in the plane of the strip at distance b away from it.

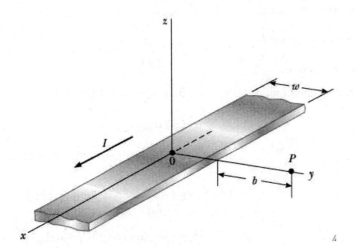

2. A long cylindrical conductor of radius R carries a current I as shown in Figure below. The current density J, however, is not uniform over the cross section of the conductor but is a function of the radius according to $J = br$, where b is a constant. Find an expression for the magnetic field B, r_1 and r_2 are measured from the axis,

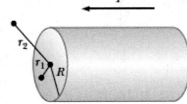

A. at a distance $r_1 < R$ and

B. at a distance $r_2 > R$

3. A long coaxial cable, a section of which is shown below, consists of a solid cylindrical conductor of radius a, surrounded by a hollow coaxial conductor of inner radius *b* and outer radius c. The two conductors each carry a uniformly distributed current I, but in opposite directions. The current is to the right in the outer cylinder and to the left in the inner cylinder. Assume $\mu = \mu_o$ for all materials in this problem.

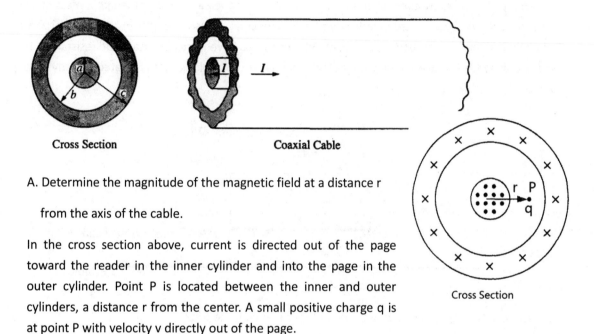

Cross Section   Coaxial Cable

A. Determine the magnitude of the magnetic field at a distance r

   from the axis of the cable.

In the cross section above, current is directed out of the page toward the reader in the inner cylinder and into the page in the outer cylinder. Point P is located between the inner and outer cylinders, a distance r from the center. A small positive charge q is at point P with velocity v directly out of the page.

Cross Section

B. Determine the force on the charge q at point P in terms of the given quantities.

C. If the current in the outer cylinder were reversed so that it is directed out of the page, how would

   your answers to A and B change?

4. In the mass spectrometer shown below, particles having a net charge +Q are accelerated from rest through a potential difference V in Region I. They then move in a straight line through Region II, which contains a magnetic field **B** and an electric field **E**. Finally, the particles enter Region III, which contains only a magnetic field **B**, and move in a semicircular path of radius R before striking the detector. The magnetic fields in Regions II and III are uniform, have the same magnitude **B**, and are directed out of the page as shown.

A. What is the relation of magnetic field **B** and the

   electric field **E** in the region II on the diagram;

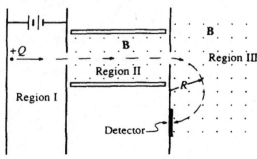

365

In terms of any or all the quantities Q, B, E, and R,

determine expressions for

B. The speed v of the charged particles as they enter Region III;

C. The mass m of the charged particles;

D. The acceleration a of the particles in Region III;

E. The time required for the particles to move along the semicircular path in Region III.

5. The circuit shown below consists of a battery of EMF ε in series with a rod of length l, mass m, and resistance R. The rod is suspended by vertical connecting wires of length d, and the horizontal wires that connect to the battery are fixed. All these wires have negligible mass and resistance. The rod is a distance r above a conducting cable. The cable is very long and is located directly below and parallel to the rod.

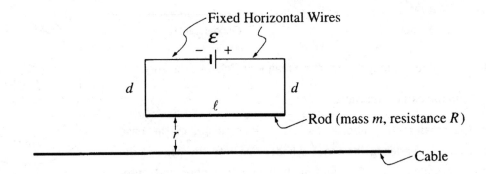

A. What is the magnitude and direction of the current I in the rod?

B. With the proper current in the cable, the rod can be lifted up such that there is no tension in the connecting wires. Determine the minimum current I_m in the cable that satisfies this situation.

C. Determine the magnitude of the magnetic flux through the circuit due to the minimum current I_m determined in part B.

Answers and Explanations

Multiple Choice Answers

1. E   2. E   3. D   4. C   5. E   6. D   7. A   8. E   9. A   10. D   11. D   12. B   13. B   14. D   15. A
16. B   17. C   18. B   19. D   20. C

Multiple Choice Explanations

1. E。通电导线在磁场中受到安培力 $F=ILB$，$B=F/IL=1\ T$。

2. E。运动电荷在磁场中受力为 $F=qvB\sin\theta$，θ 是速度v与B的夹角。所以当 $\theta=0$，q=0，或v=0 时F=0。

3. D。长直通电导线距离为d处的B=$\dfrac{\mu_0 I}{2\pi d}$，当电流增加三倍时，B增加三倍。

4. C。两通以同向电流的平行导线在中点处的B=0，所以电荷受力F=0。

5. E。$F=qvB=qv\dfrac{\mu_0 I}{2\pi d}$，d增大一倍，v变成原来的一半，F变为原来的1/4。

6. D。平面矩形线圈法向与B平行，在匀强磁场中所受和外力为零，合外力矩为零。线圈不动。

7. A。$\phi_{m1}/\phi_{m2}=r_1^2/r_2^2=1/9$

8. E。由右手螺旋法则，负电荷受力向里。

9. A。运动电荷的轨道半径 $r=\dfrac{mv}{qB}=\dfrac{p}{qB}$

10. D。单位长度导线所受作用力 $f=\dfrac{\mu_0 I^2}{2\pi d}$，d增加一倍，$I$ 增加一倍，f增加一倍。

11. D。毕奥-萨法尔定律可计算任意电流在空间中产生的磁场强度。

12. B。半圆环在圆心处产生的B=$\dfrac{\mu_0 I}{4R}$

13. B。设在下面电流的下方x处B=0，有 $\dfrac{\mu_0 6}{2\pi(0.1+x)}-\dfrac{\mu_0 4}{2\pi x}=0$，解得x=0.2m。

14. D。 运动半径相同 $r=\dfrac{mv}{qB}$，m/q相同。两个带电粒子进入磁场后受力方向相反，带有异号电荷。

15. A。 电荷受到的磁场力与电荷运动方向垂直，做功为零。

16. B。 $\phi_m=\vec{B}\cdot\vec{S}$，$S=l^2 i$；通过阴影面的磁通量 $\phi_m=\vec{B}\cdot\vec{S}=5l^2$。通过闭合面的通量为零。

17. C。 左上角和右下角的电流在中心点的**B**相同，大小为 $B=\dfrac{\mu_0 I}{\sqrt{2}\pi L}$，指向左下角；右上角和左

下角的电流在中心处的**B**也是相同的，指向右下角，大小为 $B=\dfrac{\mu_0 I}{\sqrt{2}\pi L}$。所以中心点处的合场

强为 $B=\dfrac{2\mu_0 I}{\pi L}$，指向下方。

18. B。 电流为I_2的线圈处于I_1激发的磁场中，线圈中两个半圆所受磁场力为零，两段长为L的导线受力**F**是相同的，大小为 $I_2 L\dfrac{\mu_0 I_1}{2\pi R}$，指向$I_1$的右侧。

19. D。 圆心处的场强由一无限长载流导线和圆形电流共同激发$B=\dfrac{7\mu_0}{2R}+\dfrac{7\mu_0}{2\pi R}$

20. C。 力矩大小 $\tau=NISB\sin\theta$ =50*1.2*0.3*0.4*0.866=6.24N.m，方向沿y轴反向。顺时针转动。

Free Response Explanations

1. 将宽度为w的面电流看由成无数长直细电流 $dI=\dfrac{I}{w}dy$ 组成。任意dI 在P点产生的磁场dB垂直于xy平面，沿z轴正向；大小为 $dB=\dfrac{\mu_0 dI}{2\pi(b+w/2-y)}=\dfrac{\mu_0 I}{2\pi w(b+w/2-y)}dy$

所以，P点处磁场方向沿z轴正向，大小为

$$B=\int dB=\int_{-\frac{w}{2}}^{\frac{w}{2}}\frac{\mu_0 I}{2\pi w(b+w/2-y)}dy=\frac{\mu_0 I}{2\pi w}\ln(1+\frac{w}{b})$$

2. A. 由安培环路定理 $\oint_L B \cdot dl = \mu_0 I_{encl}$，选半径为$r_1$的圆环路，环路所包围的电流

$$I_1 = \int_0^{r_1} br * 2\pi r dr = \frac{2}{3}\pi b r_1^3，所以 B * 2\pi r_1 = \mu_0 I_1，有 B = \frac{1}{3}\mu_0 b r_1^2$$

B. 同理，半径为r_2的圆环路所包围的电流为 $I_2 = \int_0^R br * 2\pi r dr = \frac{2}{3}\pi b R^3$，环路定理公式为

$$B * 2\pi r_2 = \mu_0 I_2，有 B = \frac{1}{3r_2}\mu_0 b R^3$$

3. A. $B = \dfrac{\mu_0 I}{2\pi a^2} r$ $0 < r < a$

$B = \dfrac{\mu_0 I}{2\pi r}$ $a < r < b$

$B = \dfrac{\mu_0 I}{2\pi r}(1 - \dfrac{r^2 - b^2}{c^2 - b^2})$ $b < r < c$

$B = 0$ $r > c$

B. $F = qvB = \dfrac{qv\mu_0 I}{2\pi r}$，垂直指向圆柱轴线。

C. $B = \dfrac{\mu_0 I}{2\pi a^2} r$ $0 < r < a$

$B = \dfrac{\mu_0 I}{2\pi r}$ $a < r < b$

$B = \dfrac{\mu_0 I}{2\pi r}(1 + \dfrac{r^2 - b^2}{c^2 - b^2})$ $b < r < c$

$B = \dfrac{\mu_0 I}{\pi r}$ $r > c$

运动电荷在 p 点受力不变。

4. A. **E**的方向指向上极板与**B**垂直，E=vB。

B. 正电荷Q水平穿过第二区间：QE=QvB，所以$v = \dfrac{E}{B}$

C. 加速电压V使得Q穿入第二区间前获得速度v：QV=$\dfrac{1}{2}mv^2$，所以m=$\dfrac{2QVB^2}{E^2}$

D. 在第三区间电荷受到向心力Q$vB = ma_c$，所以有$a_c = \dfrac{E^3}{2VB^2}$

E. t=T/2=$\dfrac{\pi m}{QB} = \dfrac{2\pi VB}{E^2}$

5. A. 导线棒上的电流 $I = \dfrac{\varepsilon}{R}$

B. 导体棒受到的磁场力与棒的重力相等：mg=$IlB = Il\dfrac{\mu_0 I_m}{2\pi r}$，得 $I_m = \dfrac{2\pi rmgR}{\mu_0 l\varepsilon}$，向右。

C. 线圈回路中的磁通量 $\phi_m = \displaystyle\int_r^{r+d} \dfrac{\mu_0 I_m}{2\pi y}ldy = \dfrac{mgrR}{\varepsilon l}\ln\dfrac{r+d}{r}$

Chapter 13

Electromagnetic Induction
电磁感应

Introduction：Electromagnetic Induction is the process of using magnetic fields to produce voltage, and a current in a complete circuit. The focus of our studies in electricity and magnetism so far has been the electric fields produced by stationary charges and the magnetic fields produced by currents. This chapter explores the effects produced by magnetic fields that vary in time.

Experiments show that an EMF can be induced in various processes that involve a change in a magnetic flux.

A time-varying current in a circuit produces an induced EMF opposing the EMF that initially set up the time-varying current. Self-induction is the basis of the *inductor,* this chapter concludes with an analysis of circuits that contain inductance as well as resistance and /or capacitance.

电磁感应：由变化磁场产生电势差和电流

13.1 Faraday's Law and Lenz's Law

13.1 法拉第定律和楞次定律

13.1.1 Definition of EMF

13.1.1 电动势定义EMF

A battery produces a potential difference and causes charges to move in a closed circuit and is called either a *source of electromotive force* or, more commonly, a *source of EMF.* The EMF of a battery is the maximum possible voltage that the battery can provide between its terminals. You can think of a source of EMF as a "Charge Pump".

电源提供电势差使电子在闭合回路中运动。称之电动势

EMF 或 ε 。

电源可看作电荷泵。

The circuit symbol for a battery is shown in Figure 13-1. The terminal of the source at the higher potential is marked with a "+"sign while that at the lower potential is marked with "−"sign. The battery is an unusual device: it raises the electrical potential energy of a positive charge q moving from the lower potential terminal to the higher potential terminal. The potential difference is $\Delta V = \varepsilon$ is the net work (W) done by the source on one coulomb of positive charge as it moves from the negative to the positive terminal inside or through the source. It means that there is a kind of field existing inside the battery which can act a force on a charge. We know electric field is a conservative field it can only decrease the potential of a positive charge. For the field inside the source, potential of a positive charge increases while moving a positive charge from − to +. We call this kind of field nonconservitive electric field E_k which is defined by the nonconservative force the charges experienced inside the battery

$$E_k = \frac{F_k}{q}$$

The EMF of the battery is defined as

$$\varepsilon = \int_-^+ E_k \cdot dl$$

For a closed circuit, the electric field (E_e) of a outer part of the battery is conservative field, whereas electric field (E_k) is nonconservitive inside the source, so

$$\varepsilon = \int_-^+ E_k \cdot dl = \oint_L E_k \cdot dl$$

13.1.2 Induced EMF

Faraday found that although a steady magnetic field doesn't produce current, a changing magnetic field can produce an electric current. Such a current is called an *induced current*. It says that an induced EMF is produced by a changing magnetic field. Faraday's further experiment, Figure 13-2, shows that if a magnet is moved quickly into a coil of wire, a current is induced in the wire. If the magnet is quickly removed, a current is induced in an opposite direction. The experiment shown in Figure 13-3 tells us even the

Figure 13-1 A battery provides a potential different.

电源是将正电荷从低电势移动到高电势的装置。

电源内部存在一种特殊电场。由电荷产生的电场是保守场，只能使正电荷的电势降低。电源内部的电场升高正电荷的电势，所以电源内部电场称为非保守电场。作用在电荷上的力—非静电力。

非保守场强定义：$E_k = \dfrac{F_k}{q}$

F_k：电源提供的非静电力

电源电动势定义：

$$\varepsilon = \int_-^+ E_k \cdot dl$$

单位正电荷从负极移动到正极非静电力所做的功。

闭合回路中: $\varepsilon = \oint_L E_k \cdot dl$

单位正电荷绕闭合回路一周，非静电力所做的功。

13.1.2 感应电动势

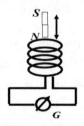

Figure 13-2 Moving a magnet up or down induces a current.

magnetic field is unchanging an EMF also can be induced when a conducting rod moving in a uniform magnetic field. What is the actually reason to induce an EMF?

磁场变化或不变化都可产生感应电动势。

13.1.3 Faraday's Law and Lenz Law

13.1.3 法拉第定律和楞次定律

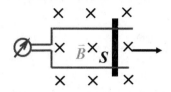

Faraday investigated quantitatively what factors actually influence the magnitude of the EMF induced. He found the EMF is not simply proportional to the rate of change of the magnetic field, B. Rather the EMF is proportional to the rate of change of the magnetic flux,

ϕ_m. We can write down the results of Faraday's investigations: the EMF induced in a circuit is equal to the rate of change of magnetic flux through the circuit

$$\varepsilon_i = -\frac{d\phi_m}{dt}$$

$\phi_m = \int_s B \cdot dS$, S is the area enclosed by the loop.

If the coil contains N closed wrapped loops, $\Psi = n\phi_m$, the EMFs induced in each add together, so

$$\varepsilon_i = -\frac{d\Psi}{dt} = -N\frac{d\phi_m}{dt}$$

The minus sign is placed there to remind us in which the direction induced EMF acts. Induced current in a closed wire is

$$I_i = \frac{\varepsilon_i}{R} = -N\frac{1}{R}\frac{d\phi_m}{dt}$$

Experiments show that:

An induced EMF gives rise to a current whose magnetic field opposes the original change in flux.

This is known as *Lenz's law*. It is valid if no current can flow:

An induced EMF is always in a direction that opposes the original change in flux that caused it.

Lenz's law is part of Faraday's Law and can help you determine the direction of the current provided you know HOW the flux is changing. Lenz's law is consistent with the law of conservation of

Figure 13-3 A conducting rod moving to right induces a current.

法拉第电磁感应定律：

$$\varepsilon_i = -\frac{d\phi_m}{dt}$$

感应电动势等于磁通量的时间变化率的负值。

ϕ_m：通过闭合面的磁通量

N 匝线圈的感应电动势：

$$\varepsilon_i = -\frac{d\Psi}{dt} = -N\frac{d\phi_m}{dt}$$

感应电流 $I_i = -N\frac{1}{R}\frac{d\phi_m}{dt}$

楞次定律：

感应电流的磁场方向与磁通量变化的方向相反。或者

感应电动势的方向总是反抗引起感应电动势的原因。

楞次定律是法拉第定律的一部分，可确定感应电动势的方向，是能量守恒定律在电

energy.

In order to decide the direction of EMF, first of all we need to set the positive direction of the loop L: *its positive direction satisfying right hand rule with magnetic field*, as shown in Figure 13-4 a.

Faraday's and Lenz's law give $\varepsilon_i = -\dfrac{d\phi_m}{dt}$, so we know

if $\dfrac{d\phi_m}{dt} > 0$, then $\varepsilon < 0$

which means ε is in opposite direction with the loop, Figure 13-4a;

if $\dfrac{d\phi_m}{dt} < 0$, then $\varepsilon > 0$.

It is shown in Figure 13-4 b which means ε is in the same direction with the loop.

Now, we know from above that the positive or negative induced EMF is related to the direction of the loop L.

Example 13.1 A coil consists of 200 turns of wire. Each turn is a square of side 18 cm, and a uniform magnetic field directed perpendicular to the plane of the coil is turned on. If the field changes linearly B=kt=$\dfrac{5}{8}$t (T) from 0 to 0.50 T in 0.80 s, what is the magnitude of the induced EMF in the coil while the field is changing?

Solution:

$$\varepsilon_i = -N\frac{d\phi_m}{dt}$$

N=200

$$\phi_m = \int_s B \cdot dS = B\,S = Kt\,S$$

$$\frac{d\phi_m}{dt} = KS = \frac{5}{8} * 0.18^2$$

$$\varepsilon_i = -N\frac{d\phi_m}{dt} = -200 * \frac{5}{8} * 0.18^2 = -4.1v$$

Example 13.2 Pulling a Coil From a Magnetic Field: A rectangular coil of a wire with two sides 5.00cm, 10.0cm contains 100 loops and

磁场中的表现。

导线回路 L 的正方向规定：
L 与 B 成右手螺旋关系。

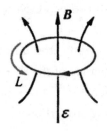

Figure13-4 a: Flux increasing $\varepsilon < 0$

磁通量增加，感应电动势与回路方向相反 $\varepsilon < 0$。

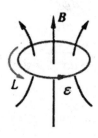

Figure13-4 b: Flux decreasing $\varepsilon > 0$

磁通量减少，感应电动势与 L 方向相同 $\varepsilon > 0$。

is placed perpendicular to a uniform B=0.600 T magnetic field, as shown in Figure 13-5. It is uniformly pulled from the field (moving perpendicular to B) to a region where B drops abruptly to zero. At t=0, the right edge of the coil is at the edge of the field. It takes 0.100s for the whole coil to reach the field-free region. Find

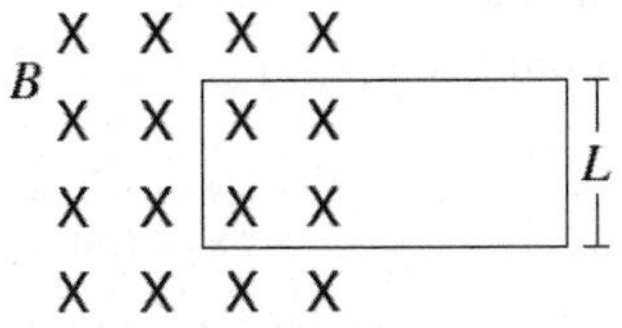

Figure 13-5 Example 13.2

a. the rate of change in flux through the coil.

b. the EMF and current induced.

c. how much energy is dissipated in the coil if its resistance is $100\,\Omega$?

d. what was the average force required?

Solution:

a. $\dfrac{d\phi_m}{dt} = \dfrac{0 - B*S}{\Delta t} = -3.00*10^{-2} Wb/s$

b. $\varepsilon_i = -N\dfrac{d\phi_m}{dt} = 3.00$ v

$I_i = \dfrac{\varepsilon_i}{R} = -N\dfrac{1}{R}\dfrac{d\phi_m}{dt} = 30.0$ mA

And, by Lenz's law, it must be clockwise to oppose the decreasing flux into the page.

c. The total energy dissipated is

E=Pt= I^2 Rt=9.00*10^{-3} J

d. The force that the magnetic field exerts on the top and bottom sections of the loop is in opposite directions and cancels each other. The magnetic force exerted on the left vertical section of the rectangular loop acts to the left because the current is up (clockwise). The right side of the loop is in the region where B=0. Hence the needed external force, to the right, has magnitude

$F_{ext} = NILB$ = 0.0900 N

13.2 Motional EMF　　　　　　　13.2 动生电动势

We describe what is called motional EMF, which is the EMF induced in a conductor moving through a constant magnetic field. Assume

导体在磁场中运动而产生的电动势称为动生电动势。

that a uniform magnetic field **B** is perpendicular to the area bounded by the U-shaped conductor and the movable rod resting on it (Figure 13-6 a). If the rod is made to move at a speed v, it travels a distance dx=vdt in a time dt. Therefore, the area of the loop increases by an amount dS=l vdt in a time dt, by Faraday's law, there is an induced EMF

$$\varepsilon = -\frac{d\phi_m}{dt} = -Blv$$

where the negative sign tell us the induced current is in counterclockwise. This conclusion is valid as long as B, l, and v are mutually perpendicular. The equivalent circuit is shown in Figure 13-6 b. We know that the moving rod is the source of the circuit. Let us see how a moving rod can be treated as a source (Figure13-7).

The electrons in the conductor experience a force **F**$_B$ = q **v** × **B** that is directed along the length l, perpendicular to both **v** and **B**. Under the influence of this force, the electrons move to the lower end of the conductor and accumulate there, leaving a net positive charge at the upper end. As a result of this charge separation, an electric field **E** is produced inside the conductor. The charges accumulate at both ends until the downward magnetic force qvB on charges remaining in the conductor is balanced by the upward electric force qE. At this point, electrons move only with random thermal motion. The condition for equilibrium requires that

$$qE = qvB \quad \text{or} \quad E = vB$$

thus, $\varepsilon = vBl$

A potential difference is maintained between the ends of the conductor as long as the conductor continues to move through the uniform magnetic field.

Example 13.3 Magnetic Force Acting on a Sliding Bar

The conducting bar illustrated in Figure 13-6 a moves on two frictionless parallel rails in the presence of a uniform magnetic field directed into the page. The bar has mass m and its length is l. The bar is given an initial velocity **v**$_i$ to the right and is released at t = 0. Using Newton's laws, find the velocity of the bar as a function of time.

Solution:

动生电动势的非静电力：

洛仑兹力

动生电动势：

$$\varepsilon = -\frac{d\phi_m}{dt} = -Blv$$

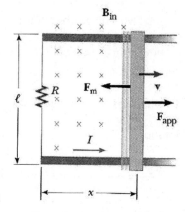

Figure 13-6 a: Motional EMF

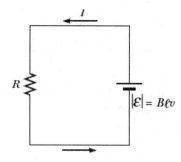

Figure 13-6 b: Equivalent circuit

磁场中运动导体是电路电源。

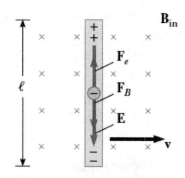

Figure 13-7 The reason for motional EMF

The upward current in the bar results in a magnetic force (F_B= $-I\,l\,$B) to the left on the bar as shown in the Figure 13-6 a. As a result, the bar will slow down, so

$$F_B = -IlB = ma$$

Induced current I =Blv/R, so

$$-\frac{B^2l^2v}{R} = m\frac{dv}{dt}$$

Solving this differential equation, we get

$$v = v_i e^{-t/\tau}$$

where $\tau = mR/B^2l^2$

磁场中运动的导体是电源：

$$\varepsilon = vBl$$

13.3 Induced EMF and Induced Electric Field

13.3 感生电动势和感生电场

When an electric current flows in a wire, there is an electric field in the wire that does the work of moving the electrons in the wire. We have seen that a changing magnetic flux induces an EMF and a current in a conducting loop. And we can relate an induced current in a conducting loop to an electric field by claiming that an induced electric field is created in the conductor as a result of the changing magnetic flux. A changing magnetic flux produces an induced electric field; this result applies not only to wires, but actually is a general result that applies to any region in space. Indeed, an induced electric field will be produced at any point in space where there is a changing magnetic field.

The EMF induced in a circuit is equal to the work done per unit charge by the electric field, which equals the integral of **E** · d**l** around the closed path.

$$\varepsilon = \oint_L \vec{E} \cdot d\vec{l}$$

We combine this with Faraday's law

磁通量的变化引起感应电动势和感应电流。

当磁场变化引起磁通量改变时，磁场的变化激发感应电场 E，作为非静电场强。

非静电场强：感生电场 **E**

非静电力：感生电场力 q**E**

回路中感应电动势等于感应电场的环流：

$$\varepsilon = \oint_L \vec{E} \cdot d\vec{l}$$

$$\oint_L \vec{E} \cdot d\vec{l} = -\frac{d\phi_m}{dt}$$

This is the general form of Faraday's law. It relates the changing magnetic flux to the electric field.

The induced electric field E in Equation above is a nonconservative field that is generated by a changing magnetic field. The field **E** cannot possibly be an electrostatic field because if the field were electrostatic, and hence conservative, the line integral of E dl over a closed loop would be zero; this would be in contradiction to Equation above.

法拉第电磁感应定律:

$$\oint_L \vec{E} \cdot d\vec{l} = -\frac{d\phi_m}{dt}$$

变化的磁场产生的感生电场是非保守场。

13.4 Self-Induction   13.4 自感

A time-varying current in a circuit produces an induced EMF opposing the EMF that initially sets up the time-varying current. This effect is called self-induction which is the basis of the *inductor,* an electrical circuit element.

When the changing current passing through a coil or a solenoid with N coils, a changing magnetic flux is produced inside the coil, and this in turn induces an EMF in the coil. This induced EMF opposes the change in flux. For example, a solenoid with a current I creates a magnetic field B, shown in Figure 13-8 a. If the current I through the solenoid is increasing, the increasing magnetic flux induces an EMF that opposes the original current and tends to retard its increase, shown in Figure 13-8 b. If the current is decreasing in the solenoid, the decreasing flux induces an EMF in the same direction as the current, thus tending to maintain the original current.

To obtain a quantitative description of self-induction, we recall from Faraday's law that the induced EMF is equal to the negative of the time rate of change of the magnetic flux. The magnetic flux is proportional to the magnetic field due to the current and it is proportional to the current in the circuit, $\Psi = N\phi_m, \phi_m \propto I$. So, we define the self-inductance L as the coefficient of the relation.

$$L = \frac{\Psi}{I}$$

回路自身电流变化产生EMF。

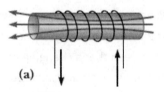

(a)

Figure 13-8 a: Solenoid with I

Lenz's law emf

(b) I increasing

Self-Inductance is the ability of a circuit to oppose the magnetic flux that is produced by the circuit itself. Running a changing current through a circuit creates a changing magnetic field, which creates an induced EMF that fights the change.

The inductance of the coil L depends on the geometry of the coil and on the presence of a ferromagnetic material. The SI unit of inductance is the Henry (H):

　　1H=1V s/A

Ψ =Nϕ_m　if the same magnetic flux passes through each turn.

Then the EMF induced in a coil of self-inductance L, from Faraday's law, is

$$\varepsilon_L = -\frac{d\Psi}{dt} = -L\frac{dI}{dt}$$

Therefore, a self-induced EMF is always proportional to the time rate of change of the current.

Resistance is a measure of the opposition to current ($R = V/I$); in comparison, inductance is a measure of the opposition to a *change* of current.

Circuits always contain some inductance, but often it is quite small unless the circuit contains a coil of many turns. A coil that has significant self-inductance L is called an inductor.

Common inductors have inductances in the range from about

$1\,\mu H$ to about 1H.

Example 13.4 Solenoid Inductance

Find the inductance of a uniformly wound solenoid having *N* turns and length ℓ. Assume that ℓ is much longer than the radius of the windings and that the core of the solenoid is air.

Solution:

Let a current I pass through the solenoid. The interior magnetic field due to the current is uniform and given by

　　B= $\mu_0 nI = \mu_0 \frac{N}{\ell}I$

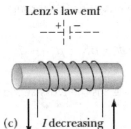

Lenz's law emf

(c) ↓ *I* decreasing ↑

Figure 13-8 b, c: Solenoid is a EMF.

自感系数定义： $L = \dfrac{\Psi}{I}$

L 表示线圈产生自感现象的能力（抵抗磁通量变化）。

自感系数 L 依赖于线圈本身的形状、大小及介质的磁导率，而与电流无关。

自感 L 的单位：亨利 H

Ψ =Nϕ_m：磁通链

自感电动势正比于自感系数和电流的时间变化率。

电阻阻碍电流，自感阻碍电流的变化。

电路本身都有自感存在，但与电路中自感元件的自感相比可略去不计。

螺线管的电感：

L= $\mu_0 n^2 V$

The magnetic flux through each turn is

$$\phi_m = BS = \mu_0 \frac{NS}{\ell} I$$

where S is the cross-sectional area of the solenoid. We have

$$L = \frac{N\phi_m}{I} = \mu_0 n^2 V$$

where V=SL is the interior volume of the solenoid.

13.5 Energy Stored in a Magnetic Field   13.5 磁场能量

When an inductor of inductance L is carrying a current I which is changing at a rate dI/dt, energy is being supplied to the inductor at a rate

外电路提供给电感的功率：

$$P = I\varepsilon_L = LI \frac{dI}{dt}$$

$$P = LI \frac{dI}{dt}$$

P stands for power. The work needed to increase the current in an inductor from zero to some value I during some time interval is

一段时间后，电流从 0 增加到 I，电感所需总电功 W。

$$W = \int dW$$

And dW= Pdt=L IdI is work done in a time dt

$$W = \int_0^I LIdI = \frac{1}{2}LI^2$$

$$W = \frac{1}{2}LI^2$$

This work done is equal to the energy U stored in the inductor when it is carrying a current I (when I =0, U=0)

电功 W 就是储存在电感中的磁场能量。

$$U = \frac{1}{2}LI^2$$

The energy in an inductor can be considered to be stored in its magnetic field. For the solenoid, L= $\mu_0 n^2 V$, B= $\mu_0 nI$

螺线管内磁场能量：

$$U = \frac{1}{2}\mu_0 n^2 V (\frac{B}{\mu_0 n})^2 = \frac{1}{2}\frac{B^2}{\mu_0} S\ell$$

$$U = \frac{1}{2}LI^2 = \frac{1}{2}\frac{B^2}{\mu_0} S\ell$$

We can think of this energy as residing in the volume enclosed by the windings which is V=Sℓ. Then the energy per unit volume or energy density is

$$u = \frac{1}{2}\frac{B^2}{\mu_0}$$

Although this expression was derived for the special case of a solenoid, it is valid for any region of space in which a magnetic field exists.

Energy stored in some magnetic field can be calculated by

$$U = \int_V u\, dV = \int_V \frac{1}{2}\frac{B^2}{\mu_0} dV$$

磁场能量密度：$u = \frac{1}{2}\frac{B^2}{\mu_0}$

u 正比于磁感应强度的平方。

尽管 u 的公式是由螺线管推出，对任何磁场分布都适用。

任意磁场的能量：

$$U = \int_V \frac{1}{2}\frac{B^2}{\mu_0} dV$$

13.6 LR Circuits / 13.6 LR电路

Because the inductance of the inductor results in a back EMF, an inductor in a circuit opposes changes in the current in that circuit. The inductor attempts to keep the current the same as it was before the change occurred.

Any inductor will have some resistance. We represent an inductor by drawing its inductance L and its resistance R separately. The resistance R could also include a separate resistor connected in series. Figure 13-9 is a RL circuit. At the instant the switch K connecting the battery is closed, the current starts to flow, increasing from zero. It is opposed by the induced EMF in the inductor. However, as soon as current starts to flow, there is also a voltage (V=IR) across the resistance. Hence the voltage applied across the inductance is reduced and the current increases less rapidly. The current thus rises gradually and approaches the steady value $I_{max} = \varepsilon / R$ when the entire voltage drop is across the resistor.

We can apply Kirchhoff's loop rule to this circuit, traversing the circuit in the clockwise direction

$$\varepsilon - L\frac{dI}{dt} - IR = 0$$

电感产生反电动势。

开关 K 连接在 1 位置，电感中磁场建立，储存能量：

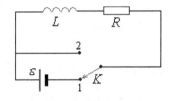

Figure 13-9 A RL circuit

基尔霍夫定律：

$$\varepsilon - L\frac{dI}{dt} - IR = 0$$

感应电动势方向与电源相反。

电流达到稳定前，电路中电流是时间的函数：

$$I = I_{max}(1 - e^{-t/\tau})$$

时间常数 $\tau = \frac{L}{R}$：描述电路

where I is the current in the circuit at any instant. Solving this differential equations we have

$$\int_0^I \frac{dI}{\varepsilon - IR} = \int_0^t \frac{dt}{L}$$

$$I = \frac{\varepsilon}{R}(1 - e^{-t/\tau}) = I_{max}(1 - e^{-t/\tau})$$

where $\tau = \dfrac{L}{R}$ is the time constant of the LR circuit. It represents the time required for a current I to reach 63 percent of its maximum value, see Figure 13-10.

We take derivative of I(t) and get

$$\frac{dI}{dt} = \frac{\varepsilon}{L} e^{-t/\tau}$$

These results tell us the induced EMF on the inductor and potential difference across on the resistor. They are

$$V_L = \varepsilon_L = -L \frac{dI}{dt} = -\varepsilon e^{-t/\tau}$$

which has the same time behavior with dI /dt

$$V_R = \varepsilon(1 - e^{-t/\tau})$$

which has the same time behavior with I (t).

Now flip the switch K to the position 2, connecting R and L together, shown in Figure 13-9. At this moment, t=0, the current is I_{max}. The differential equation from the Kirchhoff's loop rule is

$$L \frac{dI}{dt} + IR = 0$$

I=I$_{max}$ at t=0, and I at time t, solving the equation above we have

$$I = I_{max}(e^{-t/\tau})$$

The current thus decays exponentially to zero as shown in Figure 13-11.

The induced EMF on the inductor and potential difference across on

暂态过程快慢，电流达到63%所用的时间。

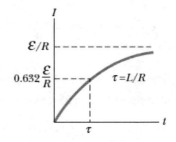

Figure 13-10 Plot of the current versus time for the *RL* circuit

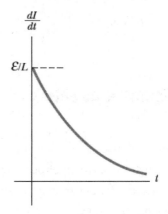

Figure 13-11 Rate of change of I in LR circuit

电感电动势：$V_L = -\varepsilon e^{-t/\tau}$

电阻上电压：$V_R = \varepsilon(1 - e^{-t/\tau})$

开关 K 连接到位置 2：

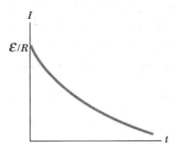

Figure 13-12 Current I in RC circuit

$$I = I_{max}(e^{-t/\tau})$$

电感电动势和电阻电压：

the resistor are

$$V_L = -\varepsilon e^{-t/\tau} \ , \ V_R = \varepsilon e^{-t/\tau}$$

$$V_L = -\varepsilon e^{-t/\tau} \ , \ V_R = \varepsilon e^{-t/\tau}$$

The analysis above shows that there is always some reaction time when an electromagnet is turned on or off. We also see that an LR circuit has properties similar to an RC circuit.

电感中磁场能量释放，电流减小直至为零。

Example 13.5 LR Circuit

At t=0, a battery ε =12v, resistor R=30 Ω , and a 220mH inductor, shown in Figure 13-9.

a. What is the current at t=0?

b. What is the time constant for this circuit?

c. How long will it take the current to reach half its maximum value?

d. At this instant, at what rate is energy being delivered by the battery?

e. At what rate is energy being stored in the inductor's magnetic field?

solution:

a. I=0 at t=0; the current can't instantaneously jump from zero to some value when the switch is closed.

开关闭合时，电感电路电流不能突变。

b. $\tau = \dfrac{L}{R}$ =7.3ms

It takes a very short time for a circuit reaching a steady state.

c. $I = I_{max}(1 - e^{-t/\tau}) = \dfrac{1}{2} I_{max}$

t=5.0 ms

d. At t=5.0ms, $I = \dfrac{1}{2} I_{max} = \dfrac{1}{2}\dfrac{\varepsilon}{R}$ =200mA, so the power being delivered by the battery is

P=IV=0.2*12=2.4W

e. The energy stored in an inductor L at any instant is

U= $\dfrac{1}{2} LI^2$

电感任意时刻的储能。

$$\frac{dU}{dt} = LI\frac{dI}{dt} = I(\varepsilon - IR)\ 0.2*(12-30*0.2)=1.2W$$

We can see that only part of the battery's power is feeding the inductor at this instant.

13.7 LC Circuits

When a capacitor C is connected to an inductor L as illustrated in Figure 13-13, the combination is an LC circuit. If the capacitor is initially charged and the switch is then closed, we find that both the current in the circuit and the charge on the capacitor oscillate between maximum positive and negative values. If the resistance of the circuit is zero, no energy is transformed to internal energy.

Suppose that at t=0, the capacitor is initially charged Q_{max}, the switch is closed. The capacitor immediately begins to discharge. As it does so, the current I through the inductor increases. Applying Kirchhoff's loop rule, we have

$$-L\frac{dI}{dt} + \frac{Q}{C} = 0$$

Because charge leaves the positive plate to produce the current I, the charge Q on the plate is decreasing, so $I = -dQ/dt$, then rewrite the equation above

$$\frac{d^2Q}{dt^2} + \frac{Q}{LC} = 0$$

It has the same form as the equation for simple harmonic motion. The solution is

$$Q = Q_{max}\cos(\omega t + \phi)$$

where $\omega = \sqrt{\dfrac{1}{LC}} = 2\pi f$

For t=0, Q=Q_{max}, ϕ =0

13.7 LC电路

电容、电感电路

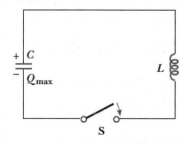

Figure 13-13 LC Circuit

开关闭合后电容器开始放电，流过电感的电流增加，产生感应电动势：

$$-L\frac{dI}{dt} + \frac{Q}{C} = 0$$

放电过程中，极板上的电荷在减少，$I = -dQ/dt$：

$$\frac{d^2Q}{dt^2} + \frac{Q}{LC} = 0$$

此微分方程和简谐振动方程相同。电容器极板上的电荷将发生周期性变化。

$$Q = Q_{max}\cos(\omega t + \phi)$$

$$\omega = \sqrt{\frac{1}{LC}} = 2\pi f$$

振动初相为零，电荷随时间

$$Q = Q_{max} \cos \omega t$$

And $I = -dQ/dt = I_{max} \sin \omega t$

The charge on the plate and the current through the conductor are both sinusoidal, shown in Figure 13-4.

The energy stored in the electric field of the capacitor at any time t is

$$U_E = \frac{Q^2}{2C} = \frac{Q_{max}^2}{2C} \cos^2 \omega t$$

The energy stored in the magnetic field of the inductor at the same instant is

$$U_B = \frac{I^2}{2L} = \frac{Q_{max}^2}{2C} \sin^2 \omega t$$

At any time, the total energy is

$$U = U_E + U_B = \frac{Q_{max}^2}{2C}$$

Hence the total energy is constant, and energy is conserved. The energy oscillates between being stored in the electric field of the capacitor and in the magnetic field of the inductor.

变化规律: $Q = Q_{max} \cos \omega t$

振动周期: $T = 2\pi \sqrt{LC}$

电流随时间变化规律:

$$I = I_{max} \sin \omega t$$

电容器电场能量 U_E:

$$U_E = \frac{Q^2}{2C} = \frac{Q_{max}^2}{2C} \cos^2 \omega t$$

电感中磁场能量 U_B:

$$U_B = \frac{I^2}{2L} = \frac{Q_{max}^2}{2C} \sin^2 \omega t$$

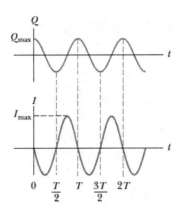

Figure 13-14 Charge on capacitor and current on the inductor

电容中储存的能量与电感中储存的能量和为常数:

$$U = \frac{Q_{max}^2}{2C}$$

能量不断地在电场和磁场中转化—电磁震荡。

第十三章总结 电磁感应

1. 电动势：电源内部存在非静电场，移动单位正电荷从负极到正极非静电力所做的功。

$$\varepsilon = \int_-^+ E_k \cdot dl = \oint_L E_k \cdot dl$$

2. 法拉第定律和楞次定律：

$$\varepsilon_i = -\frac{d\Psi}{dt} = -N\frac{d\phi_m}{dt} \quad \text{感应电动势}$$

$$\phi_m = \int_s B \cdot dS \quad \text{通过闭合回路包围的面积的磁通量}$$

$$I_i = \frac{\varepsilon_i}{R} = -N\frac{1}{R}\frac{d\phi_m}{dt} \quad \text{感应电流}$$

3. 动生电动势：$\varepsilon = vBl$

4. 感生电动势：$\oint_L E \cdot dl = -\frac{d\phi_m}{dt}$

5. 感生电场：$\oint_L E \cdot dl = -\frac{d\phi_m}{dt}$

   感生电场线是闭合曲线，感生电场是涡旋场。

6. 自感：$L = \frac{\Psi}{I}$，单位：亨利 H。

   自感电动势：$\varepsilon_L = -\frac{d\Psi}{dt} = -L\frac{dI}{dt}$

   长直螺线管的自感：$L = \mu_0 n^2 V$

7. 磁场能量：$U = \frac{1}{2}\frac{B^2}{\mu_0}S\ell = \frac{1}{2}LI^2$

   磁场能量密度：$u = \frac{1}{2}\frac{B^2}{\mu_0}$

8. RL 电路

时间常数：$\tau = \dfrac{L}{R}$

时间 t	RL 与电源相接			RL 相接（L 放电）		
	电流 I	ε_L	V_R	电流 I	ε_L	V_R
t=0	0	$-\varepsilon$	0	$I_{max} = \dfrac{\varepsilon}{R}$	$-\varepsilon$	ε
t	$I_{max}(1-e^{-t/\tau})$	$-\varepsilon e^{-t/\tau}$	$\varepsilon(1-e^{-t/\tau})$	$I_{max}(e^{-t/\tau})$	$-\varepsilon e^{-t/\tau}$	$\varepsilon e^{-t/\tau}$
$t \to \infty$	$I_{max} = \dfrac{\varepsilon}{R}$	0	ε	0	0	0

9. LC 电路：电磁振荡

电容器极板上电荷：$Q = Q_{max}\cos\omega t$

电磁震荡周期：$T = 2\pi\sqrt{LC}$

电路中的电流：$I = I_{max}\sin\omega t$

电容器内电场能量：$U_E = \dfrac{Q^2}{2C} = \dfrac{Q_{max}^2}{2C}\cos^2\omega t$

电感中的磁场能量：$U_B = \dfrac{I^2}{2L} = \dfrac{Q_{max}^2}{2C}\sin^2\omega t$

电路中的总能量是常数：$U = \dfrac{Q_{max}^2}{2C}$

Chapter 13 Electromagnetic Induction Practice

Multiple Choice Questions

1. A loop of area A lies flat on the ground. A uniform magnetic field points vertically upward with a magnitude of B. The magnetic field decreases uniformly to zero in time t. The magnitude of the EMF induced in the loop is

   A. -BA/t
   B. B/At
   C. A/Bt
   D. BAt
   E. zero

2. What is the direction of any induced current in the loop described in the question above, as viewed looking down at the loop in the ground from above?

   A. clockwise
   B. counterclockwise
   C. depends on the resistance of the loop
   D. No EMF is induced, so there is no direction.
   E. None of the above is true.

3. Moving with a velocity v through a magnetic field, a copper wire of length L may cause the wire to have a

   A. potential difference across it
   B. lower acceleration
   C. lower resistivity
   D. higher resistance
   E. current

4. A conducting loop with a radius of 0.25 m and an internal resistance of $4.0\,\Omega$ is situated in a 12.0 T magnetic field directed out of the page as shown. If the area of the loop is shrinking at a rate of 0.05 m^2/s, what is the induced current in the loop?

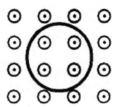

   A. 0.15 A clockwise
   B. 0.60 A clockwise
   C. 1.2 A clockwise
   D. 0.60 A counterclockwise
   E. 0.15 A counterclockwise

5. A conducting rod of length L and mass m falls with a constant velocity. It is attached to two conducting rails joined at the bottom. The total resistance of the circuit is R and there is a magnetic field of strength B perpendicular into the plane of the circuit. The velocity of the falling rod is

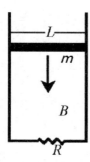

   A. BL/mgR
   B. B^2L^2R/mg
   C. B^2L^2/mgR
   D. mgR/B^2L^2
   E. mgR/BL

6. A circular loop of wire with resistance R and radius a is oriented with its plane

perpendicular to a magnetic field of strength B. A current I is induced in the loop. The rate of change of the intensity of the magnetic field is

A. I R/π a^2

B. B a^2/I R

C. 2Ba/I R

D. I R/2π a

E. aBI R

7.

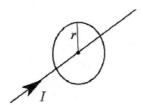

The above diagram shows a loop of wire with radius r centered around a long, straight wire that carries a current I in the direction shown. Which of the following would produce EMF in the loop?

A. changing the size of the loop

B. changing the current in the wire

C. rotating the coil about the length of the wire

D. rotating the coil about its diameter

E. moving the coil down the length of the wire

8. A rectangular loop of area A is placed in a region where the magnetic field is perpendicular to the plane of the loop. The magnitude of the field is allowed to vary in time according to $B = B_0 e^{-\frac{t}{T}}$ where B_0 and T are constants. The emf induced in the loop is given by

A. $-\dfrac{AB_0}{T} e^{-\frac{t}{T}}$

B. $-AB_0 e^{-\frac{t}{T}}$

C. $\dfrac{AB_0}{T}$

D. $\dfrac{AB_0}{T} e^{-\frac{t}{T}}$

E. AB_0

9. As $t \rightarrow \infty$, the total energy in an LC circuit

A. decreases exponentially.

B. decreases at a constant rate.

C. remains constant.

D. increases at a constant rate.

E. increases exponentially.

10. What is the period of an LC circuit with inductance L and capacitance C?

A. $2\pi\sqrt{LC}$

B. $4\pi\sqrt{LC}$

C. $2\pi/\sqrt{LC}$

D. $4\pi/\sqrt{LC}$

E. $2\sqrt{LC}$

11. Which of the following does the inductance of a solenoid inductor depend on?

A. number of turns per length

B. length

C. radius

D. physical constants

E. all of the above

12. In an RL circuit, $\varepsilon = 9$ V, $R = 30\,\Omega$, and $L = 6$ mH. How much energy is stored in the inductor's magnetic field when the current

reaches its maximum steady-state value?

A. zero

B. 1.6×10^{-4}J

C. 2.7×10^{-4}J

D. 1.6×10^{-3}J

E. 8.1×10^{-3}J

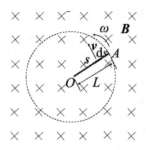

13. After an inductor in an *RL* circuit has been connected to a battery for a very long time, a switch is flipped causing the inductor to be connected to a resistor of resistance *R*. As $t \to \infty$, what does the current in the circuit approach?

A. *V/R*

B. Zero

C. Infinity

D. *LR*

E. *L/R*

14. What is the equation for the magnitude of voltage across an inductor during current growth in an *RL* circuit?

A. $V(t) = IR$

B. $V(t) = V0(1 - e^{-(R/L)t})$

C. $V(t) = V0\, e^{-(R/L)t}$

D. $V(t) = V0(1 + e^{-(R/L)t})$

E. $V(t) = V0(e^{-(R/L)t} - 1)$

15. A conducting bar with a length L rotates with a constant angular velocity ω in a uniform magnetic field B directed into the page. The bar rotates about a fixed pivot point O located at one end of the bar. The magnetic field is perpendicular to the rotational plane of the bar. What induced EMF would be introduced between the ends of the bars?

A. $\omega L^2 B$

B. $\dfrac{1}{2}\omega L^2 B$

C. $\dfrac{1}{4}\omega L^2 B$

D. $2\omega L^2 B$

E. None of the above is true.

16.

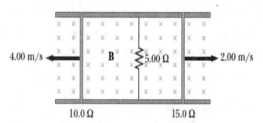

Two parallel rails with negligible resistance are 10.0 cm apart and are connected by a 5.00 Ω resistor. The circuit also contains two metal rods having resistances of 10.0 Ω and 15.0 Ω sliding along the rails. The rods are pulled away from the resistor at constant speeds of 4.00 m/s and 2.00 m/s, respectively. A uniform magnetic field of magnitude 0.0100T is applied perpendicular to the plane of the rails. The current in the 5.00 Ω resistor is

A. 0

B. 270mA

C. 327mA

D. 182mA

E. 145 mA

17. A long solenoid has n turns per meter and carries a current given by $I = I_0(1-e^{-kt})$A.

K is a positive constant. Inside the solenoid and coaxial with it is a coil that has a radius of R and consists of a total of N turns of fine wire, shown in Figure below. EMF induced in the coil by the changing current is

A. $N\mu_0 n\pi R^2 I_0$

B. $N\mu_0 n\pi R^2 KI_0 e^{-Kt}$

C. $N\mu_0 n^2\pi R^2 KI_0 e^{-Kt}$

D. $N\mu_0 nKI_0 e^{-Kt}$

E. 0

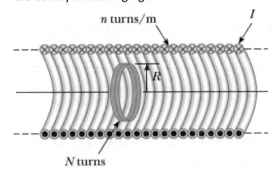

n turns/m

R

N turns

Free Response Questions

1. A circular loop of wire of radius r is in a uniform magnetic field, with the plane of the loop perpendicular to the direction of the field (shown in Figure below). The magnetic field varies with time according to $B(t) = a +bt$, where a and b are constants.

   A. Calculate the magnetic flux through the loop at $t =0$.

   B. Calculate the EMF induced in the loop.

   C. If the resistance of the loop is R, what is the induced current?

   D. At what rate is energy being delivered to the resistance of the loop?

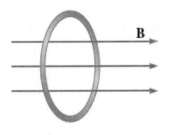

B

2.

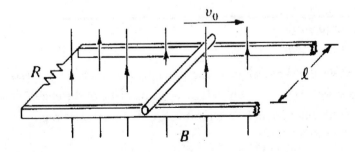

v_0

R

ℓ

B

A conducting rod of mass m can slide without friction along two horizontal conducting rails with negligible resistance and separated by a distance l. The rails are connected at left end by a resistor of resistance R, shown in the figure above. A uniform magnetic field **B** is perpendicular to the plane of the rails as shown. The rod has no resistance and is given a push to the right. Immediately after it is pushed, at the moment let time t=0, the rod has a speed v_0 to the right.

A. Determine the magnitude of the induced current in the resistor at time t=0.

B. Determine the force **F** acting on the rod at time t=0.

C. If the rod is allowed to continue to move, what will its speed as a function of time be?

D. Determine the power developed in the resistor as a function of time t.

E. Show that the total energy produced in the resistor is equal to the initial kinetic energy of the bar.

3. In the circuit shown below, resistors 1 and 2 of resistance R_1 and R_2, respectively, and an inductor of inductance L are connected to a battery of EMF ε and a switch S. The switch is closed at time $t = 0$. Express all algebraic answers in terms of the given quantities and fundamental constants.

A. Determine the current through resistor 1 immediately after the switch is closed.

B. Determine the magnitude of the initial rate of change of current, dI/dt, in the inductor.

C. Determine the current through the battery a long time after the switch has been closed.

4.

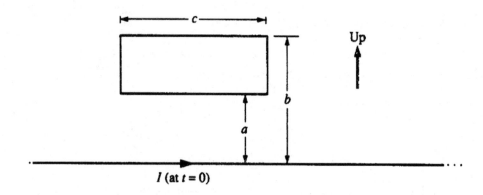

I (at $t = 0$)

The rectangular wire loop shown above has length c, width (b - a), and resistance R. It is placed in the plane of the page near a long straight wire which is in the same plane of the page. The long wire carries a current I = $\alpha(1 -\beta t)$, where α and β are positive constants and t is time.

A. Determine the magnetic flux through the loop due to the current I.

B. The induced EMF in the loop.

C. What is the net force, if any, on the loop due to the induced current at t = 0?

5. A uniform magnetic field **B** exists in a region of space defined by a circle of radius a as shown on the right. The magnetic field is perpendicular to the page and increases out of the page at a positive constant rate dB/dt. A single circular loop of wire with a resistance R and radius r is placed concentrically around the region of magnetic field.

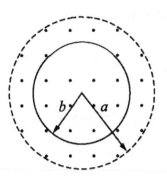

A. Determine the EMF induced in the loop.

B. Determine the current in the circuit and indicate the direction of the current in the loop at point P.

C. Determine the total energy dissipated in the loop during a time interval Δt.

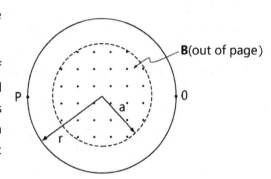

The experiment is repeated with a loop of radius b (b<a) and the same resistance R placed concentrically in the same magnetic field as before. And then, the magnetic field again increases out of the page at the same constant rate dB/dt with above.

D. What will happen compared to the results of the above parts a, b and c?

6. A magnetic field of strength B(t)=3t^2-2t+1 is directed out of the plane of a circular loop of wire with radius R as shown on the right.

A. Find the generated EMF as a function of time.

B. Determine the current through the 100-ohm loop as a function of time.

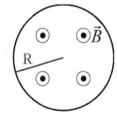

C. What is the direction of the current through the loop at time t=5s?

7. A conducting rod of length l moves with velocity v parallel to a long wire carrying a steady current I. The axis of the rod is maintained perpendicular to the wire with the near end a distance r away as shown. Show that the magnitude of the emf induced in the rod is

$$|\varepsilon| = \frac{\mu_0 Iv}{2\pi} \ln(\frac{r+l}{r})$$

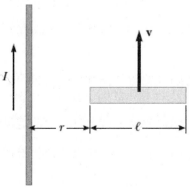

Answers and Explanations

Multiple Choice Answers

1. A   2. B   3. A   4. E   5. D   6. A   7. D   8. D   9. C   10. A   11. E   12. C   13. B   14. C   15. B
16. E   17. B

Multiple Choice Explanations

1. A。法拉第电磁感应定律 $\varepsilon = -\dfrac{d\phi}{dt} = -\dfrac{BA}{t}$

2. B。负号表示感应电动势是逆时针的。

3. A。铜导线中由于电磁感应产生感应电动势。

4. E。 $\varepsilon = -B\dfrac{dA}{dt}$, I= $\dfrac{\varepsilon}{R}$ = -0.15A，负号表示电流方向是逆时针。

5. D。 $\varepsilon = BLv$, I= $\dfrac{\varepsilon}{R}$, F=ILB= $\dfrac{B^2L^2}{R}v$ =mg, 所以 $v = \dfrac{mgR}{B^2L^2}$

6. A。感应电流 I= $\dfrac{1}{R}\dfrac{dB}{dt}\pi a^2$, $\dfrac{dB}{dt} = \dfrac{IR}{\pi a^2}$

7. D。闭合导体回路产生感应电流，回路内的磁通量必定发生变化。

8. D。 $\varepsilon = -\dfrac{d\phi}{dt} = -A\dfrac{dB}{dt}$, $\varepsilon = \dfrac{AB_0}{T}e^{-\frac{t}{T}}$

9. C。LC 电路中，电容器中的电场能量和电感中的磁场能量周期性的转化。

10. A。LC 电路震荡周期为 T= $2\pi\sqrt{LC}$

11. E。螺线管的电感 L= $\mu_0 n^2 l\pi r^2$, 所以 A、B、C、D 都是影响 L 的因素。

12. C。螺线管储能 U= $\dfrac{1}{2}LI^2$, 最大电流 I= ε / R , U=2.7*10^{-4} J

13. B。RL 电路中电感储存的能量最终都被电阻 R 消耗。

14. C。RL 电路，随着电流的增加电路趋于稳定，电感上的电压将趋于零。

15. B。旋转导体棒上各点的速度不同，产生的总感应电动势 $\varepsilon = \int_0^L \omega l B dl = \frac{1}{2} \omega B L^2$

16. E。向左运动的导体棒等效为一个电源 $\varepsilon_1 = 0.004\,v$，流过导体的电流为 I_1 沿导线向上；向右运动的导体棒的电动势 $\varepsilon_2 = 0.002v$，流过其中的电流 I_2 沿导线向下，流过 5Ω 电阻的电流为 $I_1 - I_2$，向下。由基尔霍夫定律得

$10 I_1 + 5（I_1 - I_2）= 0.004$ （1）

$-5（I_1 - I_2）+ 15 I_2 = 0.002$ （2）

求解方程得流过 5Ω 电阻的电流为：$I_1 - I_2 = 145mA$

17. B。$\varepsilon = -\dfrac{d\phi}{dt} = -\dfrac{d}{dt}(N\mu_0 n I \pi R^2) = N\mu_0 n \pi R^2 K I_0 e^{-Kt}$

Free Response questions Explanations

1. A. t=0 时，通过线圈的磁通量 $\phi_m(0) = B(0)\pi r^2 = a\pi r^2$

    B. 法拉第电磁感应定律 $\varepsilon = -\dfrac{d\phi_m}{dt} = -\dfrac{dB}{dt}\pi r^2 = -b\pi r^2$

    C. 感应电流 $I = \dfrac{\varepsilon}{R} = -b\pi r^2 / R$

    D. 消耗在回路中的电功率 P= $I^2 R = \dfrac{b^2\pi^2 r^4}{R}$

2. A. t=0 时，动生电动势 $\varepsilon = Blv_0$，感应电流 $I = \dfrac{\varepsilon}{R} = \dfrac{Blv_0}{R}$，电流方向是顺时针。

    B. 导体棒受力 F= $IlB = \dfrac{B^2 l^2 v_0}{R}$，受力方向向左。

    C. 在任意时刻 t，导体棒受力 F= $\dfrac{B^2 l^2 v}{R}$，方向向左，是时间 t 的函数（v 是时间 t 的函数）。

此时导体棒向右运动，所受合力为 $F= -\dfrac{B^2 l^2 v}{R}$，方向向左。由牛顿第二定律

$-\dfrac{B^2 l^2 v}{R} = m\dfrac{dv}{dt}$；解此微分方程得：$v = v_0 e^{-\frac{B^2 l^2}{Rm}t}$

D. t 时刻在电路中功率 $P = I^2 R = \dfrac{B^2 l^2}{R}v^2 = \dfrac{B^2 l^2 v_0^2}{R}e^{-\frac{2B^2 l^2}{Rm}t}$

E. 导体棒做减速运动，当它停止运动时电路中消耗的总电能 $E = \displaystyle\int_0^\infty P dt = \dfrac{1}{2}mv_0^2$

3. A. 时间 t=0 时，电感上的感应电动势为 $V_L = L\dfrac{dI}{dt} = V_{R_2}$，流过其中的电流 $I_L = 0$

所以，$I_{R_1} = \dfrac{\varepsilon}{R_1 + R_2}$

B. $V_L = L\dfrac{dI}{dt} = V_{R_2} = I_{R_2} R_2$，$I_{R_1} = I_{R_2}$ 当 t=0，所以 $\dfrac{dI}{dt} = \dfrac{\varepsilon R_2}{L(R_1 + R_2)}$

C. 当通电时间足够长，$I_{R_2} = 0$，有 $I = \dfrac{\varepsilon}{R_1}$

4. A. 距离水平通电导线为 r 处的 $B = \dfrac{\mu_0 I}{2\pi r} = \dfrac{\mu_0}{2\pi r}\alpha(1 - \beta t)$，t 时刻通过矩形线圈的磁通量：

$\phi_m = \displaystyle\int_a^b Bcdr = \dfrac{\mu_0}{2\pi}c\alpha(1 - \beta t)\ln\dfrac{b}{a}$

B. $\varepsilon_i = -\dfrac{d\phi_m}{dt} = \dfrac{\mu_0}{2\pi}c\alpha\beta\ln\dfrac{b}{a}$，感应电动势大于零且为常数，意味着矩形回路中的感应电动

势 ε、感应电流 I 是逆时针的且大小为常数。

C. t=0 时感应电流 $I = \dfrac{\mu_0}{2\pi R}c\alpha\beta\ln\dfrac{b}{a}$，距导线为 r 处 $B = \dfrac{\mu_0}{2\pi r}\alpha$；此时矩形线框左右两侧导线

所受磁场力大小相等方向相反，上下导线受力分别为 $I\dfrac{\mu_0}{2\pi b}\alpha c$，$I\dfrac{\mu_0}{2\pi a}\alpha c$，所以矩形线框

所受合力大小为 F=$I\dfrac{\mu_0}{2\pi a}\alpha c$ - $I\dfrac{\mu_0}{2\pi b}\alpha c$ = $\dfrac{\mu_0^2 c^2 \alpha^2 \beta}{4\pi^2 R}\ln\dfrac{b}{a}\left(\dfrac{1}{a}-\dfrac{1}{b}\right)$，方向向下。

5. A. $\varepsilon_i = -\dfrac{d\phi_m}{dt} = -\pi a^2\dfrac{dB}{dt}$，负号代表感应电动势方向是顺时针。

B. $I = \dfrac{\varepsilon}{R} = \dfrac{\pi a^2}{R}\dfrac{dB}{dt}$，电流方向也是顺时针。

C. E= $\displaystyle\int_0^{t_0} I^2 R dt = \dfrac{\pi^2 a^4}{R}\left(\dfrac{dB}{dt}\right)^2 t_0$

D. 电阻为 R 的导体圆形回路在磁场内部与导体同心，此时 r<a 有：

$\varepsilon_i = -\dfrac{d\phi_m}{dt} = -\pi r^2\dfrac{dB}{dt}$，降低

$I = \dfrac{\varepsilon}{R} = \dfrac{\pi r^2}{R}\dfrac{dB}{dt}$，减少

E= $\displaystyle\int_0^{t_0} I^2 R dt = \dfrac{\pi^2 r^4}{R}\left(\dfrac{dB}{dt}\right)^2 t_0$，减少

6. A. $\varepsilon_i = -\dfrac{d\phi_m}{dt} = -\pi a^2\dfrac{dB}{dt} = -\pi R^2(6t-2)$，

t<1/3 时，ε_i 〉0，逆时针；　　t>1/3 时，ε_i 〈0，顺时针。

B. $I = \dfrac{\pi R^2(6t-2)}{100}$ =0.01 $\pi R^2(6t-2)$，电流流向和感应电动势方向一致。

C. 当 t=5s 时，$I = 0.28\pi R^2$，顺时针。

7. 取细棒中的导体微元 dx，与电流垂直距离为 x，当 dx 沿电流方向垂直于磁场运动时产生动生电动势的大小 $d\varepsilon = Bvdx = \dfrac{\mu_0 I}{2\pi x}vdx$，整个导线在磁场中运动产生的电动势：

$$|\varepsilon| = \int d\varepsilon = \int_r^{r+l}\dfrac{\mu_0 I}{2\pi x}vdx = \dfrac{\mu_0 Iv}{2\pi}\ln\left(\dfrac{r+l}{r}\right)$$

14
Maxwell's Equations
麦克斯韦方程组

14.1 Ampere's Law and Displacement Current

14.2 Maxwell's Equations

14.1 安培定律和位移电流

14.2 麦克斯韦方程组

Introduction: The development of electromagnetic theory in the early nineteenth century by Oersted, Ampere, and others was not actually done in terms of electric and magnetic fields. The idea of the field was introduced by Faraday, and was not generally used until Maxwell showed that all electric and magnetic phenomena could be described using only four equations involving electric and magnetic fields. These equations, known as *Maxwell's equations*, are the basic equations for all electromagnetism. Maxwell's equations predict the existence of electromagnetic waves that propagate through space at the speed of light c.

所有电磁现象都可用四个电磁场方程描述-麦克斯韦方程组。

方程组预言电磁波存在。电磁波在空间以光速 c 传播。

14.1 Ampere's Law and Displacement Current   14.1 安培定律和位移电流

14.1.1 Maxwell-Ampere's Law   14.1.1 麦克斯韦–安培定律

A magnetic field is produced by an electric current and the mathematic relation of magnetic field and the current is given by Ampere's law:

稳恒电流激发稳恒磁场，磁场和电流关系由第十二章安培环路定理给出。

$$\oint_L \vec{B} \cdot d\vec{l} = \mu_0 I_{encl}$$

Ampère's law in this form is valid only if any electric fields present are constant in time. Maxwell recognized this limitation and modified Ampère's law to include time-varying electric fields.

此安培定律的形式只适用于稳恒电场、磁场情况。

From electromagnetic induction theorem we know that a changing magnetic field produces an electric field, and then perhaps the reverse might be true as well: that a changing electric field will produce a magnetic field.

在非稳状态下，变化的磁场激发感生电场，变化的电场也要产生磁场。

We can understand the problem by considering a capacitor that is being charged as illustrated in Figure 14-1. When a conduction current is present, the charge on the positive plate changes but *no conduction current exists in the gap between the plates.* Now

例如电容器充电过程：

两极板间没有电流。

consider the two surfaces S_1 and S_2 in Figure 14-1 bounded by the same path l. Ampere's law states that $\oint_l \vec{B} \cdot d\vec{l}$ around this path

must equal $\mu_0 I$, where I is the total current through *any* surface

bounded by the path l. When the path l is considered as bounding surface S_1, the conduction current passes through S_1. We have

$$\oint_{l,S_1} \vec{B} \cdot d\vec{l} = \mu_0 I$$

However, as the path is considered as bounding surface S_2, no conduction current passes through S_2. We have

$$\oint_{l,S_2} \vec{B} \cdot d\vec{l} = 0$$

Thus, we have a contradictory situation that arises from the discontinuity of the current!

The changing charge on the plates means that the electric field between the plates is changing in time. Maxwell resolved the problem of no current through surface 2 by proposing that there needs to be an extra term in Ampere's law involving the changing electric field.

Let us see what this term should be by determining it for the changing electric field between the capacitor plates which is being discharged, shown in Figure 14-2. The charge Q on the capacitor of capacitance C is Q=CV，where V=Ed is the potential difference between the plates. E is the uniform electric field between them and d is the separation of the plates. Capacitance for a parallel plates capacitor is

$$C = \varepsilon_0 \frac{S}{d}$$

S is the area of the plates. We combine these to obtain

$$Q = CV = \varepsilon_0 \frac{S}{d} Ed = \varepsilon_0 SE$$

If the charge on the plate discharges at a rate dQ/dt which is the current I flowing into or out of the capacitor, the electric field changes at a proportional rate dE/dt.

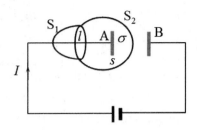

Figure 14-1 Charging a capacitor

S_1、S_2：同一回路形成的不同曲面

电流 I 穿过 S_1 面：

$$\oint_{l,S_1} \vec{B} \cdot d\vec{l} = \mu_0 I$$

没有电流穿过 S_2 面：

$$\oint_{l,S_2} \vec{B} \cdot d\vec{l} = 0$$

电流不连续，导致安培定律对同一回路得到不同结果。极板上的电荷变化，等效于板间电场的变化。

变化的电场中应引入一个新物理量。

用电容器放电来确定这个新物理量。

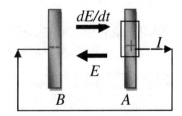

Figure 14-2 Discharging the capacitor

极板上电荷和板间场强关

系：$Q = \varepsilon_0 SE$

$$\frac{dQ}{dt} = \varepsilon_0 S \frac{dE}{dt} = \varepsilon_0 \frac{d\phi_e}{dt} = I$$

where $\phi_e = ES$ is the electric flux through the closed path.

In order to make Ampere's law work for surface 2, we write

$$\oint_L \vec{B} \cdot d\vec{l} = \mu_0 (I + \varepsilon_0 \frac{d\phi_e}{dt})$$

Although we got it for a special case, it has proved valid in general.

14.1.2 Displacement current

Maxwell thought it useful to interpret the second term on the right of Ampere's law equation as being equivalent to an electric current. He called it a displacement current I_d. An ordinary current I is then called a conduction current, so Ampere's law can be written as

$$\oint_L \vec{B} \cdot d\vec{l} = \mu_0 (I + I_d)_{encl}$$

where $I_d = \varepsilon_0 \frac{d\phi_e}{dt}$

I_d does not represent a flow of electric charge nor is there a displacement.

The central point of this formalism is that magnetic fields are produced both by conduction currents and by time-varying electric fields.

14.2 Maxwell's Equations

In his unified theory of electromagnetism, Maxwell showed that electromagnetic waves are a natural consequence of the fundamental laws expressed in the following four equations in the absence of dielectric or magnetic materials:

1) $\oint_S \vec{E} \cdot d\vec{S} = \frac{q}{\varepsilon_0}$

极板上电荷的变化率是流入或流出电容器的电流:

$$\frac{dQ}{dt} = \varepsilon_0 \frac{d\phi_e}{dt} = I$$

ϕ_e: 通过闭合回路的电通量

任意回路安培环路定律:

$$\oint_L \vec{B} \cdot d\vec{l} = \mu_0 (I + \varepsilon_0 \frac{d\phi_e}{dt})$$

此公式一般情况下也成立。

14.1.2 位移电流 I_d

位移电流 I_d: dQ/dt 可等效看作在极板间的电流。
传导电流: 电荷定向移动

变化电场中安培环路定理:

$$\oint_L \vec{B} \cdot d\vec{l} = \mu_0 (I + I_d)_{encl}$$

全电流: $I + I_d$

位移电流: $I_d = \varepsilon_0 \frac{d\phi_e}{dt}$

没有电荷流动,也没有位移。

磁场可由传导电流产生,也可由变化电场激发。

14.2 麦克斯韦方程组

麦克斯韦统一电磁场理论指出电磁波是基本电磁场理论的结果。由四个方程给出:

1)通过任意闭合曲面的电通量与该曲面所包围的自由电荷的代数和成正比。

2) $\oint_S \vec{B} \cdot d\vec{S} = 0$

3) $\oint_L \vec{E} \cdot d\vec{l} = -\dfrac{d\phi_m}{dt}$

4) $\oint_L \vec{B} \cdot d\vec{l} = \mu_0 (I + \varepsilon_0 \dfrac{d\phi_e}{dt})$

2）通过任意闭合曲面的磁通量恒等于零。

3）电场强度沿任意闭合曲线的线积分等于以该曲线为边界的任意曲面的磁通量时间变化量的负值。

4）稳恒磁场沿任意闭合曲线的线积分等于穿过以该曲线为边界的曲面的全电流。

They can be summarized in words:

1. **Gauss's law in electric field:** generalized form of Coulomb's law relating electric field to its sources-charges.

2. **Gauss's law in magnetic field:** the same for the magnetic field, except that if there are no magnetic monopoles, magnetic field lines are continuous—they don't begin or end.

3. **Faraday's law:** an electric field can be produced by a changing magnetic field.

4. **Maxwell-Ampere's law:** a magnetic field is produced by an electric current or by a changing electric field.

A changing magnetic field produces an electric field, and a changing electric field produces a magnetic field. An important outcome of these relations is the production of electromagnetic waves!

各方程的物理意义：

1. 电场是有源场，源头是电荷。

2. 没有单独存在的磁极，磁场线是闭合线，无头无尾。

3. 变化的磁场激发电场。

4. 变化的电场等效于电流，产生磁场。

变化的磁场产生电场，变化的电场产生磁场—电磁波。

第十四章总结　麦克斯韦方程组

1. 位移电流：$I_d = \varepsilon_0 \dfrac{d\phi_e}{dt}$，变化的电场等效于电流，此电流产生磁场。

　　全电流：$I + I_d$

2. 麦克斯韦-安培定律：$\oint_L \vec{B} \cdot d\vec{l} = \mu_0 (I + \varepsilon_0 \dfrac{d\phi_e}{dt})$

3. 麦克斯韦方程组：

   1) $\oint_S \vec{E} \cdot d\vec{S} = \dfrac{q}{\varepsilon_0}$；电场是有源场。从正电荷或无穷远出发，终止于负电荷或无穷远。

   2) $\oint_S \vec{B} \cdot d\vec{S} = 0$；没有单独存在的磁极。磁场是无源场，磁场线是闭合线，无头无尾。

   3) $\oint_L \vec{E} \cdot d\vec{l} = -\dfrac{d\phi_m}{dt}$；变化的磁场激发电场。

   4) $\oint_L \vec{B} \cdot d\vec{l} = \mu_0 (I + \varepsilon_0 \dfrac{d\phi_e}{dt})$；变化的电场等效于电流，产生磁场。

Chapter 14 Maxwell's Equations Practice

Multiple Choice Questions

1. Which of the following is not one of Maxwell's Equations?
   A. Gauss's Law for Electric Fields
   B. Gauss's Law for Magnetic Fields
   C. The Biot-Savart Law
   D. Faraday's Law
   E. The Ampere-Maxwell's Law

2. Which of the following creates an electric field?
   I. Electric charges
   II. Time changing magnetic fields
   III. Stationary magnetic poles

   A. I only
   B. II only
   C. I and II only
   D. II and III only
   E. I, II and III

3. Which of the following causes forces on stationary electric charges?
   I. Electric fields
   II. Magnetic fields
   III. Light

   A. I only
   B. II only
   C. I and III only
   D. II and III only
   E. I, II and III

4. Magnetic fields cause forces on which of the following?
   I. Moving electric charges
   II. Stationary electric charges
   III. Magnetic poles

   A. I only
   B. II only
   C. III only

D. I and III only
E. I, II and III

5. At a given instant, a 2.0A current flows in a wires connected to a parallel plate capacitor. If the square plates are 2.0cm on a side, the rate at which the electric field is changing between the plates is (v/ms):

   A. $\dfrac{10^4}{\varepsilon_0}$

   B. $\dfrac{10^4}{2\varepsilon_0}$

   C. $2*10^4$

   D. $\dfrac{1}{2\varepsilon_0}$

   E. $\dfrac{1}{\varepsilon_0}$

6. A circular parallel plate capacitor with radius R is being charged. At the instant, a current I is flowing into the capacitor, the integral $\oint_L \vec{B} \cdot d\vec{l}$ for a circular path L of radius R/3 centered within the capacitor will be

   A. $\mu_0 I$

   B. $\mu_0 I /3$

   C. $3\mu_0 I$

   D. $9\mu_0 I$

   E. $\mu_0 I /9$

Answers and Explanations

Multiple Choice Questions

1. C   2. C   3. A   4. D   5. B   6. E

Multiple Choice Explanations

1. C。毕奥-沙伐尔定律不是麦克斯韦方程中的方程。

2. C。电荷和变化的磁场都可以产生电场，但场的性质不同。

3. A。电场对电荷有力的作用。

4. D。磁场对运动电荷和磁极有作用力。

5. B。导线中的电流和电容器内的位移电流相等，$I = I_d$。可由位移电流公式求出电场的变化率。

由 $I_d = \varepsilon_0 \dfrac{d\phi_e}{dt} = \varepsilon_0 S \dfrac{dE}{dt}$ 求得 dE/dt= $\dfrac{10^4}{2\varepsilon_0}$。

6. E。穿过电容器的位移电流和流入电容器的电流相等。电容器内是匀强电场，电场的变化率均匀，位移电流密度也是均匀的。所以，半径为R/3的闭合回路所包围的电流由回路面积确定

$I_{encl} = I \dfrac{\pi(R/3)^2}{\pi R^2} = \dfrac{I}{9}$，B的环流是 $\oint_L B \cdot dl = \mu_0 I = \mu_0 I / 9$。

Model Test 1

Mechanics

Section I: Multiple Choice Questions—Questions 1-35 (45 minutes)

Directions: Each multiple choice question is followed by five answer choices. For each question, choose the best answer and fill in the corresponding oval on the answer sheet.

1. A car is running around the circular track of radius 50 meters. At the instant when the car's velocity is directed due east from the top view. Its acceleration is directed due north and has magnitude of $2m/s^2$. When viewed from the top, the car is moving

   A. 2m/s
   B. 4m/s
   C. 5m/s
   D. 8m/s
   E. 10m/s

2. The position of a particle moving along the x-axis is given by the equation $x(t) = 1 - t^2 + 2t^3$, where x is in meters and t is in seconds. What is the average acceleration during the interval $t = 1$ to $t = 2$?

   A. 6 m/s^2
   B. 9 m/s^2
   C. 16 m/s^2
   D. 18 m/s^2
   E. 22 m/s^2

3. Two cars approach a street corner at right angles to each other. Car 1 travels at 30 km/h moving to the East and car 2 at 50 km/h moving to the North. What is the relative velocity of car 1 as seen by car 2?

   A. 45km/h, 45^0 N of E

   B. 58km/h, 31^0 S of E
   C. 58km/h, 59^0 S of E
   D. 80km/h, 31^0 E of S
   E. 80km/h, 59^0 E of S

Questions 4-5
The position versus time graph below shows the motion of a particle on a straight line.

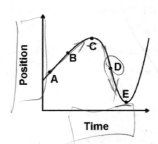

4. Which of the labeled points is the magnitude of the velocity greatest?

5. At which of the labeled points is the velocity zero?

   A. *B* only
   B. *E* only
   C. *D* only
   D. *C* and *D*
   E. *C* and *E*

6. The speed v as a function of time t for an object with mass 2 kg is $v=3t^2$. When t=0, the object is at 1 m away from the origin. Which of the following functions best represents the magnitude of the net force F exerted on

405

the object as a function of time?

A. F=2t^3

B. F=6t

C. F=2t^3+1

D. F-6t+1

E. F=12t

7. A truck traveled 1200 meters south in 80 seconds and then 500 meters west in 20 seconds. The magnitude of the average velocity of the truck is most nearly

A. 10 m/s

B. 13 m/s

C. 17 m/s

D. 25 m/s

E. 30 m/s

8. Boxes A and B are sliding to the right across a frictionless table. The hand H is slowing them down. The mass of A is larger than the mass of B. Rank in order, from largest to smallest, the magnitude of the *horizontal* forces on A, B, and H.

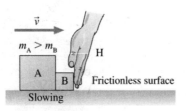

A. F_B on H = F_H on B = F_A on B = F_B on A

B. F_B on H = F_H on B < F_A on B = F_B on A

C. F_B on H = F_H on B > F_A on B = F_B on A

D. F_H on B > F_B on H > F_A on B = F_B on A

E. F_H on B < F_B on H =<F_A on B = F_B on A

9. A ball of mass *m* hangs vertically from a massless string experiencing a tension *T*. What a horizontal force is required to pull the ball out to an angle θ from the vertical?

A. *mg* sinθ

B. *mg* cosθ

C. *mg* tanθ

D. 2*mg* tanθ

E. *mg*/cosθ

10. What is the magnitude of the acceleration of an object whose position is given by the equation $x(t) = 3t^2 – 3$ and $y(t) = 3t^2 + t$?

A. 6 m/s^2

B. 6$\sqrt{2}$ m/s^2

C. 12 m/s^2

D. 12 $\sqrt{2}$ m/s^2

E. 36 m/s^2

11. A student that has a mass of 100 kg is standing on a scale in an elevator car. The elevator is accelerating downward at 5 m/s^2 in the Earth's gravitational field. The reading on the scale in the elevator is most nearly

A. 150 N

B. 500 N

C. 1000 N

D. 1500 N

E. 50 N

12. The angular position of a pendulum is represented by the equation $\theta = 0.30 \cos \omega t$, where θ is in radians and ω = 4.0 rad/s. The length of the pendulum is

A. 0.50m

B. 0.61m

C. 0.30m

D. 1.1m

E. 2.0m

13. What is the maximum speed a vehicle can travel along a circular turn without leaving the road, if the turn has a radius of 50 m and the coefficient of kinetic friction between the road and the tires is 0.20?

A. 5 m/s

B. 10 m/s

C. 15 m/s

D. 20 m/s

E. 25 m/s

14. If a force $F(t)=F_0 e^{-kt}$ acts horizontally on a mass m that is initially at rest on a frictionless surface, what is the final velocity of the object?

A. v=0

B. The velocity has no limit as time approaches infinity.

C. $v=F_0/k$

D. $v=F_0/mk$

E. $v=F_0/m$

15. An engineer wishes to design a roller coaster so that the cars will not fall when they are at the top of their circular path. Which of the following will have no effect on whether the cars remain on the track?

A. The velocity of the cars as they pass the top of the circle.

B. The radius of the circular track.

C. The mass of the cars.

D. The distance from the top of the circle to the bottom.

E. The acceleration due to gravity.

16. An ideal spring with spring constant k is cut in half. The spring constant of either one of the two half spring will be

A. k/2

B. $\sqrt{k}$

C. k

D. k^2

E. 2k

17. A horizontal force of 40 N is used to push a

block along a horizontal surface at a constant speed of 2 meters per second. How much work is done on the block in 6 seconds?

A. 80 J

B. 120 J

C. 180 J

D. 240 J

E. 480 J

Questions 18-19

A 20 kg mass, released from rest, slides 6m down a frictionless plane inclined at an angle of 30° with the horizontal. It strikes a spring of spring constant k=200 N/m as shown in the diagram above. The spring's mass is negligible. Use g=10 m/s².

18. The distance the spring has been compressed when the mass comes to rest is

A. 1m

B. 3m

C. 4m

D. 5m

E. 6m

19. The maximum speed the mass can have is

A. 6.1m/s

B. 7.7m/s

C. 7.9m/s

D. 8.1m/s

E. 10m/s

20. A force acting on an object given by the function $F(x) = 3x^2 + 4$, where F is in Newtons and x is in meters. What is the change in the

object's kinetic energy as it moves from $x = 1$ to $x = 3$ m?

A. 26 J

B. 27 J

C. 31 J

D. 34 J

E. 36 J

21. If a force moves an object of mass m so that its velocity is given by $v(t) = 4t - 2$, what is the power exerted by that force?

A. $0.5m(4t - 2)^2$

B. $4m(4t - 2)$

C. $4m(2t^2 - 2t)$

D. $4m$

E. $m(4t - 2)$

22. Two particles of masses 2 kg and 6 kg are separated by a distance of 12m. The distance of their center of mass from the heavier particle is

A. 3 m

B. 4 m

C. 6 m

D. 8m

E. 9 m

Questions 23-24

A scale is adjusted so that when a large, flat pan is placed on it, it reads zero. A water faucet at height h above is turned on and water falls into the pan at a rate R. Water level of the pan is low enough during water dropping.

23. The impact force on the pan is

A. Rgh

B. Rh

C. $R\sqrt{2gh}$

D. $\sqrt{2gh}$

E. $R\sqrt{gh}$

24. A formula for the scale reading as a function of time t is

A. $R\sqrt{2gh} + Rgt$

B. $R\sqrt{2gh}$

C. Rgt

D. $2R\sqrt{gh} + Rt$

E. $R\sqrt{gh} + Rgt$

25. A 1.0 kg mass traveling 3.0 m/s north and a 2.0 kg mass traveling 2.0 m/s east collide and stick together. After the collision, their speed is most nearly

A. 1.0 m/s.

B. 1.7 m/s.

C. 2.5 m/s.

D. 3.2 m/s.

E. 5.0 m/s.

Questions 26-27

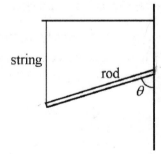

A thin rod with length L and nonuniform mass distribution is suspended by a vertical string. The rod makes an angle θ with the vertical wall shown in the diagram above.

The linear mass density is $\lambda = a + bl$, where l is the distance from the end of the rod connecting on the wall.

26. The moment of inertia of the rod about the end point on the wall is

A. $aL + \dfrac{b}{2}L^2$

B. $\dfrac{a}{2}L^2 + \dfrac{b}{3}L^3$

C. $aL^3 + bL^4$

D. $a + \dfrac{b}{2}L^2$

E. $\dfrac{a}{3}L^3 + \dfrac{b}{4}L^4$

27. The tension in the string is T

A. $T = (\dfrac{a}{2}L^2 + \dfrac{b}{3}L^3)g$

B. $T = (\dfrac{a}{2}L + \dfrac{b}{3}L^2)g$

C. $T = (aL + \dfrac{b}{2}L^2)g$

D. $T = aL + \dfrac{b}{2}L^2$

E. $T = \dfrac{a}{2}L + \dfrac{b}{3}L^2$

28. How far does a point on the edge of a wheel with radius 3 m travel in the first 2 seconds of motion if the angular velocity is given by the equation $\omega(t) = 3t + 2$?

A. 8 m

B. 10 m

C. 24 m

D. 30 m

E. 64m

29. A solid sphere of mass M and radius R rolls without slipping down an inclined plane whose incline angle with the horizontal is 30°.

What is the acceleration of the sphere's center of mass?

A. $g/3$

B. $5g/14$

C. $5g/7$

D. $2g/3$

E. g

30. An object spins with angular velocity ω. If the object's moment of inertia increases by a factor of 3 with no added torque what is the object's new angular velocity?

A. $\omega/3$

B. $\omega/2$

C. ω

D. 2ω

E. 3ω

31. A space probe is fired as a projectile from the Earth's surface with an initial speed of $2.00 * 10^4$ m/s. What will its speed be when it is very far from the Earth? Ignore friction and the rotation of the Earth. The radius of the Earth is 6400km.

A. It can't happen.
B. $1.66*10^3$ m/s
C. $2.32*10^3$ m/s
D. $2.32*10^4$ m/s
E. $1.66*10^4$ m/s

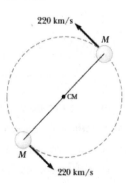

32. Plaskett's binary system consists of two stars that revolve in a circular orbit about a center of mass midway between them. This

409

means that the masses of the two stars are equal. Assume the orbital speed of each star is v=220 km/s and the orbital period of each is T=14.4 days. The mass M of each star will be

A. $1.99*10^{30}$ kg
B. $3.15*10^{30}$ kg
C. $1.26*10^{31}$ kg
D. $3.15*10^{31}$ kg
E. $1.26*10^{32}$ kg

33. An object with mass m is attached to a horizontal spring. The spring is initially stretched by x_0 m, and the object is released from rest there. It proceeds to move without friction. The next time that the speed of the object is zero is t_0 s later. What are the period of the pendulum and the maximum speed of the object?

A. $T = 2t_0, v_{max} = \dfrac{mx_0\pi}{t_0}$ m/s

B. $T = t_0, v_{max} = \dfrac{x_0\pi}{mt_0}$ m/s

C. $T = t_0, v_{max} = \dfrac{x_0\pi}{2t_0}$ m/s

D. $T = 2t_0, v_{max} = \dfrac{x_0\pi}{t_0}$ m/s

E. $T = 2t_0, v_{max} = 2\dfrac{x_0\pi}{t_0}$ m/s

34. If the Earth is assumed to be a solid sphere of mass M and radius R, suppose that a tunnel can be drilled through the center of Earth to the other side along its axis. A small object of mass m is dropped from rest into the tunnel at the surface of Earth and the friction is assumed to be negligible. The

correct expressions for the kinetic energy of the mass as it passes Earth's center include which of the following?

I. mgR

II. $\dfrac{1}{2}mgR$

III. $\dfrac{GmM}{2R}$

A. I and III only
B. II and III only
C. I only
D. II only
E. III only

35. A cylinder of mass m and radius R is supported by a rope of negligible mass, shown in the figure below. The rope is attached to the ceiling at one end and the other end of the rope is pulled upward with a force F_A which causes the cylinder to accelerate upward. The rope doesn't slip on the cylinder as the cylinder rotates. What is the linear acceleration of the cylinder?

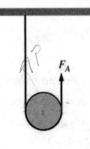

A. $\dfrac{F_A}{m} - g$

B. $\dfrac{F_A}{m} - \dfrac{1}{2}g$

C. $\dfrac{4F_A}{3m} - g$

D. $\dfrac{2}{3}(\dfrac{2F_A}{m} - g)$

E. None of the above is true.

Section II: Free Response Questions—Questions 1-3 (45 minutes)

Directions: Answer all the three questions. The suggested time is about 15 minutes for answering each of the questions, which are worth 15 points each. The parts within a question may not have equal weight.

1. A uniform chain of mass M and length L rests on a frictionless horizontal table with one end of the chain hanging slightly over the edge of the frictionless table. The chain is released from rest, and at some time later there is a length y of chain hanging over the edge, as shown below.

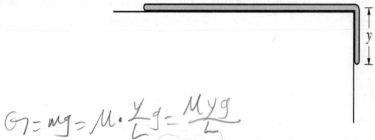

$$G_7 = mg = M \cdot \frac{y}{L}g = \frac{Myg}{L}$$

A. Determine an expression for the force of gravity on the hanging part of the rope as a function of y.

B. Determine the acceleration of the chain. $a = \frac{F}{m} = \frac{G}{M} = \frac{yg}{L}$

C. Derive an expression for the work done by gravity on the rope as a function of y, assuming y is initially zero. $\frac{y=0}{}$

D. Derive an expression for the speed v of the rope as a function of y. $W = G*0 = 0$ $V = v_0 + at = \int a = ?$

2. You are given a thin uniform rod of known mass M and length L with a pivot attached to one end, suspending from the pivot vertically. The rod is struck at the location L/3 from the bottom of the rod by a mass m whose initial velocity v is perpendicular to the rod and it sticks with the rod.

A. Determine the angular velocity of the system after the collision. $W = \frac{V}{r} = \frac{V}{L}$

B. Determine the kinetic energy of the system after the collision. $K = \frac{1}{2}mv^2$

The rod and the mass system will swing about the pivot after the collision.

C. Write the differential equation for the angle θ the rod makes with the vertical.

D. By applying the small-angle approximation to your differential equation, calculate the period of the rod's motion.

E. Write the function of θ with time t. θt

3. A particle of mass m moves in a conservative force field described by the potential energy function $U(r) = a(r/b + b/r)$, where a and b are positive constants and r is the distance from the origin. The graph of U(r) has the following shape.

411

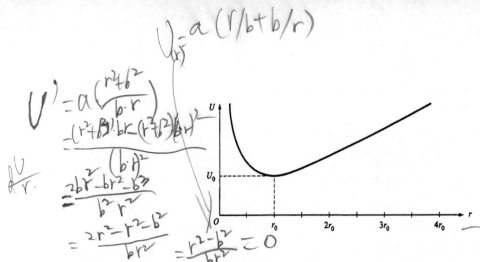

$$U_{(r)} = a\left(\frac{r}{b} + \frac{b}{r}\right)$$

$$U' = a\left(\frac{r^2 + b^2}{b \cdot r}\right)$$

$$\frac{(r^2 + b^2)' \cdot b \cdot r - (r^2 + b^2)(b \cdot r)'}{}$$

$$\frac{dU}{dr}.$$

$$\frac{2br^2 - br^2 - b^3 \cdot (b \cdot r)^2}{b^2 r^2}$$

$$= \frac{2r^2 - r^2 - b^2}{br^2}$$

$$= \frac{r^2 - b^2}{br^2} = 0$$

A. Determine the minimum potential energy U_o.

B. Graph the net force on the particle as a function of r on the figure below, considering a force directed away from the origin to be positive, and a force directed toward the origin to be negative.

$$F = -kx$$

$$U = \frac{1}{2}kx^2$$

$$F = \frac{-2U}{x}$$

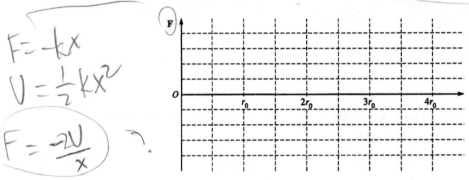

The particle is released from rest at $r = r_o/2$

C. Determine the speed of the particle when it is at $r = r_o$.

D. Find the other position where, if ever, the particle will again come to rest.

E. Describe the motion of the particle over a long period of time.

Electricity and Magnetism

Section I: Multiple Choice Questions—Questions 36-70 (45 minutes)

Directions: Each multiple choice question is followed by five answer choices. For each question, choose the best answer and fill in the corresponding oval on the answer sheet.

36. Given two electrical charges separated by a distance d, will there always be a position at which a third charge will experience no electrical force?

    A. Yes. There will always be a position at which a third charge will have no electrical force on it.
    B. Yes. There will be a position at which a third charge experiences no force only if the first two charges are of opposite sign.
    C. Yes. There will be a position at which a third charge experiences no force only if the first two charges are of the same sign.
    D. No. There will be cases in which no such position exists.
    E. Yes. The third charge must be placed between the two charges.

37. A negatively charged particle is located at a position where the electric potential is 100V and is traveling at a speed v. The particle moves to a position where the electric potential is 200V. What can you say about the speed of the particle at this location?

    A. The speed will be $v/2$.
    B. The speed will be $2v$.
    C. The speed will be less than v.
    D. The speed will be v.
    E. The speed will be greater than v.

38. Two identical conducting spheres are charged to +Q and +3Q respectively, and are separated by a distance d (much greater than the radii of the spheres). The magnitude of the force on the right sphere is F_1. After the two spheres are made to touch and then are separated again by a distance d, the magnitude of the force on the right sphere is F_2. Which of the following relationships is correct?

    A. $3F_1 = F_2$
    B. $4F_1 = 3F_2$
    C. $F_1 = F_2$
    D. $3F_1 = 4F_2$
    E. $F_1 = 3F_2$

39. The diagram below shows two charges, magnitude q, of opposite sign. Each is located a distance d from the origin A of a coordinate system. At which of the following points is the electric field greatest in magnitude?

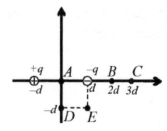

    A. Point A
    B. Point B
    C. Point C
    D. Point D
    E. Point E

40. The potential difference due to a finite rod along the x-axis is given by the equation $V(x) = C[\ln(x + L) - \ln(x)]$, where C and L are

413

constants. What is the electric field due to this rod?

A. $-C/x$
B. $-C[1/(x + L) - 1/x]$
C. $-C/(x + L)$
D. $-C/L$
E. $1/(x + L) - 1/x$

41. The Gaussian surface below is the area enclosed by the dotted line. The net flux through the Gaussian surface depends on which of the following charges?

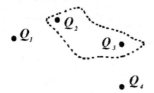

A. All four
B. Q_2 and Q_3
C. Q_1 and Q_4
D. Q_1 and Q_2
E. Q_3 and Q_4

42. The diagram below shows three particles, with the charges shown, located at corners of a square with side of length d. The work required to move a small point charge $+q$ from infinity to point P is

$+Q$ ◯ – – ◯ $-Q$

P ◯ – – ◯ $+Q$

d

A. $(2 - \dfrac{\sqrt{2}}{2}) \dfrac{Qq}{4\pi\varepsilon_0 d}$

B. $-(2 - \dfrac{\sqrt{2}}{2}) \dfrac{Qq}{4\pi\varepsilon_0 d}$

C. $(2 + \dfrac{\sqrt{2}}{2}) \dfrac{Qq}{4\pi\varepsilon_0 d}$

D. $\dfrac{Qq}{4\pi\varepsilon_0 d}$

E. $\dfrac{Qq}{2\pi\varepsilon_0 d}$

43. Suppose you have a capacitor with capacitance C charged to voltage V and a second capacitor with capacitance C charged to voltage 2V. The two capacitors are connected in parallel. What will be the voltage across the two capacitors after being connected in parallel?

A. The first capacitor will have voltage V and the second capacitor will have voltage 2V.
B. Both capacitors will be charged to voltage 3V.
C. Both capacitors will be charged to voltage 1.5V.
D. Both capacitors will be charged to voltage 0.5V.
E. The first capacitor will have voltage 2V and the second capacitor will have voltage V.

44. The circuit diagram below shows three capacitors connected to a 12 volt battery. The total energy stored in the circuit and the charge stored on the capacitor 2F are

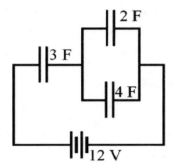

A. 24 J, 24C

B. 52 J, 16C

C. 144 J, 8C

D. 288 J, 8C

E. 312 J, 24C

45. What is the ratio of potential due to a spherical shell of radius R and a solid conducting sphere of radius R, for r < R?

A. 1:1

B. 1:2

C. 2:1

D. −1:1

E. −1:2

46. How much work is required to charge a 40 mF capacitor to a potential difference of 200 V?

A. 0.8 J

B. 1.6 J

C. 80 J

D. 160 J

E. 800 J

47. A capacitor initially has a capacitance of C. A dielectric is added to the capacitor such that its new capacitance is 3C. Which of the following best explains why this occurs?

A. The electric field is increased by the dielectric, which decreases the voltage while the charge remains the same.

B. The electric field is decreased by the dielectric, which decreases the voltage while the charge remains the same.

C. More charge is induced on the plates of the capacitor while the electric field and the voltage both remain the same.

D. Work is done in order to move the dielectric into the electric field.

E. The voltage and the charge increase in proportion due to an increase in the electric field.

48. A point charge q is placed at the center of a cube of side l. What is the flux through one face of the box?

A. $\dfrac{ql}{4\pi\varepsilon_0}$

B. $l^2 q$

C. $\dfrac{q}{6\varepsilon_0}$

D. $\dfrac{q}{4\varepsilon_0}$

E. $\dfrac{q}{\varepsilon_0}$

49. Wires A and B are made of the same material. Wire A has 4 times the resistance of Wire B. Which of the following statements about the wires is most likely true?

A. Wire A is 4 times the cross-sectional area of Wire B and has the same length as Wire B.

B. Wire A is twice the cross-sectional area of Wire B and twice the length of Wire B.

C. Wire A is half the cross-sectional area of Wire B and half the length of Wire B.

D. Wire A is half the cross-sectional area of

Wire B and has the same length as Wire B.

E. Wire A is half the cross-sectional area of Wire B and twice the length of Wire B.

50. A positive charge +Q is fixed at the origin. A charge +q in the field space moves from the position A (d, 0, 0) to position B (3d, 4d, 0). How much work does the electric force do on the +q charge?

A. zero

B. $\dfrac{qQ}{4\pi\varepsilon_0 d}$

C. $\dfrac{qQ}{8\pi\varepsilon_0 d}$

D. $\dfrac{qQ}{5\pi\varepsilon_0 d}$

E. $\dfrac{3qQ}{2\pi\varepsilon_0 d}$

51. A battery with EMF of ε and an internal resistance of r is connected to a resistor R. What is the expression for the rate at which energy is converted to heat by the resistor R?

A. ε^2 / R

B. $\varepsilon^2 / (R+r)$

C. $\varepsilon^2 r / (R+r)^2$

D. $\varepsilon^2 R / (R+r)^2$

E. $\varepsilon^2 R^2 / (R+r)^3$

52. Two nonconducting spheres (A and B) have the same net charge Q and radius R. the charge is uniformly distributed throughout the volume of sphere B and uniformly

distributed on the surface of sphere A. what are the electric field E_A and E_B inside the spheres?

A. $E_A = E_B = 0$

B. $E_A = 0$, $E_B = \dfrac{Q}{4\pi\varepsilon_0 r^2}$

C. $E_A = 0$, $E_B = \dfrac{Q}{4\pi\varepsilon_0 R^3} r$

D. $E_A = E_B = \dfrac{Q}{4\pi\varepsilon_0 R^3} r$

E. $E_A = \dfrac{Q}{4\pi\varepsilon_0 R^2}$, $E_B = \dfrac{Q}{4\pi\varepsilon_0 r^2}$

53. A long solid nonconducting cylinder of radius R contains a volume charge density $\rho(r) = 3r$, where r is the radial distance from the cylinder's central axis. The expression for the strength of the electric field inside this cylinder is

A. $\dfrac{1}{\varepsilon_0 r^2}$

B. $r / 2\varepsilon_0$

C. $2r / \varepsilon_0$

D. $r^2 / 2\varepsilon_0$

E. r^2 / ε_0

Questions 54-55

The circuit in Figure below contains two resistors, $R_1 = 2.00\ k\Omega$ and $R_2 = 3.00\ k\Omega$ and two capacitors, $C_1 = 2.00\ \mu F$ and $C_2 = 3.00\ \mu F$, connected to a battery with emf ε =120 V. No charge is on either capacitor before switch S is closed.

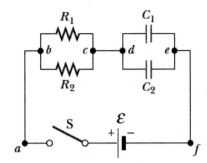

54. What is the time constant (the time for the capacitor to charge to 63% of its maximum charge) for the charging of this capacitor?

A. $(R_1 + R_2)(C_1 + C_2)$

B. $\dfrac{C_1 C_2}{C_1 + C_2}(R_1 + R_2)$

C. $\dfrac{R_1 R_2}{R_1 + R_2} C_1$

D. $\dfrac{R_1 R_2}{R_1 + R_2}(C_1 + C_2)$

E. $R_1 C_1$

55. Determine the charges q_1 on capacitors C_1 after the switch is closed.

A. $q_1 = 360(1 - e^{-\frac{1000t}{6}})\mu C$

B. $q_1 = 240(1 - e^{-\frac{1000t}{6}})\mu C$

C. $q_1 = 360(1 - e^{-\frac{t}{6}})\mu C$

D. $q_1 = 240(1 - e^{-\frac{t}{6}})\mu C$

E. zero

56. If a proton is released at the equator and

falls toward Earth under the influence of gravity, the magnetic force on the proton will be toward the _____ assuming the magnetic field is directed toward the north at this location.

A. west
B. south
C. north
D. east
E. perpendicular to the ground

57. A loop has a constant current I flowing through it while it is in a uniform magnetic field. What is a description of the most general type of motion the loop will undergo due to the interaction with the magnetic field if it is released from rest?

A. The loop will spin with constant angular speed.
B. The loop will spin with constant angular acceleration.
C. The loop will rotate back and forth.
D. The loop will accelerate with constant acceleration.
E. The loop will remain stationary.

58. A charge x is placed in an electric field and a second charge y is placed in a magnetic field. If both charges are initially held at rest, which of the following statements best describes the motion of the charges after they are released? (Ignore gravitational force)

A. charge x accelerates
B. charge y accelerates
C. both charges x and y accelerate
D. neither charge x and y accelerates
E. none of the above

59. Two long, straight, parallel wires are separated by a distance d, as shown below. They each carry a steady current I into the

page. P is midpoint of the distance of the two currents. At what points in the plane of the page and outside the wires, is the magnetic field due to the currents zero?

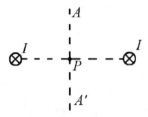

A. Only at point P
B. At all points on the line AA'
C. At all points on the line connecting the two wires
D. At all points on a circle of radius 2d centered at point P
E. At no points

60. The following statements try to explain why a magnetic field does no work on a moving charged particle. Which one is true?

A. The magnetic force is conservative.
B. The magnetic force depends on the speed of the particle.
C. The magnetic force is always perpendicular to the direction of motion.
D. There is always an electric field that cancels the work done by the magnetic field.
E. The magnetic force depends on the direction of motion of the particle.

61. For the circuit shown in Figure below, calculate the potential difference between points *a* and *b*.

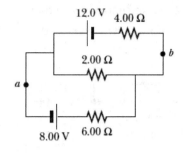

A. $V_b - V_a = -1.82\text{V}$

B. $V_b - V_a = 1.82\text{V}$

C. $V_b - V_a = 4\text{V}$

D. $V_b - V_a = -4\text{V}$

E. $V_b - V_a = 2\text{V}$

62. What is the magnetic field at point P due to the current I shown in Figure below? The arc wire BC is a semicircle with radius r and the segment of wire AB is along a diameter.

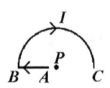

A. Zero

B. $2\mu_0 Ir$

C. $\mu_0 I / r$

D. $\mu_0 I / 2r$

E. $\mu_0 I / 4r$

63. An infinitely large current-carrying sheet lies on the xy-plane carrying current in the y-direction. Which of the following is FALSE about the magnetic field that it creates?

A. The magnetic field depends on the current density in the sheet.

B. The magnetic field can be calculated using Ampere's law.

C. The magnetic field depends on the distance away from the plane.

D. The magnetic field is in the positive x-direction.

E. The magnetic field is uniform in front of the xy plane.

64. The diagram below shows the lines of magnetic force between two north magnetic poles. Which labeled point has the greatest magnetic field strength?

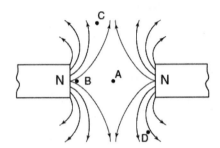

A. Point A

B. Point B

C. Point C

D. Point D

E. The magnetic field is uniform.

65. An LR circuit with no battery in the circuit has a current I at time t=0. If the circuit has a current $I/2$ at time t_1, what time does the circuit have a current $I/4$?

A. $0.5t_1$

B. $1.5t_1$

C. $2t_1$

D. $4t_1$

E. The circuit will never have a current I/4.

66. A metal rod with length L pushed along a set of conducting rails that completes a circuit with a total resistance R at a constant

velocity v to the right, as shown in Figure below. The circuit is in a magnetic field B that points out of the page. The electrical power delivered to the circuit is

A. RBlv

B. Blv/R

C. $R(Blv)^2$

D. $(Blv)^2/R$

E. $(RBlv)^2$

67. A square loop of copper wire enclosing an area of 0.10 m is initially placed perpendicular to a magnetic field of 2.0 T. The loop rotates through 90 degrees, remaining perpendicular to the field. The turn takes 0.5 s. The average emf induced in the loop during the turn is

A. 0 V

B. 0.4 V

C. 2.5 V

D. 10 V

E. 40 V

68. Which of the following will result in an induced EMF in a stationary circular loop of wire in a perpendicular magnetic field?

A. Moving the loop parallel to the magnetic field lines

B. Increasing the area of the wire loop while proportionately decreasing the magnetic field

C. Rotating the loop around an axis parallel to the magnetic field lines

D. Rotating the magnetic field to an angle 45° from the plane of the wire loop while increasing the magnetic field by a factor of

$$\sqrt{2}$$

E. Bending the wire loop into a square

69. Maxwell's equations state all of the following EXCEPT

A. the electric field is proportional to the charge enclosed by a surface.
B. there are no magnetic monopoles.
C. the induced EMF in a loop of wire is proportional to the rate of change of magnetic flux.
D. a changing electric field produces a magnetic field.
E. the magnetic flux through a closed surface is always non-zero.

70. In LC circuits which of the following act like short circuits?

I. Capacitors initially
II. Inductors initially
III. Capacitors at equilibrium
IV. Inductors at equilibrium

A. I only
B. II only
C. I and III only
D. I and IV only
E. II and III only

Section II: Free Response Questions—Questions 1-3 (45 minutes)

1.

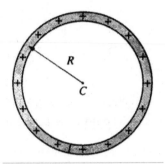

A ring of radius R carries a uniform length density λ (charge per unit length), as shown above.

    A. Calculate the electric potential V at the center C of the circle.

    B. Calculate the magnitude E of the electric field at the center C of the circle.

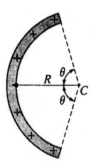

Another arc of a circle of radius R that carries the same uniform charge per unit length λ has center angle 2θ, as shown above.

    C. Determine the total charge on the rod.

    D. Determine the electric potential V at the center of curvature C of the arc.

    E. Determine the magnitude and direction of the electric field at the center of curvature C of the arc.

A proton is now placed at point C and held in place. Ignore the effects of gravity in the rest of this problem.

F. Determine the magnitude and direction of the force that must be applied in order to keep the proton at rest.

G. The proton is now released. Describe in words its motion for a long time after its release.

2.

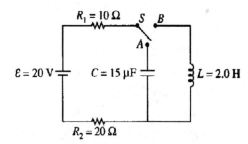

In the Figure above, the switch S is initially in the open position, and the capacitor is uncharged. A voltmeter is used to measure the potential difference across resistor R_1.

A. At sometime (let the moment is t = 0) the switch is moved to position A. Determine the voltmeter reading for the time immediately after t = 0.

B. After a long time, determine the charge on the capacitor.

C. Then at time t =T after above situation, the switch S is moved to position B. Determine the voltmeter reading for the time immediately after t = T.

D. A long time after t = T, the current in R_1 reaches a constant final value I_f. What are I_f and the final energy stored in the inductor?

E. Write and solve the differential equation for the current in resistor R_1 as a function of time t after the switch is moved to position B.

3.

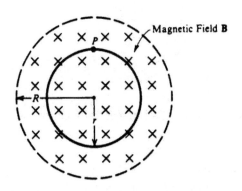

A uniform magnetic field B is confined in a cylindrical volume with radius R, perpendicular to the plane of the page as shown above. A single wire loop of radius r=R/2 is placed concentrically in the magnetic field and in the plane of the page. The magnetic field increases into the page at a constant rate of dB/dt Teslas per second.

A. Determine the induced emf in the loop.

The wire loop is moved away. A conducting rod ab with length R is placed at point p. The rod is perpendicular to the diameter passing through P.

B. Which end of the rod has a higher potential, left or right?

The conduction rod is moved away. A single electron orbits at a constant radius r=R/2 when the uniform magnetic field is constant B.

C. Determine the speed of the electron in this orbit.

D. The magnetic field is now made to increase at a constant rate of dB/dt as in part A above. Determine the tangential acceleration of the electron at the instant the field begins to increase.

Answers and Explanations

Mechanics

Section I: Multiple Choice Answers

1. E   2. C   3. C   4. D   5. E   6. E   7. B   8. C   9. C   10. B   11. B   12. B   13. B   14. D
15. C   16. E   17. E   18. B   19. C   20. D   21. B   22. A   23. C   24. A   25. B   26. E   27. B
28. D   29. B   30. A   31. E   32. E   33. D   34. B   35. D

Section I: Multiple Choice Explanations

1. E。 $a = \dfrac{v^2}{R}, v = \sqrt{Ra} = 10 m/s$

2. C。 $v = \dfrac{dx}{dt} = -2t + 6t^2$，平均加速度 $\bar{a} = \dfrac{\Delta v}{\Delta t} = \dfrac{v(2)-v(1)}{2-1} = 16 m/s^2$

3. C。 $\vec{v_{12}} = \vec{v_1} - \vec{v_2}$, $v_{12} = \sqrt{v_1^2 + v_2^2} = 58 km/h$, $\theta = \arctan \dfrac{50}{30} = 59^0$

4. D。曲线切线的斜率为速率，D 点斜率最大。

5. E。C 点和 E 点曲线切线斜率为零，速度为零。

6. E。 $a = \dfrac{dv}{dt} = 6t, F = ma = 12t$

7. B。平均速度 $\bar{\vec{v}} = \dfrac{\Delta \vec{r}}{\Delta t}$, $\Delta r = \sqrt{1200^2 + 500^2} = 1300 m$, $\bar{v} = \dfrac{1300}{80+20} = 13 m/s$

8. C。系统在手的阻力作用下做减速运动，合外力向左。由牛顿第三定律选 C。

9. C。设绳子作用于小球的拉力为 T，水平向右的力为 F，有： $T\sin\theta = F$ （水平方向），和
   $T\cos\theta = mg$ （竖直方向），得 F=$mg\tan\theta$。

10. B。加速度的两个分量分别为： $a_x = \dfrac{d^2 x}{dt^2} = 6 m/s^2$, $a_y = \dfrac{d^2 y}{dt^2} = 6 m/s^2 \rightarrow a = 6\sqrt{2} m/s^2$

11. B。N=mg-ma=100(10-5)=500N

12. B。$\omega = \sqrt{\dfrac{g}{L}} = 4.4$，$\rightarrow L = 0.61m$

13. B。$\mu mg = m\dfrac{v_{max}^2}{R}$，$\rightarrow v_{max} = \sqrt{\mu Rg} = 10m/s$

14. D。动量定理：$\displaystyle\int_0^\infty Fdt = mv_f - 0$，$\rightarrow v_f = \dfrac{F_0}{m}\displaystyle\int_0^\infty e^{-kt}dt = \dfrac{F_0}{km}$

15. C。mg=m$\dfrac{v_{min}^2}{R}$，$v_{min} = \sqrt{Rg}$，与质量无关。

16. E。F=kx=2k(x/2)=k'(x/2)，所以 k' =2k。

17. E。功 w=Fvt=480J

18. B。只有重力和弹性力做功，机械能守恒。设物体停下时，弹簧被压缩距离 x，由

$\dfrac{1}{2}kx^2 = mg(6+x)\sin 30^0$，解得 x=3m。

19. C。物体所受合外力为零时，达到最大速度，此时弹簧被压缩距离 d。有 kd=mgsin30^0，d=0.5m。

物体处于此状态时动能最大：$\dfrac{1}{2}mv_{max}^2 + \dfrac{1}{2}kd^2 = mg(6+d)\sin 30^0$，

$v_{max} = \sqrt{62.5} = 7.9m/s$

20. D。外力对物体所做的功等于动能的增量：$\Delta E_k = \displaystyle\int_1^3 Fdx = 34J$

21. B。$a = \dfrac{dv}{dt} = 4$，F=ma=4m；P=Fv=4m（4t-2）

22. A。以 6kg 物体为坐标原点：$x_{cm} = \dfrac{2*12}{2+6} = 3m$

23. C。$F = \dfrac{dp}{dt} = \dfrac{vdm}{dt} = R\sqrt{2gh}$

24. A。称的度数：$F + \Delta mg = R\sqrt{2gh} + Rgt$

25. B。碰撞后动量大小 $p=\sqrt{p_1^2 + p_2^2}$ =5kgm/s, $v=\dfrac{p}{m_1 + m_2}$ =1.7m/s

26. E。距离转点为 l 的质量微元 $dm = \lambda dl = (a+bl)dl$，其转动惯量 $dI = l^2 dm$，细杆绕端点的转

动惯量 $I = \int_0^L l^2 (a+bl)dl = \dfrac{a}{3}L^3 + \dfrac{b}{4}L^4$

27. B。细杆的质心 $L_c = \dfrac{\int_0^L l(a+bl)dl}{m} = \dfrac{1}{m}\left(\dfrac{a}{2}L + \dfrac{b}{3}L^2\right)$，m 为细杆的总质量。系统处于平衡状

态，合外力矩为零。有 $TL\sin\theta = mgL_c \sin\theta$，$\rightarrow T = \left(\dfrac{a}{2}L + \dfrac{b}{3}L^2\right)g$

28. D。$\Delta\theta = \int_0^2 (3t+2)dt = 10 rad$，$\Delta L = R\Delta\theta$ =30m

29. B。设摩擦阻力为 f。$fR = I\dfrac{a}{R}$，a 球体的加速度，球体的转动惯量 $I = \dfrac{2}{5}mR^2$。又有

$mg\sin\theta - f = ma$，解得 $a = \dfrac{5}{14}g$

30. A。角动量守恒：$I\omega = I'\omega'$，$\rightarrow \omega' = \dfrac{\omega}{3}$

31. E。设行星到质心的距离为 r：$G\dfrac{M^2}{(2r)^2} = M\dfrac{v^2}{r}$，且 T=$\dfrac{2\pi r}{v}$；有 $v = 1.66*10^4 m/s$

32. E。$\dfrac{1}{2}mv^2 = \dfrac{1}{2}mv_0^2 - G\dfrac{mM_e}{r_e}$，解得 $M = \dfrac{4Tv^3}{2\pi G} = 1.26*10^{32}kg$

33. D。周期 T=2t$_0$s, $\omega = \pi/t_0$，物体的简谐运动方程 $x = x_0 \cos\omega t$，速度方程 $v = -x_0 \omega \sin\omega t$，

$v_{max} = \dfrac{x_0 \pi}{t_0}$ m/s

34. B。物体 m 在距球心 r 处所受的引力 F=$-G\dfrac{mM(r)}{r^2} = -\dfrac{GmM}{R^3}r$

动能定理：引力使物体从 R 运动到圆心 O 所做的功等于物体的动能的增量

$\int_0^R \dfrac{GmM}{R^3}rdr = \dfrac{GmM}{2R} = \dfrac{1}{2}mgR$

35. D。牛顿第二定律：$F_A - mg + T = ma$

转动定律：$F_A R - TR = I\dfrac{a}{R}$，$I = \dfrac{1}{2}mR^2 \rightarrow a = \dfrac{2}{3}\left(\dfrac{2F_A}{m} - g\right)$

Section II: Free Response Explanations

1. A. 长度为 y 的一段绳子的质量：$m = \dfrac{M}{L}y$，重力：$F = mg = \dfrac{M}{L}yg$

B. 整个链条以相同的加速度运动，桌面与链条没有摩擦。由牛顿第二定律 $F = Ma$，求得 $a = yg/L$

C. 链条下落过程中，重力所做的功等于系统势能增量的负值：$W = \dfrac{M}{L}yg\dfrac{y}{2} = \dfrac{M}{2L}y^2 g$

D. 功等于系统动能的增量：$W = \dfrac{1}{2}Mv^2$，$\rightarrow v = \sqrt{\dfrac{g}{L}}y$

2. A. 角动量守恒：$mv\dfrac{2}{3}L = I\omega, I = \dfrac{1}{3}ML^2 + m\left(\dfrac{2}{3}L\right)^2 = \dfrac{3M + 4m}{9}L^2$，

$\rightarrow \omega = \dfrac{6m}{3M + 4m}\dfrac{v}{L}$

B. $E_k = \dfrac{1}{2}I\omega^2 = \dfrac{1}{2}\left(\dfrac{1}{3}ML^2 + m\left(\dfrac{2}{3}L\right)^2\right)\omega^2 = \dfrac{2m^2}{3M + 4m}v^2$

C. 细棒摆动到与竖直成 θ 时，对位于顶端的转点所受和外力矩为：

$\tau = -\left(Mg\dfrac{L}{2}\sin\theta + mg\dfrac{2}{3}L\sin\theta\right) = -\left(\dfrac{3M + 4m}{6}\right)gL\sin\theta$

转动定律：$\tau = I\alpha = I\dfrac{d^2\theta}{dt^2}$，$\rightarrow \dfrac{d^2\theta}{dt^2} + \dfrac{3g}{2l}\sin\theta = 0$

D. 当 $\theta \leq 5^0$ 时：$\sin\theta \approx \theta$。微分方程为 $\dfrac{d^2\theta}{dt^2} + \dfrac{3g}{2l}\theta = 0$

此时物体系统的运动为简谐振动：$\omega = \sqrt{\dfrac{3g}{2L}}$，周期 T= $2\pi\sqrt{\dfrac{2L}{3g}}$

E. 物体运动方程为：$\theta = \theta_{max} \sin \omega t = \theta_{max} \cos(\omega t - \pi/2)$

$$Mg\frac{L}{2}(1-\cos\theta_{max}) + mg\frac{2L}{3}(1-\cos\theta_{max}) = E_K$$

解得：$\cos\theta_{max} = 1 - 12\left(\frac{m}{3M+4m}\right)^2\frac{v^2}{gL}$

3. A. U(r) = a(r/b + b/r), 势能函数的最小值发生在 $\dfrac{dU}{dr} = a\left(\dfrac{1}{b} - \dfrac{b}{r^2}\right) = 0$ 处，

此时 $r = r_0 = b$，$U_0 = 2a$

B. 保守力 F（r）$= -\dfrac{dU}{dr} = a\left(\dfrac{b}{r^2} - \dfrac{1}{b}\right)$

C. 物体在 $r_0/2$（b/2）处静止释放，此位置的机械能为 $U\left(\dfrac{b}{2}\right) = \dfrac{5}{2}a$；势能最低点处的机械能

为 $\dfrac{1}{2}mv^2 + U_0$。保守力场中的机械能守恒，有：$v = \sqrt{\dfrac{a}{m}}$

D. 物体的势能达到 $U = \dfrac{5}{2}a$ 时，运动速度为零；U(r) = a(r/b + b/r) = $\dfrac{5}{2}a$，解得 r=2b, b/2.

E. 在 r=b/2 和 r=2b 之间做往复的周期运动。

Electricity and Magnetism

Section I: Multiple Choice Answers

36. C   37. E   38. B   39. A   40. B   41. B   42. A   43. C   44. C   45. A   46. E   47. B   48. C
49. E   50. D   51. D   52. C   53. E   54. D   55. B   56. D   57. C   58. A   59. A   60. C   61. A
62. E   63. C   64. B   65. C   66. D   67. A   68. E   69. E   70. D

Section I: Multiple Choice Explanations

36. C。两个等量异号点电荷组成的电荷系统称之为电偶极子。电偶极子空间场强处处不为零。两个同号电荷组成的电荷系统，在两电荷的连线方向上一定有一点场强为零。

37. E。电场力的功 $W=-q\Delta V=\Delta E_k$, $\frac{1}{2}mv_f^2-\frac{1}{2}mv^2=-q(200-100)$, $v_f^2=v^2-\frac{200q}{m}$。q 是负电荷，所以 $v_f \rangle v$。

38. B。$F_1=\frac{1}{4\pi\varepsilon_0}\frac{3Q^2}{d^2}$。这两个相同的球体接触后，各自带电荷 2Q。此时两球体的作用力

$F_2=\frac{1}{4\pi\varepsilon_0}\frac{4Q^2}{d^2}$，所以选 B。

39. A。A 点处的场强大小为 $E_A=2\frac{1}{4\pi\varepsilon_0}\frac{Q^2}{d^2}$。计算其他点处的场强，知 A 点场强最强。

40. B。由场强和电势的微分关系 E=-dV/dx 知，$E=-C[1/(x+L)-1/x]$

41. B。由高斯定理可知，穿过高斯面的电通量只与高斯面所包围的电荷成正比，故选 B。

42. A。$V_p=(2-\frac{\sqrt{2}}{2})\frac{Q}{4\pi\varepsilon_0 d}$，电荷 q 从无限远移动到 p 点外力所做的功 $W=qV_p$。

43. C。第一个电容器所带电量 $Q_1=CV$，第二个电容器所带电量为 $Q_2=2CV$。当两个电容器并联时，两电容器的电压相同，所带电量也相同，都是 1.5Q。所以 $V_1=V_2=1.5V$

44. C。电路的等效电容 $C_e=2F$，$U=\frac{1}{2}C_eV^2=144$ J; Q=CV=2*4=8C

45. A。导体球壳和实心导体球场强和电势的分布相同。球体内部是等势体。

46. E。$U=\frac{1}{2}CV^2=800$ J

47. B。电容器两极板间插入电解质，电解质的极化作用板间的场强。V=Ed，所以板间的电势差也降低，极板上的电荷不变，由 C=Q/V 知，电容升高。

48. C。电荷 q 向外发射的电力线的数目是 $\frac{q}{\varepsilon_0}$。电荷在立方体的中心，穿过每一侧面的电通量是

$\frac{q}{6\varepsilon_0}$。

49. E。$R=\rho\frac{l}{A}$。同种材料的两个电阻 $R_1=4R_2$。只能选 E。

50. D。 $\frac{qQ}{5\pi\varepsilon_0 d}$。电场力的功 W=q(V$_A$-V$_B$),V$_A$= $\frac{Q}{4\pi\varepsilon_0 d}$, V$_B$= $\frac{Q}{20\pi\varepsilon_0 d}$

51. D。电路中的电流为 $I = \varepsilon/(R+r)$，电阻 R 上的功率为：P= $I^2 R = \varepsilon^2 R/(R+r)^2$

52. C。A 球面内部没有电荷，由高斯定理可知，内部场强处处为零 E=0。B 球面：由高斯定理得

内部一点的场强正比于点到圆心的半径，E$_B$= $\frac{Q}{4\pi\varepsilon_0 R^3}r$

53. E。选一同轴柱形高斯面，半径为 r，长为 h。由高斯定理，电通量为：E 2π rh= $\frac{q_{encl}}{\varepsilon_0}$

高斯面包围的电荷 $q_{encl} = \int_0^r \rho(r)*2\pi rhdr = 2\pi hr^3$，带入高斯公式得 E= r^2/ε_0

54. D。时间常数 $\tau = RC = \frac{R_1 R_2}{R_1 + R_2}(C_1 + C_2)$ =6ms

55. B。任意时刻的电容器 1 上的电量 $q_1 = 240(1-e^{-\frac{1000t}{6}})\mu C$

56. D。赤道上的质子速度垂直地面，磁场平行于地面指向北极，质子受力 F=q$v \times B$ 将指向东。

57. C。通电线圈在磁场中受力为零，F=0，线圈不会有平动加速度。所受的磁力矩为 $\tau = ISn \times B$：
其中 S 为线圈面积，n 是线圈法向方向单位向量。线圈将发生转动，力矩随线圈位置而变。
如果线圈法向和磁场方向一致，线圈将保持不动。

58. A。电荷 q 在电场中受力 F=qE，q 将获得加速度。电荷 q 在磁场中受力 F=q$v \times B$，V=0，所
以 F=0，即静止电荷在磁场中不受力。

59. A。两平行通电长直导线，电流方向相同，连线中点处的磁场为零。

60. C。运动电荷在磁场受力的方向永远垂直于运动速度，所以磁场力不做功。

61. A。由基尔霍夫定律计算得。

62. E。电流圆环在圆心处的磁场强度为 B= $\mu_0 I/2r$。半圆环在 p 电的场强为 $\mu_0 I/4r$。线段 AB
电流的延长线通过圆心，在圆心处的 B=0。

63. C。无限大电流平板电流面密度为 i，在板两侧产生匀强磁场，平行于版面且与电流垂直。大
小为 B= $\frac{\mu_0 i}{2}$。

64. B。磁力线密集的地方场强强，稀疏的地方场强弱。

65. C。电感放电电流 $I = I_{max}(e^{-t/\tau})$，$\tau = \dfrac{L}{R}$。$\dfrac{1}{2} = e^{-t_1/\tau}$，所以 $\dfrac{1}{4} = e^{-2t_1/\tau}$，t=2$t_1$

66. D。运动导体 L 产生动生电动势 $\varepsilon = BLv$，在回路中的感应电流为 $I = BLv/R$，功率 P=I^2R

67. A。线圈旋转 90 度，但通过线圈的磁通量没有发生改变，由法拉第电磁感应定律选 A。

68. E。在磁场中环形回路的面积改变产生感应电动势。$\varepsilon = -\dfrac{d\phi}{dt} = -(S\dfrac{dB}{dt} + B\dfrac{dS}{dt})$，S：回路面积。

69. E。通过闭合曲面的磁通量为零。

70. D。刚接通电路时，电容可认为短路，电流直接流过。电路稳定时，电感可看作短路，电流直接流过。

Section II: Free Response Explanations

1. A. 均匀带电圆环在圆心处的电势：V= $\displaystyle\int \dfrac{2\pi R\lambda}{4\pi\varepsilon_0 R} = \dfrac{\lambda}{2\varepsilon_0}$

   B. 场强：E=0

   C. 圆弧所带电量：$q = \lambda R2\theta$

   D. 圆弧中心点的电势：V= $\displaystyle\int \dfrac{dq}{4\pi\varepsilon_0 R} = \dfrac{\lambda}{2\pi\varepsilon_0}\theta$

   E. 圆心 c 点竖直方向的场强为零，水平向右的场强为：

   E= $\displaystyle\int_{-\theta}^{\theta} \dfrac{\lambda Rd\theta}{4\pi\varepsilon_0 R^2}\cos\theta = \dfrac{2\lambda}{\pi\varepsilon_0 R}\sin\theta$

   F. 圆心处的质子受力为：F=eE= $\dfrac{2e\lambda}{\pi\varepsilon_0 R}\sin\theta$，质子受力方向向右。

   G. 质子受到向右的电场力作用，做加速度减小的加速运动。经过长时间运动后，质子远离带电体，受力为零，做匀速直线运动。

2. A. 开关与电容相连时：刚刚闭合时电容等效于电路短路，此时流经整个回路的

$$I = \frac{\varepsilon}{R_1 + R_2} = 0.67A$$，电阻 R_1 上的电压表读数是 $V_1 = IR_1 = 6.7V$

B. 电容通电长时间后电路相当于开路，电容器上的电压是 20V，$Q = CV = 0.3mc$

C. 此时电路中的电流为零，$V_1 = 0$

D. $t = T$ 时，开关与电感相接：相接之后瞬间电路中 $I = 0$，长时间电路稳定后

$$I = \frac{\varepsilon}{R_1 + R_2} = 0.67A$$，电感中储存的能量 $E = \frac{1}{2}LI^2 = 0.44J$

E. 在接通电感之后，电路达到稳定前的任意瞬时 t，电流时时间 t 的函数，电流变化符合的

微分方程式：$\varepsilon - L\frac{dI}{dt} = (R_1 + R_2)I$， 即 $\varepsilon - 2\frac{dI}{dt} = 30I$

解此微分方程得：$I = \frac{\varepsilon}{R}(1 - e^{-\frac{R}{L}(t-T)}) = \frac{2}{3}(1 - e^{-1.5(t-T)})$

3. A. 由法拉第电磁感应定律：$\varepsilon = -\frac{d\phi}{dt} = -\pi r^2 \frac{dB}{dt}$，负号表示感应电动势的方向沿逆时针，

在 p 点沿切向向左。

B. 左端点电势高。

C. 磁场力作为电子圆周运动的向心力：$evB = m\frac{v^2}{r}$， $v = \frac{erB}{m}$

D. 磁场随时间变化 dB/dt，在磁场存在的空间激发感应电场 $E = \frac{1}{2}\frac{dB}{dt}r$，以中心为对称轴逆时

针方向的涡旋电场。电荷在半径为 r 处受到顺时针切线方向的电场力 F=eE，在切向的加速度

为 a= $\frac{F}{m} = \frac{e}{2m}\frac{dB}{dt}r$

Model test 2

Mechanics

Section I: Multiple Choice Questions—Questions 1-35 (45 minutes)

Directions: Each multiple choice question is followed by five answer choices. For each question, choose the best answer and fill in the corresponding oval on the answer sheet.

1. A railroad train travels forward along a straight track at 80.0 m/s for 1000 m and then travels at 50.0 m/s for the next 1000 m. What is the average velocity?

   A. 65.0 m/s
   B. 61.5 m/s
   C. 63.7 m/s
   D. 70.0 m/s
   E. 68.3 m/s

2. If the displacement of an object is given in SI units by $x = -3t + 4t^2$, at $t = 2$ s its velocity and acceleration are respectively:

   A. positive, positive.
   B. positive, negative.
   C. negative, negative.
   D. negative, positive.
   E. negative, zero.

3. Which position-versus-time graph represents the motion shown in the motion diagram?

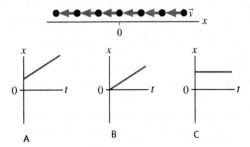

   Motion diagram

   A   B   C

   D

   E

4. The acceleration of a particle that begins at rest at the origin is given by $a(t) = \dfrac{9}{2}ti + 6tj$, where a is in m/s^2 and t is in seconds. The particle's distance from the origin at time $t = 2$ s is most nearly

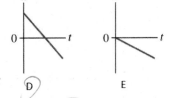

   A. 10 m
   B. 12 m
   C. 14 m
   D. 6 m
   E. 8 m

5. A plane traveling horizontally to the right at 90 m/s flies past a helicopter that is going straight up at 15 m/s. From the helicopter's perspective, the plane's direction and speed are

   A. right and down, more than 90 m/s.
   B. right and up, more than 90 m/s.
   C. right and up, less than 90 m/s.
   D. right and down, less than 90 m/s.
   E. right and down, 90 m/s.

6. A force **F** = (6**i** - 2**j**) N acts on a particle that

F = 6i + 2j N

undergoes a displacement $\Delta \mathbf{r} = (3\mathbf{i} + \mathbf{j})$ m. the work done by the force on the particle is

A. 7.1J
B. 12J
C. 16J
D. 18J
E. 20J

7. A uniform rope of weight 50 N hangs from a ceiling. A box hangs from the bottom of the rope. The ratio of tension at the top of the rope to the tension at the bottom is 3:1. What is the mass of the box?

A. 100 kg
B. 50 kg
C. 20 kg
D. 10 kg
E. 2.5 kg

8. A force of magnitude F pushes two blocks on a frictionless surface. What is the force the 4 kg block exerts on the 2 kg block?

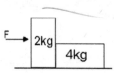

A. 4F
B. 2F
C. $\dfrac{4}{3}F$
D. $\dfrac{2}{3}F$
E. $\dfrac{1}{3}F$

9. A car of mass M is traveling around an unbanked, rough, and circular road with a radius of R at a speed of v. The minimum coefficient of kinetic friction required to allow the car to safely travel around the turn is

A. RMg
B. Rg
C. v^2/Mg
D. v^2/Rg
E. v^2/RMg

10. A ball of mass m is revolving on a string on a horizontal surface with a radius of r and a period of T. What is the tension in the string?

A. $2m\pi^2 r/T$
B. $4m\pi^2 r/T^2$
C. $2m\pi^2 r/T^2$
D. $4m\pi^2 r/T$
E. $4m\pi r/T^2$

11. A ball rolls down a curved ramp as shown in the diagram below. Which dotted line best represents the path of the ball after leaving the ramp?

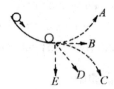

A. A
B. B
C. C
D. D
E. E

Questions 12-13

A bullet is shooting into a block of wood with mass M that is fixed in place. The block exerts a force $\mathbf{F}$ on the bullet that is proportional to the bullet's velocity $\mathbf{v}$ and in the opposite direction, that is $\mathbf{F} = -b\mathbf{v}$, where b is a constant.

12. An expression for the speed of the bullet moving inside the block before it stops is

ma
v -

F = ma
∫F = ∫ma

∫f = MV
F = MV' = -bv

A. $v = v_0 e^{-\frac{b}{m}t}$

B. $v = \frac{m+M}{m} v_0$

C. $v = v_0 \frac{b}{m} e^{-t}$

D. $v = \frac{1}{2} \frac{b}{m} t^2$

E. zero

13. An expression for the distance L that the bullet penetrates into the block is

A. $L = \frac{m}{Mb} v_0$

B. $L = \frac{M}{b} v_0$

C. $L = v_0 t$

D. $L = \frac{m}{b} v_0$

E. zero

14.

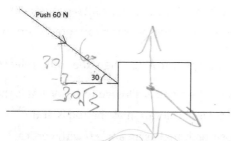

Push 60 N

A student pushes a 16 kg big box across the floor at a constant speed. He pushes with a force of 60 N angled 30° from the horizontal, as shown in the diagram above. Determine the coefficient of friction.

A. 0.10
B. 0.15
C. 0.22
D. 0.30
E. 0.42

15. The position of a vehicle of mass 1000 kg moving on a straight track along the x-axis is given by the equation $x(t) = t^3 - t^2 - 6$, where x is in meters and t is in seconds. What is the instantaneous force acting on the vehicle at t = 3 s?

A. Zero
B. 3000 N
C. 6000 N
D. 12000 N
E. 16000 N

16. If the power delivered to an object by a force acting on it is given by $P(t) = t^3 - 2t$ and the velocity of the object is given by $v(t) = 2t$, what is the force acting on the object in terms of t?

A. $F(t) = t^3 - 4t$
B. $F(t) = t^3$
C. $F(t) = t^2/2 - 1$
D. $F(t) = 3t^2 - 2$
E. More information is needed to determine the force.

17. Three homogeneous solid spheres of masses 1 kg, 2 kg and 4 kg are arranged with their centers at $(2\mathbf{i} + \mathbf{j} + \mathbf{k})$, $(3\mathbf{i} - 2\mathbf{j} + 2\mathbf{k})$ and $(4\mathbf{i} - \mathbf{j} - 2\mathbf{k})$ respectively where $\mathbf{i}, \mathbf{j}, \mathbf{k}$ are unit vectors in the x, y and z directions. All distances are in meters. The y- coordinates of the center of mass system of spheres is

A. 3.3 m
B. 2.6 m
C. 0.33 m
D. – 1 m
E. – 2 m

18. Three satellites are launched into space connected together. Once in deep space, an explosive charge separates the three satellites and they move apart. The satellites

435

each have different masses with $m_1 < m_2 < m_3$. Which of the following statements is *always* true?

A. The one with mass m_1 receives the greatest impulse.

B. The one with mass m_3 receives the greatest impulse.

C. They all must receive equal impulses.

D. Although one or more of the above statements could be true in special cases, they are not always true.

E. All of the above statements are always false.

19. A rod which is putting on x-axis with one end on the origin has a nonuniform mass density $\lambda = bx^2$, x is the distance from the origin. The rod with length L, and mass M can rotate about the origin. What are the moment of inertia I and center of mass x_c of the rod?

A. $I = ML^2, x_c = \dfrac{1}{4}L$

B. $I = \dfrac{1}{3}ML^2, x_c = \dfrac{3}{4}L$

C. $I = \dfrac{3}{5}ML^2, x_c = \dfrac{2}{3}L$

D. $I = \dfrac{3}{5}ML^2, x_c = \dfrac{3}{4}L$

E. $I = \dfrac{1}{3}ML^2, x_c = \dfrac{2}{3}L$

$\dfrac{\int x\,dm}{m}$

$\dfrac{\int x\,\lambda dx}{m}$

20. The following graphs below plot the velocity of a particle with respect to time.

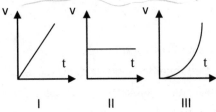

I   II   III

In which of these cases is (or are) the object's rate of change of momentum constant?

A. I only

B. II only

C. I and II

D. I and III

E. I, II, and III

21. A 100N uniform ladder, 8.0 m long, rests against a smooth vertical wall. The ladder makes an angle $\theta = 60^0$ with the floor. What is the minimum coefficient of static friction between ladder and floor before the ladder slips?

A. 0.20

B. 0.29

C. 0.35

D. 0.40

E. 0.58

22. A rod of length l, mass m is hinged at one end and is held in a horizontal position. The moment of inertia as the rod rotates around that hinge is ml^2/3. Then, the rod is released as the free end is allowed to fall. What is the angular acceleration as the rod is at the position it makes an angle θ with vertical?

A. $\dfrac{3g}{2l}\cos\theta$

B. $\dfrac{3g}{2l}\sin\theta$

C. $\dfrac{3g}{4l}\sin\theta$

D. $\dfrac{2g}{3l}\cos\theta$

E. $\dfrac{4g}{3l}\sin\theta$

23. The rod in the figure below is uniform with mass m. The tension in the supporting string is

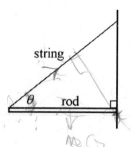

string

θ rod

A. $mg\sin\theta$

B. $mg\sin\theta/2$

C. $mg\cos\theta/2$

D. $mg/2\cos\theta$

E. $mg/2\sin\theta$

24. If an object of radius 2 m that experiences a constant angular acceleration starting from rest, rotates 18 rads in 3 s, what is its angular velocity after 2 s?

A. 2 rad/s

B. 4 rad/s

C. 8 rad/s

D. 12 rad/s

E. 16 rad/s

25. A hoop of radius 10cm and mass 2.0 kg is at rest at a height 10 m at the top of an inclined plane making an angle 30^0 with the horizontal. Rolling down the incline without slipping, what is the speed of the hoop at the bottom of the incline and what is its angular kinetic energy?

A. 10m/s, 33J

B. 7 m/s, 98J

C. 7 m/s, 49J

D. 8 m/s. 49J

E. 8 m/s, 98J

26. A figure skater spins with an angular velocity of ω on the ice holding his arms out perpendicular to his body. He then brings his arm in towards his body causing his rotational inertia to decrease by a factor of 2. What is his new angular velocity?

A. ω/4

B. ω/2

C. ω

D. 2ω

E. 4 ω

27.

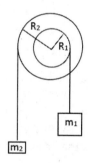

R_2

R_1

m_1

m_2

Two blocks are hanged on a pulley, shown in the diagram above. The moment of inertia of the pulley is I . The two block's masses are m_1 and m_2 ($m_1 > m_2$). What is the acceleration of the block m_1 if it is moving down without slipping?

A. $\dfrac{m_1 R_1 - m_2 R_2}{I} R_2 g$

B. $\dfrac{m_1 R_1 - m_2 R_2}{I} R_1 g$

C. $\dfrac{m_1 - m_2}{m_1} g$

D. $\dfrac{m_1 - m_2}{m_1 + m_2} g$

E. $\dfrac{m_1 R_1 - m_2 R_2}{I} g$

28. A simple pendulum is released from a height h. At the bottom of the pendulum, it strikes an object of mass m which sticks with the pendulum bob. Which of the following describes the pendulum-object system after the collision?

I. The kinetic energy of the system increases.
II. The period of the pendulum remains constant.
III. The maximum height the pendulum reaches decreases.

A. I only

B. II only

C. III only

D. II and III only

E. I, II, and III all

29. A satellite in orbit around the Earth has a period of one hour. An identical satellite is placed in an orbit having a radius four times as the first satellite. What is the period of the second satellite?

A. 1/8 hr
B. 1/4 hr
C. 2 hr
D. 4 hr
E. 8 hr

30. Two identical stars, a fixed distance D apart, revolve in a circle about their mutual center of mass. Each star has mass m and speed v. What is the centripetal acceleration of each star?

A. $\dfrac{v^2}{D}$

B. $G\dfrac{4m}{D^2}$

C. $G\dfrac{m}{4D^2}$

D. $\dfrac{v^2}{2D}$

E. $\dfrac{2v^2}{D}$

31. A particle is released at a height R_E (radius of Earth) above the Earth's surface. Determine its velocity when it hits the Earth. Ignore the air resistance.

A. $\sqrt{2gR_E}$

B. $\sqrt{gR_E}$

C. $2\sqrt{gR_E}$

D. $\dfrac{1}{2}\sqrt{gR_E}$

E. $\sqrt{\dfrac{1}{2}gR_E}$

32. A block of unknown mass is attached to a spring with a spring constant of 6.0 N/m and undergoes simple harmonic motion with an amplitude of 10 cm. When the block is halfway between its equilibrium position and the end point, its speed is measured to be 30 cm/s. The period of the motion is

A. 0.50s

438

B. 0.91s

C. 1.50s

D. 1.81s

E. 3.62s

33. The position of a simple harmonic oscillator has a function of time is given by $x(t) = 3.0\cos$ $(\dfrac{5\pi}{4}t + \dfrac{\pi}{6})$, where x is in meters and t is in seconds. The period and the maximum magnitude of its velocity are

A. T=1.0s; $v_{max} = 3m/s$

B. T=1.6s; $v_{max} = 6m/s$

C. T=1.6s; $v_{max} = 12m/s$

D. T=3.0s; $v_{max} = 12m/s$

E. T=3.0s; $v_{max} = 48m/s$

34.

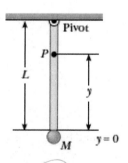

A small ball of mass M is attached to the end of a uniform rod of equal mass M and length L that is pivoted at the top, shown in Figure above. The period of oscillation for small displacements from equilibrium is

A. $T= 2\pi\sqrt{\dfrac{2L}{g}}$

B. $T=\dfrac{4\pi}{3}\sqrt{\dfrac{2L}{g}}$

C. $T=\dfrac{2\pi}{3}\sqrt{\dfrac{2L}{g}}$

D. $T= 2\pi\sqrt{\dfrac{L}{g}}$

E. $T= 2\pi\sqrt{\dfrac{2L}{3g}}$

35.

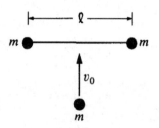

Initially, the assembly is "floating" freely at rest relative to the cabin, and the astronaut launches the clay lump so that it perpendicularly strikes and sticks to the midpoint of the rod, as shown above. The change in kinetic energy as a result of the collision will be

A. $\Delta E_k = \dfrac{1}{6}mv_0^2$

B. $\Delta E_k = \dfrac{1}{3}mv_0^2$

C. $\Delta E_k = \dfrac{1}{2}mv_0^2$

D. $\Delta E_k = \dfrac{2}{3}mv_0^2$

E. zero

Section II: Free Response Questions—Questions 1-3 (45 minutes)

Directions: Answer all three questions. The suggested time is about 15 minutes for answering each of the questions, which are worth 15 points each. The parts within a question may not have equal weight.

1. A particle moves along a line where the potential energy of its system depends on its position r as graphed in Figure below. In the limit as r increases without bound, $U(r)$ approaches +1 J.

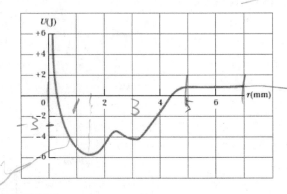

A. Identify each equilibrium position for this particle. Indicate whether each is a point of stable, unstable, or neutral equilibrium.

B. The particle will be bound if the total energy of the system is in what range?

Now suppose that the system has energy -3 J. Determine

C. the range of positions where the particle can be found,

D. its maximum kinetic energy,

E. the location where it has maximum kinetic energy, and

F. the *binding energy* of the system—the additional energy that it would have to be given in order for the particle to move out to $r \rightarrow \infty$.

2. A disk of mass M and radius R rests on a rough horizontal surface. The coefficient of friction between the disk and the surface is μ. The disk can rotate about a vertical axis through its center. It is given an initial counterclockwise angular velocity ω_0 about the center of the disk and then is gradually brought to rest by friction. The moment of inertia of the disk rotating about its vertical axis through its center is $\dfrac{1}{2}MR^2$.

A. Find the frictional torque acting on the disk about the vertical axis through the center of the disk.

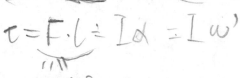

440

B. What is the angular acceleration of the disk?

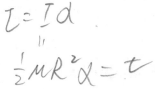

$\tau = I\alpha$

$\frac{1}{2}MR^2\alpha = \tau$

C. How long will the disk come to rest?

3. A satellite of mass m is in an elliptical orbit around the Earth, which has mass M_e and radius R_e. The orbit varies from the closest point A with a distance a to maximum distance of b from the center of the Earth at point B. At point A, the speed of the satellite is v_o. Assume that the gravitational potential energy $U_g = 0$ when masses are an infinite distance apart.

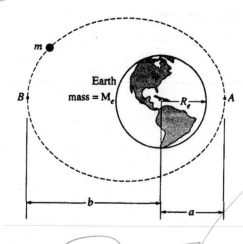

Earth
mass = M_e

$G\dfrac{M_s M_e}{a}$

A. Determine the total energy of the satellite when it is at A.

B. Determine the velocity of the satellite as it passes point B in its orbit. $M_a V_a = M_b V_b$

As the satellite passes point A, its orbit is changed to a circular orbit of radius a about the center of the Earth for some reason.

C. Determine the speed of the satellite for this circular orbit.

D. What is the total energy of the satellite?

$E = G\dfrac{mM}{r}$

441

Electricity and Magnetism

Section I: Multiple Choice Questions—Questions 36-70 (45 minutes)

Directions: Each multiple choice question is followed by five answer choices. For each question, choose the best answer and fill in the corresponding oval on the answer sheet.

36. At a distance of d from a point charge, the magnitude of the electric force on a charge q is F. What is the magnitude of the electric force if the charge is moved to a distance 3d from the other charge?

   A. 3F
   B. 9F
   C. F/3
   D. F/9
   E. F

37. A surface is an equipotential surface at a potential of zero. What is true about the electric field on the surface?

   A. The electric field on the surface is zero.
   B. The electric field on the surface is perpendicular to the surface.
   C. The electric field on the surface points parallel to the surface.
   D. The electric field on the surface has the same magnitudes.
   E. None of the above statements is necessarily true about the electric field.

38. Three identical point charges, Q, are placed at the vertices of an equilateral triangle as shown in the figure. The length of each side of the triangle is d. Determine the magnitude and direction of the total electrostatic force on the charge at the top of the triangle.

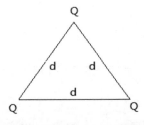

A. $\dfrac{\sqrt{3}Q^2}{4\pi\varepsilon_0 d^2}$ upwards

B. $\dfrac{\sqrt{3}Q^2}{4\pi\varepsilon_0 d^2}$ downwards

C. $\dfrac{\sqrt{3}Q^2}{2\pi\varepsilon_0 d^2}$ upwards

D. $\dfrac{\sqrt{3}Q^2}{2\pi\varepsilon_0 d^2}$ downwards

E. The net force is zero.

39. A thin semicircular conductor of radius R holds charge - q. The magnitude and direction of the electric field at the center O of the circle are

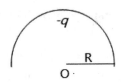

A. $\dfrac{1}{4\pi\varepsilon_0}\dfrac{q}{R^2}$, upwards.

B. $\dfrac{1}{4\pi\varepsilon_0}\dfrac{q}{R^2}$, downwards.

C. $\dfrac{1}{4\pi\varepsilon_0}\dfrac{q}{\pi R^2}$, downwards.

D. $\dfrac{1}{4\pi\varepsilon_0}\dfrac{q}{\pi R^2}$, upwards.

E. zero.

442

40. The potential at a point outside of a very long conducting cylinder of radius R and uniform charge density λ relative to the potential on the cylinder is given by the equation $V(r) = \dfrac{\lambda}{2\pi\varepsilon_0} \ln(R/r)$. What is the electric field at some distance r from the center of the cylinder?

A. $\dfrac{\lambda}{2\pi\varepsilon_0 r}$

B. $\dfrac{\lambda}{4\pi\varepsilon_0 r}$

C. $\dfrac{\lambda}{\pi\varepsilon_0 r}$

D. $-\dfrac{\lambda}{2\pi\varepsilon_0 r}$

E. $-\dfrac{\lambda}{4\pi\varepsilon_0 r}$

41. Two parallel conducting plates separated by a distance d has charge density (charge amount on one unit area) $+\sigma$ on one plate and $-\sigma$ on the other plate. An electron starts from rest on the surface of the negative plate and accelerates toward the other. Its speed as it reaches the positive plate is proportional to

A. $\dfrac{1}{\sigma d}$

B. $\dfrac{1}{\sqrt{\sigma d}}$

C. σd

D. $\sqrt{\sigma d}$

E. $(\sigma d)^2$

42. If the electric field does positive work on a negative charge as the charge undergoes a displacement from point A to point B within an electric field, then the electrical potential energy

A. is negative.

B. is positive.

C. increases.

D. decreases.

E. doesn't change.

43. In order to double the capacitance of a parallel plate capacitor you can

A. double the area of its plates.

B. double the distance between its plates.

C. double the length of each of the edges of its plates.

D. put some dielectric material between the two plates.

E. None of the above is true.

44. Two concentric, spherical conducting shells have radii r_1 and r_2 and charges $Q_1 = +1C$ and $Q_2 = -3C$, as shown below. Let r be the distance from the center of the spheres and consider the region $r_1 < r < r_2$. In this region the magnitude and direction of the electric field are

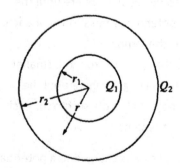

A. $\dfrac{1}{4\pi\varepsilon_0}\dfrac{4}{r^2}$; along radial, pointing away from the center.

B. $\dfrac{1}{4\pi\varepsilon_0}\dfrac{2}{r^2}$; along radial, pointing

443

towards the center.

C. $\dfrac{1}{4\pi\varepsilon_0}\dfrac{2}{r^2}$; along radial, pointing away

from the center.

D. $\dfrac{1}{4\pi\varepsilon_0}\dfrac{1}{r^2}$; along radial, pointing

towards the center.

E. $\dfrac{1}{4\pi\varepsilon_0}\dfrac{1}{r^2}$; along radial pointing away

from the center.

45. Two conducting spheres of different radii each carry a charge +Q. Which of the following occurs when the two spheres are touched together?

A. No charge flows.
B. Positive charge flows from the larger sphere to the smaller sphere until the electric field at the surface of each sphere is the same.
C. Positive charge flows from the smaller sphere to the larger sphere until the electric field at the surface of each sphere is the same.
D. Positive charge flows from the larger sphere to the smaller sphere until the electric potential at the surface of each sphere is the same.
E. Positive charge flows from the smaller sphere to the larger sphere until the electric potential at the surface of each sphere is the same.

46. A 10 μF capacitor is charged to a potential difference of 20 V. The electric energy stored in the capacitor is

A. 2×10^{-5} J
B. 2×10^{-4} J
C. 4×10^{-4} J
D. 2×10^{-3} J
E. 4×10^{-3} J

47. A voltage V_0 is initially applied to a capacitor. A dielectric of $\kappa = 3$ is added between the plates and the distance between the plates is halved. What is the new voltage that must be applied for the charge on the capacitor to remain the same?

A. $V_0/6$
B. $V_0/3$
C. V_0
D. $3V_0$
E. $6V_0$

48. In the circuit below, find the current through the 10 Ω resistor.

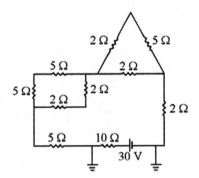

A. 0.5 A
B. 1.25 A
C. 1.5 A
D. 3 A
E. 5 A

49. A manufacturer recommends that the longer the extension cord used with an electric drill, the thicker (heavier gauge) the extension cord should be. This recommendation is made because the resistance of a wire varies

A. directly with length and inversely with cross-sectional area.
B. inversely with length and directly with cross-sectional area.
C. directly with both length and cross-sectional area.
D. inversely with both length and cross-sectional area.

E. inversely with length, and remains constant with cross sectional area.

50. A long rod containing a positive charge density of λ is putting along x axis. When the rod is moving in the +x direction with velocity v, the long rod can be considered as a current I flowing along the rod. What is the magnitude of the current, and in what direction is the conventional current flowing?

A. $I = v\lambda$ along the -x direction
B. $I = v\lambda$ along the +x direction

C. $I = v\lambda^2$ along the -x direction

D. $I = v\lambda^2$ along the +x direction

E. $I = v/\lambda$ along the +x direction

51. It requires an input energy of U joules to move a charge q from point A to point B at a constant velocity, which of the following is true?

A. $V_B - V_A = U/q$

B. $V_B - V_A = -U/q$

C. $V_B - V_A = q/U$

D. $V_B - V_A = Uq$

E. $V_B - V_A = 0$

52. In a static electric field, for the electric flux through a Gaussian surface is zero, which of the following statements must be always true?

A. The electric field has to be zero for the entire Gaussian surface.
B. There must be no charge enclosed within the Gaussian surface.
C. There is no net charge enclosed within the Gaussian surface.

D. The component of electric field perpendicular to the Gaussian surface is zero along the entire Gaussian surface.
E. None of the above is true.

53. In a certain region, the electric field varies with the radius from origin by the equation $E(r) = -3r^2+4r+15$, where r is given in meters and E in N/C. The potential difference between the origin and the point (6, 8) is

A. 69 V
B. 245 V
C. -245 V
D. 650 V
E. -650 V

Questions 54-55

In the circuit shown below, the 0.5 F capacitor is initially uncharged. The battery has no internal resistance with V=40v. The switch is closed at time $t = 0$.

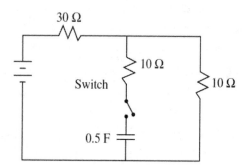

54. After a long time the switch is closed, what is the current flowing the resistor $30\,\Omega$?

A. 1A
B. 8/7 A
C. 2 A
D. 3A
E. 4A

55. After a long time the switch is closed, what is the potential difference on the capacitor?

A. 5v
B. 10v

445

C. 20v

D. 30v

E. 40v

56. If the two equal resistors R_1 and R_2 are connected in parallel to a 10V battery with no other circuit components, the current provided by the battery is I. In the circuit shown below, an inductor of inductance L is included in series with R_2. What are the currents I_1 and I_2 flowing through R_1 and R_2 when the circuit has just been connected?

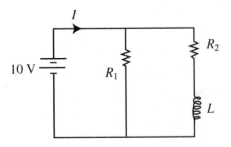

A. $I_1 = I_2 = I/2$

B. $I_1 = I, I_2 = 0$

C. $I_1 = 0, I_2 = I$

D. $I_1 = I_2 = I$

E. $I_1 = I_2 = 0$

57. Consider two long, straight, parallel wires, each carrying a current I. If the currents move in the same direction,

A. the two wires will exert a torque on each other.

B. the two wires will attract each other.

C. the two wires will repel each other.

D. neither of the two wires will exert a force on the other.

E. None of the above is true.

446   58. A rectangular loop on this page plane has

a current I flowing around the loop in a counter-clockwise direction. It is partially inserted from left to right into a region with a magnetic field pointing in the page plane. What is the direction of the magnetic force on the loop?

A. toward the top of the page

B. into the page

C. toward the right

D. toward the left

E. out of the page

59. An electron moves in a circular orbit of radius r in a magnetic field. The electron moves in a path perpendicular to the magnetic field. If the kinetic energy of the electron is doubled, what is the new radius of its path?

A. r/2

B. $\sqrt{2}\,r$

C. 2r

D. 4r

E. r/4

60. The diagram below shows two wires running parallel to the z-axis. One carries a current I towards the top of the page and intersects the x-axis at a distance of 3.0 meters from the origin. The other carries a current I towards the bottom of the page and intersects the y-axis at a distance of 4.0 meters from the origin.

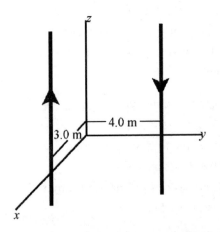

What is the magnitude of the magnetic field at the origin?

A. 0

B. $\dfrac{1}{12}\dfrac{\mu_0 I}{2\pi}$

C. $\dfrac{5}{12}\dfrac{\mu_0 I}{2\pi}$

D. $\dfrac{1}{5}\dfrac{\mu_0 I}{2\pi}$

E. $\dfrac{7}{12}\dfrac{\mu_0 I}{2\pi}$

61. In order for a magnetic field to exert a force on an object, which of the following can be true?

I. The object is charged.
II. The object is moving parallel to the field.
III. The object is moving perpendicular to the field.

A. I only
B. II only
C. III only
D. I and II only
E. I and III only

62. A current I flows around the wire below. Which segments of the wire affect the magnetic field at point P?

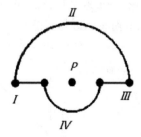

A. *I* and *III*

B. *II* and *IV*

C. *I, II* and *III*

D. *II, III* and *IV*

E. *I, II, III* and *IV*

63. The magnetic field inside a solenoid is *B*. A second solenoid has the same number of turns as the first one and is the same length, but its radius is twice the size of the radius of the first one. Both solenoids have the same current passing through them. The magnetic field inside the second solenoid is

A. *B*/4
B. *B*/2
C. *B*
D. 2*B*
E. 4*B*

64. A charged particle q can move with a constant velocity through a region containing both an electric field E and a magnetic field B (shown in Figure below) only if the

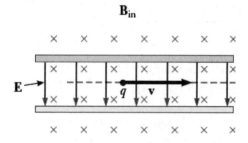

A. electric field and magnetic field are parallel. So it wouldn't happen.
B. moving charge has positive sign.
C. moving charge has negative sign.
D. velocity of the particle is $v = \dfrac{B}{E}$.
E. velocity of the particle is $v = \dfrac{E}{B}$.

65. A small object is dropped through a loop of wire connected to a sensitive ammeter on the edge of a table, as shown in the diagram below. A reading on the ammeter is most likely produced when the object falling through the loop of wire is a

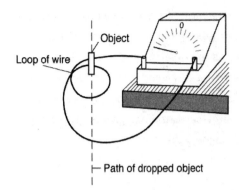

Object

Loop of wire

Path of dropped object

A. flashlight battery

B. bar magnet

C. brass mass

D. plastic ruler

E. pencil

66. Which of the three elements in an LRC series circuit always has (or have) non-negative power put into it (or them) during the operation of the circuit?

A. inductor

B. capacitor

C. resistor

D. inductor and capacitor

E. inductor and resistor

67. The diagram below shows two square loops of the same wire, with side lengths of a and $2a$. A uniform magnetic field B directed into the page is contained within the area enclosed by the square of side a.

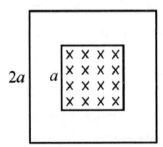

$2a$ a

The magnetic field B varies at a constant rate such that the current induced in the wire with side a is I. Find the current induced in the loop with side $2a$.

A. $I/4$

B. $I/2$

C. I

D. $2I$

E. $4I$

68. A flat ribbon of silver having a thickness t carries a steady current of I and is located in a uniform magnetic field B directed perpendicular to the plane of the ribbon. A potential difference is generated in a direction perpendicular to both the current and the magnetic field. For the four (front, back, up, bottom) surfaces of the silver ribbon, which one has the highest potential?

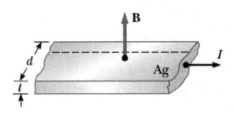

A. Up surface

B. Bottom surface

C. Front surface

D. Back surface

E. The four surfaces have equal potential.

69. A loop of wire is in a plane perpendicular to a magnetic field and is decreasing in diameter at a constant rate. The magnetic field is changing in magnitude such that no EMF is induced. Which of the following best shows the magnetic field?

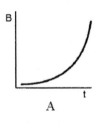

A

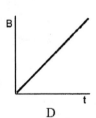

D

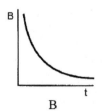

B

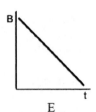

E

448

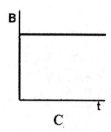

70. $\displaystyle\oint_L \vec{E} \cdot d\vec{l} = -\frac{d\phi_m}{dt}$ is one of Maxwell's equations. Choose the best statement that explains the equation.

A. A changing magnetic field produces an electric field.
B. A changing electric field creates a magnetic field.
C. The net electric flux through a closed surface depends on the charge enclosed.
D. The net magnetic flux through a closed surface depends on the current enclosed.
E. None of the above is true.

Directions: Answer all the three questions. The suggested time is about 15 minutes for answering each of the questions, which are worth 15 points each. The parts within a question may not have equal weight.

1. The long solid nonconducting cylinder of radius R shown below, with volume charge density ρ, contains a negative charge evenly distributed throughout the cylinder. Point P_1 is outside the cylinder at a distance r_1 from its center C and point P_2 is inside the cylinder at a distance r_2 from its center C.

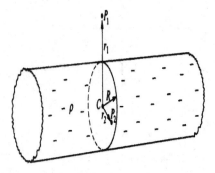

A. Derive expressions for both the electric field E inside and outside cylinder.

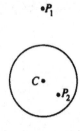

B. On the cross-sectional diagram above, draw vectors to indicate the electric field strength at points P_1 and P_2.

C. A negative charge q is placed at P_1, describe how the charge moving.

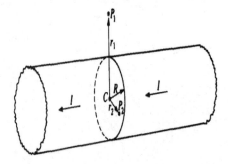

Another cylinder of the same dimensions, but made of conducting material, carries a total current I parallel to the length of the cylinder, as shown in the diagram above. The current density is uniform throughout the cross-sectional area of the cylinder.

D. Derive an expression for the magnetic field B both inside and outside the cylinder in terms of r, R, I, and fundamental constants.

E. On the cross-sectional diagram above (question B), in which the current is out of the plane of the page (toward the reader), draw vectors to indicate the magnetic field strength at the two points P_1 and P_2.

2. A capacitor with capacitance $c_1=2\ \mu F$ shown in the circuit below is fully charged by closing switch S_1 and keeping switch S_2 open, thus connecting the capacitor to the 2,000 volt power supply.

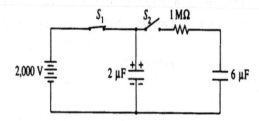

A. Determine the charge and the electrical energy stored in this fully charged capacitor.

At a later time, switch S_1 is opened. Switch S_2 is then closed, connecting the charged $2\ \mu F$ capacitor to a resistor with resistance R=1MΩ and a $C_2=6\ \mu F$ capacitor which is initially uncharged.

B. Determine the initial current in the resistor the instant after switch S_2 is closed.

The circuit reaches equilibrium after a long period of time.

C. Determine the charge on the positive plate of each of the capacitors at equilibrium.

D. Determine the total electrical energy stored in the two capacitors at equilibrium. Is the energy greater or less than the energy determined in part (A)? Why or why not?

3.

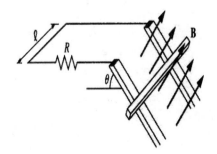

A conducting bar of mass m is placed on two long conducting rails a distance l apart. The rails are inclined at an angle θ with respect to the horizontal, as shown above, and the bar is able to slide on the rails with negligible friction. The bar and rails are in a uniform and constant magnetic field of magnitude B oriented perpendicular to the incline. A resistor of resistance R connects the upper ends of the rails and completes the circuit as shown. The bar is released from rest at the top of the incline. Both the bar and the rails have negligible resistance. And the rail is long enough.

A. Determine the constant final speed of the bar.

B. Express the speed of the bar as a function of time t from the time it is released at t = 0.

C. Suppose that the experiment is performed again, this time a second identical resistor connecting the rails at the bottom of the incline. Will this affect the final speed attained by the bar? Why?

Answers and Explanations

Mechanics

Section I: Multiple Choice Answers

1. B 2. A 3. D 4. A 5. A 6. C 7. E 8. D 9. D 10. B 11. C 12. A 13. D 14. C
15. E 16. C 17. D 18. D 19. D 20. C 21. B 22. B 23. E 24. C 25. C 26. D 27. B
28. D 29. E 30. E 31. B 32. D 33. C 34. B 35. B

Section I: Multiple Choice Explanations

1. B。 $\overline{v} = \dfrac{1000 + 1000}{\dfrac{1000}{80} + \dfrac{1000}{50}} = 61.5 m/s$ 。

2. A。 $v = \dfrac{dx}{dt} = -3 + 8t, a = \dfrac{dv}{dt} = 8m/s^2$ ，当 t=2s 时， $v > 0, a > 0$ 。

3. D。 $v = \dfrac{dx}{dt} =$ 常数且小于零。

4. A。 平面运动速度方程； $\vec{v} = \int_0 \vec{a}dt = \dfrac{9}{4}t^2\vec{i} + 3t^2\vec{j}$ ，位置方程； $\vec{r} = \int_0 \vec{v}dt = \dfrac{3}{4}t^3\vec{i} + t^3\vec{j}$ ，t=2s

    时的路程=位移（直线运动）， $\Delta s = \sqrt{x^2(2) + y^2(2)} = 10m$ 。

5. A。 飞机和直升机的速度分别为 $\vec{v_p}, \vec{v_h}$ ，飞机相对直升机的速度 $\vec{v_{ph}} = \vec{v_p} - \vec{v_h}$ 。

    $v_{ph} = \sqrt{90^2 + 20^2} > 90m/s$ ，方向由直升机指向飞机。

6. C。 $W = (6i - 2j) \cdot (3i + j) = 16J$ 。

7. E。（50+mg）/mg=3，m=2.5kg。

8. D。 两物体间的作用力为 T。F-T=2a，且 F=6a。解得 T=2F/3。

9. D。 $\mu mg = m\dfrac{v^2}{R}, \mu = \dfrac{v^2}{Rg}$ 。

10. B。 绳子中的张力 F= $m\dfrac{v^2}{r}$ ，周期 T= $\dfrac{2\pi r}{v} \rightarrow F = \dfrac{4m\pi^2 r}{T^2}$ 。

11. C。 小球做平抛运动。

12. A。 $F = -bv = ma = m\dfrac{dv}{dt}, \rightarrow v = v_0 e^{-\frac{b}{m}t}$。

13. D。 $x = \int_0^\infty v\,dt = \int_0^\infty v_0 e^{-\frac{b}{m}t}dt$，当 $t \rightarrow \infty, x = L = \dfrac{m}{b}v_0$。

14. C。摩擦力 f=50cos35=41N，支持力 N=16*10+60sin30=190N，$\mu = \dfrac{f}{N} = 0.22$。

15. E。 $v = \dfrac{dx}{dt} = 3t^2 - 2t, a = \dfrac{dv}{dt} = 6t - 2$，t=3s 时，F=ma=16000N。

16. C。 P=Fv，$F = \dfrac{1}{2}t^2 - 1$。

17. D。 $y_{cm} = \dfrac{1(1) + 2(-2) + 4(-1)}{1 + 2 + 4} = -1m$。

18. D。三颗卫星分开后的动量和保持常数。a, b, c 选项在特殊情况下可成立。

19. D。棒的总质量：$M = \int_0^L bx^2 dx = \dfrac{1}{3}bL^3$；

转动惯量：$dI = x^2 bx^2 dx, I = \int_0^L bx^4 dx = \dfrac{1}{5}bL^5 = \dfrac{3}{5}ML^2$；

质心：$x_c = \dfrac{\int_0^L bx^3 dx}{M} = \dfrac{3}{4}L$。

20. C。 $\dfrac{dP}{dt} = F = $常数，F=ma，所以 a 是常数。

21. B。光滑竖直墙面施加水平方向支持力作用于梯子上 N_2；水平地面施加于梯子竖直向上的支持力 N_1 和指向光滑竖直墙的静摩擦力 $f = \mu N_1$。梯子不滑动处于平衡状态，有力平衡：

$mg = N_1$，竖直方向；$f = N_2$，水平方向。

力矩平衡（地面上的支撑点）：$N_2 L\sin\theta - mg\dfrac{L}{2}\cos\theta = 0$，

求得：$\mu = 0.29$。

22. B。 $\tau = mg\dfrac{l}{2}\sin\theta = \dfrac{1}{3}ml^2\alpha, \alpha = \dfrac{3g}{2l}\sin\theta$。

23. E。 Tl sinθ=mg$l$/2，$\rightarrow T = \dfrac{mg}{2\sin\theta}$。

24. C。 $\Delta\theta = \dfrac{1}{2}\alpha t_1^2, \alpha = 4$ rad/s^2；$\omega = \alpha t_2 = 4*2 = 8$ rad/s。

25. C。机械能守恒定律：$mgh = \dfrac{1}{2}mv^2 + \dfrac{1}{2}(mR^2)(\dfrac{v}{R})^2$，$\rightarrow v = 7m/s$。转动动能

$$= \frac{1}{2}(mR^2)(\frac{v}{R})^2 = \frac{1}{2}mv^2 = 49J。$$

26. D。角动量守恒：$\omega' = 2\omega$。

27. B。$m_1 g R_1 - m_2 g R_2 = I\alpha, a_1 = R_1 \alpha = \frac{m_1 R_1 - m_2 R_2}{I} R_1 g$。

28. D。$T = 2\pi \sqrt{\frac{L}{g}}$，与质量无关，不变；碰撞后动能要降低，最大高度亦减小。

29. E。开普勒第三定律：$\frac{T_1^2}{R_1^3} = \frac{T_2^2}{R_2^3}$，$\rightarrow T_2 = \sqrt{(\frac{R_2}{R_1})^3} = 8hr$。

30. E。向心加速度 $a_c = \frac{v^2}{D/2}$。

31. B。机械能守恒定律：$-G\frac{mM}{2R_E} = -G\frac{mM}{R_E} + \frac{1}{2}mv^2$，$v = \sqrt{G\frac{M}{R_E}} = \sqrt{gR_E}$。

32. D。机械能守恒：$\frac{1}{2}kA^2 = \frac{1}{2}k(\frac{A}{2})^2 + \frac{1}{2}mv^2$，$\rightarrow \frac{m}{k} = \frac{1}{12}$，$\rightarrow T = 2\pi\sqrt{\frac{m}{k}} = 1.81s$。

33. C。$x(t) = 3.0\cos(\frac{5\pi}{4}t + \frac{\pi}{6})$，周期 $T = 2\pi / \frac{5\pi}{4} = 1.6s$，$v_{max} = A\omega = 3*\frac{5\pi}{4} \approx 12m/s$。

34. B。摆角为 θ 时，转动系统所受和外力矩 $\tau = -(MgL\sin\theta + Mg\frac{L}{2}\sin\theta) \approx -\frac{3}{2}MgL\theta$，系统

的转动惯量 $I = ML^2 + \frac{1}{3}ML^2 = \frac{4}{3}ML^2$；由转动定律得 $\frac{d^2\theta}{dt^2} = -\frac{9g}{8L}\theta$，$\rightarrow T = \frac{4\pi}{3}\sqrt{\frac{2L}{g}}$。

35. B。$mv_0 = 3mv$，求得 $v = \frac{v_0}{3}$。$\Delta E_k = \frac{1}{2}mv_0^2 - \frac{1}{2}3m(\frac{1}{3}v_0)^2 = \frac{1}{3}mv_0^2$。

Section II: Free Response Explanations

1. A. 平衡点发生在 $\frac{dU}{dr} = 0$ 位置处，由图中可知：

其中 r=1.5mm 和 r=3.2mm 点是稳定平衡点，

r=2.4mm 是非稳平衡点，

r>5mm 的点是中性平衡点。

B. 粒子将可能被限制在：0.2<r<5mm；此时粒子总能量 E=1J。

C. 粒子总能量 E=-3J，粒子将被限制在 0.5<r<3.5mm 范围内运动。

D. 粒子最大动能 K=3J。

E. 具有最大动能的位置是：r=1.5mm。

F. E=1-(-3)=4J。

2. A. 在半径为 r 处选取小面元 ds=$rd\theta dr$，其质量 dm=$\dfrac{M}{\pi R^2} rd\theta dr$，ds 转动过程中所受摩擦

力大小为：$df=\mu gdm$，摩擦力矩大小为：$d\tau=rdf=\mu g\dfrac{M}{\pi R^2}r^2 d\theta dr$。圆盘转动中所受

总的摩擦力矩：$\tau=\displaystyle\int_0^{2\pi}d\theta\int_0^R\mu g\dfrac{M}{\pi R^2}r^2 dr=\dfrac{2}{3}\mu MgR$。

B. 转动定律：$\tau=I\alpha$，角加速度 $\alpha=\dfrac{4}{3}\dfrac{\mu g}{R}$。

C. $\omega=\omega_0-\alpha t$ =0，t=$\dfrac{\omega_0}{\alpha}=\dfrac{3R}{4\mu g}$。经过 t 时间圆盘停止转动。

3. A. $E_A=\dfrac{1}{2}mv_0^2-G\dfrac{mM_e}{a}$。

B. 角动量守恒：$mv_0a=mv_Bb$，$\rightarrow v_B=\dfrac{a}{b}v_0$。

C. 圆周运动万有引力作为向心力：$G\dfrac{mM_e}{a^2}=m\dfrac{v_A^2}{a}$，$\rightarrow v_A=\sqrt{\dfrac{GM_e}{a}}$。

D. 总机械能：E=$-G\dfrac{mM_e}{2a}$。

Electricity and Magnetism

Section I: Multiple Choice Answers

36. D　37. B　38. A　39. D　40. A　41. D　42. D　43. A　44. E　45. E　46. D　47. A　48. D
49. A　50. B　51. A　52. C　53. D　54. A　55. B　56. B　57. B　58. D　59. B　60. C　61. E
62. B　63. C　64. E　65. B　66. C　67. B　68. D　69. D　70. A

Section I: Multiple choice Explanations

36. D。距离Q为d的点电荷受到电场力F=$\dfrac{1}{4\pi\varepsilon_0}\dfrac{qQ}{d^2}$，当两个点电荷相距3d时，相互作用的电场

力变为原来的1/9。

37. B。电场强度与等势面垂直，指向电势降落的方向。$E=-dV/dr$，与所在点的电势值无关。

38. A。场强大小为 $\dfrac{\sqrt{3}Q^2}{4\pi\varepsilon_0 d^2}$，方向向上。

39. D。由对称性分析可知，圆心处的场强方向向上，答案在A、D之间选。A选项给出的是点电荷的场强，由对称性分析可知，带电半圆环在圆心处的场强的大小要小于A选项的值，所以选D。D选项的值可由积分运算得到。

40. A。由场强和电势关系得 $E= -dV/dr=\dfrac{\lambda}{2\pi\varepsilon_0 r}$。

41. D。两极板间的电势差$V= Ed =\dfrac{\sigma}{\varepsilon_0}$d，电场力的功$qV=\dfrac{1}{2}mv^2$，所以选D。

42. D。电场力的功等于电势能增量的负值：$W=-\Delta U\rangle$ 0，所以$\Delta U<0$。

43. A。平行板电容器的电容$C=\dfrac{\varepsilon_0 S}{d}$，极板面积加倍可使电容值加倍。

44. E。$E=\dfrac{1}{4\pi\varepsilon_0}\dfrac{1}{r^2}$. 以半径为r做同心球形高斯面，高斯面上的场强只与面内包围的电荷成正比，

由高斯定理：$E\,4\pi r^2=\dfrac{Q_1}{\varepsilon_0}=\dfrac{1}{\varepsilon_0}$，E的方向沿半径向外，所以选E。

45. E。两球面的电势分别为$V_1=\dfrac{1}{4\pi\varepsilon_0}\dfrac{Q}{R_1}$，$V_2=\dfrac{1}{4\pi\varepsilon_0}\dfrac{Q}{R_2}$。如果$R_1>R_2$，那么$V_1<V_2$。电荷将从高电势$V_2$流向低电势，直到两球体电势相同，电荷不再流动。

46. D。电容器储能$U=\dfrac{1}{2}CV^2$ =2*10⁻³ J。

47. A。平板电容器电容 $C=\dfrac{\kappa\varepsilon_0 S}{d}$ =6C₀，V=Q/C=6V₀。

48. D。电流从电源直接流入地面，I=V/R=3A。

49. A。钻头的电阻$R=\rho\dfrac{l}{A}$，正比于长度l，反比于截面积A。

50. B。$I=dq/dt=vdt\lambda / dt = v\lambda$。

51. A。电荷获得能量U，电势差将发生改变：$U=q\Delta V$。

52. C。 $\phi_e = \oint_S \vec{E} \cdot d\vec{s} = \dfrac{q_{encl}}{\varepsilon_0} = 0$，所以必有 $q_{encl} = 0$。

53. D。 $\Delta V = -\int_0^{10} E(r)dr = 650V$。

54. A。RC电路稳定时，电容等效于断路。

55. B。电容器上的电压等于最右面的电阻上的电压。

56. B。电路刚刚接通时，电感等效于开路。电路中流过R₁的电流为 I，$I_2 = 0$。

57. B。无限长平行导线通以同向电流，相互作用力是引力。

58. D。通电线圈进入磁场受力为F=ILB，方向向左。

59. B。运动电荷在磁场中做匀速圆周运动，轨道半径r= $\dfrac{mv}{qB}$。当电荷的动能加倍时，其运动速度变为 $\sqrt{2}v$，半径也变为原来的 $\sqrt{2}$ 倍。

60. C。穿过y轴的电流产生的磁场垂直于y轴，大小为B_y= $\dfrac{\mu_0 I}{2\pi*4}$；穿过x轴的电流产生的磁场垂直于x轴，大小为B_x= $\dfrac{\mu_0 I}{2\pi*3}$。这两个相互垂直的场强合成大小为B= $\sqrt{B_x^2 + B_y^2} = \dfrac{5}{12}\dfrac{\mu_0 I}{2\pi}$

61. E。在磁场中运动的粒子，带有电荷、有垂直于磁场方向的速度分量，才会受到磁场力作用。

62. B。1、3电流导线的延长线通过圆心，所以在圆心处产生的场强为零。2、4电流导线是两个半径不等的半圆环，在圆心处产生的磁场方向一致。

63. C。通电长直螺线管内部为匀强磁场，B= $\mu_0 nI$。B与通过的电流强度 I 和缠绕密度n成正比。与螺线管的半径无关。

64. E。带正电运动电荷进入电磁场受磁场力F=qvB（向上），电场力F=qE（向下），两个力相等V= $\dfrac{E}{B}$ 时，电荷水平穿过电磁场，没有偏转。如果电荷带的是负电，情况相同。

65. B。运动的磁铁使导体线圈中的磁通量发生改变，产生感应电流。其他物体不行。

66. C。电容器中的电场能量和电感中的磁场能量，不断转化，功率有时正有时负。但电阻始终消耗电能，功率永远为正。

67. B。边长为a的方框中的感应电流为 $I = \dfrac{1}{R}\dfrac{d\phi}{dt} = \dfrac{a^2}{R}\dfrac{dB}{dt}$ ，边长为2a的方框中的感应电流为

$$I_2 = \frac{1}{R_2}\frac{d\phi}{dt} = \frac{a^2}{2R}\frac{dB}{dt} = \frac{I}{2}$$

68. D。导体中的自由电子的定向运动速度与电流方向相反，在磁场中受力后向前面漂移，最后在通电导体的前后面形成电势差，前面是低电势，后面是高电势。这个电势差叫做霍尔电压。

69. D。感应电动势 $\varepsilon = \dfrac{d(BS)}{dt} = \pi r^2 \dfrac{dB}{dt} + B2\pi r \dfrac{dr}{dt} = 0$ ，有 $\dfrac{dB}{dt} = -\dfrac{2B}{r}\dfrac{dr}{dt}$ 。半径以恒定速率减小，磁场加速升高。

70. A。法拉第电磁感应定理。变化的磁场激发感生电场。

Section II: Free Response Explanations

1. A. r<R：在柱形带电体内截取长为L半径为r的同轴柱形高斯面，由高斯定理

$$E* 2\pi r = \frac{1}{\varepsilon_0}\rho\pi r^2 L \text{ ，求得：} E = \frac{\rho}{2\varepsilon_0}r \text{ ，指向圆柱轴线。}$$

r>R：在柱形带电体外部截取长为L半径为r的同轴柱形高斯面，由高斯定理

$$E* 2\pi r = \frac{1}{\varepsilon_0}\rho\pi R^2 L \text{ ，求得：} E = \frac{\rho R^2}{2\varepsilon_0 r} \text{ ，指向圆柱体轴线。}$$

B. 电场强度指向C点，在P_2点E的值大。

C. 负电荷在P_1点受力垂直于轴线向外，加速远离，图中向上运动。

D. r<R：在柱形带电体内截取半径为r的同心圆环回路，由安培定律

$$B* 2\pi r = \mu_0 \frac{I}{\pi R^2}\pi r^2 \text{ ，求得：} B = \frac{\mu_0 I}{2\pi R^2}r \text{ ，指向回路切线。}$$

r>R：在柱形带电体外选取半径为r的同心圆环回路，由安培定律

$$B* 2\pi r = \mu_0 I \text{ ，求得：} B = \frac{\mu_0 I}{2\pi r} \text{ ，指向回路切线。}$$

E. P_1和P_2点的磁感应强度逆时针沿切线方向。

2. A. 电容器充电后所带电量为Q=cV=4mC，电容器储存能量为E=$\frac{1}{2}cV^2$=4J。

B. 电路刚接通时，电阻中流过的电流：$I = \frac{V}{R} = \frac{2000}{1*10^6} = 2mA$。

C. 电路达到平衡时，电阻中的电流为零，两电容器上的电压相同$V_1 = V_2$。

$$Q = Q_1 + Q_2$$

$$\frac{Q_1}{c_1} = \frac{Q_2}{c_2}，求得$$

$$Q_1 = 1mC, \quad Q_2 = 3mC$$

D. 两电容器上储存的能量分别为：

$$E_1 = \frac{1}{2}\frac{Q_1^2}{c_1} = 0.25J$$

$$E_2 = \frac{1}{2}\frac{Q_2^2}{c_2} = 0.75J$$

$$E_1 + E_2 = 1J < E = 4J，电阻R消耗能量4-1=3J。$$

3. A. 当导体棒以恒定速度V沿斜面下滑时，导体中的感应电动势$\varepsilon = BlV$。

闭合电路中的电流为：$I = \frac{\varepsilon}{R} = \frac{BlV}{R}$

此时导体棒受安培力：F=$IlB = \frac{VB^2l^2}{R}$，方向沿斜面向上。

此时导体棒沿斜面方向所受合力为零：$mg\sin\theta - \frac{VB^2l^2}{R} = 0$

解之得：$V = \frac{mgR\sin\theta}{B^2l^2}$

B. t=0时，v=0。任意时刻的速度为 v，沿斜面向下。此时导体棒所受合外力

$$mg\sin\theta - \frac{vB^2l^2}{R} = m\frac{dv}{dt}$$，解此微分方程得

$$v = \frac{mgR\sin\theta}{B^2l^2}(1 - e^{-\frac{B^2l^2}{mR}t})$$

C. 有影响。

导体棒中的电动势仍然是：$\varepsilon = BlV$

但流过导体棒的电流将变为：$I = \frac{\varepsilon}{R/2} = \frac{2BlV}{R}$

导体棒所受安培力：F= $IlB = 2\frac{VB^2l^2}{R}$

导体匀速下滑的速度：$V = \frac{mgR\sin\theta}{2B^2l^2}$

任意时刻的速度：$v = \frac{mgR\sin\theta}{2B^2l^2}(1 - e^{-2\frac{B^2l^2}{mR}t})$

Model test 3

Mechanics

Section I: Multiple Choice Questions—Questions 1-35 (45 minutes)

Directions: Each multiple choice question is followed by five answer choices. For each question, choose the best answer and fill in the corresponding oval on the answer sheet.

1. Two skaters, one of mass 75 kg, the other of mass 50 kg, stand next to each other on ice (negligible friction). If the heavier skater pushes the lighter with a force F, the ratio of the force felt by the lighter to the force felt by the heavier is

    A. 1:3
    B. 2:3
    C. 1:1
    D. 3:2
    E. 3:1

2. An object moves along the x-axis with a velocity $v(t) = t^2 - 3t + 2$, where v is in m/s and t is in seconds. What is the total distance traveled during the time interval $0 < t < 2$ s?

    A. 0.1 m
    B. 0.67 m
    C. 0.5 m
    D. 1.0 m
    E. 2.0 m

3. A particle undergoes acceleration **a** while moving from point 1 to point 2. Which of the choices shows the velocity vector **v₂** as the object moves away from point 2?

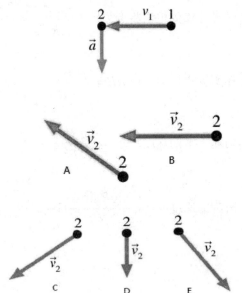

4. An object is moving in the xy-plane according to the equations $x(t) = 3sin(3t)$ and $y(t) = 4cos(3t)$. What is the maximum magnitude of the particle's acceleration?

    A. 5 m/s^2
    B. 15 m/s^2
    C. 30 m/s^2
    D. 36 m/s^2
    E. 45 m/s^2

5. Which of the following statements is true concerning the motion of an ideal projectile launched at an initial speed v_0 and angle of elevation θ to the horizontal?

A. the speed at the top of the trajectory is zero.
B. The object's speed remains constant during the entire flight.
C. The horizontal speed decreases on the way up and increases on the way down.
D. The acceleration vector points opposite to the velocity vector on the way up and in the same direction as the velocity vector on the way down.
E. The vertical speed decreases on the way up and increases in the way down.

6. A particle is moving in x-y plane along the curve below with a constant x-component of velocity given by dx/dt=constant. The components of this particle's acceleration are:

A. $a_x > 0$, $a_y > 0$.
B. $a_x = 0$, $a_y > 0$.
C. $a_x < 0$, $a_y > 0$.
D. $a_x = 0$, $a_y < 0$.
E. $a_x < 0$, $a_y < 0$.

7. A ball rolling across a flat, horizontal table has a velocity of v_1. After it leaves the edge of the table, the ball continues to travel with a constant horizontal velocity as it begins to fall. Just before the ball hits the ground, it has a net velocity of v_2. The ball's vertical speed at this moment is

A. v_2

B. $v_1 + v_2$

C. $v_2 - v_1$

D. $\sqrt{v_2^2 + v_1^2}$

E. $\sqrt{v_2^2 - v_1^2}$

8. A 20 kg block is held at rest on a ramp that makes an angle 30º with the horizontal. The coefficient of static friction between the block and the ramp is 0.7 and the coefficient of kinetic friction is 0.6. If the block is released, it will

A. remain stationary.
B. begin to accelerate down the ramp, then decelerate and stop.
C. accelerate down the ramp.
D. move down the ramp with constant velocity.
E. accelerate down the ramp until it reaches a terminal velocity, then remain traveling at that constant velocity.

9. A solid sphere with mass m and radius r has a rotational inertia of $\frac{2}{5}mr^2$ when rotated about a line passing through the center of the sphere. What is the rotational inertia of the sphere when it is rotated about an axis tangent to its surface?

A. $\frac{2}{5}mr^2$

B. $\frac{3}{5}mr^2$

C. $\frac{7}{5}mr^2$

D. $\dfrac{12}{5}mr^2$

E. $\dfrac{14}{5}mr^2$

10. A 10 g rubber ball and a 10 g clay ball are thrown at a wall with equal speeds. The rubber ball bounces, the clay ball sticks. Which statement is true about the impulse on the wall?

A. The clay ball exerts a larger impulse because it sticks.

B. The rubber ball exerts a larger impulse because it bounces.

C. The impulse on the wall is less than the impulse on the rubber ball or the clay ball.

D. They exert equal impulses because they have equal momenta.

E. Neither exerts an impulse on the wall because the wall doesn't move.

11. A toy car of mass 2 kg moving in a straight path, a net force given by a function F=-4t+2 (N) is acting on the car. The initial velocity of the car is 6 m/s at time t=0 in the positive direction. The time the car will come instantaneously to rest and the maximum velocity the car can have are respectively

A. t=1/2s, v_{max} =6.25m/s

B. t=2s, v_{max} =8.00m/s

C. t=3s, v_{max} =6.25m/s

D. t=1/2s, v_{max} =7.25m/s

E. t=3s, v_{max} =7.25m/s

12. Which of the following is true of the velocity and acceleration vectors of an object moving with a uniform speed in a circular path?

A. They are in opposite directions.

B. They are always equal in magnitude.

C. They are perpendicular in direction.

D. They are both tangent to the path of motion.

E. They are both directed toward the center of the circle.

13. A block A with mass m_A is stacked on the top of a block B with mass m_B. There is no friction between the block B and the horizontal surface. But there is a friction between the two blocks. A force F is acting on the block B. The minimum static coefficient of friction between the two blocks which will prevent the block A sliding off is

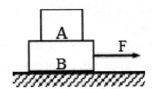

A. $\dfrac{F}{m_A g}$

B. $\dfrac{F}{m_B g}$

C. $\dfrac{F}{(m_A - m_B)g}$

D. $\dfrac{F}{(m_A + m_B)g}$

E. $\dfrac{F}{(m_B - m_A)g}$

14. A 1.0 kg object is moving along the x-axis in a region where its potential energy as a function of x is given by U(x)=2(x-1)^2, where x is in meters and U is in Joules. When the

object passes the point x=1.5 m, its velocity is +1m/s. The x-coordinate of any points at which the object has zero kinetic energy is (are)

A. $x = 1 \pm \dfrac{\sqrt{2}}{2}$

B. $x = \pm \dfrac{\sqrt{2}}{2}$

C. $x = 0$

D. $x = \pm 1$

E. $x = 1$

15. If an object sliding on a rough surface experiences an increase in kinetic energy of E while it is pushed by a constant force F through a distance d, what is the magnitude of the friction force?

A. $Fd - E$
B. $(Fd - E)/d$
C. $(F - E)/d$
D. Fd
E. $E/d - F$

16. An object with a mass of 4 kg is released from rest at the top of a ramp with length 10 m that makes an angle of 30º with the horizontal. The coefficient of kinetic friction between the block and the ramp is 0.4. The speed the block will have when it has traveled 5 m down the ramp is most nearly

A. 3.9 m/s
B. 5.6 m/s
C. 7 m/s
D. 7.9 m/s
E. 10.4 m/s

17. A force given by $F(x) = 6x + 3x^2$ acts upon a projectile that starts from rest at the origin. How much work is done on the 5 kg

projectile if it travels 5 m?

A. 155 J
B. 175 J
C. 200 J
D. 225 J
E. 400 J

18. An object that starts at rest from the origin is pushed by a constant force of 10 N which has a position given by $x(t) = 5t^2$. The power delivered to the object by the force at time

$t = 1s$ is

A. 50 J
B. 50 W
C. 100 J
D. 100 W
E. 125 W

19.

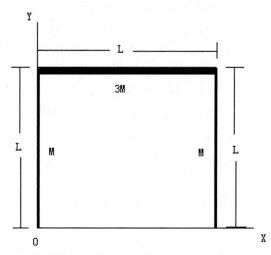

Three thin rods, each of length L, are arranged in an inverted U, as shown above. Each of the two rods on the arms of the U has mass M; the third rod has mass 3M. The center of mass of the assembly is located at

A. $\left(\dfrac{L}{2}, \dfrac{L}{2}\right)$

B. $\left(\dfrac{L}{2}, \dfrac{4}{5}L\right)$

C. $(\dfrac{L}{2}, \dfrac{3}{4}L)$

D. $(\dfrac{L}{4}, \dfrac{2}{5}L)$

E. $(\dfrac{L}{4}, \dfrac{2}{3}L)$

20.

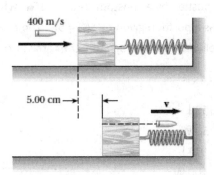

A 5.00 g bullet moving with an initial speed of 400 m/s is fired into and passes through a 1.00 kg block, as shown above. The block, initially at rest on a frictionless, horizontal surface, is connected to a spring with force constant 900 N/m. If the block moves 5.00 cm to the right after impact, the speed at which the bullet emerges from the block is

A. 100m/s
B. 200m/s
C. 300m/s
D. 399m/s
E. 1.99m/s

21. A small block of mass m is placed on a long slab of mass M. Initially, the slab is at rest and the block has a speed v to the right. The coefficient of kinetic friction between the block and the slab is μ and there is no friction between the slab and the horizontal surface on which it moves. Some time later, before the block reaches the right end of the slab, both the block and the slab attain identical speeds. The distance the slab has traveled at the moment it reaches the same speed with the small block is

A. $x = \dfrac{v^2}{2\mu g}$

B. $x = \dfrac{mM}{2\mu g(m+M)^2} v^2$

C. $x = \dfrac{m}{2\mu g(m+M)} v^2$

D. $x = \dfrac{M}{\mu g(m+M)} v^2$

E. $x = \dfrac{mM}{\mu g(m+M)^2} v^2$

22. A ball of mass m bounces off of a wall with the same speed v that it had initially. If the ball was in contact with the wall for a time t and during this time an average force F was applied to it, then the angle made between the wall and the ball's trajectory is

A. Ft/mv
B. $\cos^{-1}(Ft/mv)$
C. $\cos^{-1}(Ft/2mv)$
D. $\sin^{-1}(Ft/mv)$
E. $\sin^{-1}(Ft/2mv)$

23. A uniform, horizontal beam of length 6.0 m and weight 120 N is attached at one end to a wall by a pin connection (so that it may rotate). A cable attached to the wall above the pin supports the opposite end. The cable makes an angle of 60^0 with the horizontal. The tension in the cable needed to maintain the beam in equilibrium is

A. 35 N
B. 69 N
C. 60 N
D. 120 N
E. 150 N

24. A Ferris wheel, rotating initially at an angular speed of 0.10 rad/s, accelerates over a 5.00s interval at a rate of 0.020rad/s^2. What angular displacement does the Ferris wheel undergo in this 5s interval?

A. 0.75 rad
B. 1.5 rad
C. 3.0 rad
D. 0.50 rad
E. 0.25 rad

25. Two masses, one with mass m and the other with mass 2m, are attached to a light rigid rod as shown below. When the system is released from rest the rod begins to rotate with an angular acceleration of

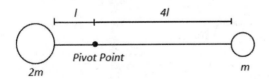

A. g/7L
B. g/5L
C. g/4L
D. g/8L
E. g/9L

26. The angular velocity of a wheel is given by $\omega(t) = 2.0t + 1.0t^3$. How many revolutions does the wheel make between time t = 1.0 s and time t = 2.0 s?

A. 15
B. 1.1
C. 51
D. 26
E. 9.0

Questions 27-28

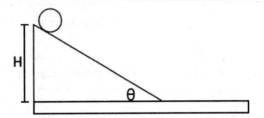

A ball of mass M and radius R with rotational inertia (2/5) MR^2 is released from rest at the top of an incline of height H at an angle θ. There is friction between the ball and incline so that the ball rolls down without slipping.

27. What is the acceleration of the ball as it rolls down the incline?

A. g/2
B. gsin θ
C. μmgcos θ
D. mgsin θ
E. 5(gsin θ)/7

28. How fast is the ball traveling at the bottom of the incline?

A. 2gH
B. gH
C. (10gH/7)$^{1/2}$
D. (2gH)$^{1/2}$
E. (H/g)$^{1/2}$

29. A solid disk of mass M and radius R is spinning with an angular velocity of ω when a disk of the same radius but mass m is placed on top. Finally they spin with the same angular velocity. The new angular velocity is

A. $\omega M/2(m+M)$
B. $\omega M/(m+M)$
C. $\omega M/2M$
D. $\omega M/2m$
E. $2\omega M/(m+M)$

30. Which of the following statements explains why astronauts feel weightless while orbiting the Earth?

A. The centripetal force on the astronaut is zero.
B. The gravitational pull of the sun cancels out the gravitational pull from the Earth.
C. The spaceship is in freefall.
D. The force of gravity decreases as the astronaut travels further away from the Earth.
E. The spaceship is traveling with a constant velocity.

31. A satellite of mass m is orbiting at a distance R_E above the surface of the Earth. The Earth's mass is M_E. How much work would be required to move the satellite from R_E above the Earth to another circular orbit which is $2R_E$ above the surface of the Earth?

A. $G\dfrac{mM_E}{2R_E}$

B. $\dfrac{1}{12}G\dfrac{mM_E}{R_E}$

C. $\dfrac{1}{6}G\dfrac{mM_E}{R_E}$

D. $G\dfrac{mM_E}{R_E}$

E. $\dfrac{1}{12}G\dfrac{M_E}{R_E}$

32. A satellite orbits the Earth at a distance of 1 Earth radius from the surface. Its velocity is v. If the satellite moves and enters a new orbit at 3 Earth radii from the Earth's surface, its new velocity will be

A. $\dfrac{v}{2}$

B. $\sqrt{3}\,v$

C. $\sqrt{2}\,v$

D. $\dfrac{v}{\sqrt{3}}$

E. $\dfrac{v}{\sqrt{2}}$

33. A restoring force that acts on a mass m is given by the equation $F(x) = -ax+bx^2$. For small amplitudes, the mass moves in simple harmonic motion with a period T. The period is

A. $2\pi\sqrt{\dfrac{a}{m}}$

B. $2\pi\sqrt{\dfrac{m}{2b-a}}$

C. $2\pi\sqrt{\dfrac{m}{2b}}$

D. $2\pi\sqrt{\dfrac{b}{m}}$

E. $2\pi\sqrt{\dfrac{m}{a}}$

34. A simple harmonic oscillator with mass m=1kg has the position function given by x(t) = 0.5sin (2t), where x is in meters and t is in seconds. At t= π /6 s, the kinetic energy of the oscillator is

A. $\dfrac{1}{8}$ J

B. $\dfrac{1}{2}$ J

C. 1J

D. 2J

E. 8J

35. A "seconds pendulum" is one that moves through its equilibrium position once each second. Anther pendulum has twice the length of a seconds pendulum. We know that the period of the pendulum is

A. 1s

B. $\sqrt{2}$ s

C. 2s

D. 2$\sqrt{2}$ s

E. 4s

Section II: Free Response Questions—Questions 1-3 (45 minutes)

Directions: Answer all the three questions. The suggested time is about 15 minutes for answering each of the questions, which are worth 15 points each. The parts within a question may not have equal weight.

1.

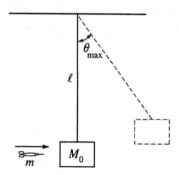

A dart of mass m is fired with the gun very close to a wooden block of mass M_0 which hangs from a cord of length l and negligible mass, as shown above. Assume the size of the block is negligible compared to l, and the dart is moving horizontally when it hits the block at its center and becomes embedded in it. The block swings up to a maximum angle θ_{max} from the vertical.

A. What is the speed v_0 of the dart immediately before it strikes the block?
B. The dart and block subsequently swing as a pendulum. Determine the tension in the cord after the collision.
C. If the motion of the mass system can be considered as SHM after the collision, how long will the block's first return to the lowest point of the swing take after the collision?
D. Determine the equation which could represent the angle that the pendulum makes with the vertical as a function of time t.

2

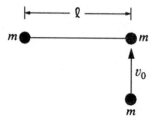

These objects with equal mass m are assembled on a frictionless surface, as shown in the above (top view). Two objects are connected with a length l rod which has negligible mass. Assume that the sizes of the masses are much smaller than the separation of them. The single object moving with velocity v_0 perpendicularly strikes and sticks to the right object connected with the rod.

A. What is the velocity of the center of mass before the collision?
B. What is the velocity of the center of mass immediately after the collision?
C. What is the angular speed of the system after the collision?
D. Determine the total energy of the system after the collision.

3.

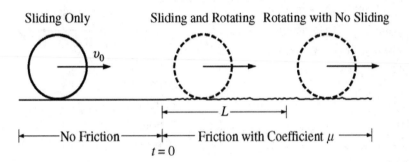

A cylinder of mass M and radius R is initially sliding on a frictionless surface at constant velocity v_0 to the direction perpendicular to its center axis, and the motion of the cross section of the cylinder is shown in the diagram above. At time t=0 it moves into a surface with coefficient μ and starts to rotate with sliding. After it travels a distance L on the rough surface, the cylinder begins rolling without slipping.

A. What is the linear velocity v and angular velocity ω of the cylinder as a function of time t while it is sliding and rotating?
B. How long will it take the cylinder to travel the distance L?
C. What is the angular velocity of the cylinder when it begins rolling without slipping?
D. Find the expression of the distance L in terms of other given quantities.

Electricity and Magnetism

Section I: Multiple Choice Questions—Questions 36-70 (45 minutes)

Directions: Each multiple choice question is followed by five answer choices. For each question, choose the best answer and fill in the corresponding oval on the answer sheet.

36. Three charges lie on a straight line. A 30 μc charge is 1.5m to the east of a -8 μc charge and 3m to the east of a +24 μc. What is the net electric force on the 30 μc charge?

    A. 0.24N west
    B. 0.24N east
    C. 0.36N west
    D. 0.36N east
    E. zero

37. Point a and point b are at the same electric potential. What can you conclude about the electric field between point a and point b?

    A. The electric field between point a and point b is zero everywhere.
    B. The electric field always points perpendicular to the line between point a and point b.
    C. Given a path from a to b, if the field has a component in the direction of the path in some region, it must have a component opposite to the path somewhere else.
    D. The electric field between point a and point b is constant.
    E. Nothing can be concluded about the electric field.

38. In the diagram below with charges of –q and +3q a distance 2L, at which of the points would a positive test charge most likely feel no electrostatic force?

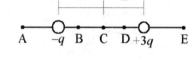

    A. Point A
    B. Point B
    C. Point C
    D. Point D
    E. Point E

39. Identical electric charges of +q are placed at the points (r,0,0), (0,r,0) and (0,0,r). What is the magnitude of the electric field at the origin?

    A. $6\dfrac{kq}{r^2}$

    B. $3\dfrac{kq}{r^2}$

    C. $\sqrt{3}\,\dfrac{kq}{r^2}$

    D. $6\dfrac{kq}{r}$

    E. $\sqrt{3}\,\dfrac{kq}{r}$

40. If the electric potential of a system is given by the equation $V(r) = 5\ln(r^2)$, what is the equation for the electric field in this system?

    A. $5\ln(r^2)/r$
    B. $-5r\ln(r^2)$
    C. $5/r^2$
    D. $-10/r$
    E. $10/r^2$

41. Which of the following statements is/are true?

I. If the electric field at a certain point is zero, then the electrostatic force on a charge at the same point is also zero.

II. If the electrostatic force on a charge at a certain point is zero, and then the electric potential at the same point is zero.

III. The electric potential is inversely proportional to the strength of the electric field.

A. I only
B. II only
C. III only
D. I and II only
E. None of the above is true.

42. The graph below shows the relationship between the work done on a charged body in an electric field and the net charge on the body. What does the slope of this graph represent?

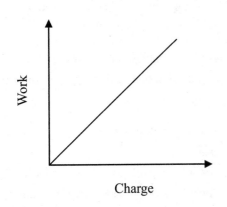

A. Power
B. Potential difference
C. Force
D. Electric field intensity
E. Resistance

43. A metal loop is placed in a uniform magnetic field as shown. The following experiments are performed:

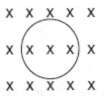

I. The magnetic field strength is changed.

II. The loop is moved up (out of the page) in the uniform field.

III. The loop is pulled to the right, and out of the field.

IV. The loop is rotated about a diameter.

A current will flow through the loop as a result of

A. I, II, and III only
B. I and III only
C. II, III, and IV only
D. I, III, and IV only
E. I, II, III, and IV

44. When a voltage V is applied to a parallel-plate capacitor, it is able to hold a charge Q. A second parallel plate capacitor has plates with half the area and twice the separation. What a voltage V must applied to it, in order to hold the same charge Q?

A. V/2
B. V/4
C. V
D. 2V
E. 4V

45. A conducting sphere of radius 0.10 meter has a charge of $+2.0 \times 10^{-6}$ coulomb. It is brought in contact with a second conducting sphere of radius 0.20 meter and no charge flows between them. What is the charge on the second sphere?

A. $+1.0 \times 10^{-6} C$

B. $+2.0 \times 10^{-6} C$

C. $+4.0 \times 10^{-6} C$

D. $+8.0 \times 10^{-6} C$

E. $+1.6 \times 10^{-5} C$

46. A 10μF capacitor is charged to a potential difference of 200kV in 20s. The average power delivered to the capacitor in this time is

    A. 100 W

    B. 200 W

    C. 10 kW

    D. 20 kW

    E. 40 kW

47. A capacitor initially has a capacitance of C_0. A dielectric, $\kappa = 2$ is placed between the plates of the capacitor and the separation between the plates is doubled. What is the new capacitance?

    A. $C_0/4$

    B. $C_0/2$

    C. C_0

    D. $2C_0$

    E. $4C_0$

48. Three identical light bulbs are connected in parallel to a voltage source. If one of the bulbs burns out,

    A. more currents will be drawn from the voltage source.

    B. the light intensity of the other bulbs will decrease, but they will not go out.

    C. the light intensity of the other bulbs will remain the same.

    D. the light intensity of the other bulbs will increase.

    E. all the bulbs will go out.

49. A cylindrical resistor of constant resistivity dissipates a power P when attached to a battery with potential V. If the resistor was replaced with one which has twice the radius and twice the length, the power dissipated would be

    A. P/2

    B. P/4

    C. P

    D. 2P

    E. 4P

50. A charged particle moves in a closed path in a region which has both an electric and a magnetic field. We know the energy of the particle at the end of the closed path is 3J greater than its energy when it began the path. Which of the following statements is correct?

    A. The magnetic force performed 3J of work on the particle.

    B. The magnetic force performed -3J of work on the particle.

    C. The electric field is produced by static charges.

    D. The electric field is conservative.

    E. None of the above is true.

51. A positive charge q is located on a 3v equipotential plane. The force on the charge q is

    A. 3q in magnitude, pointing parallel to the plane.

    B. 3q in magnitude, pointing perpendicular to the plane in the direction of decreasing potential.

    C. 3q in magnitude, pointing perpendicular to the plane in the direction of increasing potential.

    D. of unknown magnitude, pointing perpendicular to the plane in the direction of decreasing potential.

    E. of unknown magnitude, pointing

perpendicular to the plane in the direction of increasing potential.

52. A long rod has radius R and a net linear charge density λ, with the charge uniformly distributed across the cross sectional area of the rod. Which of the following is a correct application of Gauss's law (l is the length of the Gaussian cylinder)?

A. $E(\pi r^2 l) = \lambda l / \varepsilon_0$

B. $E(\pi r^2 l) = \lambda l (r^2 / R^2) / \varepsilon_0$

C. $E(2\pi r l) = \lambda l / \varepsilon_0$

D. $E(2\pi r l) = \lambda l (r^2 / R^2) / \varepsilon_0$

E. $E(\pi r^2) = \lambda l / \varepsilon_0$

53. A spherical shell has a uniform surface charge density σ and radius R. If R is changed to R/2 while holding the charge density constant, what happens on the magnitude of the electric field just outside the shell?

A. The electric field increases by a factor of 2.
B. The electric field increases by a factor of 4.
C. The electric field remains the same.
D. The electric field decreases by a factor of 2.
E. The electric field decreases by a factor of 4.

54. Determine the current through the 8.00 Ω resistor in the circuit of the figure below.

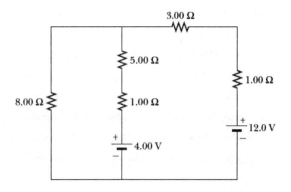

A. 6A
B. 1A
C. 0.5A
D. 0.01A
E. 0.846A

55. Three capacitors are connected to a battery as shown in Figure below. Their capacitances are $C_1 = 3C$, $C_2 = 4C$, and $C_3 = 5C$. Which statement is true about the charges Q_1, Q_2, and Q_3 they stored?

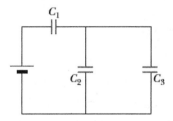

A. $Q_1 = Q_2 = Q_3$

B. $Q_1 > Q_2 > Q_3$

C. $Q_1 < Q_2 < Q_3$

D. $Q_1 > Q_3 > Q_2$

E. $Q_1 > Q_3 = Q_2$

56. An electron moves across the Earth's equator at a speed of $2.5*10^6$ m/s and in a direction 30° north of east. At this point, the Earth's magnetic field has a direction due north, is parallel to the surface, and has a value of $0.10 *10^{-4}$ T. What is the magnitude of the force acting on the electron due to its interaction with the Earth's magnetic field?

A. $2.3 *10^{-18}$ N
B. $3.4 *10^{-18}$ N
C. $5.1 *10^{-18}$ N
D. $4.0 *10^{-18}$ N
E. $6.6 *10^{-18}$ N

57. For a given length, what shape of loop will have the greatest torque for a given current and magnetic field?

A. square
B. rectangle with the long sides twice as long as the short sides
C. triangle
D. rhombus
E. circle

58. The magnitude of the magnetic field which is at a distance d from a current carrying wire is B. The magnitude of the magnetic field which is at a distance 2d from the wire is

A. 2B
B. B/2
C. 4B
D. B/4
E. B

59. In Figure below, the current in the long, straight wire is I_1 and the wire lies in the plane of the rectangular loop, which carries the current I_2. The net force exerted on the loop by the magnetic field created by the wire is

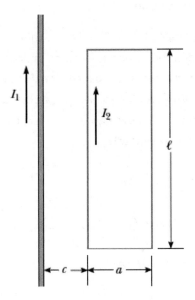

A. toward the long wire
B. away from the long wire
C. toward up
C. toward down
E. zero

60. As shown below, point P is midway between two long, straight, parallel wires which are the same distance d from each other. Wire A has current I running to the right, and Wire B has current I running to the left. Find the magnetic field at point P.

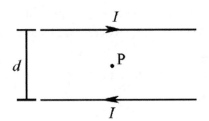

A. $\dfrac{\mu_0 I}{2d}$, out of the page

B. $\dfrac{\mu_0 I}{2\pi d}$, out of the page

C. 0

D. $\dfrac{2\mu_0 I}{\pi d}$ into the page

E. $\dfrac{\mu_0 I}{\pi d}$ into the page

61. A magnetic field exerts a non-zero force on a particle. Which of the following must be true?

A. The particle is negatively charged.
B. The particle is stationary.
C. The direction of the force is perpendicular to the magnetic field but parallel to the motion of the particle.
D. The direction of the force is parallel to the magnetic field but perpendicular to the motion of the particle.
E. The direction of the force is perpendicular to both the velocity of the particle and the magnetic field.

62. What is the magnitude and direction of the magnetic field at point P due to the segment of wire carrying current I which comes from infinity and goes to infinity?

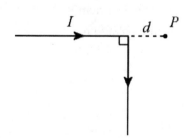

A. $\dfrac{\mu_0 I}{2\pi d}$ out of the page

B. $\dfrac{\mu_0 I}{2\pi d}$ into the page

C. $\dfrac{\mu_0 I}{4\pi d}$ out of the page

D. $\dfrac{\mu_0 I}{4\pi d}$ into the page

E. $\dfrac{\mu_0 I}{\pi d}$ out of the page

63. A tightly-wound solenoid has a length of 50 cm and contains a total of 400 turns. If it carries a current of 3A, the magnetic field inside the solenoid is

A. 24 μ_0

B. 300 μ_0

C. 1200 μ_0

D. 1600 μ_0

E. 2400 μ_0

64. A battery of emf ε_0 is connected, in series, to a capacitor C and a resistor R. The correct relationship regarding the circuit is

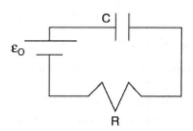

A. $\varepsilon_0 - \dfrac{q}{C} + I^2 R = 0$

B. $\varepsilon_0 + \dfrac{q}{C} - R\dfrac{dq}{dt} = 0$

C. $\varepsilon_0 - \dfrac{q}{C} + R\dfrac{dq}{dt} = 0$

D. $\varepsilon_0 - \dfrac{q}{C} - R\dfrac{dq}{dt} = 0$

E. $\varepsilon_0 + \dfrac{q}{C} + R\dfrac{dq}{dt} = 0$

65. Use dimensional analysis to determine the proportionality relationship between the inductance of a solenoid and its turns of unit length n.

A. $L \propto n$

B. $L \propto n^2$

C. $L \propto 1/n$

D. $L \propto 1/n^2$

E. None of the above is true.

66. A circular loop of wire with a radius of r=5 cm rotates clockwise at a constant angular velocity through a magnetic field B = 5 T. The plane of the loop goes from being perpendicular to the field to being at a 45º angle with the field in 0.25 s.

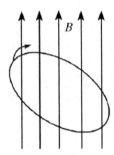

The wire has a resistivity of 7.5×10^{-8} $\Omega \bullet$m and a cross sectional area of $2.5\pi \times 10^{-7}$ m^2. What will the average current induced in the loop be? (Looking down on the loop so that B is out of the page.)

A. 0 A

B. 15 A clockwise

C. 15 A counterclockwise

D. 1.5 A clockwise

E. 1.5 A counterclockwise

67. A square wire loop of length d is pushed through a perpendicular square magnetic field of length l, with l $\geq$ d, at a constant velocity v. If the loop is completely outside the magnetic field and then is pushed through the field until it is again completely out of the field, what is the total amount of time during which an EMF is induced in the loop?

A. 0

B. d/v

C. 2d/v

D. (d + l)/v

E. (2d + l)/v

68. Which of the following creates a magnetic field?

I. Moving electric charges

II. Stationary electric charges

III. Time changing electric fields

A. III only

B. I and II only

C. I and III only

D. II and III only

E. I, II, and III

69. In LC circuits which of the following acts like open circuits?

I. Capacitors initially

II. Inductors initially

III. Capacitors at equilibrium

IV. Inductors at equilibrium

A. I only

B. II only

C. I and IV only

D. II and III only

E. II and IV only

70. The voltage across an inductor is proportional to the

A. current through the inductor.

B. the resistance of the inductor.

C. the charge on the inductor.

D. the rate of change voltage across the inductor.

E. the rate of change of current through the inductor.

Section II: Free Response Questions—Questions 1-3 (45 minutes)

Directions: Answer all three questions. The suggested time is about 15 minutes for answering each of the questions, which are worth 15 points each. The parts within a question may not have equal weight.

1.

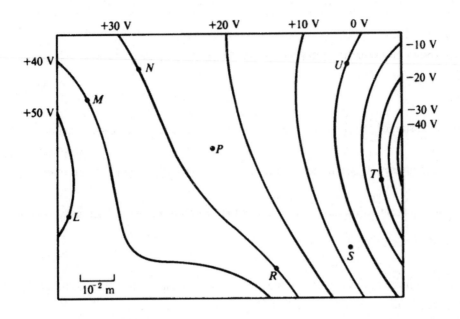

The electric equipotential lines of an electric field are shown on the diagram above.

A. At which of the lettered points is the electric field E greatest in magnitude? Why?

B. Draw the electric field vectors, **E**, at points L, N and U on the diagram.

C. Compute an approximate value for the magnitude of the electric field E at point P.

D. What is the work done by the field if a charge of +2 x 10^{-12} coulomb is moved from point M to point S?

E. What is the work done if the charge of +2 x 10^{-12} coulomb is moved from point M first to point T, and then to point S?

2.

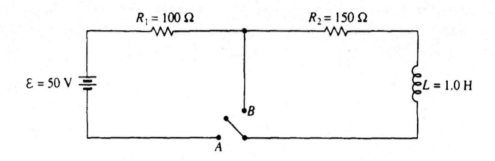

In the circuit above, the switch is initially open as shown. At time t = 0, the switch is closed to position A.

A. Find the expression of the current before a steady state situation has been reached.

B. Determine the energy stored in the inductor L when the steady state has been reached.

After the steady state situation has been reached, the switch is moved almost instantaneously from position A to position B.

C. What is the potential difference across the inductor immediately after the position of the switch is changed.

D. What happens to the energy stored in the inductor as calculated in part (b) above?

3. A closed loop is made of a U-shaped metal wire of negligible resistance and a movable metal crossbar of resistance R. The crossbar which has mass m and length L is initially located a long enough distance h_0 from the bottom of the loop. The loop is placed vertically in a uniform horizontal magnetic field of magnitude B_0 in the direction shown in the figure below. The crossbar is released from rest and slides with negligible friction down the U-shaped wire without losing electrical contact.

A. Determine the constant final speed of the bar.

B. Find the speed of the crossbar as a function of time t after it is released?

C. What is the magnitude of the current in the crossbar as it falls as a function of time?

D. How does the constant final speed change if the resistance R of the crossbar is increased?

Answers and Explanations

Mechanics

Section I: Multiple Choice Answers

1. C　2. D　3. C　4. D　5. E　6. B　7. E　8. A　9. C　10. B　11. C　12. C　13. D　14. A

15. B　16. A　17. C　18. D　19. B　20. A　21. B　22. E　23. B　24. A　25. E　26. B　27. E

28. C　29. B　30. C　31. B　32. E　33. E　34. A　35. D

Section I: Multiple Choice Explanations

1. C。牛顿第三定律，作用力等于反作用力。

2. D。路程 d= $\int_0^2 |v| dt = 1m$

3. C。$\vec{a} = \dfrac{\Delta \vec{v}}{\Delta t} = \dfrac{1}{\Delta t}(\vec{v_2} - \vec{v_1})$

4. D。$a_x = \dfrac{d^2 x}{dt^2} = -27\sin 3t, a_y = \dfrac{d^2 y}{dt^2} = -36\cos 3t$，可得 $a_{max} = a_{y,max} = 36 m/s^2$。

5. E。斜抛运动物体的加速度是常数，竖直向下。所以竖直向上物体做匀减速，向下匀加速运动。

6. B。粒子匀速向左运动 $a_x = 0$，总加速度 a 指向曲线凹的一侧，所以 $a_y > 0$。

7. E。$v = \sqrt{v_2^2 - v_1^2}$

8. A。沿斜面方向，重力的分力 F= $mg\sin 30^0$，最大静摩擦力 $f_s = \mu_s mg\cos 30^0$，

   计算可知 $F < f_s$，所以物体在斜面上不动。

9. C。平行轴定理：$I = I_{cm} + md^2 = \dfrac{2}{5}mr^2 + mr^2 = \dfrac{7}{5}mr^2$

10. B。冲量 I= ΔP，反弹的小球受到的冲量大，作用力大。

11. C。牛顿定律 F=ma，有 $a = -2t + 1$。$a = \dfrac{dv}{dx}$，$\rightarrow v = -t^2 + t + 6$，t=3s 时 v=0，

    $a = 0$ 即 t= 0.5s 时小车达到最大速度 $v_{max} = 6.25 m/s$

12. C。匀速圆周运动，速度加速度相互垂直。

482

13. D。A、B 两物体获得相同的加速度。$F = (m_A + m_B)a, \mu_s m_A g = m_A a \rightarrow \mu_s = \dfrac{F}{(m_A + m_B)g}$

14. A。当 x=1.5m 时，U(1.5)=2(1.5-1)²=0.5J，E_k=0.5J，系统的总机械能 E=1J。

当系统的动能为零时，势能 U=1J，2(x-1)²=1，得 $x = 1 \pm \dfrac{\sqrt{2}}{2}$ m。

15. B。$(F - f)d = E, f = (Fd - E)/d$

16. A。$(mg \sin \theta - \mu mg \cos \theta)l = \dfrac{1}{2}mv^2, \rightarrow v = 3.9 m/s$

17. C。$W = \int_0^5 F dx = 200J$

18. D。功率 P=$F \cdot v = F \dfrac{dx}{dt}$，t=1s 时，P=100W

19. B。三个棒的质心坐标分别为：（0, L/2），(L/2, L)，(L, L/2).

$$x_c = \dfrac{3ML/2 + ML}{5M} = \dfrac{L}{2}, \quad y_c = \dfrac{ML/2 + 3ML + ML/2}{5M} = \dfrac{4}{5}L$$

20. A。木块与子弹碰撞后速度为 V，由机械能守恒：$\dfrac{1}{2}MV^2 = \dfrac{1}{2}kx_0^2$，$\rightarrow V = 1.5 m/s$

由动量守恒：$mv_0 = mv + MV$，$\rightarrow v = 100 m/s$

21. B。动量守恒：$mv = (m + M)V$，$V = \dfrac{m}{m+M}v$，V 是两物体共同前进的速度。

下面的板受向右的摩擦力 $f = \mu mg$ 作用，这使其获得加速度 $a = \dfrac{\mu mg}{M}$，达到相同速度前板

向右运动了一段距离 $x = \dfrac{V^2}{2a} = \dfrac{mM}{2\mu g (m + M)^2}v^2$

22. E。物体所受冲量 I=Ft=$2mv \sin \theta$，$\theta = \sin^{-1} \dfrac{Ft}{2mv}$

23. B。力矩平衡：$Tl \sin 60^0 = 100 \dfrac{l}{2}, \rightarrow T = 69N$

24. A。$\Delta \theta = \omega_0 t + \dfrac{1}{2}\alpha t^2 = 0.75 rad$

25. E。合外力矩 $\tau = mg4l - 2mgl = I\alpha$，得 $\alpha = \dfrac{g}{9l}$

26. B。$\Delta \theta = \int_1^2 \omega dt$，转数 n=$\dfrac{\Delta \theta}{2\pi}$=1.1 rev

27. E。mgsinθ -f=ma，and fR=$I\dfrac{a}{R}$；$\rightarrow a = \dfrac{5}{7}g \sin \theta$

28. C。机械能守恒：$mgH = \frac{1}{2}mv^2 + \frac{1}{2}I\left(\frac{v}{R}\right)^2$，$\rightarrow v = \sqrt{\frac{10}{7}gH}$

29. B。角动量守恒：$\left(\frac{1}{2}MR^2\right)\omega = \frac{1}{2}(m+M)R^2\omega'$，$\rightarrow \omega' = \frac{M}{m+M}\omega$

30. C。宇航员失重是由于宇宙飞船在做自由落体运动。

31. B。$r = 2R_E$，卫星的能量 $E_1 = -G\frac{mM}{2r} = -G\frac{mM}{4R_E}$，外力做功卫星在轨道 $r = 3R_E$ 时的能量

$E_2 = -G\frac{mM}{6R_E}$。外力的所做功为 $w = E_2 - E_1 = \frac{1}{12}G\frac{mM}{R_E}$

32. E。卫星做圆周运动：$m\frac{v^2}{r} = G\frac{mM}{r^2}$，卫星速率 $v = \sqrt{G\frac{M}{r}}$，有 $v' = \frac{1}{\sqrt{2}}v$

33. E。小幅振动时，$F \approx -ax$ $T = 2\pi\sqrt{\frac{m}{k}} = 2\pi\sqrt{\frac{m}{a}}$

34. A。$v = \frac{dx}{dt} = \cos 2t$；当 t=$\pi$/6 s 时，$E_k = \frac{1}{2}mv^2 = \frac{1}{8}J$

35. D。秒摆的周期 T=2s。待求单摆的周期 $T' = 2\pi\sqrt{\frac{l'}{g}} = 2\pi\sqrt{\frac{2l}{g}} = \sqrt{2}T = 2\sqrt{2}s$

Section II: Free Response Explanations

1. A. 动量守恒：$mv_0 = (m+M_0)v$

   机械能守恒：$\frac{1}{2}(m+M_0)v^2 = (m+M_0)gl(1-\cos\theta_{max})$

   解得：$v_0 = \frac{m+M_0}{m}\sqrt{2gl(1-\cos\theta_{max})}$

   B. 在最低点处：$\rightarrow F_T = (m+M_0)g(3-2\cos\theta_{max}) \rightarrow F_T - (m+M_0)g = (m+M_0)\frac{v^2}{l}$

   C. 周期 T=$2\pi\sqrt{\frac{l}{g}}$，回到最低点所用时间 t=$\frac{T}{2} = \pi\sqrt{\frac{l}{g}}$

   D. $\theta = \theta_{max}\sin\left(\sqrt{\frac{g}{l}}t\right)$

2. A. 选取连杆左侧物体位置为系统的坐标原点，碰撞前任意时刻三个物体的坐标分别是$(0,0)$，$(l,0)$，和(l,y)；系统的质心坐标 $x_c=\dfrac{lm+lm}{3m}=\dfrac{2}{3}l$，$y_c=\dfrac{y}{3}$

质心速度：$v_{cx}=\dfrac{dx_c}{dt}=0$，$v_{cy}=\dfrac{dy_c}{dt}=\dfrac{1}{3}\dfrac{dy}{dt}=\dfrac{1}{3}v_0$，质心沿 y 方向匀速运动 $v_c=\dfrac{1}{3}v_0$

B. 系统所受合外力为零，质心保持匀速直线运动：$v_c=\dfrac{1}{3}v_0$

C. 和外力矩为零，系统遵循角动量守恒。碰撞前角动量 $L_1=mv_0\dfrac{1}{3}l$，碰后角动量 $L_2=I\omega$，

$I=2m(\dfrac{1}{3}l)^2+m(\dfrac{2}{3}l)^2=\dfrac{2}{3}ml^2$，所以有 $mv_0\dfrac{1}{3}l=\dfrac{2}{3}ml^2\omega$，得 $\omega=\dfrac{v_0}{2l}$

D. $E=\dfrac{1}{2}3mv_c^2+\dfrac{1}{2}I\omega^2=\dfrac{1}{4}mv_0^2$

3. A. 圆柱体进入粗糙平面后，所受摩擦力矩 $\tau=-\mu mgR$。由转动定律，圆柱体的角加速度

$\alpha=\dfrac{\tau}{I}=\dfrac{2\mu g}{R}$，$\omega=\omega_0+\alpha t=\dfrac{2\mu g}{R}t$

水平方向合外力：$-\mu mg=ma$，$a=-\mu g$；$v=v_0+at=v_0-\mu gt$

B. 圆柱体无滑动滚动的条件是：$v=\omega R$

有 $v_0-\mu gt=\dfrac{2\mu g}{R}tR$，$\rightarrow t=\dfrac{v_0}{3\mu g}$

C. 圆柱体做纯滚动运动时物体的角速度 $\omega=\dfrac{2\mu g}{R}\dfrac{v_0}{3\mu g}=\dfrac{2v_0}{3R}$

D. $L=v_0t-\dfrac{1}{2}at^2=\dfrac{5v_0^2}{18\mu g}$

Electricity and Magnetism

Section I: Multiple choice Answers

36. D   37. C   38. A   39. C   40. D   41. A   42. B   43. E   44. E   45. C   46. C   47. C   48. C

49. D   50. E   51. D   52. D   53. C   54. E   55. D   56. B   57. E   58. B   59. A   60. D   61. E

62. C   63. E   64. D   65. B   66. E   67. C   68. C   69. D   70. E

36. D. $F = k\dfrac{q_1 q}{r^2} + k\dfrac{q q_2}{r^2} = 9*10^9$ （ $\dfrac{-8\mu C * 30\mu C}{1.5^2} + \dfrac{24\mu C * 30\mu C}{3^2}$ ） = -0.24N

37. C。$\int_a^b E \cdot dl$ =0。E 不一定处处为零。

38. A。A 点场强为零，试验电荷在这点的受力为零。

39. C。三个点电荷在圆点的向量求和 $E = \sqrt{3}\,\dfrac{kq}{r^2}$

40. D。由场强和电势微分关系：$E = -\dfrac{dV}{dr} = -\dfrac{10}{r}$

41. A。场强 E=0 处，电荷受力 F=0，此处的电势 V 不确定。电势和场强是积分和微分的关系。

42. B。外力对电荷所做的功 W=qΔV，ΔV =W/q

43. E。在这几个试验中通过金属线圈的磁通量都有改变，由法拉第电磁感应定律知都会产生感应电流。

44. E。第二个电容器的电容 $C_2 = C_1/4$，其上的电势差 $V_2 = Q/C_2 = 4V_1$

45. C。第二个导体球带电 q_2，与第一个导体球等电势，$q_1/r = q_2/2r$，$q_2 = 2q_1$

46. C。20s 内电容器储存能量 U= $\dfrac{1}{2}CV^2$，平均功率 P=U/20=10 kw

47. C。电容 C= $\kappa \dfrac{\varepsilon_0 S}{d}$ =C_0

48. C。P=V^2/R，电压不变，灯泡的电阻也不变。所以 P 不变。

49. D。电阻消耗功率 P=V^2/R，R= $\rho \dfrac{l}{A}$ =R_0/2。所以功率变为原来的 2 倍。

50. E。磁场力与运动电荷速度垂直，不做功。静电场力是保守力，绕任意闭合路径所做的功为零。电场力绕闭合路径的所做的功不为零，此电场是非保守场，不是由静止电荷所激发的。

51. D。电荷所受电场力正比于场强，F=qE，且沿着 E 的方向。E=-dV/dx，场强的大小是由电势的变化率给出，不是由电势给出。场强 E 总是垂直于等势面，且指向电势降落的方向。

52. D。选取同轴柱形高斯面高为 l，高斯面内所包围的电荷为 $\dfrac{\lambda l r^2}{R^2}$，通过高斯面的电通量是

ϕ_e=E* $2\pi rl$，由高斯定理选 D。

53. C。表面附近的场强为 E，$r \approx R$。由高斯定理 E $4\pi r^2 = \dfrac{4\pi R^2 \sigma}{\varepsilon_0}$，所以 E= $\dfrac{\sigma}{\varepsilon_0}$，与半径无关。

54. E。应用基尔霍夫定律解得。

55. D。C_1 上的电荷等于 C_2、C_3 上电荷的和。C_2、C_3 上电压 $V_2=V_3=V$ 相同，$Q_2=C_2V$，$Q_3=C_3V$

56. B。磁场力 F=qvBsin60=3.4*10^{-18} N

57. E。线圈所受力矩 $\tau = ISn \times B$，线圈面积越大所受力矩就越大。

58. B。距离长直导线 d，B= $\dfrac{\mu_0 I}{2\pi d}$；距离为 2d 处，$B' = \dfrac{\mu_0 I}{2\pi 2d}$ =B/2

59. A。长直导线右侧的磁场垂直纸面向内随距离递减。线圈上下两段导线受力大小相等方向相反。左右两段导线受力方向相反，左侧受力大。

60. D。两平行导线间的 B=2 $\dfrac{\mu_0 I}{2\pi d/2} = \dfrac{2\mu_0 I}{\pi d}$，方向垂直纸面向里。

61. E。运动电荷所受磁场力 F= q**v** × **B**，力的方向垂直于 V 和 B。

62. C。半无限长水平电流延长线通过 P 点，B_P=0。竖直半无限长电流 B= $\dfrac{\mu_0 I}{4\pi d}$，方向向里。

63. E。长直螺线管 B= $\mu_0 nI$ =2400 μ_0

64. D。由基尔霍夫定律应选 D。

65. B。长直螺线管电感 L= $\mu_0 n^2 LS$

66. E。线圈的电阻 R= $\rho\dfrac{l}{A}$ =0.03 Ω。线圈中的感应电动势 $\varepsilon_i = -\dfrac{\Delta\phi_m}{\Delta t} = \dfrac{\pi r^2(1-\cos 45^0)B}{0.25}$。感

应电流 $I_i = \dfrac{\varepsilon_i}{R}$ =1.5A

67. C。线圈完全进入磁场在磁场中运动时无感应电动势。所以产生感应电动势的时间 t=2d/v

68. C。运动电荷和变化电场都可激发磁场。

69. D。LC 电路中开关刚闭合时，电感立即产生感应电动势与电源电压相反，I=0，即等效于电路
  开路。电路达到稳定时电容相当于开路。

70. E。自感电动势 $\varepsilon_L = -L\dfrac{dI}{dt}$，正比于电流的时间变化率。

Section II: Free Response Explanations

1. A. T 点等势线最密集，在此点的场强最强。

  B. 电场线指向电势降落的方向，且与等势线垂直。

  C. P 点附近区域近似可看作匀强电场，其大小为 $E_p = \dfrac{\Delta V}{\Delta l} = \dfrac{10}{0.02}$ =500 V/m

  D. W= -q $(V_s - V_M)$ =2*10^{-12}（40-5）=7*10^{-11} J

  E. 静电场是保守场，电场力做功与路径无关，只与起点和终点的位置相关。相同的起点和相

  同的终点无论沿何路径移动所做功都相同。

2. A. 电路刚刚闭合时，回路中的电流 $I=0$，长时间后电路达到稳恒状态，此时

  $I = \dfrac{\varepsilon}{R} = \dfrac{50}{250} = 0.2A$。

  电路达到稳恒前任意时刻 t，列出基尔霍夫环路方程得：

  $\varepsilon - L\dfrac{dI}{dt} = I(R_1 + R_2)$，解之求得电流：$I = \dfrac{\varepsilon}{R}(1 - e^{-\frac{R}{L}t})$ =0.2（1-e^{-250t}）

B. 电感储存能量 $E=\dfrac{1}{2}LI^2$ =0.02J

C. 开关位置迅速移到 B 位置瞬时，电路中的电流仍然是 $I=0.2A$，此时电阻 R₂ 中的电压是

V= IR_2 =0.2*150=30v

此时闭合回路中的电源是电感，感应电动势 ε_L =V=30v

D. 之后，随着电感中的能量逐渐被电路中电阻 R₂ 消耗，电流逐渐减少，电感中的磁感应强

度逐渐变弱，直至电流为零，电感中的能量全部释放出来。

3. A. 当导体棒以恒定速度 V 下滑时，导体中的感应电动势 $\varepsilon = BlV$

闭合电路中的电流为：$I = \dfrac{\varepsilon}{R} = \dfrac{BlV}{R}$

此时导体棒受安培力：F= $IlB = \dfrac{VB^2l^2}{R}$ ，方向竖直向上。

此时导体棒所受合力为零：$mg - \dfrac{VB^2l^2}{R} = 0$

解之得：$V = \dfrac{mgR}{B^2l^2}$

B. t=0时，v=0。任意时刻的速度为 v ，竖直向下。此时导体棒所受合外力

$mg - \dfrac{vB^2l^2}{R} = m\dfrac{dv}{dt}$ ，解此微分方程得：$v = \dfrac{mgR}{B^2l^2}(1-e^{-\frac{B^2l^2}{mR}t})$

C. $I = \dfrac{\varepsilon}{R} = \dfrac{Blv}{R} = \dfrac{mg}{Bl}(1-e^{-\frac{B^2l^2}{mR}t})$

D. 导体棒的终极速度 $V = \dfrac{mgR}{B^2l^2}$ ，当 R 增大时 V 增大。

附录 1　AP 物理 C 实验

科学本质上是人们认识并理解身边物理世界的过程。科学思维与其他思考方式的区别在于它靠物理世界的证据来判断假设和理论的真实性。物理学是一门以实验为基础的自然科学，实验是物理学的基础。来自真实世界的经验以及观察现象来验证科学概念的方法是物理学的重要组成部分。物理实验对相关的理论学习，对科学研究能力的培养至关重要。College Board 对 AP 物理 C 考试中关于物理实验有一定的要求，考生对此要有足够的重视。

1.　AP 物理 C 考核概述

AP 物理课程作为一门高级学习课程，其主要学习目标既要求能够理解、掌握和解决物理问题，又注重培养学生分析问题、解决问题的能力，使学生养成良好的科学思维习惯。College Board 官网对 AP 物理 C 考核提出三个方面的要求：

1）　**理论要求**：深入理解基本物理概念和原理及其在复杂问题中的应用。

2）　**实验要求**：通过实验设计和操作进行现象观察、数据采集、分析和结果说明来解决相应的物理问题。

3）　**数学要求**：掌握促进深入理解物理概念的数学工具，能应用微积分给出物理概念和原理的公式表达，并用之来解决复杂的物理问题。

从上述考核要求看，考好物理 C 要具备相应的理论水平、熟练的实验技能和坚实的数学基础。

2.　对 AP 考生实验技能要求

自 2011 年 AP 年会提出强调实验内容的考核后，每年考试的问答题中，力学和电磁学都各有一道实验相关题。同时在其他一些题目中也会出现要求画出物理量的函数表达式这样的问题，可见对实验能力和数学能力都提出了一定的要求。

AP 考生实验室技能要求：

1）design experiments；实验设计

2）observe and measure real phenomena；观察和测量

3）organize, display and critically analyze data；数据处理和分析

4）analyze sources of error and determine uncertainties in measurement；分析误差源确定测量误差

5）draw inferences from observations and data；从观察和数据给出结论

6）communicate results, including suggested ways to improve experiments and proposed questions for further study；讨论结果，提出改进实验的方案和进一步要研究的问题。

3. 真题解析

Example 1. 力学—2014 AP PHYSICS C: MECHANICS FREE RESPONSE QUESTION 1 （15 分）

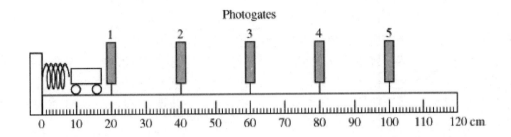

In an experiment, a student wishes to use a spring to accelerate a cart along a horizontal, level track. The spring is attached to the left end of the track, as shown in the figure above, and produces a nonlinear restoring force of magnitude $F_s = As^2 + Bs$, where s is the distance the spring is compressed, in meters. A measuring tape, marked in centimeters, is attached to the side of the track. The student places five photogates on the track at the locations shown.

(a) Derive an expression for the potential energy U as a function of the compression s. Express your answer in terms of A, B, s, and fundamental constants, as appropriate.

In a preliminary experiment, the student pushes the cart of mass 0.30kg into the spring, compressing the spring 0.040m. For this spring, $A=200N/m^2$ and $B=150N/m$, the cart is released from rest. Assume friction and air resistance are negligible only during the short time interval when the spring is accelerating the cart.

(b) Calculate the following:

    1) The speed of the cart immediately after it loses contact with the spring

    2) The impulse given to the cart by the spring

In a second experiment, the student collects data using the photogates. Each photogate measures the speed of the cart as it passes through the gate. The student calculates a spring compression that should give the cart a speed of 0.320m/s after the cart loses contact with the spring. The student runs the experiment by pushing the cart into the spring, compressing the spring the calculated distance, and releasing the cart. The speeds are measured with a precision of $\pm 0.002 m/s$. The positions are measured with a precision of $\pm 0.005 m$.

Photogate	1	2	3	4	5
Cart speed(m/s)	0.412	0.407	0.399	0.374	0.338
Photogate position(m)	0.20	0.40	0.60	0.80	1.00

(c) On the axes below, plot the data points for the speed v of the cart as a function of position x. Clearly scale and label all axes, as appropriate.

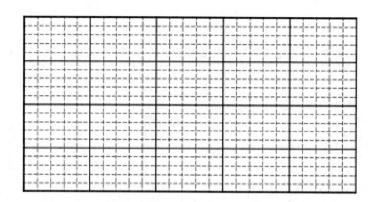

(d) 1) Compare the speed of the cart measured by photogate 1 to the predicted value of the speed of the cart just after it loses contact with the spring. List a physical source of error that could account for the difference.

2) From the measured speed values of the cart as it rolls down the track, give a physical explanation for any trend you observe.

解答：（a）写出势能函数和保守力之间的积分关系式：   1分

$$U(s) = -\int F(s)ds = -\int_0^s (As^2 + Bs)ds = -(\frac{1}{3}As^3 + \frac{1}{2}Bs^2)|_0^s$$

正确答案：$U(s) = -(\frac{1}{3}As^3 + \frac{1}{2}Bs^2)$；s=0处（弹簧原长）U(0)=0   1分

注：没有负号或表达式中有积分常数C都可以。

（b）1）机械能守恒：U(s)=K   1分

机械能守恒表达式：$\frac{1}{3}As^3 + \frac{1}{2}Bs^2 = \frac{1}{2}mv^2$ 1分

计算平衡位置速度大小：$v = 0.91m/s$ 1分

2）动量定理：$J = \Delta P = m(v - v_0)$ 1分

正确计算冲量：J=0.27kgm/s 或Ns   1分

1）和2）中的单位正确   1分

（c）正确在图中标注坐标和单位x（m）和v（m/s）。   1分

两坐标轴按线性比例对应。   1分

正确画出数据点。   1分

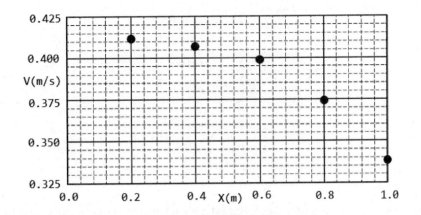

（d）1）小车在快门1的速度测量值大于小车在平衡位置的预期速度　　　　　　　1分

　　测得的小车速度的误差产生原因：　　　　　　　　　　　　　　　　　　　　1分

（1）弹簧的压缩量比计算所得的数值偏大

（2）桌子可能不是水平的，桌面有点向下倾斜。

（3）常数A、B可能不够精确。真实的A、B值可能大一些。

　2）从（C）中的数据表可知，小车速度慢慢下降。　　　　　　　　　　　　　　1分

　　产生的原因可能是：小车轮轴的摩擦、空气阻力，也可能是桌面有点向上倾斜。1分

Example 2. 电磁学—2014 AP PHYSICS C: FREE RESPONSE QUESTION（15分）

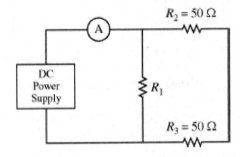

Physics students are analyzing the circuit above. A variable DC power supply is connected to an ammeter and three resistors. The resistances of two of the resistors are $R_2=R_3=50\,\Omega$, but the resistance of the third resistor is unknown. The students collect data on the potential difference across the power supply and the current measured by the ammeter, as follows.

Potential Difference(V)	2	4	6	8	10
Current(mA)	40	55	97	138	155

(a) On the grid below, plot the data points for the current as a function of the potential difference. Clearly scale and label all axes, including units if appropriate. Draw a straight line that best represents the data.

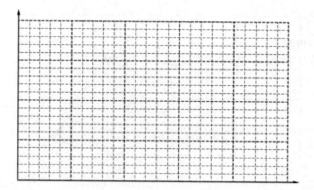

(b) Using the straight line from part (a), calculate the total resistance of the three resistor combination.

(c) Calculate the value of R_1.

The power supply is now fixed at 12V.

(d) Calculate the current through R_2.

(e) Resistor 3 is now removed and replaced by an open switch in series with an unchanged 4nF capacitor, as shown below. The power supply is still fixed at 12V.

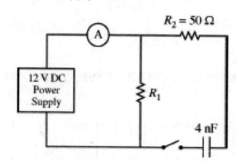

1) Calculate the current in R immediately after the switch is closed.

2) A long time after the switch is closed, will the magnitude of the current in R_2 be greater than, less than, or equal to the current though R_2 found in part (d)?

　　_Greater than;　_Less than;　_Equal to

Justify your answer.

(f) The 4nF capacitor is replaced with an uncharged 10nF capacitor. Will the magnitude of the current in R_2 immediately after the switch is closed be greater than, less than, or equal to the current in part C?

　　_Greater than;　_Less than;　_Equal to

Justify your answer.

解答：（a）两坐标轴上标出合适的变量和单位。　　　　　1分

正确地标注数据对应点。   1分

画出最佳拟合直线。   1分

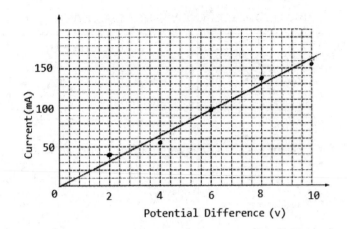

最佳拟合直线（best-fit line）是指所画直线要尽可能多的经过所描的点，而不是把所有的点连接起来，尽量让直线上方和下方的点数一样多。计算相应物理量时要在直线上取点。

（b）用图中画出的直线上的点计算斜率：$m = \dfrac{\Delta I}{\Delta V} = 0.0164A/V$ 1分

给出斜率和电阻的正确关系：$m = \dfrac{1}{R}$ 1分

计算出电阻值：R=61Ω 1分

用于计算斜率的点，一定是要在所作直线上，而不能是表格中给的数值。

（c）$\dfrac{1}{R} = \dfrac{1}{R_1} + \dfrac{1}{R_2 + R_3}, \rightarrow R_1 = 156\Omega$ 2分

（d）$I_2 = \dfrac{V}{R_2 + R_3} = 0.12A$ 2分

（e）1）$I_2 = \dfrac{V}{R_2} = 0.24A$ 1分

2）选 Less than。   1分

电容充电后R_2电路中电流为零。   1分

（f）选 equal to。   1分

开关闭合，未充电的电容等效于电路短路。   1分

从上面力学和电磁学两个真题解析可知，与实验相关的题目更注重基本物理原理，要求考生清楚如何设计合适的实验装置达到相应的实验目的；会用表格记录实验数据并画出相关曲线（注意变量的单位）；正确计算实验结果或给出预期结果；对结果和实验装置进行误差分析并能提出改进建议。对实验部分的题目训练，考生可参阅官网上的历年真题。

附录 2　力学、电磁学公式表

ADVANCED PLACEMENT PHYSICS C EQUATIONS

MECHANICS

$v_x = v_{x0} + a_x t$

$x = x_0 + v_{x0}t + \dfrac{1}{2}a_x t^2$

$v_x^2 = v_{x0}^2 + 2a_x(x - x_0)$

$\vec{a} = \dfrac{\sum \vec{F}}{m} = \dfrac{\vec{F}_{net}}{m}$

$\vec{F} = \dfrac{d\vec{p}}{dt}$

$\vec{J} = \int \vec{F}\,dt = \Delta \vec{p}$

$\vec{p} = m\vec{v}$

$\left|\vec{F}_f\right| \le \mu \left|\vec{F}_N\right|$

$\Delta E = W = \int \vec{F}\cdot d\vec{r}$

$K = \dfrac{1}{2}mv^2$

$P = \dfrac{dE}{dt}$

$P = \vec{F}\cdot\vec{v}$

$\Delta U_g = mg\Delta h$

$a_c = \dfrac{v^2}{r} = \omega^2 r$

$\vec{\tau} = \vec{r}\times\vec{F}$

$\vec{\alpha} = \dfrac{\sum\vec{\tau}}{I} = \dfrac{\vec{\tau}_{net}}{I}$

$I = \int r^2\,dm = \sum mr^2$

$x_{cm} = \dfrac{\sum m_i x_i}{\sum m_i}$

$v = r\omega$

$\vec{L} = \vec{r}\times\vec{p} = I\vec{\omega}$

$K = \dfrac{1}{2}I\omega^2$

$\omega = \omega_0 + \alpha t$

$\theta = \theta_0 + \omega_0 t + \dfrac{1}{2}\alpha t^2$

a = acceleration
E = energy
F = force
f = frequency
h = height
I = rotational inertia
J = impulse
K = kinetic energy
k = spring constant
ℓ = length
L = angular momentum
m = mass
P = power
p = momentum
r = radius or distance
T = period
t = time
U = potential energy
v = velocity or speed
W = work done on a system
x = position
μ = coefficient of friction
θ = angle
τ = torque
ω = angular speed
α = angular acceleration
ϕ = phase angle

$\vec{F}_s = -k\Delta\vec{x}$

$U_s = \dfrac{1}{2}k(\Delta x)^2$

$x = x_{max}\cos(\omega t + \phi)$

$T = \dfrac{2\pi}{\omega} = \dfrac{1}{f}$

$T_s = 2\pi\sqrt{\dfrac{m}{k}}$

$T_p = 2\pi\sqrt{\dfrac{\ell}{g}}$

$\left|\vec{F}_G\right| = \dfrac{Gm_1 m_2}{r^2}$

$U_G = -\dfrac{Gm_1 m_2}{r}$

ELECTRICITY AND MAGNETISM

$\left|\vec{F}_E\right| = \dfrac{1}{4\pi\varepsilon_0}\left|\dfrac{q_1 q_2}{r^2}\right|$

$\vec{E} = \dfrac{\vec{F}_E}{q}$

$\oint \vec{E}\cdot d\vec{A} = \dfrac{Q}{\varepsilon_0}$

$E_x = -\dfrac{dV}{dx}$

$\Delta V = -\int \vec{E}\cdot d\vec{r}$

$V = \dfrac{1}{4\pi\varepsilon_0}\sum_i \dfrac{q_i}{r_i}$

$U_E = qV = \dfrac{1}{4\pi\varepsilon_0}\dfrac{q_1 q_2}{r}$

$\Delta V = \dfrac{Q}{C}$

$C = \dfrac{\kappa\varepsilon_0 A}{d}$

$C_p = \sum_i C_i$

$\dfrac{1}{C_s} = \sum_i \dfrac{1}{C_i}$

$I = \dfrac{dQ}{dt}$

$U_C = \dfrac{1}{2}Q\Delta V = \dfrac{1}{2}C(\Delta V)^2$

$R = \dfrac{\rho\ell}{A}$

$\vec{E} = \rho\vec{J}$

$I = Nev_d A$

$I = \dfrac{\Delta V}{R}$

$R_s = \sum_i R_i$

$\dfrac{1}{R_p} = \sum_i \dfrac{1}{R_i}$

$P = I\Delta V$

A = area
B = magnetic field
C = capacitance
d = distance
E = electric field
ε = emf
F = force
I = current
J = current density
L = inductance
ℓ = length
n = number of loops of wire per unit length
N = number of charge carriers per unit volume
P = power
Q = charge
q = point charge
R = resistance
r = radius or distance
t = time
U = potential or stored energy
V = electric potential
v = velocity or speed
ρ = resistivity
Φ = flux
κ = dielectric constant

$\vec{F}_M = q\vec{v}\times\vec{B}$

$\oint \vec{B}\cdot d\vec{\ell} = \mu_0 I$

$d\vec{B} = \dfrac{\mu_0}{4\pi}\dfrac{I\,d\vec{\ell}\times\hat{r}}{r^2}$

$\vec{F} = \int I\,d\vec{\ell}\times\vec{B}$

$B_s = \mu_0 nI$

$\Phi_B = \int \vec{B}\cdot d\vec{A}$

$\varepsilon = \oint \vec{E}\cdot d\vec{\ell} = -\dfrac{d\Phi_B}{dt}$

$\varepsilon = -L\dfrac{dI}{dt}$

$U_L = \dfrac{1}{2}LI^2$

公式表来源于 2014 年美国大学理事会网站。

附录 3 数学公式表

ADVANCED PLACEMENT PHYSICS C EQUATIONS

GEOMETRY AND TRIGONOMETRY

Rectangle
$$A = bh$$

Triangle
$$A = \frac{1}{2}bh$$

Circle
$$A = \pi r^2$$
$$C = 2\pi r$$
$$s = r\theta$$

Rectangular Solid
$$V = \ell wh$$

Cylinder
$$V = \pi r^2 \ell$$
$$S = 2\pi r \ell + 2\pi r^2$$

Sphere
$$V = \frac{4}{3}\pi r^3$$
$$S = 4\pi r^2$$

Right Triangle
$$a^2 + b^2 = c^2$$
$$\sin\theta = \frac{a}{c}$$
$$\cos\theta = \frac{b}{c}$$
$$\tan\theta = \frac{a}{b}$$

A = area
C = circumference
V = volume
S = surface area
b = base
h = height
ℓ = length
w = width
r = radius
s = arc length
θ = angle

CALCULUS

$$\frac{df}{dx} = \frac{df}{du}\frac{du}{dx}$$

$$\frac{d}{dx}\left(x^n\right) = nx^{n-1}$$

$$\frac{d}{dx}\left(e^{ax}\right) = ae^{ax}$$

$$\frac{d}{dx}\left(\ln ax\right) = \frac{1}{x}$$

$$\frac{d}{dx}\left[\sin(ax)\right] = a\cos(ax)$$

$$\frac{d}{dx}\left[\cos(ax)\right] = -a\sin(ax)$$

$$\int x^n\,dx = \frac{1}{n+1}x^{n+1}, n \neq -1$$

$$\int e^{ax}\,dx = \frac{1}{a}e^{ax}$$

$$\int \frac{dx}{x+a} = \ln|x+a|$$

$$\int \cos(ax)\,dx = \frac{1}{a}\sin(ax)$$

$$\int \sin(ax)\,dx = -\frac{1}{a}\cos(ax)$$

VECTOR PRODUCTS

$$\vec{A}\cdot\vec{B} = AB\cos\theta$$

$$\left|\vec{A}\times\vec{B}\right| = AB\sin\theta$$

公式表来源于 2014 年美国大学理事会网站。

附录 4　物理常数表

CONSTANTS AND CONVERSION FACTORS

Proton mass, $m_p = 1.67 \times 10^{-27}$ kg	Electron charge magnitude, $e = 1.60 \times 10^{-19}$ C
Neutron mass, $m_n = 1.67 \times 10^{-27}$ kg	1 electron volt, 1 eV $= 1.60 \times 10^{-19}$ J
Electron mass, $m_e = 9.11 \times 10^{-31}$ kg	Speed of light, $c = 3.00 \times 10^8$ m/s
Avogadro's number, $N_0 = 6.02 \times 10^{23}$ mol^{-1}	Universal gravitational constant, $G = 6.67 \times 10^{-11}$ $(\text{N}\cdot\text{m}^2)/\text{kg}^2$
Universal gas constant, $R = 8.31$ J/(mol·K)	Acceleration due to gravity at Earth's surface, $g = 9.8$ m/s^2
Boltzmann's constant, $k_B = 1.38 \times 10^{-23}$ J/K	

1 unified atomic mass unit,	1 u $= 1.66 \times 10^{-27}$ kg $= 931$ MeV/c^2
Planck's constant,	$h = 6.63 \times 10^{-34}$ J·s $= 4.14 \times 10^{-15}$ eV·s
	$hc = 1.99 \times 10^{-25}$ J·m $= 1.24 \times 10^3$ eV·nm
Vacuum permittivity,	$\varepsilon_0 = 8.85 \times 10^{-12}$ C$^2/(\text{N}\cdot\text{m}^2)$
Coulomb's law constant,	$k = 1/(4\pi\varepsilon_0) = 9.0 \times 10^9$ $(\text{N}\cdot\text{m}^2)/\text{C}^2$
Vacuum permeability,	$\mu_0 = 4\pi \times 10^{-7}$ (T·m)/A
Magnetic constant,	$k' = \mu_0/(4\pi) = 1 \times 10^{-7}$ (T·m)/A
1 atmosphere pressure,	1 atm $= 1.0 \times 10^5$ N/m$^2 = 1.0 \times 10^5$ Pa

UNIT SYMBOLS							
	meter,	m	mole,	mol	watt,	W	farad, F
	kilogram,	kg	hertz,	Hz	coulomb,	C	tesla, T
	second,	s	newton,	N	volt,	V	degree Celsius, °C
	ampere,	A	pascal,	Pa	ohm,	Ω	electron volt, eV
	kelvin,	K	joule,	J	henry,	H	

PREFIXES		
Factor	Prefix	Symbol
10^9	giga	G
10^6	mega	M
10^3	kilo	k
10^{-2}	centi	c
10^{-3}	milli	m
10^{-6}	micro	μ
10^{-9}	nano	n
10^{-12}	pico	p

VALUES OF TRIGONOMETRIC FUNCTIONS FOR COMMON ANGLES

θ	0°	30°	37°	45°	53°	60°	90°
$\sin\theta$	0	1/2	3/5	$\sqrt{2}/2$	4/5	$\sqrt{3}/2$	1
$\cos\theta$	1	$\sqrt{3}/2$	4/5	$\sqrt{2}/2$	3/5	1/2	0
$\tan\theta$	0	$\sqrt{3}/3$	3/4	1	4/3	$\sqrt{3}$	∞

The following assumptions are used in this exam.
I. The frame of reference of any problem is inertial unless otherwise stated.
II. The direction of current is the direction in which positive charges would drift.
III. The electric potential is zero at an infinite distance from an isolated point charge.
IV. All batteries and meters are ideal unless otherwise stated.
V. Edge effects for the electric field of a parallel plate capacitor are negligible unless otherwise stated.

公式表来源于 2014 年美国大学理事会网站。